PROCEEDINGS OF THE SECOND INTERNATIONAL TURFGRASS RESEARCH CONFERENCE

a publication of the American Society of Agronomy and the Crop Science Society of America

Eliot C. Roberts, editor

This conference was sponsored by the International Turfgrass Society in cooperation with the American Society of Agronomy and the Crop Science Society of America.

Matthias Stelly, *editor-in-chief*
American Society of Agronomy
John W. Dudley, *editor-in-chief*
Crop Science Society of America
D. A. Fuccillo
Managing Editor
Margaret E. Davis
Laura H. Paskin
Assistant Editors

Library of Congress Catalog Card Number: 74-84163

Cover and book design by Ruth C. Poulsen.

Printed in the United States of America.

FOREWORD

At the request of the International Turfgrass Society (ITS), the American Society of Agronomy (ASA) and the Crop Science Society of America (CSSA) agreed to publish the proceedings of the Second International Turfgrass Research Conference. It is the hope and belief of all three societies that this joint effort will make a significant contribution toward the advancement of turfgrass science around the world.

The ITS is a very young organization, having been organized at the First International Turfgrass Research Conference in Harrogate, England, in July 1969. The ASA and CSSA take pride in the role played by their Turfgrass Division (C-5) in the organization of the First Conference and the formation of the ITS. The wisdom of the organizing committee and other supporters of that conference becomes more apparent from the vantage point of time. Both public interest in improved turfgrasses and research effort with the goal of improving sports fields, recreational areas, roadsides, and lawns have increased throughout the "developed" world since the first conference in Harrogate. One hundred ninety-two turfgrass scientists representing 15 countries attended the Second Conference. As evidence of increased worldwide interest in turfgrass, more scientists from countries other than the United States attended the Second Conference in Blacksburg, Virginia, USA, than attended the First Conference in England. Total attendance at the Second Conference was more than twice that of the First Conference.

This Proceedings of the Second Conference represents a mammoth effort by both authors and editors. In addition to the usual problems of preparing a publication, language barriers and international differences in style of writing had to be overcome. All concerned have the gratitude of the officers of the three societies involved with this joint effort.

Darell E. McCloud, President
American Society of Agronomy

Richard R. Davis, Chairman
Executive Committee,
International Turfgrass Society;
President, Crop Science Society
of America

PREFACE

The second research conference of the International Turfgrass Society featured more than 80 presentations concerned with turfgrass culture and use throughout the world. Representatives of 15 countries discussed the significance of research findings and commented on research approaches and techniques of importance in their varying geographic locations. The compilation of these papers and the discussions provides a unique presentation of current turfgrass scientific information of the widest practical importance.

These proceedings are dedicated to the objective of providing turfgrass information that can be used in the synthesis of concepts to better serve the needs of people who grow and use turf under diverse landscape and sports situations. In order to provide this type of information, subject matter is approached in several different ways. Some papers emphasize fundamental and applied research and provide detail concerning research techniques and methodology. Other papers consider developmental research approaches or demonstrations and evaluations of various cultural practices. Still other papers are concerned with reviews of the current "state of the art" and with formulation of new approaches based on past experience in the culture of fine turf.

Subject matter presented is arranged in eight topic areas. Reports have been grouped within these areas on the basis of continuity of subject matter and relevance to a common theme for discussion. Considerable overlap exists between areas, and thus the subject index is recommended in use of this volume for reference purposes.

Transactions of this conference included the presentation of current practical information relating to turfgrass production and use throughout the world and involved both cool- and warm-season grasses. Turfgrass breeding and cultivar evaluation topics emphasize the importance of induced mutations, isolation barriers and self-compatibility, flowering, seed characteristics and quality, variety registration, and evaluation under actual and simulated wear and by use of infrared photography. Cultural practices are described for turfgrass types varying from roadside to putting green. Fertilization effects on carbon assimilation, carbohydrates, and proteins; clipping and use of growth regulators; watering, including subirrigation; topdressing; and thatch control and overseeding are discussed. Environmental influences such as temperature, including soil warming; moisture; and light intensity and quality are related to turf management practices. Soils and their modification through use of organic matter and other amendments to improve root development are featured in papers concerning vertical drainage bands, the Prescription Athletic Turf System, and the United States Golf Association Green Section specifications. Disease, insect, and weed control reports consider both cultural and chemical practices. Proneness of grasses to disease and tolerance to fungicides, effects of herbicides on establishment of turf from seed and sod, and use of charcoal to deactivate pesticides are presented as key concepts in turfgrass management for the 1970's.

These reports demonstrate the existence of considerable variation in the research base upon which conclusions are generated. Some investigators present research data from field experiments conducted over periods of several years, and these results reflect the influence of changing environmental conditions and variations in the cultivars evaluated. Other investigators have reported on short-term studies conducted under controlled environmental conditions, with one to a few cultivars represented. These studies may be considered preliminary when related to general response situations or they may be viewed as providing insight for a better understanding of the cultural requirements of a specific cultivar under a narrow range of growth conditions. Many of these investigators report important new leads for further study, trial, and evaluation. Thus, the varying degree of generality or in-depth study provides overall variability in approach and subsequent strength regarding the usefulness of these proceedings in the formation of new concepts of practical importance for turfgrass specialists and landscape horticulturists.

The various reports also reflect current needs for turfgrass related information in the geographic location represented by the research specialist. Turfgrass cultural and environmental conditions vary throughout the world and, thus, information needs vary from place to place. As these needs change at any given location so do research methods and procedures for evaluations of turfgrass response. Further, how turfgrass research information is used varies throughout the world. For example, courses of study in turfgrass management and in landscape horticulture may provide an informational demand of primary importance in some areas. Cooperative extension programs, which are well developed in the United States, as well as various consultation services and agencies, utilize applied, developmental, and feasibility research results in drafting specifications and in making practical recommendations. Fundamental research provides a foundation of knowledge upon which all of turfgrass science is based. Also, uses of turfgrasses differ throughout the world not only because of climatic and soil variables but also because of varying quality standards established by the public. Maintenance and cultural practices and problems are often related, either as cause or effect, to the established quality of turf produced. These proceedings provide insight towards a better understanding of turfgrass science in the broadest sense.

In order to present these concepts in the most universally accepted format, an editorial board of specialists active within the American Society of Agronomy has served in a review and advisory capacity. All measurements have been standardized using metric units so that reference may be made between different articles without conversion. A table of conversion factors is included for the convenience of those who wish to relate data presented to other units of measurement.

Recorded in an appendix are the transactions of the business meeting for the International Turfgrass Society. This meeting holds historic significance because of the adoption of a Constitution and Bylaws for the organization. This document and other related information are presented in Section IX.

Thus, these proceedings provide a significant informational resource for turf managers and for commercial consultants. They serve as reference material for instructors in landscape and turfgrass maintenance courses of study and as important aids to students assigned special topic problems or completing preparations for seminar presentations. In addition, they provide a reference resource for members of the International Turfgrass Society and for all turfgrass research and extension personnel who strive to keep up-to-date in this rapidly developing science of turfgrass culture and management.

Eliot C. Roberts, Ph.D.
Editor

CONTENTS

SECTION II NUTRITION AND FERTILIZERS

Conversion factors for English and metric units

To convert column 1 into column 2 multiply by	Column 1	Column 2	To convert column 2 into column 1 multiply by
	Length		
0.621	kilometer, km	mile, mi	1.609
1.094	meter, m	yard, yd	0.914
0.394	centimeter, cm	inch, in	2.540
	Area		
0.386	kilometer^2, km^2	mile^2, mi^2	2.590
247.1	kilometer^2, km^2	acre, acre	0.00405
2.471	hectare, ha	acre, acre	0.405
	Volume		
0.00973	meter^3, m^3	acre-inch	102.8
3.532	hectoliter, hl	cubic foot, ft^3	0.2832
2.838	hectoliter, hl	bushel, bu	0.352
0.0284	liter	bushel, bu	35.24
1.057	liter	quart (liquid), qt	0.946
	Mass		
1.102	ton (metric)	ton (English)	0.9072
220.5	quintal, q	pound, lb	0.00454
2.205	kilogram, kg	pound, lb	0.454
0.0353	gram, g	ounce (avdp), oz	28.35
	Yield or Rate		
0.446	ton (metric)/hectare	ton (English)/acre	2.242
0.892	kg/ha	lb/acre	1.121
0.892	quintal/hectare	hundredweight/acre	1.121
	Pressure		
14.22	kg/cm^2	lb/inch^2, psi	0.0703
0.968	kg/cm^2	atmospheres, atm	1.033
0.9807	kg/cm^2	bar	1.0197
	Temperature		
1.80 C + 32	Celsius, C	Fahrenheit, F	0.555 (F−32)
	−17.8	0	
	0	32	
	20	68	
	100	212	

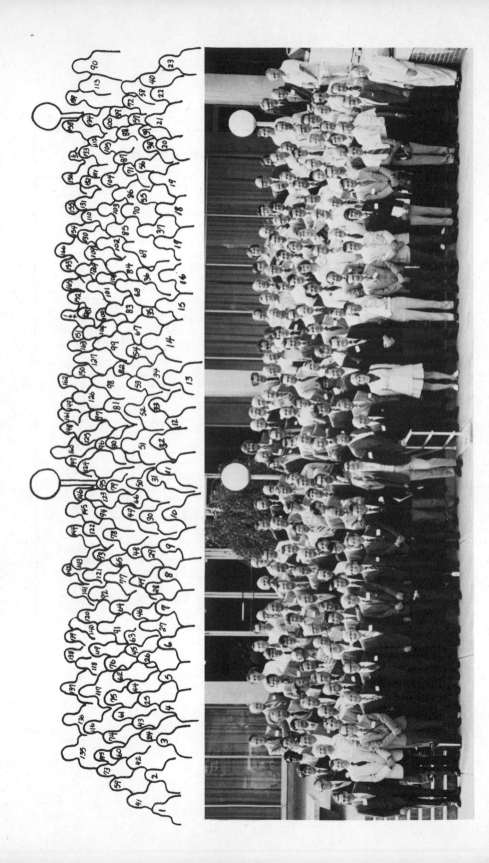

INTERNATIONAL TURFGRASS SOCIETY

Identification of Delegates
Second Research Conference Photograph
Virginia Polytechnic Institute and State University
Blacksburg, Virginia
June 19, 1973

1. J. F. Shoulders (U.S.A.)
2. R. C. Wakefield (U.S.A.)
3. G. M. Wood (U.S.A.)
4. A. M. Radko (U.S.A.)
5. W. W. Huffine (U.S.A.)
6. F. V. Juska (U.S.A.)
7. Yoshisuke Maki (Japan)
8. Toyoji Hosotsuji (Japan)
9. Kaoru Ehara (Japan)
10. Saburo Kakuta (Japan)
11. B. H. Baba (Japan)
12. Tom Mascaro (U.S.A.)
13. Any Castaings (France)
14. J. B. Beard (U.S.A.)
15. G. M. Kozelnicky (U.S.A.)
16. D. T. Duff (U.S.A.)
17. A. J. Powell (U.S.A.)
18. J. L. Kidwell (U.S.A.)
19. A. E. Dudeck (U.S.A.)
20. C. T. Blake (U.S.A.)
21. W. B. Gilbert (U.S.A.)
22. W. R. Kneebone (U.S.A.)
23. L. H. Taylor (U.S.A.)
24. G. V. Johnson (U.S.A.)
25. G. G. Fisher (Neth.)
26. H. M. Day (U.S.A.)
27. M. Fukui (Japan)
28. Y. Kamon (Japan)
29. E. Kawazoe (Japan)
30. J. P. Shildrick (U.K.)
31. R. M. Endo (U.S.A.)
32. Richard Brunner (W. Ger.)
33. Peter Boeker (W. Ger.)
34. J. P. van der Horst (Neth.)
35. C. W. Goldberg (U.S.A.)
36. Ian Greenfield (U.K.)
37. G. C. Nutter (U.S.A.)
38. C. J. Gould (U.S.A.)
39. J. H. Dunn (U.S.A.)
40. S. W. Bingham (U.S.A.)
41. R. E. Schmidt (U.S.A.)
42. W. C. Morgan (U.S.A.)
43. C. R. Skogley (U.S.A.)
44. B. V. Daugherty (U.S.A.)
45. E. C. Roberts (U.S.A.)
46. Don Parsons (U.S.A.)
47. C. A. Kouskolekas (U.S.A.)
48. J. B. Powell (U.S.A.)
49. P. F. Colbaugh (U.S.A.)
50. K. W. Kurtz (U.S.A.)
51. Hans Prun (W. Ger.)
52. Roger Loiseau (France)
53. Francois Loiseau (France)
54. Marc Masson (France)
55. E. R. Steiniger (U.S.A.)
56. A. C. Ferguson (Canada)
57. W. M. Lewis (U.S.A.)
58. V. A. Gibeault (U.S.A.)
59. J. E. Kaufmann (U.S.A.)
60. W. H. Bengeyfield (U.S.A.)
61. R. E. Engel (U.S.A.)
62. J. J. Murray (U.S.A.)
63. R. E. Blaser (U.S.A.)
64. G. W. Burton (U.S.A.)
65. R. W. Nelson (U.S.A.)
66. D. F. Marion (U.S.A.)
67. R. R. Davis (U.S.A.)
68. J. M. Latham (U.S.A.)
69. J. R. Watson (U.S.A.)
70. J. E. Gallagher (U.S.A.)
71. Hal Weitz (U.S.A.)
72. V. B. Youngner (U.S.A.)
73. H. H. Williams (U.S.A.)
74. R. M. Schmit (U.S.A.)
75. W. A. Meyer (U.S.A.)
76. C. R. Funk (U.S.A.)
77. G. E. Jurgensen (U.S.A.)
78. M. M. Fulton (U.S.A.)
79. J. R. Hall (U.S.A.)
80. H. Vos (Neth.)
81. C. H. Hamrle (Austria)
82. B. A. Rieger (Canada)
83. R. J. Hull (U.S.A.)
84. T. W. Cook (U.S.A.)
85. F. J. Wray (Canada)
86. H. W. Indyk (U.S.A.)
87. E. H. Odell (U.S.A.)
88. W. E. Sieveking (Canada)
89. S. G. Fushtey (Canada)
90. K. T. Payne (U.S.A.)
91. D. R. Fyfe (N. Zeal.)
92. H. D. Niemczyk (U.S.A.)
93. R. T. Westfall (U.S.A.)
94. Sven-Ove Dahlsson (Sweden)
95. Kyosti Raininko (Finland)
96. D. J. Glas (Neth.)
97. J. D. Smith (Canada)
98. K. M. Beckman (U.S.A.)
99. T. J. Gillespie (Canada)
100. J. L. Eggens (Canada)
101. J. F. Wilkinson (U.S.A.)
102. D. P. Martin (U.S.A.)
103. R. W. Miller (U.S.A.)
104. J. R. McCloud (U.S.A.)
105. L. M. Callahan (U.S.A.)
106. P. M. Halisky (U.S.A.)
107. W. C. Stienstra (U.S.A.)
108. C. W. Winstead (U.S.A.)
109. H. D. Palmertree (U.S.A.)
110. D. E. Brown (U.S.A.)

(continued on next page)

111. D. V. Waddington (U.S.A.)
112. B. J. Johnson (U.S.A.)
113. J. Lauwers (Belgium)
114. R. C. O'Knefski (U.S.A.)*
115. S. J. Han (U.S.A.)
116. Werner Skirde (W. Ger.)
117. Rudolph Pietsch (W. Ger.)
118. Reimar Vogel (W. Ger.)
119. Amand Chesnel (France)
120. R. W. Schery (U.S.A.)
121. H. M. Griffin (U.S.A.)
122. Hans Baukloh (W. Ger.)
123. L. G. Akesson (Sweden)
124. H. C. H. Ghijsen (Neth.)
125. Martin Kamps (Neth.)
126. R. A. Keen (U.S.A.)
127. F. B. Ledeboer (U.S.A.)
128. R. A. Moore (U.S.A.)
129. J. B. Moncrief (U.S.A.)
130. Ralph Smalley (U.S.A.)
131. T. L. Watschke (U.S.A.)
132. J. D. Butler (U.S.A.)
133. R. E. Burns (U.S.A.)
134. E. O. Burt (U.S.A.)
135. Wouter Versteeg (Neth.)
136. R. L. Goss (U.S.A.)
137. R. L. Morris (U.K.)

*Not present in this picture

138. R. W. Duell (U.S.A.)
139. K. McVeigh (U.S.A.)
140. W. F. Cordukes (Canada)
141. P. McMaugh (Australia)
142. William Dickens (U.S.A.)
143. D. T. Hawes (U.S.A.)
144. Andre Hentgen (France)
145. E. de Vilmorin (France)
146. L. H. J. Korsten (Neth.)
147. C. Schaepman (Neth.)
148. W. A. Small (U.S.A.)
149. V. Worrel (U.S.A.)
150. J. A. Jagschitz (U.S.A.)
151. D. J. Wehner (U.S.A.)
152. J. C. Harper (U.S.A.)
153. C. Y. Ward (U.S.A.)
154. D. L. Klingman (U.S.A.)
155. P. E. Rieke (U.S.A.)
156. Howard Kaerwer (U.S.A.)
157. Milton Archer (U.S.A.)
158. D. B. White (U.S.A.)
159. E. W. Schweizer (Switz.)
160. R. B. Anda (U.S.A.)
161. C. M. Switzer (Canada)
162. Noel Jackson (U.S.A.)
163. J. M. Vargas, Jr. (U.S.A.)
164. R. J. Peterson (U.S.A.)
165. D. K. Taylor (Canada)
166. W. G. Brown (U.S.A.)

PARTICIPANTS
& CONTRIBUTORS

L. G. Aakesson — 5-270-50, Hommenhog, Sweden

W. A. Adams* — Soil Science Unit, University College of Wales, Aberystwyth, Dyfed, Wales, United Kingdom

R. B. Anda — Crops and Soils Department, Michigan State University, East Lansing, MI 48823

M. Archer — 1023 Darwick Center, St. Louis, MO 63132

M. Armand — C.N.R.A. Route de St. Cyr 78000 Versailles, France

H. Baba — 1-17-3 Shiraitodai, Fuchu, Tokyo, Japan

R. T. Bangs — O. M. Scott and Sons, Marysville, OH 43040

H. Baukloh — Kleinwanzlebener Saatzucht Ag., 3352 Einbeck/Hannover, Postfach 146, West Germany

J. B. Beard* — Professor, Department of Crop and Soil Science, Michigan State University, East Lansing, MI 48824

K. M. Beckman — The Upjohn Company, Kalamazoo, MI 49001

W. H. Bengeyfield — U. S. Golf Association Green Section, Post Office Box 567, Garden Grove, CA 92642

W. Bidwell — Congressional Country Club, Bethesda, MD 20034

Claude Billot* — Institut National de la Recherche Agronomique, I.N.R.A.-S.E.I., Domaine Expérimental de Gotheron, 26320 Saint-Marcel-Les-Valence, France

S. W. Bingham* — Professor, Department of Plant Pathology and Physiology, Virginia Polytechnic Institute and State University, Blacksburg, VA 24061

Gustaaf Blaak — Zwaan and de Wiljes, Ltd., Post Office Box 2, Scheemda, Netherlands

C. T. Blake — Crop Science Department, North Carolina State University, Raleigh, NC 27607

G. R. Blake — Soil Science Department, University of Minnesota, St. Paul, MN 55101

R. E. Blaser* — University Professor of Agronomy, 236 Smyth Hall, Virginia Polytechnic Institute and State University, Blacksburg, VA 24061

Peter Boeker* — Professor, Institute for Agronomy, University of Bonn, Katzenburgweg 5, 53 Bonn, West Germany

B. Bourgoin* — Institut National de la Recherche Agronomique, SAPF-INRA, 86600 Lusignan, France

---

*All names followed by an asterisk indicate contributors.

xvii

D. E. Brown	Virginia Department of Agriculture, Post Office Box 1163, Richmond, VA 23209
W. G. Brown*	Department of Horticultural Science, University of Minnesota, St. Paul, MN 55101 (present address: Ciba-Geigy Canada, Agrichemicals Division, 1 Westside Drive, Etobicoke, Ontario)
A. Bruneau	O. M. Scott and Sons, Marysville, OH 43040
R. Brunner	Sachsenspiegel 11, 8 Munich, West Germany
P. J. Bryan*	Estates Department, Kent County Council, Maidstone, Kent, England
R. E. Burns*	Associate Professor, Georgia Experiment Station, University of Georgia, Experiment, GA 30212
E. O. Burt	Agricultural Research Center, University of Florida, Institute of Food and Agricultural Sciences, 3205 S.W. 70 Avenue, Fort Lauderdale, FL 33314
G. W. Burton*	Research Geneticist, Agricultural Research Service, USDA, and the University of Georgia, Georgia Coastal Plain Experiment Station, Tifton, GA 31794
J. D. Butler*	Extension Associate Professor, 137 Agriculture Building, Colorado State University, Fort Collins, CO 80523
L. M. Callahan	Department of Ornamental Horticulture and Landscape Design, Post Office Box 1071, University of Tennessee, Knoxville, TN 37901
R. A. Cappellini	CAES, Post Office Box 231, Rutgers University, New Brunswick, NJ 08903
R. N. Carrow	Plant and Soil Science Department, University of Massachusetts, Amherst, MA 01002
A. Castaings	B. P. 36, 85003 LaRoche Sur Yon, France
A. Chesnel	E Vilmorin, 49750, La Menitre, France
G. E. Coats	Department of Plant Pathology and Weed Science, Post Office Box P. G., Mississippi State University, Mississippi State, MS 39762
P. F. Colbaugh*	Department of Plant Pathology, University of California, Riverside, CA 92502
Herbert Cole, Jr.*	Professor, Department of Plant Pathology and Pesticide Research Laboratory, 211 Buckhout Lab, The Pennsylvania State University, University Park, PA 16802
T. W. Cook	Department of Plant and Soil Science, University of Rhode Island, Kingston, RI 02881
W. F. Cordukes	Plant Research Institute Agriculture Canada, Ottawa, Ontario, Canada
H. B. Couch	Department of Plant Pathology and Physiology, Virginia Polytechnic Institute and State University, Blacksburg, VA 24061
Sven-Ove Dahlsson*	Weibull s Turf Grass Section, S-261 20 Landskrona, Sweden
W. H. Daniel*	Professor, Department of Agronomy, Purdue University, West Lafayette, IN 47907
B. Daugherty	Capitol Building, Charleston, WV 25305
R. R. Davis	Ohio Agricultural Research and Development Center, Wooster, OH 44691
W. B. Davis*	Department of Environmental Horticulture, University of California, Davis, CA 95616
H. M. Day	Stauffer Chemical Company, Westport, CT 06880
R. den Engelse	Dr. Augustynlaan 50, Ryswyk (2.H.) Netherlands
E. de Vilmorin	1 Rue Des Marronniers, 77 – Villemer Par Moret, France

R. Dickens	Department of Agronomy and Soils, Auburn University, Auburn, AL 36830
W. Dickens	Soils and Crops Department, Lipman Hall, Rutgers University, New Brunswick, NJ 08903
G. Donohue	Hercules, Inc., 910 Market Street, Wilmington, DE 19899
A. T. Dore*	Plant and Soil Science Department, College of Resource Development, University of Rhode Island, Kingston, RI 02881 (present address: U. S. Soil Conservation Service, Warwick, RI 02881)
R. L. Duble*	Associate Professor, Texas Agricultural Experiment Station, Soil and Crop Sciences Department, Texas A&M University, College Station, TX 77843
J. P. Duchatelet	Vitseroel 60, B-1740 Ternat, Belgium
A. E. Dudeck*	Associate Professor, IFAS, University of Florida, Agricultural Research Center, Fort Lauderdale, Florida (present address: IFAS, University of Florida, Gainesville, FL 32601)
R. W. Duell*	Associate Research Professor, Soils and Crops Department, Cook College, Rutgers University, Post Office Box 231, New Brunswick, NJ 08903
D. T. Duff*	Assistant Professor, Department of Plant and Soil Science, University of Rhode Island, Kingston, RI 02881
J. M. Duich	Department of Agronomy, Pennsylvania State University, University Park, PA 16802
J. H. Dunn	Horticulture Department, University of Missouri, Columbia, MO 65201
R. Duyvendak*	Institute for Research on Varieties of Field Crops, Post Office Box 32, Wageningen, Netherlands
A. N. Ede*	Managing Director, Land and Water Management Limited, 88a Girton Road, Cambridge, CB3 OLN, England.
J. L. Eggens*	Assistant Professor, Department of Horticultural Science, University of Guelph, Guelph, Ontario, Canada N1G 2W1
K. Ehara	1-10-19 Minamidai, Kamifukuoka-Shi, Saitama-Ken, Japan
B. G. Ellis*	Professor, Department of Crop and Soil Sciences, Michigan State University, East Lansing, MI 48824
R. M. Endo*	Professor, Department of Plant Pathology, University of California, Riverside, CA 92502
R. E. Engel*	Professor, Soils and Crops Department, Cook College, Rutgers University, New Brunswick, NJ 08903
A. C. Ferguson	Department of Plant Science, University of Manitoba, Winnipeg, Canada
W. Fines	11 Amble Road, Chelmsford, MA 01824
G. G. Fisher*	Land and Water Management Limited, 88a Girton Road, Cambridge CB3 OLN, England
R. P. Freeborg*	Department of Agronomy, Purdue University, West Lafayette, IN 47907
T. E. Freeman*	Professor, Plant Pathology Department, University of Florida, Gainesville, FL 32611
M. Fukui	Toyo Green Company, Ltd., 1-6 Kobunacho 2-Chome, Nihonbashi Chuoku, Tokyo 103, Japan
D. E. Fulton	16 H. Grad. Circle, University Park, PA 16802
M. M. Fulton	O. M. Scott and Sons, Marysville, OH 43040
J. L. Fults*	Professor, 115a Weed Research Lab, Colorado State University, Fort Collins, CO 80523
C. R. Funk*	Research Professor, Soils and Crops Department, Cook

	College, Rutgers University, New Brunswick, NJ 08903
S. G. Fushtey	Department of Environmental Biology, University of Guelph, Guelph, Ontario, Canada
D. Fyfe	Post Office Box 51-134, Pakuranga, Aukland, New Zealand
J. E. Gallagher	Amchem Products, Inc., Ambler, PA 19002
H. C. H. Ghijsen	Wezelaan 12, Wageningen, Netherlands
V. A. Gibeault	1145 Batchelor Hall, University of California, Riverside, CA 92502
W. Gilbert	Crop Science Department, North Carolina State University, Raleigh, NC 27607
T. J. Gillespie*	Associate Professor, Department of Land Resource Science, University of Guelph, Ontario, Canada N1G 2W1
D. J. Glas	D. J. van der Have B. V., Rilland 3648, Netherlands
C. W. Goldberg	Department of Plant Pathology, Pennsylvania State University, University Park, PA 16802
R. L. Goss*	Western Washington Research and Extension Center, Washington State University, Puyallup, WA 98371
C. J. Gould*	Plant Pathologist, Western Washington Research and Extension Center, Washington State University, Puyallup, WA 98371
F. V. Grau	Box AA, College Park, MD 20740
J. T. Green, Jr.*	Instructor, Department of Agronomy, 339 Smyth Hall, Virginia Polytechnic Institute and State University, Blacksburg, VA 24060
Ian Greenfield*	Chairman, The Cayford Group (now known as Cayford International), 18 Hadham Road, Bishop's Stortford, Herts, United Kingdom
H. M. Griffin	U. S. Golf Association Green Section, Post Office Box 5563, Charlottesville, VA 22903
W. K. Griffith	Potash Institute of North America, 865 Seneca Road, Herndon, VA 22070
E. Grundler	Soatzucht Steinback Dr., M. V. Schmieder Nachf, 8441 Steinach, West Germany
P. M. Halisky	CAES, Post Office Box 231, Rutgers University, New Brunswick, NJ 08903
J. R. Hall*	Assistant Professor, Department of Agronomy, 1112 H. J. Patterson Hall, University of Maryland, College Park, MD 20740
C. Hamrle	Fa. Agromotor Franz Zimmer, A 1141 Wien, Keisslergasse 26-28, Austria
S. J. Han	CAES, Post Office Box 231, Rutgers University, New Brunswick, NJ 08903
J. C. Harper	Department of Agronomy, Pennsylvania State University, University Park, PA 16802
D. T. Hawes	Agronomy Department, University of Maryland, College Park, MD 20742
André Hentgen*	Institut National de la Recherche Agronomique, I.N.R.A.-S.E.I., Route de Saint-Cyr, 78000 Versailles, France
J. J. Hintzen	Mommersteeg International B. V., Vlijmen, Netherlands
T. Hosotsuji	1-10-19 Minamidai, Kamifukuoka-Shi, Saitama-Ken, Japan
J. E. Howland	Plant, Soil and Water Science Division, University of Nevada, Reno, NV 89507
W. W. Huffine	Department of Agronomy, Oklahoma State University, Stillwater, OK 74074

T. D. Hughes	Department of Ornamental Horticulture, University of Illinois, Urbana, IL 61801
R. J. Hull*	Associate Professor, Plant and Soil Science Department, University of Rhode Island, Kingston, RI 02881
H. W. Indyk	Soils and Crops Department, Rutgers University, New Brunswick, NJ 08903
Noel Jackson*	Associate Professor, Plant Pathology-Entomology Department, 223 Woodward Hall, University of Rhode Island, Kingston, RI 02881
J. A. Jagschitz*	Assistant Professor, Rhode Island Agricultural Experiment Station, Plant and Soil Science Department, University of Rhode Island, Kingston, RI 02881
B. J. Johnson*	Associate Professor, University of Georgia College of Agriculture Experiment Station, Experiment, GA 30212
G. V. Johnson*	Assistant Professor, Department of Soils, Water and Engineering, University of Arizona, Tucson, AZ 85721
G. Jurgensen	Jacklin Seed Company, Inc., East 8803 Sprague Avenue, Spokane, WA 99213
F. V. Juska* (deceased)	Turf-Research Agronomist, Agricultural Research Service, USDA, Plant Genetics and Germplasm Institute, Turfgrass Laboratory, Room 338, Building 001, BARC-West, Beltsville, MD 20705
H. Kaerwer	Northrup-King Company, 1500 Jackson Street N. E., Minneapolis, MN 55343
S. Kakuta	1-10–19 Minamidai, Kamifukuoka-Shi, Saitama-Ken, Japan
Yasuhiko Kamon*	Kansai Golf Union Green Section Research Center, 1303-2 Yamahata, Kurando, Takarazuka 665, Hyogo, Japan
M. Kamps	Van Engelen Zaden, Post Office Box 5, Vlijmen, Netherlands
J. E. Kaufmann	17 Plant Science Building, Cornell University, Ithaca, NY 14850
E. Kawazoe	1-10–19 Minamidai, Kamifukuoka-Shi, Saitama-Ken, Japan
R. A. Keen	Department of Horticulture, Kansas State University, Manhattan, KS 66506
M. Kerguelen*	Institut National de la Recherche Agronomique, Geves La Miniere, 78000 Versailles, France
J. L. Kidwell	Kidwell Turf Farms, Route 3, Box 16A, Culpeper, VA 22701
D. L. Klingman	ARC-West, Beltsville, MD 20705
W. R. Kneebone	Department of Agronomy and Plant Genetics, University of Arizona, Tucson, AZ 85721
L. H. J. Korsten	Veredlingsbedrijf Cebeco-Handelsraad, 36 Lisdoddeweg, Lelystad, Netherlands
C. A. Kouskolekas*	Associate Professor, Department of Zoology-Entomology, Auburn University, Auburn, AL 36830
G. M. Kozelnicky	Department of Plant Pathology and Plant Genetics, University of Georgia, Athens, GA 30602
J. V. Krans*	Department of Soils, Water and Engineering, University of Arizona (present address: Department of Crop and Soil Science, Michigan State University, East Lansing, MI 48823)
K. W. Kurtz	1547 North Boulder, Ontario, CA 91762
J. Latham	Milwaukee Sewerage Commission, Box 2079, Milwaukee, WI 53201

J. Lauwers — Gerard Le Grellelaan, 5 Antwerp, Belgium

F. B. Ledeboer* — Assistant Professor, Clemson University, Clemson, SC (present address: Loft Pedigreed Seed, Inc., Post Office Box 146, Bound Brook, NJ 08805)

W. M. Lewis — Crop Science Department, North Carolina State University, Raleigh, NC 27607

F. Loiseau — 157 Rue Gambetta, 72000 Le Mans, France

R. Loiseau — Les Goderies, Ruaudin, 72000 Le Mans, France

J. H. Madison* — Professor, Department of Environmental Horticulture, University of California, Davis, CA 95616

Y. Maki — Hokkaido National Agricultural Experiment Station, Sapporo, Japan

P. Mansat* — Institut National de la Recherche Agronomique, SAPF-INRA, 86600 Lusignan, France

D. Marion — Department of Plant Pathology-Entomology, University of Rhode Island, Kingston, RI 02881

D. P. Martin — Department of Agronomy, Ohio State University, 1827 Neil Avenue, Columbus, OH 43210

T. Mascaro — 2210 NE 124th Street, Keystone Point, North Miami, FL 33161

M. Masson — Ets. L. Clause - 91220 Bretigny s/Orge, France

H. B. Mayer — 565 Solingen, Focher Strausse 30–34, West Germany

J. R. McCloud — Post Office Box 419, Norfolk, VA 23501

N. McCollum — Department of Horticultural Science, University of Guelph, Guelph, Ontario, Canada

P. McMaugh — 4F Eastwood Avenue, Eastwood, N.S.W. Australia 2122

K. McVeigh — Box 1741, State Highway 27, Somerset, NJ 08873

E. L. McWhirter* — Mississippi Agricultural and Forestry Experiment Station, Post Office Box 5248, Mississippi State, MS 39762

W. A. Meyer — 8400 West 111th Street, Palos Park, IL 60464

R. T. Miller — Biochemicals Department, DuPont Company, Wilmington, DE 19898

R. W. Miller* — Professor, Department of Agronomy, Ohio State University, Research Agronomist, Chem-Lawn Corporation (mailing address: 5532 Shier-Rings Road, Dublin, OH 43017)

J. B. Moncrief — U. S. Golf Association Green Section, Post Office Box 4213, Campus Station, Athens, GA 30601

R. A. Moore — Post Office Box 385, Delair, NJ 08110

W. C. Morgan — Kellogg Supply, Inc., 23813 Cholame Drive, Diamond Bar, CA 91766

R. L. Morris — Fisons Limited-Fertilizer Division, Levington Research Station, Levington, Ipswich IPIO OLU, England

C. K. Mruk — Hercules, Inc., 34 Pontiac Avenue, Providence, RI 02907

J. J. Murray* — Research Agronomist, Agricultural Research Service, USDA, Plant Genetics and Germplasm Institute, Turfgrass Laboratory, Room 338, Building 001, Beltsville Agricultural Research Center-West, Beltsville, MD 20705

B. Muse — Stark Campus, Kent State University, Canton, OH 44720

R. R. Muse — Plant Pathology Department, Ohio Agricultural Research and Development Center, Wooster, OH 44691

R. W. Nelson — Jacobsen Manufacturing Company, 1721 Packard Avenue, Racine, WI 53403

H. D. Niemczyk — Department of Entomology, Ohio Agricultural Research and Development Center, Wooster, OH 44691

D. Nikolic	6209 Loran Street, St. Louis, MO 63109
F. J. Nudge*	Department of Plant Sciences, University of California, Riverside, CA 91720
G. C. Nutter	Box 5082, Lake City, FL 32055
E. H. Odell	Post Office Box 1326, Chesapeake, VA 23320
R. C. O'Knefski	Nassau County Extension Agent, 66 Scudders Lane, Glen Head, NY 11545
Wilhelm Opitz von Boberfeld*	Institute for Agronomy, University of Bonn, Katzenburgweg 5, 53 Bonn, West Germany
G. Osburn	Hercules, Inc., 910 Market Street, Wilmington, DE 19899
G. Otten	Proctor and Gamble Company, Ivorydale Technical Center, Cincinnati, OH 45217
H. D. Palmertree*	Mississippi Cooperative Extension Service, Box 5425, Mississippi State, MS 39762
D. Parsons	25232 Vermont Drive, Newhall, CA 91321
J. L. Paul*	Associate Horticulturist, Department of Environmental Horticulture, University of California, Davis, CA 95616
K. T. Payne	Department of Crop and Soil Science, Michigan State University, East Lansing, MI 48823
H. D. Perry*	Research Associate, 339 Smyth Hall, Virginia Polytechnic Institute and State University, Blacksburg, VA 24061
Martin Petersen*	L. Dashnfeldt Ltd., Post Office Box 185, DK-5100 Odense, Denmark
R. J. Peterson	E. F. Burlingham and Sons, Post Office Box 217, Forest Grove, OR 97116
R. Pietsch	Wolf-Gerate GmbH, 524 Betzdorf/Sieg, Gregor-Wolf-StraBe, West Germany
R. H. Pluenneke*	Associate Professor, Mississippi Agricultural and Forestry Experiment Station, Box 5248, Mississippi State, MS 39762
A. J. Powell, Jr.*	Assistant Professor, Agronomy Department, Virginia Polytechnic Institute and State University, Blacksburg, VA 24061
J. B. Powell*	Research Geneticist, Turfgrass Laboratory, Plant Genetics and Germplasm Institute, Agricultural Research Service, USDA, Room 333, B-001, BARC-West, Beltsville, MD 20705
H. Prun	Landw. Versuchsstation der BASF, D6703, Limburgerhof, West Germany
A. M. Radko*	National Research Director, U. S. Golf Association Green Section, Post Office Box 1237, Highland Park, NJ 08904
K. Raininko	Hankkija, Keskusosuusliike, Salomonkatu 1, 00100 Helsinki 10, Finland
R. Randell	165 Natural Resources, University of Illinois, Urbana, IL 61801
B. A. Rieger*	Department of Horticultural Science, University of Guelph, Guelph, Ontario, Canada N1G 2W1
P. E. Rieke*	Professor, Department of Crop and Soil Sciences, Michigan State University, East Lansing, MI 48824
E. C. Roberts	Plant and Soil Science Department, University of Rhode Island, Kingston, RI 02881
R. L. Robertson	Department of Entomology, North Carolina State University, Raleigh, NC 27607
M. J. Robey*	Athletic Department, Purdue University, West Lafayette, IN 47907

E. Roschel	Wolf-Gerate GmbH, 524 Betzdorf/Sieg, Gregor-Wolf-StraBe, West Bermany
P. L. Sanders*	Department of Plant Pathology, 111 Buckhout Lab, Penn State University, University Park, PA 16802
G. D. Sanks*	Department of Horticulture, University of Illinois, Urbana, IL 61801
C. Schaepman	Barenbrug Holland B. V., Postbus 4, Arnhem, Netherlands
R. W. Schery*	The Lawn Institute, Route 4, Kimberdale, Marysville, OH 43040
R. E. Schmidt*	Associate Professor, Agronomy Department, Virginia Polytechnic Institute and State University, Blacksburg, VA 24061
R. M. Schmit*	Soils and Crops Department, Cook College, Rutgers University, Post Office Box 231, New Brunswick, NJ 08903
E. W. Schweizer	Post Office Box 360, CH-3601, Thun, Switzerland
R. L. Self*	Plant Pathologist in Charge, Auburn University, Ornamental Horticulture Field Station, Post Office Box 8276, Mobile, AL 36608
J. P. Shildrick*	Assistant Director, Sports Turf Research Institute, Bingley, Yorkshire, BD 16 1AU, England
J. F. Shoulders*	Associate Professor, Agronomy Department, Virginia Polytechnic Institute and State University, Blacksburg, VA 24061
W. E. Sieveking	Research Center, Maple Leaf Mills Ltd., RR 2, Georgetown, Ontario, Canada
J. A. Simmons	O. M. Scott and Sons Company, Marysville, OH 43040
Werner Skirde*	Justus Liebig-Universität, Schlossgasse 7, Brandplatz 1, Giessen 63, West Germany
C. R. Skogley	Plant and Soil Science Department, University of Rhode Island, Kingston, RI 02881
W. A. Small	Mallinckrodt Chemical Works, 3600 North Second Street, St. Louis, MO 63160
R. Smalley	Box 451, Cobleskill, NY 12043
J. D. Smith*	Plant Pathologist, Research Station, Research Branch, Agriculture Canada, University Campus, Saskatoon, Saskatchewan S7N 0X2, Canada
L. M. Smith*	University of Rhode Island (present address: O. M. Scott and Company, 2619 Greenleaf Drive, Orlando, FL 32810)
Vincent Snyder*	Department of Agronomy, Virginia Polytechnic Institute and State University, Blacksburg, VA 24061
E. R. Steiniger	Pine Valley Golf Club, Clementon, NJ 08021
W. C. Stienstra	6035 McKinley Street, Minneapolis, MN 55432
C. M. Switzer	College of Agriculture, University of Guelph, Guelph, Ontario, Canada
D. K. Taylor*	Research Scientist, Research Branch, Agriculture Canada, Post Office Box 1000, Agassiz, British Columbia V0M 1A0 Canada
L. H. Taylor*	Professor, Agronomy Department, Virginia Polytechnic Institute and State University, Blacksburg, VA 24061
W. R. Thompson, Jr.*	Potash Institute of North America, 810 Howard Drive, Starkville, MS 39759
R. W. Toler*	Professor, Department of Plant Sciences, Texas A&M University, College Station, TX 77843

J. Troll	Plant and Soil Science Department, University of Massachusetts, Amherst, MA 01002
A. J. Turgeon*	Assistant Professor, Department of Horticulture, 202 Ornamental Horticulture Building, University of Illinois, Urbana, IL 61801
J. P. van der Horst*	Netherlands Sports Federation, van Karnebeeklaan 6, The Hague, Netherlands
J. M. Vargas	Department of Botany and Plant Pathology, Michigan State University, East Lansing, MI 48823
W. Versteeg	Heidemij Nederland N. V., Postbus 33, Arnhem, Netherlands
R. Vogel	D-59 Siegen, Bruderweg 33, West Germany
H. Vos*	Institute for Research on Varieties of Field Crops, Post Office Box 32, Wageningen, Netherlands
D. V. Waddington	Department of Agronomy, Pennsylvania State University, University Park, PA 16802
R. C. Wakefield*	Professor, Plant and Soil Science Department, College of Resource Development, University of Rhode Island, Kingston, RI 02881
G. E. Walker*	Newport High School, Monmouthshire, Wales, United Kingdom
R. H. Walker*	Agronomy Department, Mississippi State University (present address: 1129 Joel Drive, Albany, GA 31707)
C. Y. Ward*	Professor, Mississippi Agricultural and Forestry Experiment Station, Post Office Box 5248, Mississippi State, MS 39762
C. G. Warren*	Department of Plant Pathology and Pesticide Research Laboratory, The Pennsylvania State University, University Park, PA 16802
H. Watkins	Agronomy Department, Agricultural Science Center North, Lexington, KY 40506
T. L. Watschke*	Assistant Professor, Department of Agronomy, 20 Tyson Building, The Pennsylvania State University, University Park, PA 16802
D. J. Watson	Hercules, Inc., Wilmington, DE 19899
J. R. Watson*	Vice President, The Toro Company, 8111 Lyndale Avenue South, Bloomington, MN 55420
W. L. Watson	Box 327, Virginia State College, Petersburg, VA 23803
R. W. Weaver*	Assistant Professor, Texas Agricultural Experiment Station, Soil and Crop Sciences Department, Texas A&M University, College Station, TX 77843
D. J. Wehner	119 Tyson Hall, Pennsylvania State University, University Park, PA 16802
H. Weitz	Box 10, Somerset, NJ 08873
R. Westfall	RR 1, Marysville, OH 43040
D. B. White*	Professor, Department of Horticultural Science, University of Minnesota, St. Paul, MN 55101
J. F. Wilkinson*	Department of Crop and Soil Science, Michigan State University, East Lansing, MI 48824 (present address: Department of Agronomy, Ohio State University, 1827 Neil Avenue, Columbus, OH 43210)
H. H. Williams*	Plant Physiologist, Los Angeles State and County Arboretum (present address: 1128 East 80th Street, Los Angeles, CA 90001)
C. W. Winstead*	Mississippi State College (present address: Horticulture

Department, Louisiana Tech University, Post Office Box 5136, Tech Station, Ruston, LA 71270)

G. M. Wood* Associate Professor, Plant and Soil Science Department, University of Vermont, Burlington, VT 05401

J. M. Woodruff* Assistant Professor, Virginia Polytechnic Institute and State University (present address: Cooperative Extension Service, University of Georgia, Post Office Box 1209, Tifton, GA 31794)

V. Worrel 2055 White Bear Avenue, St. Paul, MN 55109

F. J. Wray* Assistant Professor, Plant Science Department, Nova Scotia Agricultural College, Truro, Nova Scotia, Canada

V. B. Youngner* Professor, Department of Plant Sciences, University of California, Riverside, CA 91720

M. A. Zanko Mallinckrodt Chemical Works, International Division, 675 Brown Road, Hazelwood, MO 63042

Turfgrass breeding and cultivar evaluation

Section I

1

Induced mutations in turfgrasses as a source of variation for improved cultivars[1]

J.B. POWELL

Mutation breeding of vegetatively propagated turf bermudagrasses (*Cynodon* spp.) has resulted in an unusually large number of mutations, many of which may be economically important. Gamma radiation of dormant rhizomes of 'Tifgreen' and 'Tifway' cultivars and actively growing stolons of 'Tufcote' bermudagrass slightly alter the characteristics of otherwise excellent cultivars. Genotypic differences among the cultivars influenced the visible mutations. The nonsectoring mutant propagules were more common than were the chimera-derived propagules. Thus, diplontic selection and chimeral formation do not hinder the use of mutation-breeding techniques in bermudagrass. The most common types of mutations observed were lighter green plants, dwarfing, rate of spread changes, dark reddish-purple plants, and a number of leaf morphology changes. Ionizing radiation should be considered an additional tool for the plant breeder to improve vegetatively propagated turf bermudagrasses. Additional index words: Chimeras, Dwarfing, Vegetative propagation, Rhizomes, Stolons, Dosages, Gamma radiation, Morphological mutants, Radiosensitivity, Rads, Physical mutagens, *Cynodon* spp.

Many of the grasses used for special-purpose turf, including residential lawns, golf courses, athletic fields, and highway rights-of-way, are reproduced by vegetative sod, sprigs, or asexual caryopses. The breeding improvement of some of these cool- and warm-season cultivars is impeded by apomixis, sparse development of the inflorescence, complete sterility, or very poor seeding characteristics. New techniques are needed to circumvent these breeding barriers to further improve those turfgrass cultivars that are presently commercialized. Induction of mutations in vegetatively propagated grasses by ionizing radiation is one approach.

In 1970 Powell, Burton, and Young (7) induced distinct mutations in two vegetatively propagated bermudagrasses (*Cynodon* spp.) by ionizing radiation. The induced variants were of such frequency that mutation breed-

---

[1]Contribution from the Turfgrass Laboratory, Plant Genetics and Germplasm Institute, Agricultural Research Service, U. S. Department of Agriculture, Beltsville, MD 20705.

ing was suggested as a practical approach to permanent modification and improvement of these cultivars. The two closely related cultivars tested in the previous work were triploid, sterile hybrids. Further experimentation was needed to test whether the same or unrelated cultivars of bermudagrass responded in a similar manner. The findings reported here are the results of tests with three commercially available turf bermudagrasses.

MATERIALS AND METHODS

'Tifgreen' (5) and 'Tifway' (3) bermudagrass, crosses of *Cynodon transvaalensis* Burtt-Davy with *C. dactylon* (L.) Pers., and 'Tufcote' (4) *C. dactylon* were selected for the experimental materials. Tifgreen and Tifway were collected from breeders' source nurseries at Tifton, Georgia, and Tufcote was taken from experimental plots at Beltsville, Maryland. During December 1970 and January 1971, dormant sod of Tifgreen and Tifway was removed from the field nurseries and stored at Tifton. Rhizomes were collected from the dense sod by shaking the soil from sod pieces and then hand-removing the fleshy rhizomes. Except during periods of hand-separation at ambient temperatures, all vegetative material was kept cooled to 4 to 5 C to maintain dormancy.

On February 24, 1971, rhizomes of Tifgreen and Tifway were removed from the refrigerated room, chopped into short lengths (15 to 25 mm), placed into polyethylene bags, and irradiated. Dosages of 8,100 and 9,700 rads were applied to Tifgreen and Tifway with a 4,500-Ci Gamma-Rad Irradiator, Model GR-12, U. S. Nuclear Division of International Chemicals and Nuclear Corporation.[2] The dosage rate was 3,900 rads/min.

The irradiated rhizomes of Tifgreen and Tifway were planted in flats of sterilized soil in the greenhouse. A total of 760 g of Tifgreen rhizomes was divided among 28 flats, while 1,964 g of Tifway rhizomes were divided among 46 flats. Four flats of each cultivar were maintained as a control. The number of emerged shoots was counted 21 days after planting.

Subsequently, single shoots and attached rhizome pieces were transplanted to the field and spaced on 45-cm centers. Observations of the growing propagules were noted weekly or more frequently, and mutations were labeled.

Both stolons and rhizomes of Tufcote were treated, in contrast to only rhizomes for Tifgreen and Tifway. Selected sod was washed free of soil and chopped into 20- to 25-mm lengths. A total of 1,506 g of this material was equally divided among two replicates of four treatments placed into cloth bags and irradiated. Gamma radiation was applied in August 1972 at the rate of 300 rads/min by a ^{60}Co source located in a large room at the Goddard Space Flight Center, Greenbelt, Maryland. The irradiated Tufcote and control were then planted directly into the field, covered lightly with straw, and irrigated frequently to maintain soil moisture. Propagules from sprouting stolons and rhizomes were transplanted to a spaced nursery for observation.

---

[2]Mention of a trademark or proprietary product does not constitute a guarantee or warranty of the product by the U. S. Department of Agriculture, and does not imply its approval to the exclusion of other products that may also be suitable.

RESULTS AND DISCUSSION

Because of radiosensitivity, Tifgreen and Tifway were noticeably different from the controls in shoot emergence 21 days after irradiation (Table 1). Tifway, the stouter and more vigorously elongating of the two cultivars, had fewer surviving plants (12%) at the high dosage. More than twice as many plants of Tifgreen as Tifway survived the high-dose treatment (29%). This differential response of the cultivars was in marked contrast to previous studies (7) in which 'Tifdwarf' and Tifgreen were virtually identical in shoot emergence after gamma ray treatment.

Since special effort was taken to subject both cultivars to identical environmental conditions during processing and treatment, the radiosensitivity response is believed to express a basic difference between these two cultivars. Both cultivars have 27 chromosomes, and both are interspecific sterile hybrids. The small chromosomes of *Cynodon* species may account for the comparatively higher dosages that are needed to obtain the desired response (8).

Tufcote, a winter-hardy, turf-forming selection of *C. dactylon*, responded in a manner similar to that of Tifway for sensitivity to radiation. Although dosages and treatment conditions differed, the highest dosage left few surviving plants (Table 2).

One purpose of the experiments reported here was to repeat the treatments of Tifgreen to determine if mutations were induced and if types similar

Table 1—Shoot emergence of two vegetatively propagated turf cultivars 21 days after gamma radiation.

Cultivars	Treatments, rads	Rhizomes in treated flats		Shoot emergence			
				Per flat		Per gram of rhizomes	
		No.	Wt, g	Mean	S.D.	Mean	% of control
Tifgreen	control	4	22	171	19	7.8	100
	8,100	12	28	92	9	3.3	42
	9,700	12	28	63	5	2.3	29
Tifway	control	4	51	157	5	3.1	100
	8,100	20	44	53	3	1.2	39
	9,700	20	44	16	3	0.3	12

Table 2—Number of sprouting buds and new shoots produced following gamma radiation of Tufcote rhizomes and stolons.

Treatments, rads	Average*
Control	2000 a*†
5,700	715 b
8,600	223 c
11,500	25 d

* Averages with a common letter are not significantly different at a probability of < 0.05, by Duncan's Multiple Range test.   † Number of sprouting buds and new shoots in the control, based on subsample counts.

Table 3—Types and frequencies of morphological mutations selected from two vegetatively propagated turfgrass cultivars after gamma radiation.

Tifgreen		Tifway	
Single major change	Freq.	Single major change	Freq.
Light green	22	Dwarf	11
Dwarf	5	Small stolons	6
Tall growing	3	Long runners	2
Slow growing	2	Fine leaves	1
Fine leaves	2	Slow growing	1
Erect leaves	1	Lax growth	1
Purple	1	Strongly heading	1
Multiple changes	Freq.	Multiple changes	Freq.
Light green—lax	8	Light green—small leaf	2
Light green—fine leaf	4	Dwarf—fine leaf	2
Light green—dwarf	3	Light green—fine leaf	1
Dwarf—reddish-purple	2	Light green—vigorous	1
Purple—lax	1	Light green—variegated	1
Light green—small leaf	1	Dwarf—stiff leaf	1
Less green—dwarf	1	Small—long runners	1
Small stolons—rootless	1	Light green—slow growing	1
Light green—slow growing	1	Tall—lax	1
Light green—vigorous	1	Light green—dwarf	1
Dwarf—leafy	1		
Dwarf—fine leaf	1		
Dwarf—dark green	1		

to those noted previously occurred. The observed mutations were color hue mutants, dwarfing, and other morphological changes (Table 3). Most of the mutant types were similar to the induced changes in the 1970 study (7). Fewer reddish-purple mutants were induced (1 out of 62) than were expected in this cultivar, since 1 in 24 was observed in the previous experiments. However, screening of plants during the warm summer gives poor expression of the reddish-purple pigment. The weakly reddish-purple pigment types may have been overlooked, because 1971 experiments were screened during a warmer period than the 1970 experiments. The 62 mutations induced in Tifgreen (Table 3) were mostly whole-propagule mutations.

More than 3% of the mutations were obtained from the 8,100-rad treatment of Tifgreen (Table 4). A comparison of Tifgreen and Tifway indicated that Tifgreen gave a smaller percentage of mutations at the higher dose. This trend was reversed in Tifway. Sufficient data were not available to draw firm conclusions on dosage and mutational response.

Only 8 of the 62 mutations in Tifgreen were of chimeral origin (Table 4). In Tifway, only 2 of 35 mutants were obtained from chimeras (Table 4). These results indicate that chimeral formation is infrequent and does not impose a barrier to effective use of mutation breeding in bermudagrass.

The observable mutations in Tifway were different from those found in Tifgreen (Table 3). The dwarfing mutants were present in both cultivars; however, the light green mutants, which predominated in Tifgreen, occurred infrequently in Tifway.

Only preliminary screening in the greenhouse for morphological changes has been conducted with Tufcote stolons and rhizomes irradiated in 1972. One very dwarfed mutation has been discovered. Dwarfing in this cultivar

Table 4—Effect of gamma radiation on frequency of morphological mutations in Tifgreen and Tifway bermudagrass.

Cultivars	Treatments, rads	Propagules planted	Mutants		
			Chimeral	Total	%
Tifgreen	control	642	0	0	0.0
	8,100	1,054	5	36	3.4
	9,700	1,449	3	26	1.8
Tifway	control	625	0	0	0.0
	8,100	1,694	1	24	0.9
	9,700	437	1	11	2.5

would be very desirable, because the cultivar has rapidly elongating stolons. Tufcote often grows into flower beds and over curbing, making it difficult for the homeowner to control. Thus, induced dwarfing could perhaps reduce its strong spreading habit while maintaining its excellent cold hardiness, color, and late fall growth.

These experiments and the previous work on mutagenesis of turf bermudagrass (7) have yielded 168 mutations. Some of these mutants were very weak and were subsequently lost. Numerous others, although of fundamental interest, involved undesirable color changes to light green and may be of little practical value. However, some of the mutations have important modifications that may be of commercial value. Mutants were produced that did not turn reddish-purple during cool weather. The more dwarfed mutants may find their place on bowling greens or grass tennis courts. Several of the dwarfs remained dwarfed under greenhouse glass and may find a place in indoor gardens. The selected mutations are being tested for shade tolerance, herbicidal phytotoxicity, and susceptibility to plant pests.

Ionizing radiation should be considered as an additional tool for the breeder to improve vegetatively propagated turf bermudagrass. In cases where dwarfing in a cultivar is desired, its induction by irradiation may be the most efficient breeding method available. In principle, there is no reason to limit the procedure to bermudagrasses. Vegetatively propagated grasses may be modified by implementing the methods reported here; however, each genus may present a different screening problem. Studies in other vegetatively propagated crops, fruits, tubers, and ornamentals have demonstrated diverse techniques and differing responses (1, 2, 6). Kentucky bluegrass (*Poa pratensis* L.) is usually propagated by seed but can be vegetatively propagated by rhizomes. Thus, dormant rhizomes may be amenable to induction of mutation. Selected mutants from rhizomal material could then be increased by seed propagation. The mutants would be maintained by apomictic reproduction. Work is continuing to clarify the methodology for best use of physical and chemical mutagens on turfgrasses and related grasses.

ACKNOWLEDGMENT

The author thanks Glenn W. Burton for his assistance and acknowledges support of this investigation in part by the U. S. Atomic Energy Commission, Contract No. AT–(38–1)637; U. S. Golf Association, Green Section; and Golf Course Superintendents' Association of America. Availability and use of NASA Goddard Space Flight Radiation Facility, Greenbelt, Maryland, is also appreciated

REFERENCES

1. BROERTJES, C. 1969. Induced mutations and breeding methods in vegetatively propagated species. p. 325-329. *In* Proc. Symp. Induced Mutations in Plants (Pullman, Wash.) Int. Atomic Energy Agency, Vienna.

2. ———, and J. M. BALLEGO. 1967. Mutation breeding of *Dahlia variabilis*. Euphytica 16:171-197.

3. BURTON, Glenn W. 1966. Tifway (Tifton 419) bermudagrass (Reg. No. 7). Crop Sci. 6:93-94.

4. DEAL, Elwyn E., and Joseph L. NEWCOMER. 1967. Tufcote bermudagrass. Univ. Maryland, Agron. Memo. No. 70.

5. HEIN, M. A. 1961. Registration of varieties and strains of bermudagrass (Reg. No. 5). Agron. J. 53:276.

6. NYBOM, N. 1970. Mutation breeding of vegetatively propagated plants. p. 141-147. *In* Manual on mutation breeding. Tech. Rep. 119. Int. Atomic Energy Agency, Vienna.

7. POWELL, Jerrel B., Glenn W. BURTON, and John R. YOUNG. 1973. Induced mutations in vegetatively propagated turf bermudagrasses by gamma radiation. Crop Sci. 14:327-330.

8. SPARROW, A. H., L. A. SCHAIRER, and R. C. SPARROW. 1963. Relationship between nuclear volumes, chromosome numbers, and radiosensitivity. Science 141: 163-166.

2

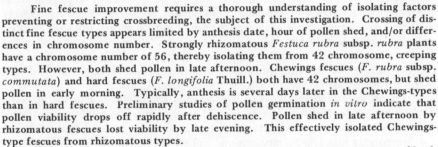

Isolation barriers and self-compatibility in selected fine fescues[1]

R.M. SCHMIT, R.W. DUELL, C.R. FUNK

Fine fescue improvement requires a thorough understanding of isolating factors preventing or restricting crossbreeding, the subject of this investigation. Crossing of distinct fine fescue types appears limited by anthesis date, hour of pollen shed, and/or differences in chromosome number. Strongly rhizomatous *Festuca rubra* subsp. *rubra* plants have a chromosome number of 56, thereby isolating them from 42 chromosome, creeping types. However, both shed pollen in late afternoon. Chewings fescues (*F. rubra* subsp. *commutata*) and hard fescues (*F. longifolia* Thuill.) both have 42 chromosomes, but shed pollen in early morning. Typically, anthesis is several days later in the Chewings-types than in hard fescues. Preliminary studies of pollen germination *in vitro* indicate that pollen viability drops off rapidly after dehiscence. Pollen shed in late afternoon by rhizomatous fescues lost viability by late evening. This effectively isolated Chewings-type fescues from rhizomatous types.

Wide variability in seed set under terylene bags occurred in selected clones of both Chewings and spreading fescues. Practical applications of self-compatibility in hybridization are discussed. Additional index words: Anthesis, Pollination, Polyploids, Rhizomes, Selfing, Speciation.

Recently, considerable breeding effort has been undertaken to develop improved fine fescue cultivars. Unfortunately, however, the taxonomy of these grasses has been the subject of much confusion in turf literature. According to Hubbard (3), *Festuca tenuifolia* Sibth., *F. ovina* L., *F. longifolia* Thuill., and *F. rubra* L. are morphologically distinct, occupy different habitats, and perform differently under turf conditions. The following discourse provides considerable evidence for the subdivision of *F. rubra* into three morphologically distinct species which are reproductively isolated by ploidy levels and/or hour of anthesis.

MATERIALS AND METHODS

In an effort to clarify the breeding interrelationships of the fine fescues, superior fine fescue clones and selections from commercial cultivars were

[1]Paper of the Journal Series, Soils and Crops Department, New Jersey Agricultural Experiment Station, Cook College, Rutgers University, The State University of New Jersey, New Brunswick, NJ 08903.

characterized morphologically from spaced plant nurseries established in late Summer 1970 and 1971. Plants were observed for date of first anthesis, dates of peak pollen shed, and daily time of anthesis during 1971 and 1972. In addition, similar entries were observed in 1 and 2-year-old turf trials at New Brunswick, New Jersey, maintained under 3 cm, twice weekly mowing and three applications of 48 kg of N/ha from NH_4NO_3 during the growing season.

Characteristics of the fine fescues that were compared included leaf morphology, rhizome development, flowering dates, and hours of anthesis in spaced plant nurseries. Three plug replicates were sampled from turf plots and were examined for the presence of rhizomes. Cross sections were made through the widest part of the leaf blade. Number of ridges on the adaxial epidermis were counted and leaf width was measured with a micrometer.

Fine fescue plants selected for chromosome counting were potted and grown in the greenhouse under natural daylength supplemented by fluorescent light which extended daylength to 18 hours. Culms were sampled at the time of emergence of the panicle tips from the boot. The anthers were dissected out, squashed in propionocarmine, and examined microscopically. Panicles having cells undergoing meiosis were fixed in Carnoy's mixture of 3:1 ethanol propionic acid. This fixed material was macerated in proprionocarmine for further study and counting. Chromosomes in favorable meiotic configurations were counted and photographed.

Pollen germination studies were conducted *in vitro* on a medium described by Teare, Maun, and Canode (4) containing 0.74 g Bactoagar (Difco Laboratories, Detroit, Michigan), 15 g sucrose, 5 ppm boric acid, and 10 ppm calcium nitrate in a 100 ml suspension. Pollen was collected from panicles of selected fine fescue clones grown in the greenhouse and maintained during the pollen germination study. During the experiment, the temperature ranged from 15 to 20 C with a relative humidity of 80 to 95%. Light intensity was low due to cloudy, rainy weather.

Pollen was removed by tapping the anthers directly over petri dishes of the above medium at 90-min intervals. Viable pollen began germination within 10 min after contacting the agar surface. Germination counts were made after 30 min. Each randomly selected microscope field constituted a sample. Ten random counts were made for each entry on each dish by examination at 100 X. Counts were expressed as a percentage of germinated pollen tubes to the total grains present in each field.

The degree of self-compatibility of selected fine fescue clones and commercial types was assessed in the greenhouse. Plants dug from the space-planted nursery were transplanted to clay pots containing 2:1 sand to loam soil. Temperatures were regulated from 18 to 25 C (day) and 10 to 15 C (night) to promote flowering.

After emergence of panicles from the leaf sheaths, pairs of panicles of equal maturity were enclosed in selfing bags. Plants were grouped into pollination blocks according to similar morphology, maturity, and hour of anthesis. During periods of peak pollen shed plants were shaken to facilitate interpollination. Panicles in the selfing bags and equivalent sets of typical open pollinated panicles were harvested for comparison in later counting of seeds set. Data were subjected to analysis of variance. Confidence intervals were calculated for the mean of each entry.

RESULTS AND DISCUSSION

Under mowed turf conditions, species differences are apparent in leaf width and in number of epidermal ridges (Table 1). Fine-leaved sheeps fescue (*F. tenuifolia* Sibth.) had the narrowest leaf and lacked prominent epidermal ridges, resulting in a roundly infolded leaf. Sheep fescue (*F. ovina* L.) had a

Table 1—Vegetative characteristics of selected fine fescues taken from the 1972 regional test at New Brunswick, New Jersey.

Fescue type and species	Variety	Number of prominent epidermal ridges	Range of leaf width, mm
Fine-leaved sheep:	S70-2	0	
F. tenuifolia	S70-2	0	0.2–0.5
Sheeps:			
F. ovina	Barok	0*,1	0.3–0.5
Hard:			
F. longifolia	HZ-71-4	0*,1	0.5–0.7
	C-26	1*,rarely 3	0.4–0.8
	Scaldis	1*,rarely 3	0.4–0.7
Chewings-types:			
F. rubra subsp. *commutata*	Banner	3,4,5*	0.8–1.2
	Horritine	3,5*	0.7–1.3
	Scarlet†	3,5*	0.8–1.2
	Waldorf	3,4,5*	0.8–1.2
	Polar	3,4,5*	0.8–1.2
	Ore K	3,4,5*	0.9–1.3
	Flevo†	3,4,5*	0.8–1.5
	Amboise	3,4,5*	1.0–1.2
	ERG 11	4,5*	1.1–1.4
	Jamestown	3,4,5*	1.0–1.4
	Koket	3,4,5*	1.0–1.5
	Barfalla	3,4,5*	1.0–1.5
	Encota	5	0.9–1.3
	Menuet	5	0.9–1.5
	Highlight	5	1.0–1.5
Rhizomatous cultivars			
Creeping (small rhizome):	HF-11	3.5*	0.8–1.2
F. rubra subsp. *tricophylla*	Dawson	4,5*	1.0–1.4
Spreading (coarse rhizome):			
F. rubra subsp. *rubra*	Boreal	4,5*6,7	1.0–1.8
	Pennlawn	3,4,5*	1.2–1.5
	F-84	3,5*	1.2–1.8
	Roda	5	1.0–1.4
	Fortress	5	1.2–1.8
	Durlawn	5	1.3–1.7
	Novarubra	5	1.3–1.8
	S59	5	1.0–1.5

* Most common number observed.   † Described as Chewings types, but plants with rhizomes were found.

narrow V-shaped leaf with an indistinct epidermal midrib. Hard fescues (*F. longifolia* Thuill.) appeared similar, possessing a V-shaped leaf but typically were wider with a well-defined midrib and two less distinct epidermal side ridges. Chewings and spreading fescue (*F. rubra*) cultivars had five or more epidermal side ridges and were distinctly greater in leaf width than the sheeps or hard fescues.

Presence or absence of and size of rhizomes were useful characters to categorize types of *F. rubra*. Chewings-type fescue (*F. rubra* subsp. *commutata* Guad., 2n = 6x = 42) always lacked rhizomes. Strongly rhizomatous types of *F. rubra* subsp. *rubra* Guad. were octoploid (2n = 8x = 56). These were characterized by aggressive spread in old turf (Fig. 1) and in the nursery (Fig. 2).

These spreading types were distinct from the hexaploid (2n = 42) types which had small rhizomes (originally described as *F. rubra* subsp. *trichophylla* Guad.) and which should remain designated as 'creeping' fescue. However, there is no term in current popular useage to distinguish the octoploid, strongly rhizomatous types from the creeping fescues. Therefore, to make this distinction more apparent, we propose that the term 'spreading' fescue should be used to refer to octoploid, strongly rhizomatous types of *F. rubra* var. *rubra*.

Chromosome counts of the fine fescues were in agreement with those previously reported (3). Hard, sheep, and Chewings-type fescue clones and cultivars examined had 21 bivalents in the pollen mother cells or 2n = 42 in the somatic tissue. Red fescue as previously reported (3) exists at two ploidy levels with Chewings fescue (2n = 42) being hexaploid and *F. rubra* subsp.

Fig. 1—A dark green spreading (*F. rubra* L. subsp. *rubra*) fescue clone growing on the median of U.S. Highway 130 near Robbinsville, New Jersey.

tricophylla Guad. also hexaploid (as typified by Dawson creeping fescue). *F. rubra* subsp. *rubra* Hack. is octoploid (2n = 56) and is represented in this study by 'Ruby' and clonal parents of 'Fortress (RU-6S)'. Differences in ploidy levels within the subspecies of *F. rubra* should place a complete isolation barrier between the creeping (2n = 42) types and strongly rhizomatous (2n = 56) types.

Further evidence for reproductive isolation is that with clones selected from locally adapted populations in a space-planted nursery, there were considerable differences among sheep, hard, and red fescue with respect to flowering date and the time at which the bulk of the pollen was shed (Table 2). Generally, sheep fescue types flowered earliest in the season, followed successively by hard and red fescue, so that one group sheds the majority of its pollen before another group initiated flowering. Differences in flowering date may thus account for considerable reproductive isolation between species.

Perhaps more important, in terms of reproductive isolation, however, were differences in time of day when flowering occurred (Table 2). Chewings-type fescues shed their pollen prior to 6 a.m. while anthesis of creeping and spreading fescues occurs from 3 to 5 p.m. at New Brunswick, N. J. These times have been observed on days favorable for pollination during four

Fig. 2—Masses of rhizomes removed from typical spaced plants from the nursery at Adelphia, New Jersey. Spreading-type fescues (*F. rubra* L. subsp. *rubra,* 2n = 56) as 'Fortress' and 'Nova rubra' have larger and thicker rhizomes than creeping-type fescues (*F. rubra* subsp. *trycophylla,* 2n = 42) such as 'Dawson' and 'Golfrood'.

Table 2—Date of flowering and hour of anthesis of fine fescue clones and cultivars in the nursery at Adelphia and New Brunswick, New Jersey.

Types	1970	1971	1972	Hour of anthesis
Chewings	May 28-June 3 53 clones	May 31-June 8 5 cultivars	June 5-June 12 14 clones	Prior to 6 a.m.
Spreading	June 5-June 10 7 clones	June 1-June 6 2 cultivars	June 6-June 12 23 clones	3-5 p.m.
Creeping	–	June 1-June 6 2 cultivars	–	2-4 p.m.
Sheeps	–	May 23-June 5 4 cultivars	May 24-June 1 11 clones	11-12 a.m.
Hard	–	May 25-May 28 2 cultivars	May 26-June 1 7 clones	Prior to 8 a.m.

flowering seasons. Likewise, there appears to be a difference in hour of anthesis between the sheep and hard fescues. Hard fescues initiated anthesis prior to 8 a.m. while sheep fescues shed pollen abundantly just prior to noon.

Time of flowering, or hour of pollen shed, is an important mechanism of isolation enforcing speciation if grass pollen is very short-lived. Percentages of germinated fescue pollen grains were tabulated to assess pollen longevity *in vitro* (Fig. 3). It was apparent that pollen shed at 6 a.m. was incapable of germinating in the early afternoon. A similar reduction in pollen germination occurred in the spreading fescues which flowered in the late afternoon.

Thus, pollen viability is of most practical concern with regard to the reproductive isolation occurring within subspecies of *F. rubra*. It is apparent from field observations and the above date that Chewings-type and spreading-type fescues are reproductively isolated by the relatively short period of pollen viability and the large time difference between time of anthesis of Chew-

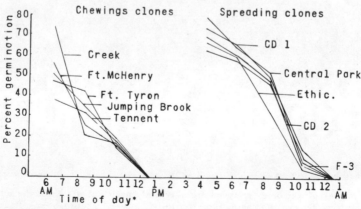

Fig. 3—Germination of red fescue pollen collected at different times of the day. *Counts made at 90-min intervals.

ings- and spreading-types. Pollen shed by the Chewings fescue in the early morning is dead by early afternoon, several hours prior to anthesis of spreading fescues. Likewise, pollen shed in the late afternoon by the spreading fescue is incapable of pollinating stigmas of Chewings fescues flowering the next morning.

It is likely that under field conditions grass pollen is even more short-lived due to higher temperature and higher solar radiation during the season of pollination in late May and early June.

The abundance of pollen grains available to a receptive stigma (Fig. 4) at anthesis and the speed with which these germinate support the hypothesis

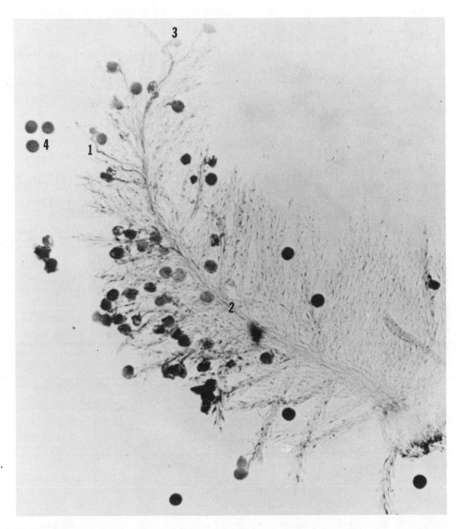

Fig. 4—Many pollen tubes (1) have grown into the stigma (2) 1 hour after arrival of pollen. Germinated pollen grains (3) stain lightly and appear collapsed. Ungerminated grains are round and dark (4).

of reproductive isolation based on hour of anthesis. Once pollen grains have grown deep into the stigma to insure fertilization, the subsequent application of pollen from a later flowering plant would have no effect. This would combine a short period of stigma receptivity in the presence of abundant pollen with a limited period of pollen viability. This would be effective in preventing outcrossing of plants belonging to different flowering groups.

Attempts to make interspecific crosses between the fine fescue species under discussion and within the subspecies of *F. rubra* have met with little success in isolated crossing and the usual result is selfing. Emasculation of fescue panicles because of their small size and structure is particularly tedious and difficult. However, the chances for hybridization could be improved through the use of highly self-incompatible parents to make reciprocal crosses. Therefore, another phase of investigation was to assess self-compatibility of promising fescue clones.

A preliminary study in 1971 using terylene pollination bags on plants in isolation indicated no significant difference between percent seed set among bagged panicles and panicles setting seed in isolation. Hence, use of pollination bags provides a reasonable estimate of self-compatibility under greenhouse conditions.

Selfing studies on clones of Chewings-type (Table 3) and spreading-type (Table 4) fescues revealed that seed set was reduced by selfing in all instances.

Table 3—Effect of self-pollination in terylene isolation bags versus open pollination on percentage seed set of Chewings-type fescue clones in 1972.

Clone	Selfed pollination		Open pollination	
	Mean	95% confidence interval estimate	Mean	95% confidence interval estimate
Ft. McHenry—1	1.1	0.0, 7.6	43.5	3.8, 83.7
Ft. McHenry—1	1.3	0.0, 6.9	43.8	3.8, 83.7
Jumping Brook	2.6	0.0, 8.0	28.7	0.0, 61.7
Ft. Tyron	3.6	0.0, 12.9	70.6	14.1, 127.2
Tennant	6.4	1.0, 11.7	41.8	9.2, 89.7
Plainfield	6.8	0.0, 16.0	69.5	12.9, 100.0
Wakil	16.0	6.7, 25.3	50.6	0.0, 107.1
Philadelphia	18.3	9.0, 27.6	77.9	21.4, 100.0

Table 4—Effect of self-pollination in terylene isolation bags versus open pollination on percentage seed set of spreading fescue clones in 1972.

Clone	Selfed pollination		Open pollination	
	Mean	95% confidence interval estimate	Mean	95% confidence interval estimate
Beachmont	0.1	0.0, 5.5	29.7	4.9, 54.5
130-17	0.4	0.0, 5.7	45.7	20.9, 70.5
Ethic 121-6	0.6	0.0, 5.9	47.3	23.5, 72.1
Radko	2.8	0.0, 10.3	13.5	0.0, 48.6
CD-1	2.8	0.0, 10.3	59.3	0.0, 94.4
Central Park	3.0	1.4, 7.3	34.6	14.2, 54.9
130-23	3.4	0.0, 8.7	42.4	17.6, 67.2
130-18	4.6	0.0, 12.1	12.1	0.0, 47.2
Ethic 122-3	7.9	2.6, 13.3	41.8	17.0, 66.6

Some clones set almost no seed when selfed, while in some others the percent seed set approached that of open-pollinated panicles from the same plant. It was apparent that differences in degree of self-incompatibility existed in both species, with the greatest differences occurring among the Chewings-type fescues.

CONCLUSIONS

F. rubra should be subdivided into three distinct, noninterbreeding species, corresponding to spreading, Chewings, and creeping, respectively, based upon comparative morphology, turf characteristics, chromosome number, and reproductive isolation including different flowering times and longevity of pollen.

Nonrhizomatous fine fescues including Chewings fescue, hard fescue, sheep fescue, and fine-leaved sheep fescue can be distinguished by leaf morphology, rhizome development, and date and hour of anthesis. In particular, hard fescue (*F. longifolia*), often regarded as a variety of sheep fescue (*F. ovina* L.), sheds pollen prior to 6 a.m. Sheeps fescue sheds pollen prior to noon.

All fine fescues examined appear to belong to highly crossbred populations. It is possible to select for types possessing different degrees of self-compatibility.

Furthermore, it is the opinion of the authors that the taxonomic basis for classification of *F. rubra* and the other turf-type fine fescues species should be reexamined with particular regard to isolating factors. Preferably this should be done by breeders and systematists, in cooperation, on a worldwide basis. The adequacy of the present nomenclature should be reassessed to determine whether the three subspecies of *F. rubra* are in fact distinct species. Changes should be proposed consistent with the knowledge of the breeding behavior of these species and the performance of improved cultivars of fine fescue species.

ACKNOWLEDGMENT

The authors wish to acknowledge the financial support for research by the New Jersey Department of Transportation and the U.S. Department of Transportation, Federal Highway Administration.

The contents of this report reflect the views of the authors who are responsible for the facts and accuracy of the data presented herein. The contents do not necessarily reflect the official views or policies of the State of New Jersey or the Federal Highway Administration. This report does not constitute a standard specification or regulation.

REFERENCES

1. DUELL, R. W., and R. M. SCHMIT. 1974. Grass varieties for roadsides. p. 541–550. *In* E. C. Roberts (ed.) Proc. Second Int. Turfgrass Res. Conf. Amer. Soc. Agron., Madison, Wis.
2. HACKEL, E. 1882. Monographia Festucarum Europaeareum. Kasel and Berlin Publ., Germany.
3. HUBBARD, C. E. 1968. Grasses. Penguin Books Ltd., Hammondsworth, England.
4. TEARE, I. D., M. A. MAUN, and C. L. CANODE. 1970. Viability of Kentucky bluegrass (*Poa pratensis* L.) pollen as influenced by collection time and temperature. Agron. J. 62:515–516.

3

Breeding bermudagrass for turf[1]

G.W. BURTON

Bermudagrass (*Cynodon* spp.) is one of the world's most versatile turfgrasses. It is a highly variable species that reproduces sexually. Out of the natural variation in the species have come selections better suited to specific turf demands. 'U-3', discovered on a Georgia golf course, was the first of these. 'Tiflawn,' the first controlled hybrid for turf between two *C. dactylon* (L.) Pers. selections, was released in 1952. It is still superior for football fields and heavy-duty turf. *C. dactylon* ✕ *C. transvaalensis* Burtt-Davy hybrids, 'Tiffine', 'Tifgreen', and 'Tifway' are sterile, fine-textured hybrids better suited to golf and home lawns. 'Tifdwarf', a dwarf mutant of Tifgreen, mowed at 5 mm and properly managed, makes a putting surface comparable with the best bentgrasses. Radiation breeding (exposing dormant sprigs of these sterile hybrids to gamma irradiation) offers a means of improving them. A total of 158 mutants, currently being evaluated at Tifton, Georgia, show many promising variations from their parent clones, including greater resistance to root knot nematode. Excellent turfgrasses with greater winterhardiness than those currently available should be found within the 480 F_1 hybrids recently made between selected *C. transvaalensis* introductions and a very winter-hardy *C. dactylon* from Berlin. Additional index words: Dwarfing, Gamma radiation, Mutants, Radiation breeding, Vegetative propagation, *Cynodon* spp.

Bermudagrass is one of the world's most versatile turfgrasses. When properly managed it is able to withstand daily defoliation to a height of 6 mm on the golf green, tolerate severe punishment on the football field, or make a beautiful lawn.

Bermudagrass is a highly variable species that reproduces sexually. Common bermudagrass *Cynodon dactylon* (L.) Pers. (2n = 36) and African bermudagrass *C. transvaalensis* Burtt-Davy (2n = 18) are the two species best suited for turf. Although bermudagrass is generally classed as a subtropical species, selected clones from Europe have survived in northcentral Michigan in the northern United States. The tough, rapidly spreading stolons and rhizomes that characterize bermudagrass make vegetative propagation prac-

---

[1] Cooperative investigations of the U.S. Department of Agriculture, Agricultural Research Service, and the University of Georgia, College of Agriculture Experiment Stations, Coastal Plain Station, Tifton, Georgia. Supported in part by U.S. Atomic Energy Commission contract No. AT(38-1)-637.

ticable and all improved varieties are planted in this way. The bermudagrass seed sold in the United States is the common type and is produced largely in Arizona.

Good turf results when a grass variety interacts with an environment usually altered by management. Obviously the best turf is realized when variety, environment, and management are compatible. Frequently the balance required for good turf can be most easily and economically achieved by altering the grass to more nearly fit the environment and the management that must be imposed. Altering the grass is usually the job of the plant breeder.

The ideal turfgrass should be a dependable perennial capable of maintaining a green, dense, weed-free turf under frequent mowing. It should be resistant to pests (diseases, insects, etc.) and wear; tolerant of shade, cold, drought, heat, and chemicals; and it should possess low weed potential—all this at low cost for establishment and maintenance. Plant breeding can create plants that more nearly embody these ideals.

Out of the natural variation in the species have come selections better suited to specific turf demands. U-3, discovered on a Georgia golf course, was the first of these in the United States. 'No-mow,' collected on the Mobile Country Club in the early 1960s, is another clone of *C. dactylon* that falls into this category.

We began breeding bermudagrasses for turf in 1946 when we started evaluating, in plots (maintained as golf greens), bermudas collected from old golf greens and hybrids from our forage breeding program that had turf potential. Characteristics sought in these grasses were dependability, good green color throughout the growing season, frost resistance, drought tolerance, weed resistance, disease resistance, and compatability with overseeded winter grasses. Relative visual ratings from 1 to 5, or 1 to 10, with 1 always being the most desirable condition, proved to be the most practical way of taking notes on individual clones. The best of these bermudas, based on 3 years of testing, was an F_1 hybrid between very dense dwarf and highly disease resistant selections of *C. dactylon* made in 1942. Officially released as 'Tiflawn' ('Tifton 57') in 1952, this bermudagrass continues to be the best variety for football fields, playgrounds, and other areas that receive rough treatment.

The next product of our turf breeding program was Tiffine (Tifton 127), a cross between Tiflawn and *C. transvaalensis* (5). This sterile triploid had a softer, finer texture and was better suited for golf greens than Tiflawn. It was soon replaced, however, by Tifgreen (Tifton 328), an F_1 triploid hybrid between *C. transvaalensis* and a superior *C. dactylon* from a golf green at the Charlott Country Club (2) in North Carolina.

Tifgreen, officially released in 1956, made a better putting surface than other varieties and has been extensively planted on golf greens. It has also been used to a lesser degree on fairways, tees, and lawns.

Our fourth improved turf variety (released in 1960) was Tifway (Tifton 419), a dark green sterile triploid (*C. transvaalensis* X *C. dactylon*) hybrid with greater frost tolerance (1). Its stiffer leaves and greater pest resistance made it particularly well suited for golf fairways and tees, lawns, and athletic fields with moderate wear.

In 1965, we released Tifdwarf, a vegetative mutant of Tifgreen (3). Tifdwarf has finer stems, shorter internodes and a smaller, softer, darker green leaves than Tifgreen. It makes a denser turf and, when mowed at 5 mm and properly managed, makes a putting surface comparable with the best bentgrasses. Although planted on lawns, it is best suited for golf greens.

Most of the other named varieties of turf bermudagrasses such as 'Everglades', 'Ormond', 'Bayshore', 'Pee Dee', 'Santa Ana', and 'Sunturf', are *C. dactylon* × *C. transvaalensis* F_1 hybrids that occurred naturally, frequently on golf courses when *C. transvaalensis* was being tested on golf greens. Their superiority in part of a golf green led to their isolation, increase, naming, and release.

All interspecific *C. dactylon* × *C. transvaalensis* hybrids are sterile and shed no pollen. This makes them attractive lawn grasses for people who are allergic to bermudagrass pollen. Such sterility facilitates their control, yet it imposes no serious handicap on their use, because they can be easily propagated by planting sprigs. The sterility of these hybrids does, however, prevent their improvement by the common plant breeding methods of hybridization and selection.

A turf bermudagrass with greater winterhardiness than any now available would have a market in the United States. Currently, there are attempts to develop such a variety, using as a source of winter-hardy genes a bermudagrass I collected in Berlin in 1966. This *C. dactylon* clone, tested by Dr. Milo Tesar, Agronomy Department, University of Michigan, has survived a number of winters in northcentral Michigan. We are testing the seed-producing properties of selfed seedlings from this clone, hoping to find one that will produce enough seeds to make seed propagation practicable. Since this winter-hardy clone is too coarse for superior bermudagrass turf, we have crossed it with two superior introductions of *C. transvaalensis* from South Africa. The 460 F_1 hybrids we have obtained from this effort will be evaluated for winterhardiness, with the help of Dr. Charles Shilling, Forestry Department, University of Kentucky, in a field planting in the mountains of eastern Kentucky and by Dr. Jerrel Powell, USDA, Beltsville, Maryland.

Attempts in recent years to improve the 'Tif'-bermudagrass by making new interspecific hybrids have failed. The best of these (nearly as good as the 'Tifs') are being kept in our nursery as insurance against a possible disaster such as the 1970 corn-blight disease. It now appears that radiation breeding will be the most practical way of improving these highly successful sterile varieties.

The success of the natural mutant Tifdwarf suggested to us several years ago that increasing the natural mutation rate with the aid of mutagenic agents could create other useful varieties. Such mutants should retain most of the superior traits of the 'Tif'-bermudagrasses, while differing in such traits as plant color, size, and pest resistance. Theoretically, treatment of highly heterozygous plants, such as our 'Tif'-bermudagrasses, with mutagens should create mutations that can be seen in the immediate M-1 generation. Our radiation breeding research with dallisgrass in the 1950s confirmed this expectation.

Thus in the winter of 1969–70, we began research designed to produce mutants in Tifdwarf and Tifgreen bermudagrasses (4). Dormant sprigs (stolons and rhizomes), washed free of soil and cut into one- or two-node sections, were treated with EMS (ethylmethanesulfonate, a chemical mutagenic agent) and gamma rays. EMS, even at levels that killed many of the dormant buds, failed to create noticeable variants.

Exposing the dormant sprigs to gamma rays from a Cobalt-60 source, however, gave rise to a number of distinctly different bud mutations. These were isolated from normal tissue as soon as they appeared, a necessary practice to keep them from being overgrown and masked by the normal tissue. Striking differences in plant and leaf size, stem diameter, internode length, and basic plant color were observed in the 60 mutants produced in Winter 1969–70.

In Winter 1970–71, dormant sprigs of Tifgreen and Tifway bermudagrass were exposed to various dosages of gamma rays ranging from 5 to 12 kr. In these studies, exposure to 9 or more kr killed most, if not all, of the sprigs. Treated sprigs were planted in flats of sterile soil and were space-planted in the field as soon as the survivors had produced several shoots 7.62 to 12.70 cm long. Mutants were selected by examining the plants early in the morning or on cloudy days when small color differences could be easily detected. Tifgreen produced a higher frequency of mutants than Tifway. Generally, only a small sector of a plant was different and occasionally these sectors, when isolated, sectored to produce two or more types. These isolated sectors were planted in pots in the greenhouse and were increased to permit field planting for evaluation.

We now have 158 mutants of Tifdwarf, Tifgreen, and Tifway, produced by exposing dormant sprigs of these varieties to gamma rays. They are currently being evaluated in field plots at Tifton, Georgia, and Beltsville, Maryland. Several of these are so much smaller and slower growing than Tifdwarf that they would seem to have no economic use except perhaps in some miniature garden. Mutants with a lower level of the purple basic plant color do not develop the undesirable brownish purple color that characterizes Tifdwarf when exposed to low (but above freezing) temperatures. These should be useful on golf greens where overseeding is practiced only to avoid the brownish purple discoloration during winter. One of the mutants has a higher level of the basic plant color than its normal parent. With the assistance of Dr. A. W. Johnson, USDA nematologist, resistance to root knot nematode, *Meloidogyne graminis* (Sledge and Golden) Whitehead, was determined by planting ten stem cuttings of each mutant in a greenhouse bed of soil artificially infested with this nematode. Small plants that developed from these stems were carefully lifted from the soil and their roots were washed free of soil, stained, and examined under a binocular microscope for the presence of root knot nematodes. Counts of the number of nematodes per plant indicated that several of the radiation-induced mutants are more resistant to root knot nematode than their parental clones.

REFERENCES

1. BURTON, Glenn W. 1960. Tifway bermudagrass. U.S. Golf Assoc. J. Turf Manage. July p. 28–30.

2. ————. 1964. Tifgreen (Tifton 328) bermudagrass for golf greens. U.S. Golf Assoc. Green Sec. Rec. May p. 11–13.

3. ————, and J. Earl ELSNER. 1965. Tifdwarf—a new bermudagrass for golf greens. U.S. Golf Assoc. Green Sec. Rec. 2(5):8–9.

4. ————, and Jerrel B. POWELL. 1971. Developing new bermudagrass for golf. Golf Superintendent. June p. 21–24.

5. HANSON, A. A., F. V. JUSKA, and Glenn W. BURTON. 1969. Species and varieties. *In* A. A. Hanson and F. V. Juska (eds.) Turfgrass science. Agronomy 14:370–409. Amer. Soc. Agron., Madison, Wis.

4

Wear tolerance of turfgrass cultivars in the United Kingdom[1]

J.P. SHILDRICK

One of the most important criteria in choosing cultivars for use in the United Kingdom is what is loosely described as wear tolerance. "Wear", meaning the many different ways in which force is applied to turf, depends on so many factors that it is misleading to postulate or look for a single character labelled "wear tolerance". "Wear" needs to be defined and assessed in terms appropriate to each turf use, and assessment is always complicated by the interaction of wear effects and turf recovery.

Three machines are used for artificial wear treatments at the Sports Turf Research Institute at Bingley, England. In recent trials, turf cultivars of *Lolium perenne* L. such as 'Manhattan' and 'Sprinter' have shown better resistance to wear and have required less mowing than most other cultivars. Mowing and artificial wear treatments on *Poa pratensis* L. have indicated several promising cultivars, particularly 'Sydsport', but no cultivar yet excels in establishment. Cultivars of *Phleum bertolonii* DC. and *Phleum pratense* L. have established themselves vigorously and withstood hard wear. Some nonrhizomatous or short rhizomatous cultivars of *Festuca rubra* L. are very valuable for turf mown at 5 mm, although some of the short rhizomatous cultivars are seriously susceptible to disease. Additional index words: Wear, Cultivar trials, *Lolium perenne*, *Poa pratensis*, *Phleum bertolonii*, *Festuca rubra* L.

There is no published or recognized set of characters by which turf cultivars are judged and chosen in the United Kingdom. The accidents of convenience, advertising, recommendation, and fortunate experience play a large part. Nevertheless certain points are kept in mind when considering cultivars. The ability of turf to withstand wear is certainly the main point because of increasing use of sports turf. Response to various heights of cut is given less attention than response to wear. However, for ornamental turf in parks and domestic lawns there is much interest in "minimum maintenance" and demand for grass to look attractive with little attention, particularly with less frequent mowing than at present. More information is needed on cultivar performance at low mowing intensities.

Disease, cold, heat, and drought tolerance are of rather low importance in cultivar choice in the United Kingdom. Color and appearance of turfgrass

---

[1]Contribution from the Sports Turf Research Institute, Bingley, Yorkshire, BD16 1AU, England.

are not yet considered very important, although official advice takes account of them.

Rate of establishment is an important criterion in cultivar selection. *Lolium perenne* L. might be used less if cultivars of other species gave an equally rapid cover. *Poa pratensis* L. seems to be particularly handicapped in the United Kingdom by its poor establishment.

DEFINITION OF WEAR, AND ITS EFFECTS

"Wear" is a convenient, omnibus term for all the ways in which force is applied to turf. Force may be applied gently or violently, vertically downward or slanted at various angles by people walking or playing games, by vehicles and machines, and even by grazing animals. "Traffic" seems a less satisfactory term, as it suggests only the passage of people and vehicles without implying some of the more random and destructive elements of wear on sports turf, such as the scrum in rugby football, the sliding tackle in association football, or the impact of the ball delivered by a fast bowler in cricket. Similarly, the Dutch and German terms "betreden" and "betreten" imply only treading by people walking or running.

Wear can affect turf by direct physical damage, by compaction of the soil, and by increasing susceptibility to disease and various stress factors. Compared with the relatively simple processes and effects of grass defoliation by mowing or grazing, the possible forms of wear and the conditions under which it occurs are almost infinite.

"Wear resistance" and "wear tolerance" are terms that apply to the ability of turf to remain unaltered under wear. Wear tolerance, better than wear resistance, recognizes that turf is damaged to some extent by any wear and that the damage has to become serious before much notice is taken of it. Wear tolerance depends on factors such as compactness (shoot density), anatomy and morphology, amount of leaf and thatch, growth rate, power of recovery, etc. Wear resistance and wear tolerance only have meaning in relation to a defined type of wear, and complete wear resistance is virtually impossible as even the lightest wear must have some effect however slight.

The terms "wear resistance" and "wear tolerance" will obviously remain convenient to outline a certain general area for thought and discussion, but it should be recognized that there is no single quality of wear tolerance. Table 1 compares several recent rankings for wear resistance or tolerance in the United States, all broadly similar, with an appreciably different Dutch ranking for resistance to treading. The comparison suggests major differences in the conditions, techniques, and assessments on which are based the United States and Dutch versions of what one would expect to be the same turf character.

A further difficulty arises in assessing the extent to which the turf has remained "unaltered for the purposes for which the turf is grown and used." For football or horse racing the appearance of the turf is less important than its properties as a foothold or level cushioning surface. Dead leaf, "thatch," or underground organs may be more important than green leaf in providing grip or traction on such fields. For sports requiring very smooth turf, as on

Table 1—Some published rankings of cool-season turfgrasses for response to wear.

Wear resistance		Wear tolerance	Resistance to treading
1	2	3	4
HIGH	HIGH	GOOD	HIGH
	Fa	Fa	
Fa			9. Lp (w), Pop
	MEDIUM	MEDIUM	
Lp	Lp	Lp	8. Php (w), Phb, Cc
	Fp	Pop	
	Pop	Fp	7. Lp (h)
Pop	Fr	Fr	
			6. Pot, Dg, Frc, Fa, Fl, Frr (s)
Fp		POOR	
		As, At	5. Fp (w), Fo, At, Php (h), Frr (t)
Frr	LOW	VERY POOR	
			4. Fp (h), Acc, As, Pon
	At	Php	
As	As	Pot	3. Acm
LOW			LOW

	Recovery from		
Recovery from wear	Moderate wear	Severe injury	Recuperative potential
5	6	7	8
HIGH	FAST		GOOD
	As		Pop
As			As
	MEDIUM	MODERATE	
Pop	Fa	As	INTERMEDIATE
	Pop	Pop	Fr
Frr	Lp	At	At
	Fp		
Fa	Fr		POOR
		PARTIAL	Fp
Fp		Fr	Fa
	SLOW	Fp	
Lp	At	Fa	VERY POOR
		Lp	Lp
LOW			Php

* Sources by column: 1—Youngner, 1969; 2—Madison, 1971; 3—Beard, 1973; 4—I.V.R.O., 1973; 5—Youngner, 1969; 6—Madison, 1971; 7—Madison, 1971; 8—Beard, 1973.

Key to Table

Acc or m	*Agrostis canina* L. spp. *canina* or *montana (arida)*	Lp	*Lolium perenne* L.
As	*Agrostis stolonifer* L. (*A. palustris* Huds.)	Phb	*Phleum bertolonii* DC. = *P. nodosum*
At	*Agrostis tenuis* Sibth.	Php	*Phleum pratense* L.
Cc	*Cynosurus cristatus* L.	Pon	*Poa nemoralis* L.
Dg	*Dactylis glomerata* L.	Pop	*Poa pratensis* L.
Fa	*Festuca arundinacea* Schreb.	Pot	*Poa trivialis* L.
Fl	*Festuca longifolia* Thuill.	h	hay cultivars
Fo	*Festuca ovina* L.	s	slender rhizome cultivars
Fp	*Festuca pratensis* Huds.	t	thick rhizome cultivars
Frc or r	*Festuca rubra* L. spp. *commutata* or *rubra*	w	pasture cultivars

bowling or golf greens, minor irregularities of surface and small differences in growth or compactness can be important. Any lack of uniformity in appearance or texture, however slight, can be disturbing. Equally, in parks and ornamental areas, people like to see an unspoiled smooth surface. At an other extreme, on cricket wickets the grass leaves are often considered less important than the grass roots. Provided the roots remain to help bind the soil, it does not matter much if the leaves disappear. Indeed, on all heavily worn areas the most important parts of the grass are those which are least visible—the crowns, the roots, and the rhizomes. Thus, according to the use, assessment of survival ought to relate to green leaf, to all aboveground plant tissues, to underground parts, or to the complete plant.

Finally, there is the time factor, and the problem of distinguishing between survival and recovery. Unless assessment of survival is made immediately after wear there will be some element of recovery in the turf when it is assessed. If wear is brief and severe or if it occurs in the dormant season— either in actual use or in some accelerated wear simulation—survival can be isolated from recovery. When wear and recovery occur simultaneously, the parallel processes of destruction and repair cannot be separated, quite apart from the confusing effects of environment and management on growth. "Recovery from wear" or "recuperative potential" has been taken as a distinct turfgrass character (some recent United States rankings are included in Table 1), but for many practical situations it is part of the whole complex process which enables the turf to remain more or less unaltered for its essential purpose.

Four points have been discussed:
1) A definition of wear which recognizes its variable nature;
2) The difficulties likely to arise in postulating and looking for a single character labelled "wear tolerance";
3) The need to assess wear in terms of turf use; and
 4) The problems—which may not matter in practice—of separating wear effects from turf recovery.

These points have become evident from artificial wear testing done during the last 3 years at the Sports Turf Research Institute at Bingley, England. They serve as background to the data reviewed below, and as acknowledgement of the shortcomings of the work so far. This has been done with limited time and resources and, because of the urgent need in the United Kingdom for information on cultivar performance under heavy wear, it has been done without either the comparisons with wear in real turfgrass use or the detailed studies of plant behavior under various treatments which ought to have preceded any cultivar testing.

TECHNIQUES FOR ARTIFICIAL WEAR

One of the first machines for simulating wear on turfgrasses was designed and used in California (Perry, 1958; Youngner, 1961). It had two sets of wear elements consisting of corrugated wooden feet to give abrasive wear and rollers covered with golf shoe spikes to punch and tear the turf. Each plot was given enough revolutions to reach a standard "end point" of wear, with all leaf blades removed. All pure grass swards treated were more resistant to the scuffing than to the tearing, and recovered sooner. It was suggested that this was due to the spiked roller having at least two effects, injury to crowns, roots, and rhizomes, and compaction of the soil. Tests were also made on mixtures mown at different heights prior to treatment (Youngner, 1962).

A machine designed primarily to give compaction was developed in Washington State (Goss and Roberts, 1964). Metal feet on a JR aerifier (West Point Corp., West Point, Pennsylvania)[2] gave, according to their size, pressures ranging from 0.56 kg/cm^2, given as the approximate pressure of a walking man, to 1.2 kg/cm^2 or more. A similar machine was used at Ottawa, (Cordukes, 1967) to make compaction studies on turfgrass mixtures and the soil underneath.

Recently, compaction treatments have been adopted by various workers in Germany and the Netherlands. These are made either with heavy studded rollers (van der Horst, 1970; Skirde, 1970) or with modified aerators (Kamps, 1969). At the Institute for Research on Varieties of Field Crops (I.V.R.O.) in the Netherlands, the roller of an Atco trailer seat fitted with studs has been used.

A man of 80 to 90 kg standing in football boots each with seven studs of diameter 12 mm exerts a pressure of 5 to 6 kg/cm^2. Beard (1973) quotes that a 90-kg man standing in ordinary shoes exerts pressures of 0.4 kg/cm^2, 1.2 kg/cm^2 putting his heel down in walking, 10 kg/cm^2 standing in football boots each with seven cleats of 9 mm diameter, and two or three times this pressure when running.

MATERIALS AND METHODS

Normal mowing and fertilizer regimes for cultivar trials at Bingley, England have been described elsewhere (Shildrick, 1969, 1971, 1972).

A typical soil textural analysis from the Experiment Ground is:

Soil	Size, mm	%
Sand		
Very coarse	2.0 –1.0	3
Coarse	1.0 –0.5	12
Medium	0.5 –0.25	13
Fine	0.25 –0.125	17
Very fine	0.125–0.050	14
Silt		
Coarse	0.050–0.020	10
Fine	0.020–0.002	12
Clay	< 0.002	14

Soil pH ranges from 5.5 to 7.0, according to the nature of each trial. The average annual rainfall for 1968-72 was 914 mm.

---

[2] Mention of a trade name does not constitute an endorsement of the product.

Artificial wear treatment

Three machines were used in artificial wear studies at the Sports Turf Research Institute. A Ryan Ren-O-Thin aerator (RA) (Ryan Equipment Co., St. Paul, Minnesota) with special stud-ended tines gave battering wear to the turf. As the reel height is altered, the studs either act like flail mowers, simply removing leaf, or cut into the crowns of plants or even into the ground, leaving a more or less grooved effect. The machine is intended to simulate hard scuffing and sliding with studded boots, as in football. A Webb trailer seat (TR) (Wolseley-Webb Ltd., Witton, Birmingham, England) fitted with studs on the roller was towed behind a mower to give crushing wear and soil compaction. With the full weight of the rider on one line of studs, the maximum pressure at rest is about 2.8 kg/cm². A Sisis self-propelled Auto-Outfield Spiker (SS) gave scuffing wear by sections of auto tires fastened to slightly curved plates fitted round the periphery of the discs that normally carry the spikes. The plates with facing of rubber tread are drawn across the turf slightly slower than the forward speed of the machine. This machine causes less damage than the modified aerator, and is intended for more closely mown turf.

The first two machines have previously been described in more detail (Shildrick, 1971). The modified aerator (RA) is normally followed by the trailer roller with studs (TR) to give compaction and tread back the tufts of grass exposed by the aerator. The aerator has been used at all seasons, the studded roller mostly when the ground is neither frozen nor baked hard. Both have mainly been used on species and mixtures that might be suitable for heavy use in winter, such as football. With both machines, each pass is made at right angles to the previous one. Usually two passes are made on each treatment date, and treatments usually take place once a week.

Artificial wear treatments were made on trials on cultivars and species mixtures. Individual plots were 2 to 4 m² in size, more or less square, in random layout, with three or four replicates. With the modified aerator, the largest possible size of plot and number of replicates is desirable because wear is rather uneven. However level the turf seems to be, slightly raised areas are scalped and hollows left relatively undamaged. The effects of the studded roller and the scuffer are more uniform.

Results have generally been assessed as percentage ground cover of identifiable material of the species (green and dead leaf), measured by point quadrat (first hits only), or sometimes estimated visually.

Assessment is in terms of ground cover, rather than shoot number or tiller number (used by Kamps, 1969), because it is probably the main character which the turf user considers in assessing the survival or recovery of turf after wear, and to economize in time.

Growth of cultivars under infrequent cutting

Most cultivar trials at Bingley are mown once or twice a week. Relative regrowth rates were determined from small individually cut plots (0.3 to 0.4 m², replicated twice). They were measured once or twice according to growth, and each time the top leaf level reached 100 mm or more, the plots were cut to 50 mm, using an electric hedge cutter sliding over a wooden frame placed round the plot to give a standard cutting level.

RESULTS AND DISCUSSION

Lolium perenne L.

Tables 2 and 3 show some results from recent trials. 'Aberystwyth S.23' is an acceptable turf cultivar, and is widely used in the United Kingdom. The majority of cultivars in the two trials were not significantly different from Aberystwyth S.23 when mown at 19 mm (Table 2, Cols. 1 and 2), but under the artificial wear treatments 'Manhattan' and 'Sprinter' were significantly better than Aberystwyth S.23. Manhattan in particular has been outstanding among the cultivars so far tested in this way. Manhattan, Sprinter, and 'Romney' (a selection out of 'Kent Indigenous') have been characterized by good filling-in in the first few months after sowing, continuing high shoot density, and lower growth rate than average. Although all three cultivars have tended to show more than average symptoms of red thread disease in ordinary mown plots, where the winter appearance of Manhattan has also been rather poor, no disease symptoms have appeared on the plots receiving artificial wear, and there has been no fault in the winter appearance of Manhattan.

Table 2—Percentage ground cover (in month shown) of cultivars of *Lolium perenne* L. after three treatments (Trial sown, June 1969).

| | Nitrogen levels* | | |
| | High | Average | |
Cultivar	No wear, October 1971	No wear, October 1971	Wear,† April 1971
Manhattan	51	36	40
Barenza pasture	54	35	29
Aberystwyth S.23	48	36	29
Kent Indigenous	46	36	28
Romney	58	39	27
Lamora	36	23	23
Sportiva	44	26	21
Aberystwyth S.101	42	29	20
Compas	37	32	20
Aberystwyth S.321	42	30	16
Stadion	49	28	14
Aberystwyth S.24	28	11	11
Average	45	30	23
LSD (P = 0.05)	12.4	12.7	8.9

* N levels (kg/ha) high of 300 in 1970, 408 in 1971; average 168 in 1970, 258 in 1971.
† Wear October 1970–March 1971. Thirty-eight treatments with a Ryan Ren-O-Thin aerator (RA) 1/week, 1970 and 2/week, 1971. Mowing height was 19 mm. Figures include slight amounts of weed grasses.

Table 3—Percentage ground cover (in January 1973) in plots of cultivars of *Lolium perenne* L. after artificial wear treatment (Trial sown, Aug. 1971).

Cultivar	Percent all grass leaf	Percent bare slippery mud
Manhattan	39	27
Sprinter	27	37
Romney	26	38
Mom Lp16	26	44
Kent Indigenous	24	48
Pelo	22	47
Aberystwyth S.23	22	52
Melle pasture	22	56
Angela	21	63
Barenza pasture	20	59
Splendor	20	60
HE 33	20	60
Sportiva	20	62
Bar Lp 7	19	59
Lamora	19	60
Caprice	17	68
Cropper	17	70
Stadion	17	73
Aberystwyth S.24	15	72
LSD (P = 0.05)	4.0	9.8

* Wear treatment: March to Aug. 1972, 52 treatments with TR; Aug. 1972 to Jan. 1973, 34 treatments with RA, 34 with TR, and eight plain roller treatments.

Table 3 shows that the studded roller alone was first used in summer on this trial. It created no perceptible differences between cultivars, so the modified aerator was used. This at once gave differences. A heavy plain roller was substituted for the studded roller, to follow the aerator on eight occasions when the ground was baked hard.

The slower rate of growth of Manhattan and Sprinter has been observed in normal trial plots, and is also now being assessed in small plots cut down to 50 mm each time they reach 100 mm. Over the 9 months from sowing in mid-July 1972 until the end of April 1973, Manhattan and Sprinter required seven to eight cuts, Aberystwyth S.23 eleven cuts, and 'Aberystwyth S.24' twelve.

Poa pratensis L.

Table 4 shows that in one trial of 12 cultivars, eight retained good ground cover after their first year with mowing brought down to 19 mm. Continued artificial wear reduced stands on all cultivars with severe stand losses for 'Primo,' 'Arista,' and 'Campus.' 'Sydsport' was most consistent and maintained stand best throughout the test. Although handicapped by initial poor stands, 'Merion' retained ground cover under wear and was among the group. Rankings from the initial wear treatment were merely accentuated in the next 18 months. Whether other types of treatment and other dates would give different results is open to question, although in another earlier trial most of the same cultivars were given wear in spring and gave similar

Table 4—Percentage ground cover (in months shown) of cultivars of *Poa pratensis* L. before and after artificial wear treatment (Trial sown, July 1970).

Cultivar	Percent cover before wear; mown at 19 mm Aug 1971	Percent cover during wear			Percent cover after recovery Mar 1973
		Nov 1971	May 1972	Aug 1972	
Sydsport	82	63	73	58	67
Fylking	86	68	72	48	59
Birka	89	73	61	46	53
Baron	90	68	62	44	54
Merion	43†	51†	50†	43	54
Prato	78	48	64	40	44
Primo	84	36	46	18	21
Arista	70	46	38	11	15
Campus	81	58	44	7	6
LSD (P = 0.05)	7.6	19.4	13.9	20.6	18.9

* Wear treatment in periods between assessments: Sept. to Nov. 1971—22 treatments with RA and 4 with TR; Nov. to May 1972—22 treatments with RA and 30 with TR; May to Aug. 1972—22 treatments with RA and 22 with TR; Aug. to Sept. 1972—14 treatments with RA and 4 with TR.
† Sample contamination by *Poa annua*: cover of Merion unduly low at first.

results, the average ranking order in three assessments (April, May, Sept.) being Sydsport, Merion, 'Birka', 'Fylking', and 'Prato' ('Baron' not in trial) (Shildrick, 1971).

Of the six cultivars at the head of the list in Table 4, Sydsport, Baron, and Prato appeared to be better in speed and vigor of establishment than Fylking, Birka, or Merion.

The shoot density (sward compactness) of Sydsport has been outstanding in recent trials at the Sports Turf Research Institute, and this seems to have been the main cause of its good performance under artificial wear. Moreover, whereas in mown plots Sydsport shows many unattractive dead yellow leaves in winter, in plots under wear treatment there is little or no dead leaf but instead a healthy green color from live shoots even in winter.

Phleum bertolonii DC. and *P. pratense* L.

The cultivars of *P. bertolonii* (e.g., 'Aberystwyth S.50', 'Evergreen', 'Maris Paviour', 'Pedestra', 'Sport') and the late-heading ("pasture") cultivars of *P. pratense* (e.g., 'Aberystwyth S.48', 'King', 'Pastremo') have considerable interest in the United Kingdom for sports turf mown at 12 to 25 mm. At Bingley, establishment of these timothy grasses is much stronger and is successful over a longer season than that of *Poa pratensis*. Height of growth is appreciably less than that of *Lolium perenne*, and winter color and early spring growth are good. There has been no disease problem. The main disadvantage compared with *Poa pratensis* is lack of rhizomes. *P. bertolonii* has stolons but these are easily damaged by heavy wear. The yellow to blue green color is less attractive than that of *Lolium perenne* and *Poa pratensis* and the leaf, especially that of *P. pratense*, coarser.

The four *Phleum* cultivars shown in Table 5 were persistent under artificial wear. The *Phleum* cultivars survived artificial wear more or less as

Table 5—Percentage ground cover in April 1971 of all grass in plots of cultivars of *Phleum* spp. and *Lolium perenne* L. under almost identical artificial wear treatment in separate but adjacent trials (Trial sown, June 1969).

Species and cultivar	Mown prior to wear treatment* at		
	11 mm	19 mm	25 mm
Lolium perenne (168 kg/ha N in 1970)			
Manhattan		40	
Aberystwyth S.23		29	
Aberystwyth S.24		11	
Phleum bertolonii (129 kg/ha N in 1970)			
Aberystwyth S.50	33		24
Sport	30		18
Phleum pratense (129 kg/ha N in 1970)			
Aberystwyth S.48	33		28
King	33		24
LSD (P = 0.05)	N.S.	8.9	5.9

* Wear treatments Oct. 1970–March 1971. Thirty-eight RA treatments on *L. perenne*, 42 RA treatments on *Phleum* spp.; 1/week in 1970 and 2/week in 1971.

well as Aberystwyth S.23 in a similar test adjacent to them. (This is in accord with the I.V.R.O. ratings in Table 1.) It is interesting to note the better survival of the plots mown at 11 mm than those mown at 25 mm.

Festuca spp.

Festuca rubra L. ssp. *commutata* Gaud. (Chewings fescue) is widely used in the United Kingdom for fine turf, giving a denser, stronger, less disease-prone sward than some of the smaller *Festuca* spp. (e.g., *F. ovina* L., *F. tenuifolia* Sibth.), and a finer-leaved, healthier, and more persistent sward under 5 mm mowing than cultivars of *F. rubra* ssp. *rubra* (creeping red fescue). In recent years, however, it has become clear that *F. rubra* ssp. *rubra* consists of at least two main types, called here Group I and Group II. Group I is a fine-leaved type, with relatively short or fine rhizomes, tolerant of close mowing but often susceptible to dollar spot disease. Group II is a coarser, more vigorous type, with strong rhizomes. Vos and Scheijgrond (1969) separate the two groups on chromosome number (2n = 42 and 2n = 56, respectively).

Table 6 shows how, in performance under mowing at 5 to 8 mm, the Group I cultivars overlap Chewings fescues at one end of the range and the more typical creeping red fescues at the other end. A major defect, however, has been serious susceptibility to dollar spot disease at Bingley. 'Cumberland Marsh', 'Dawson', 'Golfrood' and 'Oasis' have all shown this. They are also rather susceptible to red thread disease, in common with cultivars of Group II. Most cultivars of Chewings fescue are little affected by either disease.

Table 6—Average ground cover after three years mowing at 5 to 8 mm of some cultivars of *F. rubra* L.

Species and cultivar			
	Creeping red fescue		
Chewings fescue	Group I	Group II	Percent ground cover
Barfalla ⎫ Highlight ⎬			64 a*
Famosa ⎭			58 ab
Koket			57 abc
Encota			56 bc
	Dawson		51 c
Oregon			43 d
Erika			40 de
	Golfrood	Gracia ⎫ Novorubra ⎬	34 efg
	Oasis		33 efgh
		Dasas	31 fgh
		Canadian	28 ghi
		Bargena	26 hi
		Agio ⎫ Danish ⎬	22 i

* Cultivars with a common letter are not significantly different (P = 0.05) using Duncan's Multiple Range test.

Table 7—Some representative cultivars of *Festuca* spp. rhizome development in rows and growth under infrequent cutting.

		Rhizome shoots		No. of cuts
Species	Cultivar	1971*	1972†	at 100 mm‡
Festuca tenuifolia	Barok	--	0	0
Festuca pseudovina	Vendôme	--	0	1
Festuca ovina	Charming	--	0	0
Festuca longifolia	Biljart	0	0	0
Festuca rubra	Cascade	--	0	3
ssp. *commutata*	Highlight	0	0	2½
Festuca rubra	Cumberland Marsh	--	9	½
ssp. *rubra* Group I	Dawson	8	--	--
(short or fine rhizomes)	Golfrood	3	16	2½
	Oasis	5	--	3½
Festuca rubra	Bargena	22	--	4½
ssp. *rubra* Group II	Boreal	--	21	3
(typically with strong rhizomes)	Canadian	18	--	4
	Durlawn	--	33	2
	Echo Daehnfeldt	--	54	6½
	Novorubra	11	--	5½
	Rapid	18	31	3

* Number of shoots per 3-m row, Jan. 1972, 6 months after sowing.   † Number of shoots per 2.5-m row, Nov. 1972, 5 months after sowing.   ‡ Number of times leaves grew to 100 mm and were then cut to 50 mm, in first 8 months after sowing (Aug. 1972–Apr. 1973). ½ = only one of two replicates cut.

Table 7 includes a range of representative cultivars of various *Festuca* spp. from over 70 cultivars and selections of *F. rubra* and 20 of other fine-leaved species at present in trials at Bingley, and gives preliminary data on two aspects under study. As an indication of ability to form and repair a turf for hard wear, rhizome development is being studied in row plots. In two series, sown in July 1971 and July 1972, shoots from rhizomes were apparent in the interrow spaces within 5 or 6 months. Although the average level of numbers in the second series was greater than in the first series, the numbers shown in Table 7 are fewer for the cultivars of creeping red fescue Group I than for those in Group II.

The final column of Table 7 shows the progress in the first 8 months (mainly winter months) of a trial to compare growth of cultivars under infrequent mowing for "minimum maintenance". In this, the species at the top of the list score best, though for practical use their slow weak establishment would be a disadvantage. Chewings fescue cultivars occupy a midway position, and the low growth of Cumberland Marsh is notable.

REFERENCES

1. BEARD, J. B. 1973. Turfgrass: Science and culture. Prentice-Hall, Inc., Englewood Cliffs, N. J.
2. CORDUKES, W. E. 1967. Compaction and wear of turf grasses. Greenhouse, Garden, Grass 6(3):1–5.
3. GOSS, R. L., and J. ROBERTS. 1964. A compaction machine for turfgrass areas. Agron. J. 56:522.
4. INSTITUTE FOR RESEARCH ON VARIETIES OF FIELD CROPS. 1973. 48e rassenlijst voor landbouwgewassen. (48th list of varieties of field crops). I.V.R.O., Wageningen, The Netherlands.
5. KAMPS, M. 1970. Effects of real and simulated play on newly sown turf. p. 118–123. In Proc. First Int. Turfgrass Res. Conf. Sports Turf Research Institute, Bingley, England.
6. MADISON, J. H. 1971. Practical turfgrass management. Van Nostrand Reinhold Co., N. Y.
7. PERRY, R. L. 1958. Standardized wear index for turfgrasses. S. Calif. Turfgrass Culture 8(4):30–31.
8. SHILDRICK, J. P. 1970. Turfgrass variety trials in the U. K. p. 88–99. In Proc. First Int. Turfgrass Res. Conf. Sports Turf Research Institute, Bingley, England.
9. ————. 1971. Grass variety trials, 1971. J. Sports Turf Res. Inst. 47:86–127.
10. ————. 1972. Trials of fescue and bent cultivars, 1971–72. J. Sports Turf Res. Inst. 48:44–101.
11. SKIRDE, W. 1970. The development, present position and future objectives of turf research in Giessen. J. Sports Turf Res. Inst. 46:33–45.
12. VAN DER HORST, J. P. 1970. Sports turf research in the Netherlands. J. Sports Turf Res. Inst. 46:46–57.
13. VOS, H., and W. SCHEIJGROND. 1970. Varieties and mixtures for sports turf and lawns in the Netherlands. p. 34–44. In Proc. First Int. Turfgrass Res. Conf. Sports Turf Research Institute, Bingley, England.
14. YOUNGNER, V. B. 1961. Accelerated wear tests on turfgrasses. Agron. J. 53:217–218.
15. ————. 1962. Wear resistance of cool-season turfgrasses: effects of previous mowing practices. Agron. J. 54:198–199.
16. ————. 1969. A review of recent turfgrass research in Southern California. Calif. Turfgrass Culture 19(1):6–7.

5

Behavior of turfgrass species in France[1]

B. BOURGOIN, C. BILLOT, M. KERGUELEN, A. HENTGEN, P. MANSAT

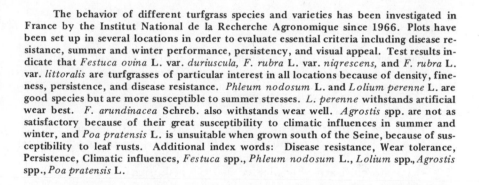

The behavior of different turfgrass species and varieties has been investigated in France by the Institut National de la Recherche Agronomique since 1966. Plots have been set up in several locations in order to evaluate essential criteria including disease resistance, summer and winter performance, persistency, and visual appeal. Test results indicate that *Festuca ovina* L. var. *duriuscula*, *F. rubra* L. var. *niqrescens*, and *F. rubra* L. var. *littoralis* are turfgrasses of particular interest in all locations because of density, fineness, persistence, and disease resistance. *Phleum nodosum* L. and *Lolium perenne* L. are good species but are more susceptible to summer stresses. *L. perenne* withstands artificial wear best. *F. arundinacea* Schreb. also withstands wear well. *Agrostis* spp. are not as satisfactory because of their great susceptibility to climatic influences in summer and winter, and *Poa pratensis* L. is unsuitable when grown south of the Seine, because of susceptibility to leaf rusts. Additional index words: Disease resistance, Wear tolerance, Persistence, Climatic influences, *Festuca* spp., *Phleum nodosum* L., *Lolium* spp., *Agrostis* spp., *Poa pratensis* L.

Interest in turf in France is recent, but continually growing. The quantity of seed used has increased from some 50,000 quintals in 1966 to about 80,000 in 1972 (*Lolium perenne* L. 40,000, *Festuca rubra* L. 18,500, *Poa pratensis* L. 14,500 quintals). About all is imported from other parts of Europe (Holland and Denmark) and from the United States.

It is important to know whether the species and varieties imported are suited for pure or for mixed sowings. A wide range of different climate zones are found in France. In general the French climate outside the Mediterranean zone is oceanic with continental tendencies being increasingly marked toward the east. Broadly, six zones can be designated based on January and July temperatures and summer rainfall.

    I. Flemish oceanic climate—cool in winter and summer, with a regular but poor rainfall which is lowest in summer.

    II. Breton oceanic climate—mild in winter, cool in summer with abundant rainfall throughout the year, particularly in autumn and winter.

[1]Contribution from Institut National de la Recherche Agronomique, France.

III. Aquitain oceanic climate—mild in winter, hot in summer. Rainfall is plentiful, particularly in the spring. Significant summer rainfall is carried by storms.

IV. Paris Basin oceanic climate with continental tendencies—rainfall is low (approximately 550 mm) but well spaced throughout the year (frequent summer storms).

V. Eastern French oceanic climate with continental tendencies—severe winters and reasonably warm summers. Rainfall is abundant, especially in summer when it is associated with violent storms.

VI. Mediterranean climate—mild in winter (except in the Rhone valley which is chilled by wind) and hot in summer. Rainfall is poor, though a little better than that of Paris. It is abundant in autumn but practically non-existant in summer.

A series of trials was established by the Institut National de la Recherche Agronomique regions to judge the value of the main species for disease resistance, summer and winter performance, persistence, and general appearance, which are important for any site and intended use.

MATERIALS AND METHODS

There were six trial sites: Douai, zone I on clay silt soil; Rouen, between zones I and II and also on a clay silt; Versailles, zone IV on silt; Valence, between zones V and VI on a stoney sandy silt; Avignon, zone VI on a very fine, impervious silt; and Lusignan, between zones II and III on a calcareous clay.

The trials at the first 5 sites, which included 36 cultivars representing 9 turfgrass species, were established in 1969. Fifteen cultivars of *Festuca rubra* and seven of *Poa pratensis* were chosen for further study.

The same cultivars were planted in 1970 at Lusignan where a turf research laboratory has been established.

At all sites, seedings were made in the spring (early in the south and late in the north) to take advantage of the rain which is always abundant at that season. Seeding rates were approximately 30 g/m² for *Lolium perenne* and *Festuca rubra*, 25 g/m² for *F. ovina* L., 20 g/m² for *Poa pratensis* and *Cynosurus cristatus* L., 10 g/m² for *Phleum nodosum* L., and 5 g/m² for the *Agrostis* spp. Maintenance of the trials varied with the site. Annual nitrogen fertilization varied from 120 to 280 of K/ha applied in 3 to 7 dressings of 40 units of K/ha. Phosphate and potassium dressings were similar, about 120 kg/ha at the end of autumn.

Irrigation was practiced in the Mediterranean zone. At Valence, 25 mm of water was applied every 10 days in the spring and every 4 days in summer. There were several applications of 40 mm of water at Avignon.

Mowing, carried out with a reel mower at Lusignan and with rotary mowers elsewhere, varied in height and frequency. Different types of management were compared at certain sites. The extremes were weekly cuts to 2-cm height during the growing season at Lusignan, Rouen, Douai, and Valence, and a monthly cut to 5-cm height at Avignon and Versailles.

RESULTS AND DISCUSSION

Disease resistance

The principal turf diseases in France are the rusts, incited by *Puccinia* sp. (with bright yellow-orange uredospores) on *Poa pratensis,* evident from late spring to midautumn; *Puccinia graminis* Pers. on *Poa pratensis* and *Festuca rubra* in late summer; *Puccinia coronata* Corda on *Lolium perenne,* also in late summer.

Puccinia sp. attack on *Poa pratensis* is the most prevalent. Attack is increasingly severe from north to south, so that *P. pratensis* is not suitable for use south of the Seine, the sward becoming an undesirable orange-brown color. In the south, the plants may even die. However, there are differences between cultivars in susceptibility. 'Parade,' 'Monopoly,' 'Baron,' and 'Fylking' are the least susceptible while 'Merion' and 'Prato' are severely attacked.

The other rusts are rarely or hardly visible on plots which are frequently and closely mown, especially on *Festuca rubra.* However, some attacks on *Lolium perenne* are severe, depending on the cultivar. 'Manhattan' was particularly susceptible to *Puccinia coronata.*

Other diseases were noted, especially in the north. *Corticium* sp. and *Fusarium* sp. were observed on *Lolium perenne* and *Festuca rubra.* In winter at Lusignan, *Fusarium* attacks on *Agrostis* spp. and *Festuca rubra* were observed, as were attacks of *Helminthosporium vagans* Drechsler on *Poa pratensis,* 'Silo,' 'Park,' and 'Delft' being the most susceptible cultivars and Prato and Merion the most resistant. In contrast to the rusts, these diseases are less severe toward the south.

Winter and summer performance

In Summer 1971, without irrigation and in relatively dry conditions at Lusignan and Douai, certain cultivars of *Festuca rubra littoralis* ('Oase,' 'Dawson,' and 'Golfrood') remained green, as did *Lolium perenne* cut weekly to 2 cm and the *F. ovina duriuscula* cultivars 'Biljart' and 'Scaldis.' By contrast all the other species studied were brown or pale green in color: *Phleum nodosum, Poa pratensis, Festuca rubra nigrescens, F. rubra rubra, Agrostis* sp. *Cynosurus cristatus,* and *Lolium perenne* cut less frequently. *F. arundinacea* and other *F. ovina* cultivars observed only at Lusignan showed the same fault. In the moister areas (Rouen) or with irrigation all species remain green.

In winter at Avignon, Douai, Lusignan, Valence, and Versailles, the *Festuca rubra nigrescens* cultivars ('Highlight,' 'Koket,' 'Encota') were greener than those of *F. rubra littoralis* (Golfrood, Oase, Dawson) and *F. rubra rubra* ('Rapid,' 'Silo,' 'Roda,' 'Rubina roskilde').

At Rouen, the *Festuca rubra* cultivars as a group were more definitely yellowed during the winter period. In contrast, *Lolium perenne, Festuca ovina duriuscula, Cynosurus cristatus* and especially *Phleum nodosum* were very green. The appearance of *Poa pratensis* varied by cultivar. Prato, Merion, and Baron were very green while 'Sydsport,' Fylking, 'Captan,' and Monopoly were whitish in color.

The *Agrostis* spp., especially *A. canina* L., were red-brown in winter at all sites; of these, however, the cultivar 'Tracenta' of *A. tenuis* Sibth. had the least discoloration.

At Lusignan, *F. arundinacea* cultivars were pale except for Mediterranean types which were grown in frost-free periods.

Persistence

Persistence depends on the site, but even more so on the species, its management and use. *Festuca rubra* was the most persistent species observed. A sward analysis at Rouen in 1971 of a trial of 15 cultivars of the principal turf species laid down in 1966 and mown regularly to 4 cm every fortnight showed that the cleanest and least debilitated was *Festuca rubra*. The *F. rubra nigrescens* varieties, notably Highlight, appeared to be better than the others. 'Melle Pature' (*Lolium perenne*), 'Sport' (*Phleum nodosum*) and Merion (*Poa pratensis*) were judged fairly persistent. The other cultivars of *P. pratensis,* those of *F. ovina,* of the *Agrostis* spp., and of *Cynosurus cristatus* had practically disappeared.

Comparisons of different managements at Rouen, Douai, and Valence showed that *Lolium perenne, Festuca rubra,* and *Poa pratensis* deteriorated faster with fortnightly cuts to 2 cm than with weekly cuts to 2 cm or with fortnightly cuts to 4 cm.

Studies of resistance to wear by treading have been carried out at Lusignan since 1972 with a 200-kg simulation roller of the type developed by J. P. van der Horst. Two intensities were applied, one calculated to be equivalent to 2 to 3 football matches per week and the other 8 to 10 matches.

When wear is strongest, *Lolium perenne* is the most resistant species ahead of *Festuca arundinacea. Poa pratensis* and *Phleum nodosum* are not as good, this being particularly marked if the treatment occurs over summer. *F. ovina* and the *Agrostis* spp. are practically valueless. After ceasing wear treatments, *Poa pratensis* with a recolonized rhizome system quickly patches areas from which it had disappeared, followed by *Phleum nodosum* with the other species very much slower.

When the wear is less intensive, *Lolium perenne* is still the most resistant, ahead of *Festuca arundinacea* and *F. rubra,* particularly *nigrescens* and *littoralis*. This is important for this last species presents a more pleasing appearance than the other two. Hence, its attraction increases for amenity lawns, public gardens, and urban green areas subject to less wear than sports grounds. Conversely, for intensive sporting use, *L. perenne* and *F. arundinacea* seem to be the two most wear-tolerant species.

Visual appeal

Visual appeal was noted monthly at Lusignan and at least twice each season elsewhere. It encompasses the characters already discussed, apart from resistance to wear, as well as resistance to weed invasion and the quality of the plant cover.

At all sites the *Festuca rubra nigrescens* cultivars (notably Highlight, 'Flevo,' Encota), those of *F. rubra littoralis* (Golfrood, Oase, Dawson), as well as some of the *F. rubra rubra* (*'Nova rubra,'* Rapid) and the *F. ovina duriuscula* cultivar Biljart were the most attractive. Their aesthetic value (fine leaves, plant cover, and regular green color throughout the year), their satisfactory plant health, and their persistence were responsible for the superiority of these species.

Lolium perenne

While less aesthetically pleasing (less dense, more open sward) and growing faster, *Lolium perenne* was the next most attractive after *Festuca rubra nigrescens*. When well managed, it was shown to be of value in all trials. The most attractive cultivars were 'Perma,' 'Scotia,' Melle Pature, 'Parcour,' 'Pelo,' 'S.23'. Manhattan would have been the best if it had not been the most susceptible to rust.

Phleum nodosum

Except for its undesirable pale appearance throughout the summer (similar in this respect to badly managed *Lolium perenne*), *Phleum nodosum* was fairly appealing. *Cynosurus cristatus* was inferior to *Phleum nodosum*.

The different *Agrostis* spp., in spite of their fine plant cover, are not attractive as they are too sensitive to an adverse climate. However, *Agrostis tenuis* is not as sensitive as the others, the best cultivars being Tracenta, 'Holfior,' 'Orbica,' and 'Bardot.'

Festuca arundinacea

Festuca arundinacea, particularly the cultivar 'Ludion' which was the best at Lusignan, performed very well whatever the mowing height, 2, 4, or 6 cm; but the plants were coarse and appeared whitish in color in summer and somewhat so in winter.

Poa pratensis

Finally, *Poa pratensis* is of very little interest at present, particularly south of the Seine, mainly because of its general susceptibility to rust which gives it an undesirable color from late May through to the end of October and causes deterioration of the sward. The better cultivars were Parade, Baron, Monopoly, and Fylking.

GENERAL CONCLUSIONS

For all the climates and soils in which trials took place *Festuca rubra* is the most satisfactory species, because of satisfactory plant health, excellent general appearance, persistence, and broad adaptability. However, it can not

Table 1—General quality of species according to sites.*

Species	Zone I, Douai	Zone between V–VI, Valence	Zone IV, Versailles	Zone between II–III, Lusignan	Zone VI, Avignon	Zone between I–II, Rouen
Festuca rubra						
nigrescens	Good	Good	Average	Good	Average	Good
littoralis	Good	Good	Average	Good	Average	Good
rubra	Average	Good	Average	Good	Average	Average
Festuca ovina						
duriuscula	Good	Good	Average	Good	Good	Good
tenuifolia				Average		
Festuca arundinacea				Average		
Lolium perenne	Good	Good	Average	Good	Average	Good
Poa pratensis	Average	Bad	Bad	Bad	Bad	Average
Phleum nodosum	Bad			Average		Good
Cynosurus cristatus	Bad			Bad		Bad
Agrostis stolonifera	Bad	Bad	Bad	Bad	Bad	Bad
tenuis	Bad	Average	Average	Average	Average	Average
canina	Bad	Average	Average	Average	Bad	Bad

*According to the species and criteria used, a variability exists that may or may not be important.

be recommended at present for situations where wear is likely to be heavy (Table 1).

The next most satisfactory is *Lolium perenne,* which is attractive visually and more open and faster growing, but shows excellent resistance to wear.

While the currently available cultivars of these two species include some which can be used in most French conditions, a breeding program is needed to improve their adaptation, not only to climate but also to their intended use. Thus, selection would have diverse objectives: 1) resistance to wear in *Festuca rubra*; and 2) visual appeal and slower growth in *Lolium perenne.* The present qualities of these species would of course be conserved and improved in the process.

To this, one might add the improvement of *Festuca arundinacea,* particularly in its visual appeal, because this species seems promising for intensive use under less finely controlled conditions (leisure areas and sports grounds). Resistance to parasites, summer performance, and persistence for these three species must be kept in mind. Other species might be considered for specialized or localized use, for example, *Agrostis tenuis* in golf greens or *Poa pratensis* north of Paris.

For the Mediterranean zone, these conclusions are not absolutely valid unless there is irrigation. Other species must be sought since the application of water could in time pose problems.

6

Poa pratensis L. as a turfgrass in Britain[1]

W.A. ADAMS & P.J. BRYAN

Eight cultivars of *Poa pratensis* L. were examined under conditions of establishment and low management typically encountered on school and local-authority playing fields in Britain. *Poa pratensis* L. was grown alongside and in mixtures with turfgrasses normally used in Britain on sports fields where the winter games of soccer and rugby are played. The time of emergence was similar for all turfgrasses examined. *Lolium perenne* L. 'S.23' reached a height of 5 cm 14 days before any of the examined cultivars of *Poa pratensis* L., indicating a much more rapid rate of establishment. When sown in a 6:1 seed number ratio with *Lolium perenne* L. or in a 2:1 seed number ratio with *Phleum pratense* L. and at an overall seeding rate of 24 g/m^2, *Poa pratensis* L. failed to establish.

Two severe infections of rust affected only *Poa pratensis* L. The most resistant cultivar was 'Baron.' 'Nugget' and 'Arista' were virtually eliminated by the infections. 'Fylking,' although infected, recovered well.

Rugby was played over the trial plots throughout a winter period and there was no evidence that *Poa pratensis* L. cultivars tolerated wear less well than cultivars of the other turfgrass species examined.

The evidence produced suggests that the main obstacles to the success of *Poa pratensis* L. as a turfgrass in Britain are its slow rate of establishment and disease susceptibility, rather than intolerance of wear. Additional index words: Fertilizer use, Mowing regime, Seeding rate, Sports fields, Turfgrass establishment, Turfgrass maintenance, *Poa pratensis* L., *Lolium perenne* L., *Phleum pratense* L.

Poa pratensis L. displays a number of characteristics including depth of color, leafiness, hardiness, and tolerance of mowing which make it a desirable turfgrass. Selections have been made and varieties bred to strengthen its useful attributes. In consequence, *P. pratensis* is now recognized, especially in the United States and continental Europe, as a very important turfgrass.

Although *P. pratensis* is indigenous to Britain, it is seldom found as a dominant grass in natural and seminatural grassland. Experience with this grass outside Britain suggests that it might prove a useful constituent of turf. However, despite the renown of the species in the United States and elsewhere, it has never emerged as a successful turfgrass in Britain.

[1] Contribution from Soil Science Unit, University College of Wales, Aberystwyth, Wales.

P. pratensis is susceptible to fungal attack, and disease is an important consideration in varietal selection. A number of fungal pathogens have been recorded on the turfgrass, including *Helminthosporium* spp. (leaf spot, root rot, and melting out), *Erysiphe graminis* DC. (powdery mildew), and *Puccinia* spp. (rust). Melting out caused by *Drechslera poae* (Baudys) Shoem, and related diseases caused by *Helminthosporia* are probably the most damaging (Couch and Cole, 1957; Couch and Moore, 1960; Shildrick, 1971). Rust infections are usually limited and varieties vary in their susceptibility (Britten and Butler, 1965). Nevertheless, under some circumstances, damage can be considerable (Elliott, 1962; Rogerson, 1958). There is some evidence linking climate with susceptibility to fungal attack (Endo, 1961). The general lack of acceptance of *P. pratensis* in Britain may be due to a higher disease incidence in a maritime, cool-temperature climate.

This paper describes a plot trial which included fertilizer use, seeding rate, and mowing regime generally practiced in the establishment and maintenance of school and local-authority playing fields in Britain. The aim of the experiment was to compare several *P. pratensis* cultivars with cultivars of other turfgrass species which are used or found in similar sportsfield situations.

MATERIALS AND METHODS

The experiment was carried out on the University College of Wales playing fields at Aberystwyth. The soil was a silty clay loam with pH of 6.0 (soil/solution ratio, 1:2.5). The experimental area was cultivated and then sprayed with paraquat (1,1'-dimethyl-4,4'-bipyridinium ion) after allowing time for weed emergence. The cultivation and weed-killing operation was repeated. Preseeding fertilizer was applied at a rate of 30, 20, 25 kg/ha of N, P, and K, respectively. A further dressing supplying 50, 22, 42 kg/ha of N, P, and K, respectively, was applied 3 months after sowing.

The main experimental plots were 4 m X 40 m. Smaller plots approximately 2 m X 20 m were used for the *P. pratensis* cultivars 'Nugget', 'Barones', 'Arista', 'Golf', and 'Prato' for which seed was limited. Seeding was carried out using a Contravator and Lospred seeder [Sisis Equipment (Macclesfield) Ltd., Cheshire, England], at a rate of 24 g/m² for *P. pratensis* and at equivalent seed numbers for other species. Species cultivars and seed sources for turfgrasses used in the plot trials are given below.

Species, cultivar	Origin of seed
Poa pratensis L., Windsor	United States
Poa pratensis L., Fylking	United States
Poa pratensis L., Nugget	United States
Poa pratensis L., Baron	Netherlands
Poa pratensis L., Barones	Netherlands
Poa pratensis L., Arista	Netherlands
Poa pratensis L., Prato	United Kingdom
Poa pratensis L., Golf	Sweden
Poa trivialis L., Commercial	United Kingdom

Poa annua L., Commercial	United Kingdom
Lolium perenne L., S.23	United Kingdom
Agrostis tenuis L., Highland	United Kingdom
Phleum pratense L., S.48	United Kingdom
Phleum pratense L., Bariton	Netherlands
Phleum bertolonii DC., S.50	United Kingdom

Plots were seeded on June 5, 1971. Time to emergence was recorded as was also the time taken for seedlings to reach a height of 5 cm. This latter measurement was regarded as a useful indication of speed of establishment. Plots were maintained for the first month at 5 cm using a rotary mower. Subsequently they were maintained at 4 cm by gang mower. Clippings were collected at 6, 14, and 18 weeks after sowing to obtain a comparison of grass growth on the various plots.

Two major rust infections occurred on *P. pratensis* during the Autumn 1971. Disease ratings by visual assessment were made on these occasions.

In order that the effect of play wear could be examined, the plots were laid out across a rugby field. Although the intensity of wear cannot be considered uniform over the whole field, the choice of rugby rather than soccer and the fact that each major plot covered approximately two-thirds of the width of the field meant that wear was reasonably even. The plots were played over once a week during a 4-month winter period. Percentage cover of sown grasses was measured using a randomly thrown 15-m quadrat 4, 10, and 12 months after sowing.

RESULTS AND DISCUSSION

Table 1 shows the time to emergence and time to reach 5-cm height for the turfgrasses examined. The data show the considerable discrepancy in time for the *P. pratensis* cultivars to reach 5 cm compared with the most widely used coarse-textured turfgrass in Britain, *Lolium perenne* L. 'S.23.' *P. pratensis* lagged by approximately 2 weeks in reaching this stage of establishment and this constitutes a considerable handicap when the grounds staff is faced with very short interseason establishment periods. The two cultivars of *Phleum pratense* L. plus *Phleum bertolonii* DC. 'S.50' were similar in their establishment periods and were approximately 1 week ahead of

Table 1—Length of time required for turfgrass establishment.

Species	Cultivar	Days to emerge	Days to reach 5 cm
L. perenne L.	S.23	9	18
P. bertolonii DC.	S.50	8	26
P. pratense L.	S.48	9	26
P. pratense L.	Bariton	9	26
P. annua L.	Commercial	9	27
P. trivialis L.	Commercial	9	26
Agrostis tenuis L.	Highland	9	32
P. pratensis L.	8 cultivars*	10 to 14	32 to 34

* Arista, Baron, Barones, Fylking, Golf, Nugget, Prato, Windsor.

Table 2—Percentage cover in mixtures 4 months after sowing.

Constituent	Percent by weight in mixture	Percent cover	Constituent	Percent by weight in mixture	Percent cover
L. perenne L. S.23	60	74	Poa pratensis L.*	40	1
P. pratense L. Bariton	50	72	Poa pratensis L.*	50	5
Agrostis tenuis L. Highland	30	56	Poa pratensis L.*	70	26
P. trivialis L. "Commercial"	50	37	Poa pratensis L.*	50	24
P. annua L. "Commercial"	50	47	Poa pratensis L.*	50	10

* Poa pratensis L. cultivars Merion plus Baron plus Windsor.

the *P. pratensis* cultivars. The slow rate of early development of *P. pratensis* (Table 2) suggests that it would be quite difficult to establish in turf using a mixture containing significant amounts of *Lolium perenne*. These data are limited in that a range of *P. pratensis* cultivars were used and only one mixture composition and seeding rate with *L. perenne* was employed. Nevertheless, it is noteworthy that when sown either with *L. perenne* S.23 at a seed number ratio of approximately 6:1 in favor of *P. pratensis* or with *Phleum pratense* 'Bariton' at a seed number ratio of approximately 2:1 in its favor *P. pratensis* failed to establish. Undoubtedly, wider seed ratios and lower seeding rates would increase the *P. pratensis* in the turf, nevertheless the composition of the established turf would probably be so sensitive to these factors as to be unpredictable except under closely controlled experimental conditions.

The pattern of clipping yields was similar on the three monitored occasions. The data in Table 3 are for yields measured at 18 weeks from sowing and show that under the relatively low fertility conditions employed in this experiment the growth of the *P. pratensis* cultivars was less than that of any of the other sown species. The yield of *L. perenne* S.23 was more than three times that of 'Fylking,' the highest yielding variety of *P. pratensis*. It is again worth mentioning that the experimental conditions were not designed to favor particular grasses but were typical of very large areas of playing fields in Britain. *P. pratensis* appeared much less tolerant of such conditions than *L. perenne*, *P. pratense*, or *P. bertolonii*.

Table 3—Yield of fresh clippings obtained over an 8-day period 18 months from sowing.

Species	Cultivar	Yield of clippings
		kg/ha
L. perenne L.	S.23	1694
P. bertolonii DC.	S.50	983
P. pratense L.	Bariton	847
P. annua L.	"Commercial"	1210
P. trivialis L.	"Commercial"	771
Agrostis tenuis L.	Highland	816
P. pratensis L.	eight cultivar mean*	338
P. pratensis L.	Fylking (max.)	484

* Arista, Baron, Barones, Fylking, Golf, Nugget, Prato, Windsor.

Table 4—Incidence of rust on varieties of *P. pratensis* L.

Cultivar	August 1971	September 1971
Baron	0	1
Golf	1	2
Barones	1	2
Fylking	2	7
Arista	4	9
Windsor	5	7
Prato	6	8
Nugget	8	10

Although *P. pratensis* is susceptible to a range of fungal pathogens, rust was by far the most devastating in this trial. The first infection was noted during the first week of August approximately 2 months after sowing and the second in September. Visual assessment of infection is given in Table 4. No other sown species (including *Poa annua* L. and *Poa trivialis* L.) were affected.

The infected plots took on an orange color. The uredosori were bright orange and mostly adaxial. Spores were echinulate and round. No paraphyses were noted in the uredia and no telial stage was observed. The disease was identified as *Puccinia poarum* Niels (Cummins, 1971; Grove, 1913; Sampson and Western, 1954; Wilson and Henderson, 1966).

Meteorological data showed that the first infection coincided with a week of high rainfall (80 mm), high humidity (80 to 90%), and small diurnal variation in temperature (11 C ± 1 C).

The plots were subjected to wear during the winter, and the damaging effect of rust cannot be isolated from any differential response to wear. Nevertheless, there was a significant linear correlation ($r = 0.768*$) between the percentages of 4-month cover remaining at 10 and 12 months and disease ratings at the second and more serious infection. The second infection occurred at 4 months from sowing. Of the eight cultivars examined, the most severely affected were 'Nugget,' 'Arista,' 'Prato,' and 'Windsor.' 'Baron' was the most resistant and maintained its percentage cover (Table 5). Fylking maintained good cover despite a severe rust infection. The rust susceptibility of Nugget is particularly interesting since it never showed rust infection at Palmer, Alaska, where it was selected. This observation highlights the dangers of predicting turfgrass performance across climatic boundaries.

Rust infections frequently cause little damage and we are cautious to attribute all the disease damage to rust. This is because large numbers of *Fusarium* spores were found on rust infected leaves and it is possible that rust, although visually the most important, acted to weaken susceptible cultivars with ultimate death caused by *Fusarium* spp.

Poa pratensis is not grown widely in Britain and until now little significance had been attached to rust. In order to ascertain incidence of the disease in Britain, fifteen stations where grass breeding or trials are carried out were contacted. Seven stations had no *P. pratensis* under trial. Five had not noted the disease and three had observed severe infections. The three stations where infections had been recorded were situated in Northern Ireland,

Table 5—Percentage cover of sown species estimated on three occasions using 15-cm quadrat.

Species	Cultivar	4 months	Time since sowing 10 months	12 months
L. perenne L.	S.23	69	52	53
P. pratense L.	Bariton	74	43	49
Agrostis tenuis L.	Highland	93	24	22
P. trivialis L.	"Commercial"	53	21	20
P. annua L.	"Commercial"	52	29	43
P. pratensis L.	Baron	58	41	54
P. pratensis L.	Golf	28	21	33
P. pratensis L.	Barones	24	7	17
P. pratensis L.	Fylking	53	40	49
P. pratensis L.	Arista	27	2	1
P. pratensis L.	Windsor	45	9	17
P. pratensis L.	Prato	22	3	2
P. pratensis L.	Nugget	17	1	3

the mid-lowlands of Scotland, and eastern England. This limited survey suggests that our experience of rust on *P. pratensis* is not an isolated one and would appear to present a further problem in varietal selection.

Of the eight cultivars of *P. pratensis* examined, none had a cover prior to wear treatment comparable with *L. perenne, P. pratense,* or *Agrostis tenuis* (Table 5). However, taking this into account, the rust resistant cultivars Baron, 'Barones,' and 'Golf,' and the infected but undamaged Fylking maintained their cover well. Of the other turfgrasses, *L. perenne* S.23 tolerated wear best. *P. annua* L. was reduced substantially in cover at 10 months but by 12 months had shown its potential for recovery. *A. tenuis* L. 'Highland' withstood wear least well and it would seem that the tightly knit turf it produces is more liable to "tear" wear than that of the looser growing *L. perenne* S.23.

The data obtained from this trial indicate that the slow establishment of *P. pratensis* and its disease susceptibility constitute severe and possibly decisive handicaps to its success in Britain. This becomes evident when *P. pratensis* is compared to the aggressive *L. perenne* cultivars, which are now used for low management sports field situations. However, no evidence was produced to suggest that cultivars of *P. pratensis* are more susceptible to wear than the examined cultivars of *L. perenne, P. pratense,* or *P. bertolonii.*

ACKNOWLEDGMENTS

The authors thank the several organizations who supplied seed for the trial and those who gave information on rust indicence on *P. pratensis.* P. J. Bryan is grateful to the Sports Council for financing his research work.

REFERENCES

1. BRITTEN, M. P., and J. D. BUTLER. 1965. Resistance of seven Kentucky bluegrass varieties to stem rust. Plant Dis. Rep. 49:708–710.

2. COUCH, H. B., and H. COLE, Jr. 1957. Chemical control of melting out of bluegrass. Plant Dis. Rep. 41:205-208.

3. ————, and L. D. MOORE. 1960. Broad spectrum fungicides tested for control of melting out of bluegrass and *Sclerotinia* dollar spot of 'Seaside' bentgrass. Plant Dis. Rep. 44:506-509.

4. CUMMINS, G. B. 1971. The rust fungi of cereals, grasses and bamboos. Springer-Verlag, Berlin.

5. ELLIOTT, E. S. 1962. Disease damage in forage crops. Phytopathology 52:448-451.

6. ENDO, R. M. 1961. Turfgrass diseases in southern California. Plant Dis. Rep. 45:869-876.

7. GROVE, W. B. 1913. The British rust fungi. Cambridge University Press, Cambridge.

8. ROGERSON, C. T. 1958. Diseases of grasses in Kansas 1956-1957. Plant Dis. Rep. 42:346-353.

9. SAMPSON, K., and J. H. WESTERN. 1954. Diseases of British grasses and herbage legumes, 2nd ed. Cambridge University Press, Cambridge.

10. SHILDRICK, J. P. 1971. Grass variety trials 1971. J. Sports Turf Res. Inst. 47:86-127.

11. WILSON, M., and D. M. HENDERSON. 1966. British rust fungi. Cambridge University Press, Cambridge.

7

Cultivar response in turfgrass species mixture trials with mowing at two heights[1]

D.K. TAYLOR

A study of the response of turfgrass cultivars and species in mixtures, seeded in various proportions, to two cutting-height managements was observed over 3 years. Results of competition among species and the effects of cultivar, seeding ratio, and cutting height on the plant populations were determined by shoot counts. The mixture components were *Festuca rubra* L. 'Boreal' and 'Pennlawn,' *Poa pratensis* L. 'Park' and 'Merion,' and *Agrostis tenuis* Sibth. 'Highland.' The bentgrass component was the most aggressive of the three species and dominated all mixtures in which it was seeded, especially at the lower cutting height. However, differences in performance between cultivars were large and indicate the importance of using adapted disease-resistant cultivars when formulating turfgrass seeding mixtures. Additional index words: Cultivar competition, *Festuca rubra* L., *Poa pratensis* L., *Agrostis tenuis* Sibth.

Turfgrass seed mixtures for coastal British Columbia often contain two or more turfgrass species. It is generally acknowledged that a species mixture is more widely adapted than a single species to the potential variability of environment and management. Commonly *Festuca rubra* L. and *Agrostis tenuis* Sibth. and, to a lesser extent, *Poa pratensis* L., are recommended for western Washington State and coastal British Columbia (Goss et al., 1968; Turley et al., 1972). *P. pratensis* and *F. rubra* appear to be well adapted in the interior of the province (McLean, 1960). However, experimental evidence upon which to base recommendations of species, cultivars, and mixtures for this area is limited.

In the northern United States and central Canada, *P. pratensis* and *F. rubra* are the main turfgrasses recommended for lawns (Davis, 1958; Juska and Hanson, 1959; Taylor, 1969). In much of this area *A. tenuis* is considered a weed because of its aggressive, competitive behavior in mixtures, even at low percentages (Musser, 1948; Juska and Hanson, 1959) and especially when maintained at low cutting height (Davis, 1958). It is known in Europe for its suppressive tendency toward other species on sandy acid

[1]Contribution No. 206 of the Research Station, Agriculture Canada, Agassiz, British Columbia.

soils (Eschauzier, 1970; Vos and Scheijgrond, 1970). In sports fields, early dominance by *A. tenuis* is a disadvantage since it declines rapidly under wear. The percentage of *A. tenuis* used in a mixture may vary widely with little effect on the ultimate composition of the stand (Juska and Hanson, 1959; Musser, 1948).

The short-rhizomed varieties of *F. rubra* are reported to be finer leaved and denser than the more strongly creeping cultivars (Eschauzier, 1970). 'Pennlawn' was superior to common creeping red fescue in survival and resistance to weeds during 5 years of test in Ohio (Davis, 1958).

Vos and Scheijgrond (1970) reported that good survival depended upon resistance to disease, e.g., *Helminthosporium vagans* Drechsler on *P. pratensis*. Davis (1958) found that although 'Park' had more seedling vigor than common *P. pratensis*, its susceptibility to *H. vagans* limited its usefulness in the northern humid area. High fertility favored the *P. pratensis* component of 'Merion'-*F. rubra* mixtures (Juska, Tyson, and Harrison, 1955).

Merion has been superior to other named cultivars of *P. pratensis* when cut at 1.27 cm (Wood and Burke, 1961). Madison (1962) has shown that more plants survive at lower cutting heights but the amount of living turfgrass above ground is less. Population density at germination is a function of seeding rate, but populations of *P. pratensis* converge to a common level with time (Madison, 1966).

In view of the absence of data in the literature for a comparable climate, this study was undertaken. Shoot counts were determined annually over a 3-year period to assess species and cultivar competition, and the effect of seeding ratio and cutting height on plant population.

MATERIALS AND METHODS

In June 1969 at Agassiz, British Columbia, five turfgrass cultivars, *F. rubra* 'Boreal' and Pennlawn, *P. pratensis* Park and Merion, and *A. tenuis* 'Highland' were seeded alone and in all possible combinations in Test 1. In adjacent Test 2, some of the cultivar mixtures used in Test 1 were seeded at three different ratios. A summary of the numbers of treatments, type of mixture, seeding ratios, and rates by weight is given in Table 1.

The 20 treatments of Test 1 were seeded in 1.5 × 3.0 m unreplicated plots arranged in random order. In Test 2, the treatments were arranged in randomized split-plot design with two replications at each cutting height. Each mixture main plot was similar in size to the plots in Test 1 but each in turn was divided into three ratio treatments.

The soil, a silt loam of pH 6.2 and organic matter content of 4.4%, was plowed, disced, fumigated with methyl bromide, tilled, leveled, firmed, and seeded by hand using plot-sized shelters. Following seeding, each plot was topdressed lightly and rolled. Sprinkler irrigation provided adequate moisture for good establishment and continuous growth. Biweekly mowing, except for early spring and late fall, commenced in July 1969 at two heights of cut (1.9 and 3.8 cm). Clippings were removed.

Prior to planting, plant nutrients were worked into the surface 15 cm of the seed bed at rates in kg/are of 0.67 N, 1.46 P, 1.12 K, 0.34 Mg, and

Table 1—Number of cultivar mixture treatments, seeding ratios, and rates by weight of turfgrass species seeded in Test 1 and 2 at Agassiz, British Columbia, June 1969.

Number of treatments	Mixture	Seeding ratio	Seeding rate, kg/are
	Test 1		
3	*F. rubra* (incl. cv. blend)	--	2.00
3	*P. pratensis* (incl. cv. blend)	--	1.50
1	*A. tenuis*	--	.50
4	*F. rubra/P. pratensis*	3:1	1.87
2	*F. rubra/A. tenuis*	6:1	1.75
2	*P. pratensis/A. tenuis*	9:2	1.37
5	*F. rubra/P. pratensis/A. tenuis*	5:3:1	1.80
	Test 2		
4	*F. rubra/P. pratensis*	3:1, 1:1, 1:3	2.00
2	*F. rubra/A. tenuis*	16:1, 8:1, 4:1	1.75
2	*P. pratensis/A. tenuis*	12:1, 6:1, 3:1	1.40

22.5 finely ground calcium carbonate. Subsequent fertilizer applications were made at 6-week intervals to provide a 7:1:4 ratio of N:P:K at a seasonal nitrogen level of 1.5 kg/are in 1969 and 1970, and 2.5 kg/are in 1971 and 1972.

The number of viable seeds per dm^2 sown was determined. Population densities were determined in June of 1970, 1971, and 1972 by taking 4 to 5 random cores from each plot. The total areas of the cores examined per treatment at each date were 89 and 71 cm^2 for Test 1 and 2, respectively. The number of shoots was counted for each of the three main species. The dry weight of 400 shoots of each species, at each height of cut, was determined in order to compare the accumulation of aboveground growth of each species.

RESULTS AND DISCUSSION

Mean shoot counts at yearly intervals are given in Table 2 for five cultivars and two blends grown in pure stands of each species. Over the 3-year period the shoot numbers of Highland increased rapidly. On the other hand, shoot numbers for the *F. rubra* tended to remain relatively constant, while those of *P. pratensis* decreased to a lower level than either of the other two species. However, since the individual shoot weight for *P. pratensis* was greater than for the other two species (Table 3) the total shoot dry weight of Merion approached that of Pennlawn.

The low values for Park were the result of successive severe attacks of leaf spot-melting out disease followed by invasion and competition from grass weeds (mainly *A. tenuis*). The seed of *A. tenuis* may have originated as a windblown contaminant following seeding and once established it became dominant in certain treatments (Table 2). These results support the concern of Davis (1958) with *Agrostis* contamination of *Poa* seed planted in the northern humid area.

Table 2—Shoot counts over a 3-year period and percentage weeds in 1972 for five cultivars of turfgrass (three species) grown in pure stands at two mowing heights in Test 1.

| Species and cultivar | Shoots/dm^2 | | | | | | % Grass weeds 1972 | |
| | Mowing ht, 1.9 cm | | | Mowing ht, 3.8 cm | | | Mowing ht | |
	1970	1971	1972	1970	1971	1972	1.9 cm	3.8 cm
F. rubra								
Boreal	404	269	232	215	365	480	78	9
Pennlawn	673	853	698	348	609	568	2	1
Boreal-Pennlawn	583	773	683	301	383	366	19	3
Mean	553	632	538	288	452	447	33	4
P. pratensis								
Park	361	20	57	214	40	17	90	93
Merion	467	231	413	291	238	232	9	11
Park-Merion	396	207	261	249	167	172	61	15
Mean	408	153	244	347	148	140	53	40
A. tenuis								
Highland	554	812	2163	448	609	1464	0	0

With the exception of the 1971 and 1972 results for Boreal, there were more shoots at the lower cutting height, which agrees with results obtained by Madison (1962). The lower shoot count and higher percentage grass weeds for Boreal at the 1.9-cm mowing height is an indication that this cultivar is poorly adapted to the lower height of mowing.

The *P. pratensis* cultivar blend approached Merion in shoot count, indicating that the stand of the blend in 1972 must be mostly disease-resistant Merion. The performance of the *F. rubra* cultivar blend was not as clear-cut, as it approached Pennlawn in shoot density only at the lower cutting height, where the selection pressure was perhaps greater.

The results of interspecies competition provided additional evidence of the competitive ability of *A. tenuis* in three-species mixtures with *F. rubra* and *P. pratensis* (Table 3). Over the period, the number of *A. tenuis* shoots increased rapidly while the number of *F. rubra* and *P. pratensis* shoots decreased after the first year. At the end of the 3-year period, *A. tenuis*

Table 3—Mean shoot count, percentage, and dry weight for five combinations of three-species mixtures cut at two mowing heights over a 3-year period in Test 1.

| Mowing height, cm | Species | Mean viable * seeds sown/dm^2 1969 | Mean number/dm^2 | | | Percentage | | | Dry weight, g/400 shoots |
			1970	1971	1972	1970	1971	1972	
1.9	*F. rubra*	77	116	80	45	22	12	2	1.6
	P. pratensis	155	180	81	50	33	13	3	2.4
	A. tenuis	139	244	490	1836	45	75	95	1.2
3.8	*F. rubra*	77	33	47	15	9	12	1	2.0
	P. pratensis	155	102	71	41	29	18	4	4.0
	A. tenuis	139	217	273	1126	62	70	95	1.7

* Seeding ratio *F. rubra*–*P. pratensis*–*A. tenuis* 5:3:1 at 1.8 kg/are.

Table 4—Comparison of the shoot count of Boreal versus Pennlawn and Park versus Merion in mixture competition at two heights of mowing over a 3-year period in Test 1.

| Competitive cultivar | Comparison | Viable seeds sown/dm^2 | Shoots/dm^2 | | | | | |
| | | | Cut at 1.9 cm | | | Cut at 3.8 cm | | |
			1970	1971	1972	1970	1971	1972
Park	Boreal	93	103	239	429	50	140	378
	Pennlawn	155	304	476	334	215	524	492
Merion	Boreal	93	79	98	157	89	97	95
	Pennlawn	155	268	291	347	162	385	250
Highland	Boreal	72	62	20	0	11	0	0
	Pennlawn	124	434	303	116	118	116	0
Boreal	Park	93	196	100	58	156	56	10
	Merion	109	300	242	383	204	162	172
Pennlawn	Park	93	143	77	24	99	58	39
	Merion	109	221	272	236	166	103	138
Highland	Park	181	324	25	0	163	9	2
	Merion	222	502	132	203	239	152	40

dominated the turf, contributing 95% of the shoots at both heights of mowing.

The difference in seed size was responsible for the large difference between Boreal and Pennlawn in viable seed sown per unit area (Table 4). For this reason, Boreal was at a disadvantage, having a lower shoot count initially. Boreal had increasing shoot counts in competition with Park; Pennlawn reached a peak in 1971. Merion was more competitive than Park, and both red fescue cultivars tended to have lower counts in mixtures with Merion. Pennlawn was reasonably competitive with Highland over a 2-year period but was much reduced in stand the third year. Boreal was never seriously competitive with Highland.

Because of its disease susceptibility, Park was never as competitive as Merion at any time in the three mixtures studied. While Merion had good shoot counts in mixtures with Boreal and Pennlawn, it had a slowly declining shoot count in a mixture with Highland.

The 1972 results for eight two-cultivar mixtures seeded at three ratios are expressed as a percentage of the accumulated growth at the time of sampling (Table 5). It is apparent that Highland dominated all mixtures in which it was a component, supporting the findings in other areas (Juska and Hanson, 1959; Musser, 1948). Only with Merion and Pennlawn was there any residual competition. Since mixtures with Highland are almost completely Highland within 2 years, the choice of seeding ratios is not critical and appears of minor importance only with mixtures involving the more strongly competitive cultivars.

Even among many of the *F. rubra-P. pratensis* combinations, one species dominated the mixture within a 3-year period. There was a balance of species only where the mixture combination involved equally competitive cultivars such as Pennlawn-Merion at both cutting heights and Boreal-Park at the higher cutting height. For these, seeding ratios of 3:1 or 1:1 appeared to give a

Table 5—Calculated percentage species composition for turfgrass mixtures seeded at three ratios and cut at two mowing heights, 3 years after seeding in Test 2.

Cultivar mixture	Seeding ratio	Calculated percentage species composition					
		Cut at 1.9 cm			Cut at 3.8 cm		
		Festuca	*Poa*	*Agrostis*	*Festuca*	*Poa*	*Agrostis*
Boreal-Merion	3:1	5	69	26*	23	35	42*
	1:1	6	78	16*	16	54	30*
	1:3	7	83	11*	8	72	20*
Pennlawn-Merion	3:1	45	51	4*	38	24	38*
	1:1	51	45	4*	42	52	6*
	1:3	19	74	7*	31	62	7*
Boreal-Park	3:1	25	3	72*	48	31	21*
	1:1	32	1	67*	61	21	18*
	1:3	19	4	77*	63	13	24*
Pennlawn-Park	3:1	70	3	27*	67	12	21*
	1:1	37	1	62*	77	2	21*
	1:3	87	1	12*	83	11	6*
Boreal-Highland	16:1	3	0	97	0	0	100
	8:1	0	0	100	0	0	100
	4:1	0	1*	99	0	0	100
Pennlawn-Highland	16:1	13	0	87	7	0	93
	8:1	9	1*	90	2	0	98
	4:1	1	0	99	1	0	99
Park-Highland	12:1	0	1	99	0	0	100
	6:1	0	1	99	0	0	100
	3:1	0	1	99	0	0	100
Merion-Highland	12:1	0	23	77	0	10	90
	6:1	0	19	81	0	4	96
	3:1	0	14	86	0	6	94

* Unsown species estimate.

good balance of each species. It is apparent that a balance of competitive ability among cultivars as well as species is essential to the survival of all components in a mixture seeding.

REFERENCES

1. DAVIS, R. R. 1958. The effect of other species and mowing height on persistence of lawn grasses. Agron. J. 50:671-673.
2. ESCHAUZIER, W. A. 1970. Turfgrass breeding in the Netherlands. p. 34-44. *In* Proc. First Int. Turfgrass Res. Conf. Sports Turf Research Institute, Bingley, England.
3. GOSS, Roy L., K. J. MORRISON, A. E. LAW, O. C. MALOY, H. S. TELFORD, and C. J. GOULD. 1968. Home lawns. Washington Agr. Exp. Sta. Ext. Bull. 482 (Rev.).
4. JUSKA, F. V., and A. A. HANSON. 1959. Evaluation of cool-season turfgrasses alone and in mixtures. Agron. J. 51:597-600.
5. ———, J. TYSON, and C. M. HARRISON. 1955. The competitive relationships of Merion bluegrass as influenced by various mixtures, cutting heights and levels of nitrogen. Agron. J. 47:513-518.
6. MADISON, John H. 1962. Turfgrass ecology. Effects of mowing, irrigation and nitrogen treatments of *Agrostis palustris* Huds., 'Seaside' and *Agrostis tenuis* Sibth., 'Highland' on population, yield, rooting and cover. Agron. J. 54:407-412.

7. ―――. 1966. Optimum rates of seeding turfgrasses. Agron. J. 58:441–443.

8. MC LEAN, A. 1960. Home lawn establishment in the southern interior of British Columbia. Canada Dep. Agr. Publ. 1079.

9. MUSSER, H. B. 1948. Effects of soil acidity and available phosphorus on population changes in mixed Kentucky bluegrass-bent turf. J. Amer. Soc. Agron. 40:614–620.

10. TAYLOR, J. C. 1969. Lawns. Ontario Dep. Agr. Publ. 448.

11. TURLEY, R. H., R. M. ADAMSON, N. V. TONKS, and D. K. TAYLOR. 1972. Lawns for coastal British Columbia. Canada Dep. Agr. Publ. 1306 (Rev.).

12. VOS, H., and W. SCHEIJGROND. 1970. Varieties and mixtures for sports turf and lawns in the Netherlands. p. 70–79. *In* Proc. First Int. Turfgrass Res. Conf. Sports Turf Research Institute, Bingley, England.

13. WOOD, G. M., and Jane A. BURKE. 1961. Effect of cutting height on turf density of Merion, Park, Delta, Newport, and common Kentucky bluegrass. Crop Sci. 1:317–318.

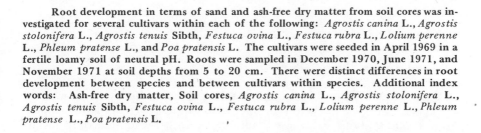

8

Root development of selected turfgrass species and cultivars[1]

P. BOEKER

Root development in terms of sand and ash-free dry matter from soil cores was investigated for several cultivars within each of the following: *Agrostis canina* L., *Agrostis stolonifera* L., *Agrostis tenuis* Sibth, *Festuca ovina* L., *Festuca rubra* L., *Lolium perenne* L., *Phleum pratense* L., and *Poa pratensis* L. The cultivars were seeded in April 1969 in a fertile loamy soil of neutral pH. Roots were sampled in December 1970, June 1971, and November 1971 at soil depths from 5 to 20 cm. There were distinct differences in root development between species and between cultivars within species. Additional index words: Ash-free dry matter, Soil cores, *Agrostis canina* L., *Agrostis stolonifera* L., *Agrostis tenuis* Sibth, *Festuca ovina* L., *Festuca rubra* L., *Lolium perenne* L., *Phleum pratense* L., *Poa pratensis* L.

Cultivars of grasses are generally described in terms of their aboveground appearance and by measurements of aboveground parts, e.g., leaf color, leaf width, etc. These are the most important and obvious indications of quality and potential for uses to which the grasses may be put. Root depth is also important and can be especially important for turfgrasses used on heavily used sports fields or for erosion control. Deep and ample rooting facilitates the regeneration of turf.

Currently there is considerable information on the amount of roots and their vertical distribution in soils for grasses. There is as well, some information on the changes in root mass with time (Troughton, 1957). Most of this information, however, has been obtained for herbage grasses under less frequent grazing or mowing than is usual for turfgrasses. Until recently, only limited information on root development of turfgrasses in Europe has been available. Recent studies by Boeker (1971), van der Horst (1970), van der Horst and Kappen (1970), and Skirde (1971) suggest that root development may be used for evaluation and identification of turfgrass cultivars.

---

[1]Contribution from Institute für Pflanzenbau, Katzenburgweg 5, 53 Bonn, West Germany.

MATERIALS AND METHODS

Trial plots of the following were seeded in April 1969 on the experimental field of the Institute for Agronomy of the University of Bonn (numbers in parenthesis indicate the number of cultivars for each species or grouping): *Agrostis canina* L. (8); *Agrostis tenuis* L. and *Agrostis stolonifera* (14); *Festuca ovina* L. (11); *Festuca rubra* L. (30); *Lolium perenne* L. (21); *Phleum pratense* L. (6); and *Poa pratensis* L. (22).

The test area is in the Rhine Valley on a soil with medium loam texture, good structure, a pH of 6.9 (in KCl), and high nutrient levels. Mean annual precipitation is 606 mm and temperature 9.7 C. During the period 1969–1972 fertilizer totaling 20 g of N/m^2, 4.4 g of P/m^2, and 1.64 g of K/m^2 was applied to the plot area. The plot area was not irrigated. The area was mowed once a week at 3 cm with the exception of the *Agrostis* cultivars which were mowed at two heights, 3 cm once a week and 1 cm twice a week.

Roots were first sampled in December 1970 with additional samples taken in June 1971 and in November 1971. Six samples were taken from each cultivar at each sampling using a steel tube 6.5 cm in diameter. Initial samples were to a depth of 10 cm, the second series to 15 cm, and the third series to 20 cm. Opitz von Boberfeld (1972), who used the same material, has discussed the sampling variation.

RESULTS

Agrostis spp.

Height and frequency of cut had little apparent effect on root mass in the upper 5 cm (Table 1) with the exception of the November 1971 samples from *A. tenuis* and *A. stolonifera* cultivars. Percentages of total root mass in the upper 5 cm were similar for cutting treatments at all three sampling dates.

Table 1—Mean sand and ash-free root dry matter values at various soil depths for *Agrostis* species.

Species*	Cut at	Sample date	Sampling depth, cm			
			0–5	5–10	10–15	15–20
			dry matter, g/1000 cm²			
A. canina (8)	3 cm	Dec 1970	31.79	3.43	---	---
		Jun 1971	41.70	4.92	2.09	---
		Nov 1971	38.09	2.70	0.90	0.42
	1 cm	Dec 1971	31.24	2.42	---	---
		Jun 1971	39.10	2.90	1.74	---
		Nov 1971	42.93	1.86	1.04	0.53
A. tenuis	3 cm	Dec 1971	34.79	5.20	---	---
A. stolonifera (14)		Jun 1971	39.92	6.73	3.84	---
		Nov 1971	56.72	3.94	1.75	0.91
	1 cm	Dec 1971	31.67	3.86	---	---
		Jun 1971	39.73	4.72	2.46	---
		Nov 1971	31.95	3.13	1.35	0.65

* Numbers in parentheses indicate numbers of cultivars.

Table 2—Root percentages at various soil depths for *Agrostis* species.

Species*	Cut at	Sample date	Sampling depth, cm			
			0–5	5–10	10–15	15–20
			——————% of total roots ——————			
A. canina (8)	3 cm	Dec 1970	90.3	9.7	---	---
		Jun 1971	85.6	10.1	---	---
		Nov 1971	90.5	6.4	2.1	1.0
	1 cm	Dec 1970	92.8	7.2	---	---
		Jun 1971	89.4	6.6	4.0	---
		Nov 1971	92.6	4.1	2.2	1.1
A. tenuis *A. stolonifera* (14)	3 cm	Dec 1970	87.0	13.0	---	---
		Jun 1971	79.1	13.3	7.6	---
		Nov 1971	89.6	6.2	2.8	1.4
	1 cm	Dec 1970	89.1	10.9	---	---
		Jun 1971	84.7	10.1	5.2	---
		Nov 1971	86.2	8.4	3.6	1.8

* Numbers in parentheses indicate numbers of cultivars.

Both the percentages of total roots (Table 2) and actual amounts present were higher with the less frequent 3-cm cutting height.

Root masses increased from December until June and probably reflect the vigorous top growth occurring at that time. Roots of the *A. canina* cultivars tended to be more concentrated in the upper portions of the soil than those from *A. tenuis* and *A. stolonifera* (Table 2).

Festuca spp.

Although there were more roots recovered from the 0 to 5 cm layer for *F. ovina* than for *F. rubra* on the first sampling (Table 3), the root masses for *F. rubra* were greater than those for *F. ovina* at all other samplings and sampling depths. Because both species leave a high amount of dead material on the soil surface after cutting, it is difficult to distinguish between this debris and actual roots in the upper portions of the soil. For this reason comparisons between species and cultivars might best be made on the basis of roots in lower layers.

Table 3—Mean sand and ash-free root dry matter values at various soil depths for *Festuca* species.

Species*	Sample date	Sampling depth, cm			
		0–5	5–10	10–15	15–20
		——————— dry matter, g/1000 cm^2 ———————			
F. ovina (11)	Dec 1970	42.81	4.35	---	---
	Jun 1971	40.21	5.63	3.11	---
	Nov 1971	76.83	4.97	2.23	1.13
F. rubra (30)	Dec 1970	38.47	6.34	---	---
	Jun 1971	49.71	6.84	4.33	---
	Nov 1971	90.01	6.59	3.51	1.90

* Numbers in parentheses indicate numbers of cultivars.

Table 4—Root percentages at various soil depths for *Festuca* species.

Species*	Sample date	Sampling depth, cm			
		0-5	5-10	10-15	15-20
		% of total roots			
F. ovina (11)	Dec 1970	90.8	9.2	---	---
	Jun 1971	82.1	11.5	6.4	---
	Nov 1971	90.2	5.9	2.6	1.3
F. rubra (30)	Dec 1970	85.9	14.1	---	---
	Jun 1971	81.7	11.2	7.1	---
	Nov 1971	88.2	6.5	3.4	1.9

* Numbers in parentheses indicate numbers of cultivars.

F. rubra cultivars had a larger root mass in the deeper layers than had those of *F. ovina* and the percentages of total root mass in the deeper layers were greater for *F. rubra* (Tables 3 and 4).

Lolium perenne, Phleum pratense, and Poa pratensis

As with the *Festuca* spp. the root mass in the upper soil layer increased considerably with age (Table 5), particularly for *Poa pratensis*. Again, accumulation of debris from clipping played a part, but *Poa pratensis* also produces with time a large number of shallow rhizomes. *Phleum pratense* cultivars had the mass in the upper 5 cm increased because of the haplocorms which their tillers form just below the soil surface. *Poa pratensis* cultivars had more roots at lower depths than did those of *Lolium perenne* which in turn were superior to those of *Phleum pratense*. Because of the relatively high volume of material produced by *Poa pratensis* near the soil surface, percentages of roots at lower depths were similar to those for *Lolium perenne* (Table 6).

Table 5—Mean sand and ash-free root dry matter values at various soil depths for *Lolium perenne, Phleum pratense,* and *Poa pratensis*.

Species*	Sample date	Sampling depth, cm			
		0-5	5-10	10-15	15-20
		dry matter, g/1000 cm²			
L. perenne (21)	Dec 1970	39.96	3.59	---	---
	Jun 1971	51.49	5.02	3.20	---
	Nov 1971	71.79	3.30	1.74	0.89
P. pratense (6)	Dec 1970	45.96	3.89	---	---
	Jun 1971	65.87	4.69	2.84	---
	Nov 1971	74.79	2.61	1.67	0.81
P. pratensis (22)	Dec 1970	59.40	5.28	---	---
	Jun 1971	82.14	6.75	3.52	---
	Nov 1971	113.49	5.53	2.29	1.16

* Numbers in parentheses indicate numbers of cultivars.

Table 6—Percentage of total roots at various soil depths for *Lolium perenne, P. pratense,* **and** *P. pratensis.*

Species*	Sample date	Sampling depth, cm			
		0–5	5–10	10–15	15–20
		% of total roots			
L. perenne (21)	Dec 1970	91.8	8.2	---	---
	Jun 1971	86.2	8.4	5.4	---
	Nov 1971	92.4	4.3	2.2	1.1
P. pratense (6)	Dec 1970	92.2	7.8	---	---
	Jun 1971	89.7	6.4	3.9	---
	Nov 1971	93.6	3.3	2.1	1.0
P. pratensis (22)	Dec 1970	91.8	8.2	---	---
	Jun 1971	88.9	7.3	3.8	---
	Nov 1971	92.7	4.5	1.9	0.9

* Numbers in parentheses indicate numbers of cultivars.

Differences within species

Thirteen of the cultivars of *Festuca rubra* were identified as the subspecies *rubra* and 17 as the subspecies *commutata*. Those in the creeping subspecies *rubra* always had higher root masses in the uppermost layer than those of *commutata* which produced no rhizomes. This difference was also apparent in percentages of the total root mass (Table 7). *Commutata* types tended to have more of their roots and a higher proportion of them at lower depths than did the *rubra* cultivars.

Some of the range of root mass values among *Festuca rubra* cultivars is shown by Table 8. As mentioned before, the most consistent comparative values are for the lower depths. Cultivar differentials were most distinct with

Table 7—Mean and ash-free root dry matter values and percentage total roots at various soil depths for *Festuca rubra* **subspecies** *rubra* **and** *commutata.*

Subspecies	Sample date	Sampling depth, cm			
		0–5	5–10	10–15	15–20
		dry matter, g/1000 cm²			
rubra	Dec 1970	45.45	5.61	---	---
	Jun 1971	54.93	6.05	3.95	---
	Nov 1971	93.00	6.09	3.00	1.72
commutata	Dec 1970	33.14	6.89	---	---
	Jun 1971	45.72	7.44	4.62	---
	Nov 1971	87.96	6.97	3.90	2.03
		% of total roots			
rubra	Dec 1970	89.0	11.0	---	---
	Jun 1971	84.6	9.3	6.1	---
	Nov 1971	89.6	5.9	2.9	1.6
commutata	Dec 1970	82.8	17.2	---	---
	Jun 1971	79.1	12.9	8.0	---
	Nov 1971	87.2	6.9	3.9	2.0

Table 8—Mean sand and ash-free root dry matter values at various soil depths for selected cultivars of *Festuca rubra*.

Sampling date	Sample depth	Cultivar					LSD .05
		Reptans	Linora	Topie	Oase	Lifalla	
	cm			dry matter, g/1000 cm^2			
Dec 1970	0–5	45.38	33.53	29.94	32.33	35.06	12.81
	5–10	3.74	5.35	6.87	7.08	7.78	2.12
Jun 1971	0–5	48.61	38.50	43.64	60.55	46.12	22.87
	5–10	5.86	5.64	7.55	6.64	7.52	2.36
	10–15	3.82	3.90	5.55	4.11	5.24	1.33
Nov 1971	0–5	102.82	77.93	101.48	93.98	110.09	45.64
	5–10	6.51	6.47	6.46	4.78	6.05	3.37
	10–15	3.06	3.56	2.56	2.80	5.23	2.08
	15–20	1.66	2.27	1.86	1.45	2.05	1.21

the early samplings and newest growth, e.g., the 5 to 10 cm layer in December 1970 and the 10 to 15 layer in June 1971.

Among 21 *Lolium perenne* cultivars tested, root masses for the 5 to 10 cm layer varied from 2.5 to 5.2 g/1,000 cm^2 in December 1970, 2.7 to 7.2 g/1,000 cm^2 in June 1971, and 1.8 to 5.2 g/1,000 cm^2 in November 1971 (Table 9). The cultivar 'Wilstermarsch' was high in every case, while the cultivar 'Pacey's,' formerly very popular in Europe but now of little importance, had especially low values.

There were distinct differences among the 22 *Poa pratensis* cultivars in root mass values at the 5- to 10-cm depth. These are illustrated by the five examples given in Table 10. Two of these, 'Barkenta' and 'Captan,' had consistently low values, whereas 'Merion,' 'Fylking' and 'Campus' were consistently high in root mass.

Table 9—Mean sand and ash-free root dry matter values at various soil depths for selected cultivars of *Lolium perenne*.

Sampling date	Sample depth	Cultivar					LSD .05
		Pacey's	Semper-weide	Combi	Barlenna	Wilster-marsch	
	cm			dry matter, g/1000 cm^2			
Dec 1970	0–5	48.42	38.19	36.52	43.56	45.76	21.95
	5–10	2.05	3.16	3.47	3.84	5.16	1.05
Jun 1971	0–5	33.36	42.89	58.72	55.54	44.13	16.89
	5–10	2.66	3.79	4.92	5.99	7.19	1.26
	10–15	1.88	2.71	3.06	3.81	4.18	1.58
Nov 1971	0–5	56.74	58.40	91.29	64.99	62.47	35.50
	5–10	2.84	3.43	3.35	3.44	5.18	2.24
	10–15	1.39	1.82	2.27	1.87	2.32	1.05
	15–20	0.65	0.91	0.87	1.01	1.34	0.74

Table 10—Mean sand and ash-free root dry matter values at various soil depths for selected cultivars of *Poa pratensis.*

Sampling date	Sample depth	Cultivar					LSD .05
		Barkenta	Captan	Merion	Fylking	Campus	
	cm	dry matter, g/1000 cm²					
Dec 1970	0-5	62.42	61.46	57.88	68.10	61.47	14.48
	5-10	4.21	4.61	4.93	6.59	8.13	2.92
Jun 1971	0-5	82.94	78.84	103.85	115.27	91.91	19.78
	5-10	4.19	3.84	6.30	9.93	7.72	2.21
	10-15	1.90	2.18	3.61	5.12	4.47	1.18
Nov 1971	0-5	105.40	105.23	109.04	130.24	114.18	38.18
	5-10	2.97	4.82	6.72	8.98	6.21	2.68
	10-15	0.78	1.40	3.18	2.19	2.66	1.32
	15-10	0.24	0.56	1.57	0.79	1.42	0.89

DISCUSSION

There were considerable differences in amounts and percentages of roots in various soil depths both between and within turfgrass species. In the upper 0- to 5-cm layer, total roots increased with age of stand. Differentials in this layer were confounded by varying amounts of debris from clipping and by vegetative growth characteristics (rhizomes and/or haplocorms). By use of values found for depths lower than 5 cm, comparisons could be made and cultivars distinguished as having high or low root mass values. Investigations at other localities (Boeker, 1971) have shown similar results. Values were generally higher for the June 1971 sampling, suggesting that seasonal effects on root growth must be considered when making comparative studies and sampling should be standardized both as to technique and time.

REFERENCES

1. BOEKER, P. 1971. Wurzelmassenenwicklung unter einigen Rarsengraeserarten und -sorten. Protokellheft, DLG.:25–35.
2. OPITZ VON BOBERFELD, W. 1972. Zur Problemstik des Stichprobenumfanges bei Wurzelgewichsfeststellungen von Rasengraesern. Rasen-Turf-Gazon 3:51–53.
3. SAGLAMTIMUR, T., and G. BOGDAN. 1970. Untersuchungen ueber dem Einfluss von Nutsungshaeufigheit and Stickstoffduengung auf Sorten vom Deutschces Weidelgrass (*Lolium perenne* L.). 2. Acker-u. Pflbau. 132:16–35.
4. SKIRDE, W. 1971. Bewurzelung der Rasendecke mit Beispielen fuer Abhaengigkeit und Beeinflussung. Rasen-Turf-Gazon 2:112–115.
5. TROUGHTON, A. 1957. The underground organs of herbage grasses. Commonwealth Bureau Bull. 44. Farnham Royal, England.
6. VAN DER HORST, J. P. 1970. Die Pruefung von Sportrasengraesern in den Niederlanden. Rasen-Turf-Gazon 1:88–90.
7. ———, and L. M. KAPPEN. 1970. Bewurzelung vom Rasengraesern. Rasen-Turf-Gazon 1:15–16.

9

Registration and evaluation of turfgrasses in the Netherlands[1]

R. DUYVENDAK & H. VOS

The Dutch Seeds and Planting Materials Act provides legal provisions regarding the Dutch register of varieties, breeders rights, the list of varieties, and marketing of seeds and certification. In 1972 the act was adjusted to the Directives of the European Economic Community. To be included in the register of varieties, a seed sample and a short description of the grass variety must be provided. The seed, which is tested by an official institution, is judged by the registration criteria: distinctness, homogeneity and stability, and on application for breeders right at world novelty. The testing is concluded with a distinguishing varietal description stating morphologic characteristics. Besides the register of varieties there is a varieties list which is issued each year. A national authority chooses and describes those varieties judged to be of agriculture value and importance for the Netherlands.

Registration examination of sufficient distinctness and homogeneity of the varieties is explained in more detail for Kentucky bluegrass (*Poa pratensis* L.) and red fescue (*Festuca rubra* L.). Before 1973 about 40 varieties of Kentucky bluegrass were distinguished with respect to: presence of anthocyanin in leaf sheath and panicle, presence of hairs on different parts of leaf sheath, leaf blade and ligule, dimensions of culm and leaves, shape of the panicle, heading date, resistance to different diseases. The chromosome number is not used. About 30 varieties of red fescue have been distinguished with respect to: chromosome number, growth habit, rhizome development, presence of anthocyanin in leaf sheath, dimensions of culm and leaves, heading date, resistance to diseases.

For the testing on cultural value chiefly other characteristics are taken into account such as: persistence, competitive ability, color in winter and summer, resistance to diseases, frost and treading, rapidity of establishment and growth, and leaf blade width. The testing is executed under the same conditions as those under which the varieties are used in practice, or with methods which give comparable results. The best varieties are described in the varieties list issued yearly. Additional index words: Breeders rights, Turfgrass registration, Distinctness, Homogenity, Stability, Morphological characteristics, *Poa pratensis* L., *Festuca rubra* L.

STATUTORY REGULATIONS

In the Netherlands there have been regulations for the protection and the sale of plant varieties for decades. The original regulations for agricul-

---

[1] Institute for Research on Varieties of Field Crops (IVRO), Wageningen, The Netherlands.

tural crops were set up to give farmers advice about the qualities of the varieties and to ensure guarantees of seed quality. In 1967 the Seed and Plant Materials Act came into force. The Act was adapted to the legal regulations of the International Convention for the Protection of New Varieties of Plants, signed at Paris on December 2, 1961 and ratified by the Netherlands in 1966. In 1972 the Act was adjusted to the Directives of the European Economic Community (EEC). This act gives legal provisions with respect to the inscription of varieties in the Netherlands Plant Variety Register, the granting of plant breeders rights, the variety lists, and the certification of and the trade with propagation material. The law includes agricultural crops, vegetables, ornamentals, forest and fruit trees. Both for seed certification and for variety recommendations clear descriptions for identification are desirable. Furthermore, in order to guarantee the predictive value of the results obtained in the merit trials, the varieties should be stable in their characters.

The important contributions of new varieties make it desirable to stimulate plant breeding by the granting of plant breeders rights.

In several countries some form of variety protection exists. The United States already protects varieties of vegetatively propagated crops and in 1970 the Plant Variety Protection Act stated that the breeder of any novel variety of sexually propagated plant (other than fungi, bacteria, or first generation hybrids) would be entitled to plant variety protection. In contrast to the Dutch act, potatoes, carrots, and F_1 hybrids are excluded from breeders rights in the United States.

Varieties entered in the *Netherlands Variety Register* must comply with the requirements for distinctness, homogeneity, and stability. In order to be considered distinct, a variety must be clearly distinguishable by one or more important characteristics, and be capable of precise description and recognition from any other variety whose existence is known at the time of application. The variety is judged for homogeneity through consideration of its manner of reproduction. The level of homogeneity required is not the same in cross-fertilized crops as in self-fertilized or in vegetatively propagated crops. Also the characteristics taken into consideration for judging homogeneity in the various crops are different. For a variety to be considered stable, it is required that the variety remains true to its description after repeated reproduction. The application for inclusion of a variety in the register must be presented to the Board of Plant Breeders Rights. The application must include a provisional reference, an indication of the group and the distinctive characteristics by which it can be distinguished from the existing varieties it most closely resembles. At the same time a representative seed sample of the variety must be delivered.

The registration research of agricultural crops is executed by the Institute for Research on Varieties of Field Crops (IVRO). The IVRO is also charged with the registration research of turfgrass varieties. After 2 to 3 years of investigations a report is delivered to the Board of the Plant Breeders Rights with data from which the decision for registration can be made. This report contains a description of the established characteristics of the variety and the differences with other varieties. A reference sample of the registered varieties is also available. This makes it possible to add further characteristics to the original description if it becomes necessary for distinguishing new varieties. Plant breeders rights are only granted to varieties that are new. At the time of the application, seed of the variety must not have been offered for sale or commercialized, with the agreement of the breeder, in the Netherlands or for longer than 4 years in the territory of any other State, or longer than 5 years prior to the application without permission of the breeder. For grasses rights are granted for a period of 20 years.

Apart from the variety register there is a variety list naming those varieties whose cultivation in the Netherlands is considered to be of importance; the essential characters are described and further information thought to be useful is given. To be included in the variety list for field crops a variety not only must be distinguishable, sufficiently homogeneous, and stable, it must also possess a satisfactory value for cultivation or use. A satisfactory value implies that the variety concerned, in comparison with the other listed varieties by the totality of its qualities, can be considered to be an improvement.

As a consequence of the EEC regulations the national variety list is now restrictive with respect to the agricultural crops. Only listed varieties may be commercialized. Varieties admitted to the national list will go forward for entry in the *Common Catalogue* of the EEC. In general, varieties entered in the *Common Catalogue* will be given free access to all the EEC member states.

The requirement of satisfactory value for cultivation and use is not prescribed if the breeder declares that the variety is destined for "nonfodder purposes." This implies that for turfgrasses there are no minimum requirements for merit and that all registered varieties may be marketed. The variety list is not a restrictive list but a recommended list. Actually the marketing of seeds of turfgrasses is limited to the varieties included in the *Netherlands Register of Varieties*. When the provisions of the EEC *Common Catalogue* become effective all varieties included in this catalogue will also have free entry in the Netherlands. The sale restriction will be that only certified seed may be marketed, that is seed produced under the control of the person responsible for this variety, i.e., generally the breeder.

With respect to a few species however, e.g., *Agrostis canina* L., *A. gigantea* Roth, *A. tenuis* Sibth., *A. stolonifera* L., *Cynosurus cristatus* L., *Festuca ovina* L. (inclusive var. *tenuifolia* and var. *duriuscula* (L) Koch.), *Poa annua* L., *P. nemoralis* L., *P. palustris* L. and *P. trivialis* L., not only certified seed of the approved varieties may be marketed, but also commercial seed which is true to species, but for which no statement as to variety name is given on the label.

An account of testing for registration and merit is given in this report (see also Duyvendak and Vos, 1971).

TESTING FOR DISTINCTNESS, HOMOGENEITY, AND STABILITY

Tests for the registration criteria are executed with the standard sample that is delivered together with the application for inscription in the register. The tests include assessments on the dry seeds and seedlings and field trials with single plants and rows. Every variety is sown in ± 2 to 3 consecutive years.

Distinctness

Every application is tested to ascertain if the sample is really new. The last-issued OECD-list is taken as the main source of information. Whenever it might appear that a variety was already known at the date of application, the inscription in the Variety Register is nullified.

The investigation must confirm that the variety is different from those already known. This confirmation must be backed by measurements and counts and expressed in a characterizing description.

Homogeneity

In varieties with apomictic seed formation homogeneity does not cause problems. Many varieties of Kentucky bluegrass (*Poa pratensis* L.) appear to consist of a single seed clone. Varieties that consist of more than one apomictic seed clone are not considered to be sufficiently homogeneous and are not admitted to the variety register. The different components of such a variety can be registered separately; naturally there are no objections to the commercialization of a blend of several varieties, but the blend cannot be registered.

In the case of cross-fertilizing crops it is more difficult to define sufficient homogeneity. The varieties are genetically heterogenic as is also evident from their morphological characters. Experiments with cross-fertilizing grasses have made it clear that all linear measurable characters follow the normal or Gausz distribution. Varieties with normal distributions appear to be constantly reproducible; varieties for which a character does not show a normal distribution will in general tend to shift in the course of generations.

A normal distribution is characterized by two parameters, viz., the mean ($\bar{x}$) and the standard deviation (SD). On the basis of the mean values of the characters the varieties are classified and described. The standard deviation is not made a part of the variety description, but must fall within certain limits. The standard deviation of each of the investigated characters is compared with but may not exceed that of the established varieties grown in the same trial.

Stability

Stability is required for the registration tests because new varieties are always compared with ones already registered. If these latter should change there would be no stable basis for the comparison.

For the breeder stability is important for if his variety changes the new product is not covered by a registration and may not be marketed under the registered name. Nor can the breeder assert rights on a product that does not comply with the description on which rights have been granted.

The merit testing requires stability in order that the testing results maintain their predictive value. Generally speaking when executing continuous selection there is more chance of spoiling a good variety than of improving it.

REGISTRATION OF VARIETIES OF *POA PRATENSIS* L. AND *FESTUCA RUBRA* L.

Preferably characters are used that are not or only little influenced by the environment, so that the relative position of the varieties remains the same irrespective of the conditions. Characters with a large variety—environment or variety—year interaction are often considered to be less attractive for registration. However, it is probable that for the purpose of variety identification that more use will be made of the interactions of variety—extreme conditions in the near future. Nittler (1972) has already acquired experience in this direction by inducing varietal differences under extreme nutrient conditions.

In the Netherlands a large number of Kentucky bluegrass varieties were distinguished by means of some 15 morphological characters. Since the expression of some characters is modified by the environment the morphological description depends on the conditions under which the trials have taken place. This holds especially true for such characters as anthocyanin pigmentation and heading date. The classification given here is based on observations on the IVRO trial fields at Wageningen. The 15 characters used were the following:

leaf sheath— color
        — hairs on margin
        — hair tuft just before top of the sheath
hairs on ligule
leaf   — width
        — fringe of hairs at junction of leaf blade and sheath
        — hairs on upper surface
        — hairs on lower surface
length of full grown plant
panicle   — color
        — bend in rachis opposite lower side branches
        — collar of rachis opposite lower side branches
        — angle of lower side branches
seed   — size
date of ear emergence

For illustration of these characters see Duyvendak (1972).

In Table 1 a classification is given of a number of *Poa pratensis* L. varieties on the basis of five characteristics. Some varieties have the same classification in this table; they can be distinguished with the aid of other characteristics mentioned above.

A classification of a number of varieties of red fescue is given as an example of the distinction of varieties of a cross-fertilizing species. Based on the presence or absence of rhizomes red fescue is commonly divided into two groups, *Festuca rubra* L. var. *rubra* and *F. rubra* var. *commutata* Gaud. The first group, creeping red fescue, has 42 or 56 chromosomes, the second group, chewings fescue, has 42 chromosomes. By further consideration it appears that the varieties of creeping red fescue with 42 chromosomes have shorter and finer rhizomes, whereas the varieties with 56 chromosomes have thicker and longer rhizomes. The varieties with the long creeping rhizomes with 56 chromosomes agree with the description of *Festuca rubra* by Linnaeus.

Table 1 – Classification of varieties of *Poa pratensis*.

length of culm	leaf sheath	early			medium early				medium late				late		
emergence date															
hairs on ligule		−	−	+	−	−	+	+	−	−	+	+	−	−	+
hairs on upper leaf surface		−	+	+	−	+	−	+	−	+	−	+	−	+	+
long	not red														
	red	Atlas			Ensma	Apoll Dynamo					Monopoly				Parade Entensa
medium long	not red				Windsor										
	red		Delta Pondorosa			Park				Newport Primo					
medium short	not red						Captan					Geronimo			
	red			Adorno			Delft	Barkenta			Spaths Olymprisp			Merion	
short	not red						Fylking		Prato						
	red							Minimo	Baronie	Arista		Barones HV 3		Baron Birka Golf	Continental

The varieties with the shorter and finer rhizomes with 42 chromosomes fit the description of *Festuca rubra* var. *trichophylla* by Gaudin (1828), recognized by Hackel (1882).

A distinction between the two groups of varieties within creeping red fescue seems justified on account of their many and conspicuous differences, such as number of chromosomes, plant height, differences in turf density, resistance to short mowing, resistance to treading.

The main classification of red fescue is: *Festuca rubra* L. var. *rubra* (long rhizomes, 2n = 56), *Festuca rubra* var. *trichophylla* Gaud. (short rhizomes, 2n = 42), and *Festuca rubra* var. *commutata* Gaud. (no rhizomes, 2n = 42). For the distinction of the varieties the following characters are studied: number of chromosomes; degree of rhizome formation; date of ear emergence; leaf, open or closed, color; leaf sheath, color; culm, length of upper internode, total length, length of panicle.

For sufficient homogeneity the investigated characters should show a normal distribution with a limited standard deviation. In Fig. 1 the frequency distributions of the heading date of two homogeneous varieties has been plotted. The standard deviations are also indicated. From the data for a third variety it appears that the emergence dates are not normally distributed and that the standard deviation is much higher than that of the other two accepted varieties. This third "variety" was not accepted in the variety register because of its insufficient homogeneity.

With the aid of six characteristics several varieties are classified in Table 2.

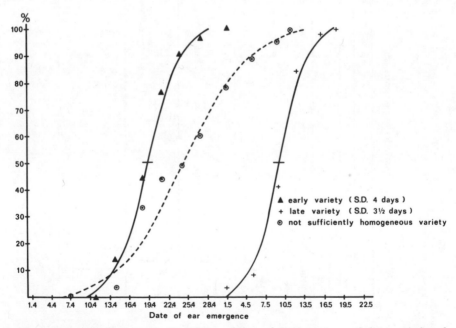

Fig. 1—Cumulative frequency distribution of date of ear emergence of three varieties of red fescue. ▲ early variety (SD 4 days), + late variety (SD 3½ days), ⊙ not sufficiently homogeneous variety.

Table 2—Classification of varieties of *Festuca rubra*.

chromosomes		2n = 42							2n = 56		
rhizomes		absent				short			long		
leaf		closed			open	closed	open		open		
length upper internode		short	medium long	long	long	short	short	medium long	short	medium long	long
leaf sheath	emergence date										
not red	early		Highlight	Encota Koket						Engina	Rapid Enzet
red	early	Tenora	Menuet		Flevo	Golfrood	Dawson	Oase	Agio	Novorubra	Envira
red	medium early	Waldorf Halifax	Barfalla Atlanta							Bargena Ruby	Patio Reptans
red	medium late								Gracia		
red	late								Roda		

VARIETY TESTING FOR MERIT

In general, variety testing for merit is begun after application of a variety for insertion in the register of varieties. On behalf of variety testing for merit other characteristics are studied than those for registration. Though sometimes these two methods of research support each other. When testing for registration the question is to which extent do the various characteristics of a variety differ from those of the other registered varieties. When testing for merit the question is how much better or worse is a variety for a definite characteristic than the assortment of good varieties. A merit, a quality is thus fixed.

The varieties are judged as well as possible under various conditions on lawns, sports grounds, roadsides, recreation grounds, under conditions of shade, etc.

In various cases there is a variety—management interaction. To prevent false conclusions being drawn it is necessary to determine the merit of a variety under those conditions for which the varieties have been bred and under which they will be used in practice. This gives the advantage of judging the level of sufficient quality in the right way and of determining the order of the varieties for the purpose in question.

The relative value of *Poa pratensis* L. varieties under close mowing clearly is different from that exhibited under heavy wear. Cultivars of *Agrostis* species rank differently depending on closeness of mowing while N fertilization influences varietal differences in *Poa pratensis* L. with respect to resistance to leaf spot disease (*Drechslera vagans* (Drechs.) Shoem.).

Important performance criteria

Persistence

Persistence is clearly one of the most essential variety characteristics. Persistence is defined as the capacity to survive in a monoculture under a given management. For turfgrasses persistence is assessed under turfgrass management, but this can include a wide range of environments and treatments. The ranking of the varieties by persistence can change as a result of differences in cutting heights, nutrient regimes, etc. It is, therefore, necessary to state the growing conditions when an evaluation for persistence is given with respect to a series of varieties.

Competitive ability, recuperative potential, quick establishment

Rapid emergence suppresses undesirable species or gives them little chance to establish. Rapid emergence leads, at least in the beginning, to great competitive ability which further depends on the growth habit, persistence, environment, and treatment. A strong competitive ability raises the objection that the variety in question may dominate so much that the mixture turns into a monoculture. When it concerns a desirable variety one wonders if this will in fact be an objection; generally speaking a high competitive ability therefore seems favorable.

Lawns or playgrounds may be damaged by disease or as a result of hard use. Recuperative potential differs considerably among the various species and varieties.

Resistance to diseases, frost, and drought

For turfgrasses only a few diseases are of essential importance in the Netherlands, viz.:

Disease	Turfgrass
Drechslera vagans (Drechs.) Shoem	*Poa pratensis* L.
Fusarium nivale (Fr.) Ces. and	*Agrostis* spp., *Lolium perenne* L.,
Fusarium culmorum (W.G. Smith)Sacc.	*Festuca rubra* L.
Puccinia poarum Niels.	*Poa pratensis* L.
Puccinia poae-nemoralis Otth.	*Poa pratensis* L.
Puccinia coronata Corda	*Lolium perenne* L.
Corticium fuciforme (Berk) Wakef.	*Festuca rubra* L., *Agrostis* spp. and *Lolium perenne* L.

Much attention is given to genetic disease resistance, since control by chemical means is thought to be less desirable from the viewpoint of environmental quality. Most turfgrasses in the Netherlands are winterhardy enough so that winter damage is not a problem. *Lolium perenne* L. and *Cynosurus cristatus* L. can sometimes be damaged by winter. Varieties of these two species show big differences in sensitivity, which are assessed both in field trials and in artificial freezing tests. Good winterhardiness is especially required for sports grounds which are used in winter after removing the snow cover.

Drought and/or heat damage are an exception in the Dutch maritime climate, and in addition many lawns and some sports grounds are watered. There are slight varietal differences in the rate of losing color during dry periods in summer although there isn't any serious damage done to the turf.

Wear tolerance

Wear tolerance is of special importance for sports grounds and public lawns. More and more lawns are recognized as a functional element rather than merely an ornamental element in the garden or park. Good varieties of *Lolium perenne* L., *Poa pratensis* L., and *Phleum pratense* L. are the most tread resistant in the Netherlands.

From investigations both on sports grounds and with artificial "treading" with a roller, especially on *Poa pratensis* L., it appears that although several varieties form a dense turf and show good resistance to diseases, there are other specific characteristics which determine wear tolerance. Rather quick growing varieties with a good winter color have a better recovery potential after being damaged by intensive treading.

Color and leaf width

There is no definite preference for either dark or light colored varieties. It is important, however, that varieties stay green both in winter and in summer and that they do not become yellow or brown. In particular, varieties showing winter dormancy, which is often associated with a fading color, are considered undesirable. A late nitrogen application may improve the winter color without increasing the risk of a *Fusarium* attack.

As a rule, fine-leaved varieties and species are preferred for lawns. For sports grounds the leaf width is hardly a matter of consideration—treading resistance is far more important.

Growth rate

There is a general desire that grasses form a nice green turf needing only little mowing for lawns and roadsides as well as for sports grounds. An interest has developed, therefore, in species and varieties that remain short. A disadvantage of these shorter grasses is their insufficient competition potential in relation to *Poa annua* L. Many varieties of *Poa pratensis* L. remain shorter than those of *Lolium perenne* L. but the former cannot compete sufficiently in many regions of the Netherlands. There is a special interest, therefore, for short varieties of *Lolium perenne* L. possessing the advantages of this species, viz., quick establishment, good competitive ability, resistance to treading, and good recuperative potential.

THE LIST OF VARIETIES

In the 48th descriptive list of varieties of field crops 25 pages are devoted to turfgrasses. Fourteen grass species are listed: four *Agrostis* species, four *Festuca* species, two *Poa* species, two *Phleum* species, and also *Lolium perenne* L. and *Cynosurus cristatus* L. A detailed description for 56 varieties and their qualities as turfgrass is given.

The list concerns those varieties that on the basis of detailed experiments can be recommended for the Netherlands. A new variety should be an improvement of the existing varieties for one or more characteristics or for its characteristics taken as a whole. The varieties are listed by species in order of recommendation. Next to the name of the variety the names of the breeder and his representative are given.

In the list of varieties special chapters are dedicated to the various purposes of turfgrasses, viz., lawns, sports grounds, recreation fields, roadsides, and dikes. Not only varieties that suit most of the stated purposes but also mixtures of grass species, which according to research, have performed well are described

These seed mixtures have to be certified by the field inspection service. Mixtures of species are almost always sown; monocultures are little used, although since better varieties are coming to the front the possibilities of using monocultures have become attractive. A mixture often deteriorates so that almost a monoculture is left after a few years. Therefore the question is obvious, why do we not start directly from these monocultures? A monoculture isn't as adaptible to various environmental conditions and treatments as a mixture that in most cases cannot be predicted and moreover can change.

Mixtures for various purposes are already as simple as possible. For lawns, mixtures of *Agrostis tenuis* Sibth., *Festuca rubra* var. *commutata* Gaud. and *Festuca rubra* var. *trichophylla* Gaud. are used; for lawns to be trodden mixtures of *Festuca rubra* L. and *Poa pratensis* L. are used. For sports grounds mixtures principally consist of *Poa pratensis* L. and *Lolium perenne* L., whereas for hockey grounds a mixture of *Poa pratensis* L. and *Phleum* species is used (Vos and Scheijgrond, 1969). For roadsides on sandy soils various *Festuca* species with *Agrostis tenuis* Sibth. are used; for roadsides on clay soil principally *Poa pratensis* L. and *Festuca rubra* L. For good results a combination of varietal research and mixture testing is necessary. For each turfgrass environment both the choice of species and the choice of varieties is decisive for achieving an optimal result.

REFERENCES

1. Beschrijvende Rassenlijst voor landbouwgewassen (48th ed.). 1973. Leiter-Nypels, Maastricht, The Netherlands. 312 p.
2. DUYVENDAK, R. 1972. Characters used for identification of *Poa pratensis* cultivars. Proc. Int. Seed Test. Ass. 37(2):462–468.
3. ————, and H. VOS. 1971. Sortenprüfung von Rasengräsern in den Niederlanden. Rasen-Turf-Gazon 2(2):40–45.
4. GAUDIN, J. F. G. P. 1828. Flora Helvetica. Turici. p. 288.
5. HACKEL, E. 1882. Monographia Festucarum europaearum. Kassel and Berlin. 216 p.
6. NITTLER, L. W., and T. J. KENNEY. 1972. Cultivar differences among calcium deficient Kentucky bluegrass seedlings. Agron. J. 64(1):73–75.
7. VOS, H., and W. SCHEIJGROND. 1970. Varieties and mixtures for sports turf and lawns in the Netherlands. p. 34–44. *In* Proc. First Int. Turfgrass Res. Conf. Sports Turf Research Institute, Bingley, England.

10

Flowering response of several selections of St. Augustinegrass[1]

A.E. DUDECK

The flowering response of ten clones of St. Augustinegrass *Stenotaphrum secundatum* (Walt.) Kuntze was studied in the field and under controlled conditions. Under field conditions in South Florida, the maximum number of inflorescences in all clones emerged during June. However, some clones flowered sporadically year-round. A study involving 8-, 10-, 12-, and 13.5-hour photoperiods confirmed that all plants flowered best under long photoperiods but that three clones flowered to some degree under all photoperiods. Maximum flowering at the 13.5-hour photoperiod occurred 6 to 7 weeks after initiation of the study. Uniform flowering could be induced in the greenhouse by preconditioning the plants for 3 weeks with 8-hour photoperiods at 24 C and 16-hour dark periods at 10 C followed by 7 weeks at 27 C with 2 hours of interrupted light at midnight. Additional index words: Grass breeding, Preconditioning, Photoperiod, *Stenotaphrum secundatum* (Walt.) Kuntze.

St. Augustinegrass *Stenotaphrum secundatum* (Walt.) Kuntze is a warm-season perennial grass widely used for turf purposes and pastures in Florida and in the Gulf Coast region of the United States.

All of the presently available cultivars of St. Augustinegrass are propagated vegetatively. Seeded types are not commercially available. However, Long (1958) indicated that some Texas types were good seed producers and that establishment from seed may be feasible.

Very little breeding work on St. Augustinegrass has been reported in the literature. Long and Bashaw (1961) found three cytological groups in *S. secundatum*. Yellow stigma types had a normal diploid complement of 2N = 18. Some purple stigma types had a triploid complement of 27 chromosomes; while one purple stigma type was a tetraploid containing 36 chromosomes. They found that the diploids reproduced normally and produced seedling progeny which differed widely in morphological characters, thus indicating considerable heterozygosity in common St. Augustinegrass in Texas.

In order to broaden the genetic base in St. Augustinegrass, an attempt was made at the University of Florida Agricultural Research Center (ARC),

[1] Journal Series No. 4956 from the Florida Agricultural Experiment Station, Gainesville, FL 32601.

Fort Lauderdale, to polycross ten superior clones. However, this attempt failed due to sporadic flowering under greenhouse conditions. Several clones produced a few inflorescences while others did not flower at all. Consequently, this study was undertaken to document the flowering response of St. Augustinegrass in the field and to identify those floral induction treatments that would maximize uniform flowering under greenhouse conditions.

MATERIALS AND METHODS

Clonal material for this study was obtained from the turfgrass nursery of the Florida Agricultural Experiment Station, Gainesville. Ten superior turfgrass types were selected out of 79 clones after 3 years of field evaluation for ten different characteristics at ARC, Fort Lauderdale.

During the 1972 growing season all clones were evaluated for flowering under field conditions. Individual plots were 1.8 X 2.7 meters and replicated three times in a randomized block design. All inflorescences within a randomly placed 15 X 60 cm quadrat were counted monthly and were removed with a power mower after counting.

On the basis of field results, two floral induction studies were conducted. In the first study, photoperiods of 8, 10, 12, and 13.5 hours were used. In the second study all clones were preconditioned under relatively cool temperatures with short days for varying periods before being transferred to a warm greenhouse with long days.

In both studies, each clone was propagated by planting a 10-cm plug in a 15-cm pot containing a soil mixture of 30% muck and 70% sand. Throughout the experiments all pots were fertilized weekly with a water-soluble complete fertilizer with minor elements at the rate of 123 g N, 27 g P, and 77 g K/100 m².

In the first study, all clones were potted on April 12, 1972 and allowed to establish in the greenhouse until June 5, 1972. All pots were then clipped to 2.5 cm. Three replicates of each clone were randomly assigned to the following treatments:

1) Outdoors for an 8-hour photoperiod but placed in a dark room at 30 C each night,
2) In a growth chamber for a 10-hour photoperiod with 21.52 klux of light at 30 C constant temperature,
3) In a growth chamber for a 12-hour photoperiod with 21.52 klux of light at 30 C constant temperature,
4) Control treatments kept outdoors with 13.5-hour photoperiods with mean temperature of 26 C.

All seed heads were counted weekly for a 2-month period. Inflorescences were not removed after each count.

For the second study, all clones used in the first study were clipped to 2.5 cm on August 8, 1972 and allowed to recover in an unshaded greenhouse until September 1, 1972. The clones were randomly reassigned new treatment numbers. Control samples were left in the greenhouse while the other clones were preconditioned in a growth chamber with 21.51 klux for 8 hours at 24 C followed by a 16-hour dark period at 10 C daily. Each week, two

Table 1—Monthly flowering of St. Augustinegrass selections in the field during the 1972 growing season at Fort Lauderdale, Florida.

Clone	April	May	June	July	Aug	Sept	Mean†
							Mean inflorescences/10 dm²*
118	0.4	1.1	23.7	22.9	2.5	0	9.5 a
108	1.2	1.2	20.1	20.8	1.4	0	8.2 a
110	2.9	0.6	18.6	14.6	2.5	0	7.0 ab
201	0.4	1.2	13.7	10.8	3.2	0	5.4 abc
34	0.1	0.3	12.2	8.9	2.2	0	4.4 bcd
159	0.0	0.6	12.6	7.5	2.5	0	4.3 bcd
223	0.0	0.5	7.8	5.7	3.6	0.3	3.4 cd
38	0.0	0.8	7.2	4.6	2.2	0	2.8 cd
26	0.0	0.5	6.8	5.7	1.1	0	2.6 d
2	0.1	0.3	6.1	4.3	2.5	0	2.5 d
Mean†	0.5 z	0.7 z	12.9 w	10.6 x	2.4 y	0.0 z	

* Mean of three replicates per clone per month.　　　† Means with the same letter are not significantly different at the 5% level using Duncan's Multiple Range Test.

replications of each clone were transferred to a greenhouse with a mean temperature of 27 C. The dark period was interrupted with 2 hours of light from midnight to 2 a.m. with incandescent lamps that provided a minimum of 430.40 lux of light at plant height. Inflorescences were counted weekly for 14 weeks and were not removed after each count. Those aspects relating to fertility and seed production were not evaluated in any of these studies. All data were statistically analyzed using the square root transformation ($\sqrt{X + 1}$) after Snedecor (1956).

RESULTS AND DISCUSSION

St. Augustinegrass flowered best under long days as maximum flowering of all ten clones occurred during June (Table 1). However, some clones flowered continuously from April to August. One clone not involved in this study has flowered year-round in the field for the past 2 years in South Florida. Significant differences in inflorescence production were found between clones, indicating clonal differences for seed production potential (Table 1).

The photoperiodic study confirmed the field results in that all clones flowered best when subjected to a long photoperiod and that clonal differences in inflorescence production are real (Table 2). A minimum of 6 weeks was required at the 13.5-hour photoperiod to induce uniform flowering in all replicates of each clone. Flowering under the shorter photoperiods was quite sporadic between clones, possibly indicating that flowering in St. Augustinegrass is not controlled entirely by photoperiod. Clones 108, 110, and 118 flowered to some degree under all photoperiods. They also flowered earliest in the spring in the field (Table 1).

To simplify the results of the preconditioning study, the data were summarized within preconditioning treatments and are presented graphically in Fig. 1. For each preconditioning period only the post-treatment (weeks of

Table 2—Photoperiodic effects on St. Augustinegrass flowering. Values are total inflorescences per pot after 8 weeks of exposure averaged over three replicates.

Clone	Photoperiod in hours			
	8	10	12	13.5
108	2.0 b*	2.7 b	7.0 ab	27.7 a
118	6.7 a	6.3 a	5.0 b	27.3 a
110	5.7 a	2.3 bc	10.7 a	25.7 ab
34	0.0 b	0.0 c	0.7 c	21.3 abc
26	0.3 b	0.0 c	0.3 c	19.3 bc
38	0.3 b	0.0 c	0.0 c	19.0 bc
201	1.0 b	0.3 bc	0.3 c	17.3 c
223	0.0 b	0.3 bc	0.0 c	16.7 c
159	0.7 b	0.0 c	0.0 c	14.0 c
2	0.7 b	0.0 c	0.7 c	7.0 d
Mean†	1.7 z	1.2 z	2.5 z	19.5 y

* Means within photoperiods with the same letter are not significantly different at the 5% level using Duncan's Multiple Range Test. † Means between photoperiods with the same letter are not significantly different at the 5% level using Duncan's Multiple Range Test.

post-treatment) yielding the greatest number of new inflorescences in the shortest period of time is presented.

Preconditioning the plants with short days and cool temperatures had a marked effect on inflorescence production (Fig. 1). The best flowering in the shortest period of time was obtained by preconditioning the clones for 3 weeks followed by 7 weeks of warm temperatures with interrupted dark periods. A minimum of 3 weeks was required to induce uniform flowering within all clones as all replicated clones did not flower in treatments 0 + 13,

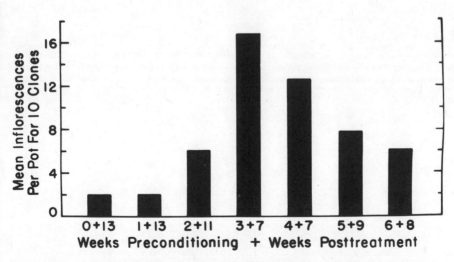

Fig. 1—Effects of preconditioning on floral development in St. Augustinegrass. Maximum inflorescence emergence for each preconditioning period. The first number represents weeks of cool temperatures with short days. The second number represents weeks of warm temperatures with interrupted dark periods after the clones were transferred from the preconditioning chambers.

1 + 13, and 2 + 11. These data confirm that flowering in St. Augustinegrass is controlled by a combination of temperature and photoperiod.

During Spring 1973 another polycross with ten replicates was attempted in the greenhouse. The ten clones were planted on March 21, 1973 after natural preconditioning in the field during the winter. All plants began to flower uniformly after 8 weeks in a greenhouse at 28 C minimum with 2 hours of light near midnight.

From a breeding standpoint it now appears possible to manipulate flowering in St. Augustinegrass. Maximum flowering can be induced by preconditioning the plants for at least 3 weeks at cool temperatures with short days. This can be accomplished naturally in the field during the winter or with growth chambers. The plants should then be placed in a warm greenhouse with at least 13.5 hours of light or the night period should be interrupted with 2 hours of light near midnight.

REFERENCES

1. LONG, J. A. 1958. A compilation of major turf reserach in the U. S. Park Maintenance Turf Annual Vol. II.
2. ———, and E. C. BASHAW. 1961. Microsporogenesis and chromosome numbers in St. Augustinegrass. Crop Sci. 1:41–43.
3. SNEDECOR, G. W. 1956. Statistical methods, 5th ed. Iowa State College Press, Ames, Iowa.

11

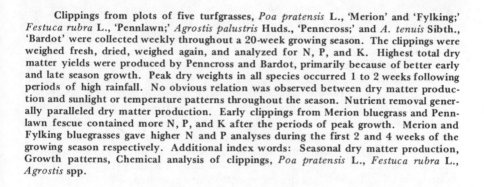

Seasonal growth and major nutrient uptake of turfgrasses under cool, wet conditions[1]

F.J. WRAY

Clippings from plots of five turfgrasses, *Poa pratensis* L., 'Merion' and 'Fylking;' *Festuca rubra* L., 'Pennlawn;' *Agrostis palustris* Huds., 'Penncross;' and *A. tenuis* Sibth., 'Bardot' were collected weekly throughout a 20-week growing season. The clippings were weighed fresh, dried, weighed again, and analyzed for N, P, and K. Highest total dry matter yields were produced by Penncross and Bardot, primarily because of better early and late season growth. Peak dry weights in all species occurred 1 to 2 weeks following periods of high rainfall. No obvious relation was observed between dry matter production and sunlight or temperature patterns throughout the season. Nutrient removal generally paralleled dry matter production. Early clippings from Merion bluegrass and Pennlawn fescue contained more N, P, and K after the periods of peak growth. Merion and Fylking bluegrasses gave higher N and P analyses during the first 2 and 4 weeks of the growing season respectively. Additional index words: Seasonal dry matter production, Growth patterns, Chemical analysis of clippings, *Poa pratensis* L., *Festuca rubra* L., *Agrostis* spp.

Different grass species have individual growth patterns, and vary in the amount of dry matter they produce at any given time of the year. Leaf growth is influenced by seasonal patterns of rainfall and sunlight, while root growth is primarily influenced by soil temperature and the supply of carbohydrates translocated from the leaves (Stuckey, 1941; Beard and Daniel, 1965). Few textbooks give either seasonal growth patterns of the important turfgrasses or chemical tissue analyses obtained under specified conditions. The older literature (Graber et al., 1927; Brown, 1943) considers root growth in relation to their sugar and other carbohydrate contents. No information is available concerning seasonal patterns of dry matter production or variations in chemical analyses of leaf tissues for the cool humid (Atlantic) regions of Canada and the United States, although analyses of clippings from eight turfgrass species grown in pots are recorded by Waddington and Zimmerman (1972) for Pennsylvania.

Such data are necessary for advisory purposes as well as turf management. Analytical laboratories require chemical analyses from turfgrasses

[1]Contribution from Plant Science Department, Nova Scotia Agricultural College, Truro, Nova Scotia, Canada.

grown under specified conditions for diagnostic comparisons; while good turf management involves the correct, most economical timing of fertilizer applications. Consequently, a knowledge of the growth patterns of turf grasses is important from the economic point of view. The objectives of this work were to record dry matter removed weekly as clippings of the important turfgrass species. These figures could be used together with weekly chemical analyses of the leaf tissues to calculate both weekly and seasonal removal of major plant nutrients.

MATERIALS AND METHODS

Experiments were conducted in 1972 with 2 to 3-year-old well-established plots of single turfgrass species or varieties which were mowed weekly. These plots were on a sandy loam soil adjacent to the Truro, Nova Scotia, meteorological station from which climatic information was obtained. Single 11-m^2 plots were used for *Poa pratensis* L., 'Merion' and 'Fylking' and *Festuca rubra* L., 'Pennlawn.' Two 6-m^2 plots were used for *Agrostis palustris* Huds., 'Penncross' and *A. tenuis* Sibth., 'Bardot.' Replication was not possible, and the results presented are from single plots. Both bluegrasses and fescue were cut at 32 mm, while the bentgrasses were cut at 6.5 mm. Fertilizer, in the form of sewage sludge, was applied weekly, additional potassium chloride was applied twice each month, and additional superphosphate at the beginning of the growing season. This form of N, and the patterns of application of fertilizer were chosen to prevent their causing variations in growth patterns. Over the entire season 152.5 kg/ha N, 44.9 kg/ha P (103 kg/ha P_2O_5), and 81.3 kg/ha K (101 kg/ha K_2O) were applied. Irrigation was used as sparingly as possible, approximately 10 mm of water being applied at three times during very hot, dry conditions.

The leaf clippings were weighed, dried at 105 C, and weighed again to calculate the dry matter percentage. A sample of the dried tissue was ground, digested in a sulfuric acid-peroxide mixture, and analyzed. N was determined colorimetrically on an auto-analyser, using the Berthelot phenol-hypochlorite reaction following a sodium hydroxide-tartrate treatment to remove heavy metals. P was determined colorimetrically, using the phospho-molybdate blue produced in H_2SO_4 solution reduced by ascorbic acid. K was determined on the flame emission spectrograph, while Ca, Mg, and the minor elements were determined using an atomic absorption spectrograph.

RESULTS AND DISCUSSION

These results do not give total dry matter production and nutrient utilization of the grasses concerned because it was not possible to collect root samples.

Table 1 gives analytical values for N, P, K, Ca, Mg, and minor elements for each of the five turfgrasses during each month of the growing season. Dry weight percentages are also tabulated here. Penncross tissue had lower dry

Table 1—Typical dry weight and chemical analyses of leaf tissue of five turfgrasses at different times.

Date	Turfgrass	Dry wt	N	P	K	Ca	Mg	Fe	Mn	Zn	B
		%			%				ppm		
May 20	P. pratensis L., Merion	21	5.80	0.67	6.03						
	P. pratensis L., Fylking	20	4.85	0.59	6.05						
	F. rubra L., Pennlawn	24	3.75	0.45	2.56	0.29	0.14	404	95	75	8
	A. palustris Huds., Penncross	19	4.00	0.58	2.65	0.28	0.14	1280	156	75	8
	A. tenuis Sibth., Bardot	33	3.15	0.37	2.14						
June 12	P. pratensis L., Merion	32	3.50	0.53	2.35	0.27	0.13	105	45	25	
	P. pratensis L., Fylking	28	3.70	0.46	2.70	0.36	0.08	78	59	25	
	F. rubra L., Pennlawn	31	3.40	0.48	2.36	0.29	0.12	105	50	25	
	A. palustris Huds., Penncross	13	4.05	0.51	2.41	0.39	0.16	465	170	25	
	A. tenuis Sibth., Bardot	33	3.35	0.46	2.48	0.41	0.15	700	320	28	
July 7	P. pratensis L., Merion	35	4.15	0.56	3.52	0.31	0.10	225	150	33	12
	P. pratensis L., Fylking	24	3.70	0.47	2.65	0.27	0.07	70	112	23	9
	F. rubra L., Pennlawn	23	3.95	0.51	2.86	0.48	0.11	100	95	19	10
	A. palustris Huds., Penncross	21	4.05	0.68	2.81	0.44	0.13	155	133	30	12
	A. tenuis Sibth., Bardot	20	3.50	0.60	2.89	0.56	0.18	195	285	39	17
Aug 12	P. pratensis L., Merion	30	3.85	0.47	2.67	0.34	0.31	400	100	27	
	P. pratensis L., Fylking	30	3.95	0.43	2.90	0.28	0.20	100	113	24	
	F. rubra L., Pennlawn	35	3.30	0.57	2.65	0.24	0.23	80	57	24	
	A. palustris Huds., Penncross	25	3.70	0.54	2.88	0.38	0.36	300	143	29	
	A. tenuis Sibth., Bardot	35	3.60	0.53	2.64						
Sept 30	P. pratensis L., Merion	28	3.80	0.48	2.34						
	P. pratensis L., Fylking	28	3.90	0.42	2.34						
	F. rubra L., Pennlawn	29	3.35	0.55	2.30						
	A. palustris Huds., Penncross	21	4.40	0.58	2.90						
	A. tenuis Sibth., Bardot	27	3.85	0.48	2.27						
Oct 14	P. pratensis L., Merion	27	3.00	0.43	2.54	0.25	0.11	412	70	28	
	P. pratensis L., Fylking	25	3.60	0.47	2.80	0.25	0.06	210	80	22	
	F. rubra L., Pennlawn	26	2.43	0.45	2.58	0.18	0.05	210	78	25	
	A. palustris Huds., Penncross	26	3.50	0.57	3.05	0.24	0.08	515	93	27	
	A. tenuis Sibth., Bardot	27	3.65	0.54	2.65	0.18	0.07	550+	267	26	

weights than Bardot tissue throughout the season, while Pennlawn tissue had higher dry weights than both bluegrass tissues. During the warmer months, the lower dry matter content of Penncross tissue was often associated with higher N contents. There was a similar association between tissue dry weights and high N, P, K analyses for both bluegrasses in May. This cannot be attributed to the same cause as for the Penncross bentgrass, since in May bluegrass growth was poor and in May and June Penncross grew well.

In turf management, an accepted "rule of thumb" assumes an N:K ratio of 2:1 for fertilizer requirements. These analyses show a closer ratio of approximately 2:1.5 is required, with an N:P ratio of approximately 2:0.3 to compensate for clipping removal.

Minor element analyses show higher Fe values for Merion over the Fylking bluegrass, which was also found in separate pot experiments. Bentgrasses show higher Fe and Mn analyses than bluegrasses and fescue during May, June, and October, this also is found for A. tenuis Sibth., 'Boral.'

Seasonal variations in dry weights of clippings removed weekly throughout the season, together with their associated weights of N, P, and K, are given in Fig. 1 through 5. These figures should be examined in relation to Fig. 6 which also summarizes the 1972 climatic data (rainfall, hours bright sunlight, average maximum and minimum air temperatures, and soil temperature at 5-cm depth) at weekly time intervals. The data in Fig. 1 through 5 are presented in the form of bar diagrams, the heights of each bar representing

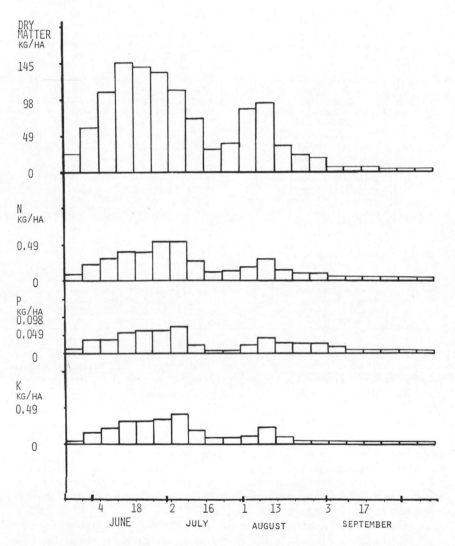

Fig. 1—Growth curve for 'Merion' Kentucky bluegrass (*Poa pratensis* L.) showing the dry weight, elemental N, P, and K removed weekly over the growing season in kilograms per hectare.

the appropriate quantity removed in a 7-day period. These show that the seasonal pattern of leaf growth depends mainly on rainfall and temperature.

Bentgrasses and Pennlawn fescue began growth when the soil temperature rose above 7.6 C, and the rapid spring growth of Penncross and Bardot bentgrasses is clearly shown. These bentgrasses continued growth into mid-October until terminated by frost. The Maritime season is short; although calendar autumn begins on September 21st, grass growth is normally finished

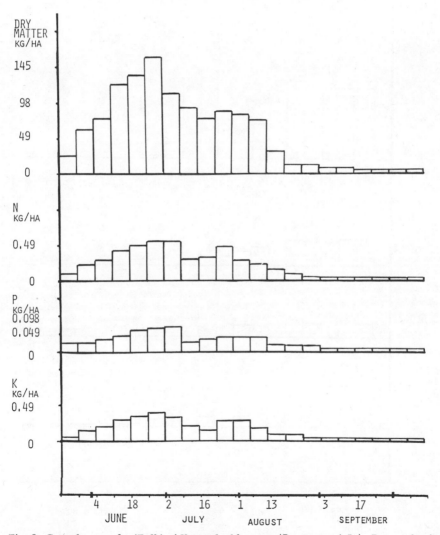

Fig. 2—Growth curve for 'Fylking' Kentucky bluegrass (*Poa pratensis* L.). Data and units identical to Fig. 1.

by this date. Consequently Maritime growth maxima in August correspond to "autumn" secondary growth peaks in warmer climates with longer seasons.

The three periods of heavy rainfall (early June, late July, and an unusually wet September and October) produced increased growth 1 to 2 weeks later. No clear relation existed between dry matter production and hours of bright sunlight or temperature variations, except where low temperatures simply prevented growth.

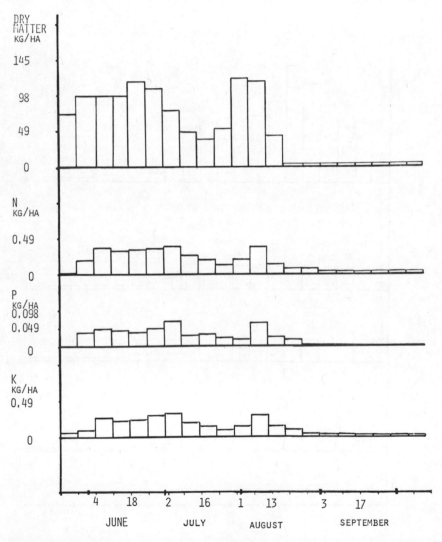

Fig. 3—Growth curve for 'Pennlawn' creeping red fescue (*Festuca rubra* L.). Data and units identical to Fig. 1.

Nutrient removal of major elements paralleled dry matter production. The areas under the bar graphs give the total dry weight and N, P, and K weights removed in the clippings over the season. These data are summarized in Table 2. Both bentgrasses produced more dry matter than the bluegrass or fescue species. All plots received identical fertilizer treatments of approximately 150 kg/ha N, 100 kg/ha P_2O_5, and 100 kg/ha K_2O which were not

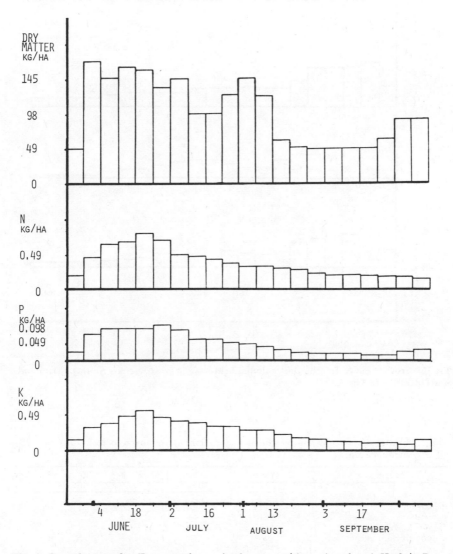

Fig. 4—Growth curve for 'Penncross' creeping bentgrass (*Agrostis palustris* Huds.). Data and units identical to Fig. 1.

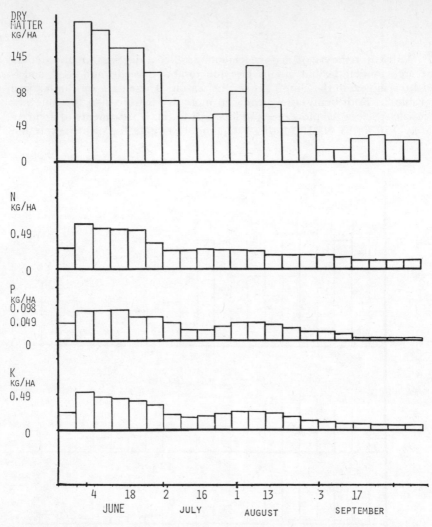

Fig. 5—Growth curve for 'Bardot' colonial bentgrass (*Agrostis tenuis* Sibth.). Data and units identical to Fig. 1.

Table 2—Total dry weight and weight of major elements removed as leaf tissue in a 20-week growing season.

Turfgrass	Dry wt	N	P	K
		kg/ha		
P. pratensis L., Merion	1234	45	5.8	32
P. pratensis L., Fylking	1210	48	5.4	33
F. rubra L., Pennlawn	1156	39	5.8	29
A. palustris Huds., Penncross	2064	78	10.5	56
A. tenuis Sibth., Bardot	1828	59	8.7	48
Total nutrients applied		152	45	81
			102 P_2O_5	98 K_2O

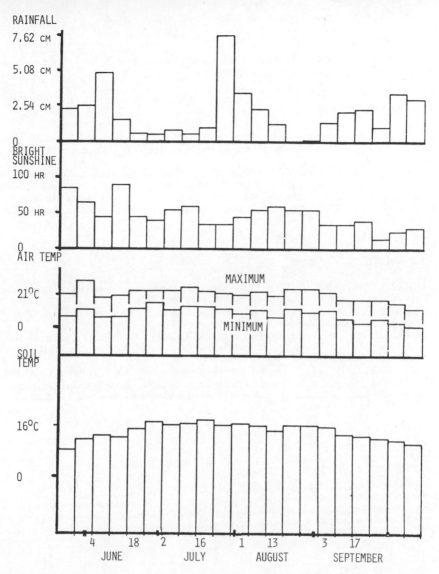

Fig. 6—Weekly pattern of climatic conditions (Truro, Nova Scotia) during the 1972 growing season. Total weekly rainfall in centimeters, total weekly bright sunlight in hours, weekly average air temperatures (maxima and minima) in C, weekly average soil temperature at 5-cm depth in C.

excessive by golf course standards, but these plots were not subject to excessive wear or mowing. Both bluegrasses produced similar weights of tissue to Pennlawn fescue which, however, is earlier to both start and finish growing.

Approximate recoveries of applied nutrients were 30% N, 13% P, and 40% K for the bluegrasses and fescues; while the bentgrass recoveries were 45% N, 21% P, and 60% K. This neglects nutrients in the roots. Soil analyses

(May 17 and October 31) were similar and showed low N, and medium-high P_2O_5, and K_2O in their exchangeable forms.

ACKNOWLEDGMENTS

This work was supported by grants from the Royal Canadian Golf Association, the Atlantic Superintendents' Association, and the Nova Scotia Department of Agriculture and Marketing.

The author is particularly grateful to Mr. B. Harnish, Analytical Laboratory, Nova Scotia Department of Agriculture (Soils and Crops) for carrying out the tissue and soil analyses; and to Mr. R. S. Morton, Nova Scotia Department of Agriculture (Horticulture and Biology Services) for the provision of established plot areas on which these studies were carried out.

REFERENCES

1. BEARD, J. B., and W. H. DANIEL. 1965. Effect of temperature and cutting on the growth of creeping bentgrass roots. Agron. J. 57:249–250.
2. BROWN, E. M. 1943. Seasonal variations in the growth and chemical composition of Kentucky bluegrass. Missouri Agr. Exp. Sta. Res. Bull. No. 360.
3. GRABER, L. F., N. T. NELSON, W. A. LUEKEL, and W. B. ALBERT. 1972. Organic food reserves in relation to the growth of alfalfa and other perennial herbaceous plants. Wisconsin Agr. Exp. Sta. Res. Bull. No. 80.
4. STUCKEY, I. H. 1941. Seasonal growth of grass roots. Amer. J. Bot. 28:486–491.
5. WADDINGTON, D. V., and T. L. ZIMMERMAN. 1971. Growth and chemical composition of eight grasses grown under high water table conditions. Soil Sci. Plant Anal. 3(4):329–337.

12

Development of improved Kentucky bluegrass cultivars for the transition zone of the eastern United States [1]

L.H. TAYLOR, J.F. SHOULDERS, A.J. POWELL, JR.,
R.E. SCHMIDT

Turfgrass performance is reviewed for a transition zone in the eastern United States where neither warm-season or cool-season turfgrasses give satisfactory performance. Kentucky bluegrass, *Poa pratensis* L., is widely grown in this area but cultivars now available are not sufficiently tolerant to summer temperature and drought stresses even with careful management. Characteristics of Kentucky bluegrass strains that may be important to their performance under high temperature stress are reviewed. A breeding approach for improvement of the species is suggested and progress to date is reported. Additional index words: High temperature stress, Intraspecific hybridization, Facultative apomixis, *Poa pratensis* L.

Between areas in the United States where warm-humid and cool-humid conditions prevail, there is a zone of transition where present turfgrasses are not well adapted. We are exploring variability within Kentucky bluegrass (*Poa pratensis* L.) and attempting to develop strains that will give more satisfactory performance in this zone.

In the eastern United States this transition zone includes southern New Jersey, all of Delaware, the eastern two-thirds of Maryland, most of Virginia east of the Blue Ridge Mountains, much of the piedmont of North Carolina, and areas of higher elevations in South Carolina and Georgia (Juska, Cornman, and Hovin, 1969). In general, within this climatically variable zone, warm-season grasses have a long dormant season and may be subject to winterkill while cool-season grasses have problems related to high temperature stresses, high humidity, and drought (Holt, 1969). Midsummer temperatures appear crucial. A climatograph of summer temperature regimes proposed by Madison (1971) indicates that no species being grown for fine turf in the transition zone is well adapted to the effective day and night temperatures.

In the transition zone, Kentucky bluegrass has been the most widely grown cool-season grass for lawns and general purpose turf. It is subject to summer dormancy during heat and drought stress. Most cultivars have been developed in cooler regions and are susceptible to warm-season diseases

[1] Contribution from the Department of Agronomy, Virginia Polytechnic Institute and State University, Blacksburg, VA 24061.

(Keen, 1969). The fine-leaved fescues, *Festuca rubra* L. and related species, are even less adapted to warm-season survival but are often included in mixtures with Kentucky bluegrass because of their shade tolerance. Tall fescue *Festuca arundinacea* Schreb., especially the cultivar 'Kentucky 31,' is used where Kentucky bluegrass is difficult to maintain, where use is heavy, and where its coarse texture is not objectionable. Bermudagrass *Cynodon dactylon* L. and zoysiagrass *Zoysia japonica* Steud. are the most commonly used warm-season grasses. They can provide excellent summer turf but are not attractive after frost in the fall and until full recovery has been attained the next spring (Juska and Hanson, 1959; Keen, 1969; Ward, 1969).

Kentucky bluegrass in the transition zone performs better if careful attention is given to management factors that relate to summer performance. Of prime importance are rate and timing of fertilizer application to promote fall and winter root and rhizome growth and higher mowing to reduce summer stress (Madison, 1969; Powell, Blaser, and Schmidt, 1967). With late fall and winter fertilization and irrigations during summer droughts, Kentucky bluegrass cultivars have been maintained for 5 years at Newport News, Virginia, (an area of high temperature stress) as an attractive summer and winter turf. Most sites and management regimes are less favorable and it would appear that genetic improvements must be made if Kentucky bluegrass is to be grown successfully in the transition zone (Watschke, Schmidt, and Blaser, 1970).

Limited data are available on the characteristics of Kentucky bluegrass strains which are important to satisfactory performance under summer temperature stresses. Differences in drought resistance among cultivars may be related to the depth of the root system (Beard, 1973). 'Merion,' a cultivar from an area of relatively high July temperature, had higher carbohydrate reserves and produced more top growth at warm temperatures than cultivars originating in cooler areas (Youngner and Nudge, 1968). In a Virginia study, five bluegrass strains from a range of latitudes were grown at three temperature regimes and at high and low nitrogen levels. A higher temperature tolerance of bluegrasses originating in warmer regions appeared related to higher carbohydrate levels and inherently lower nitrate absorption (Watschke et al., 1970). In a further study, ten bluegrass strains were grown under high temperature stress for 4 weeks. Bluegrasses growing best at high temperatures were usually higher in foliar carbohydrates and had higher photosynthesis and lower respiration rates. It was suggested that bluegrasses with genetically high photosynthetic efficiency be selected for use in areas of high temperature stresses (Watschke et al., 1972). There is need for suitable techniques to screen temperate turfgrasses for photosynthetic efficiency at high temperature (Watschke et al., 1973).

Important to the improvement of Kentucky bluegrass for the transition zone is the great diversity present within the species which has been grown over a wide area and subjected to natural selection under a variety of climates. It is also a facultative apomict with a range of plant types from the largely sexual to the almost entirely apomictic. Most important cultivars developed until recently likely originated from chance hybrids in nature. Superior chance hybrids undoubtedly exist in old turf areas and while efforts to collect and evaluate them are justified, the frequency of elite plants from this source is rather low. Local ecotypes may be of value in themselves, but it is more likely they will be useful as parents to provide characteristics of persistence and disease resistance when crossed with other parental strains with desirable turf characteristics. It appears that an efficient procedure would be hybridization of selected parents and selection within promising progenies. This procedure has resulted in the production of promising types, some of which are highly apomictic (Pepin and Funk, 1971).

In the turfgrass improvement program at Virginia Polytechnic Institute and State University several hundred bluegrass selections (produced by the breeding program of the New Jersey Agricultural Experiment Station at Rutgers) are being evaluated for turf performance under Virginia conditions. Clonal collections from a number of sources, especially from sites in the transition zone not considered favorable for Kentucky bluegrass, are also being evaluated. The most likely value of these clonal selections will be as parents with some tolerance for high temperature stress in a crossing program with another group of clones with desirable turf characteristics. Progenies of 55 crosses are currently being screened for promising types. Selections that appear to have desirable turf and seed production characteristics in preliminary tests will be observed under high temperature stress and evaluated for turfgrass performance at several locations in the transition zone.

REFERENCES

1. BEARD, J. B. 1973. Turfgrass science and culture. Prentice Hall, Inc., Englewood Cliffs, New Jersey.
2. FUNK, C. R., and S. J. HAN. 1967. Recurrent intraspecific hybridization: a proposed method of breeding Kentucky bluegrass, *Poa pratensis* L. p. 3–14. *In* 1967 Report of Turfgrass Research. New Jersey Agr. Exp. Sta. Bull. 818.
3. HOLT, E. C. 1969. Turfgrasses under warm, humid conditions. *In* A. A. Hanson and F. V. Juska (ed.) Turfgrass science. Agronomy 14:513–528. Amer. Soc. Agron., Madison, Wis.
4. JUSKA, F. V., J. F. CORNMAN, and A. W. HOVIN. 1969. Turfgrasses under cool, humid conditions. *In* A. A. Hanson and F. V. Juska (ed.) Turfgrass science. Agronomy 14:491–512. Amer. Soc. Agron., Madison, Wis.
5. ———, and A. A. HANSON. 1959. Evaluation of cool-season turfgrasses alone and in mixtures. Agron. J. 51:597–600.
6. KEEN, R. A. 1970. Grasses for the transition zone. p. 84–85. *In* Proc. First Int. Turfgrass Res. Conf. Sports Turf Research Institute, Bingley, England.
7. MADISON, J. H. 1970. Relationships between plants and mowing. p. 469–480. *In* Proc. First Int. Turfgrass Res. Conf. Sports Turf Research Institute, Bingley, England.
8. ———. 1971. Principles of turfgrass culture. Van Nostrand Reinhold Co., New York.
9. PEPIN, G. W., and C. R. FUNK. 1971. Intraspecific hybridization as a method of breeding Kentucky bluegrass (*Poa pratensis* L.) for turf. Crop Sci. 11:445–448.
10. POWELL, A. J., R. E. BLASER, and R. E. SCHMIDT. 1967. Physiological and color aspects of turfgrasses with fall and winter nitrogen. Agron. J. 59:303–307.
11. WARD, C. Y. 1969. Climate and adaptation. *In* A. A. Hanson and F. V. Juska (ed.) Turfgrass science. Agronomy 14:27–79. Amer. Soc. Agron., Madison, Wis.
12. WATSCHKE, T. L., R. E. SCHMIDT, and R. E. BLASER. 1970. Responses of some Kentucky bluegrasses to high temperature and nitrogen fertility. Crop Sci. 10:372–376.

13. ———, ———, E. W. CARSON, and R. E. BLASER. 1972. Some metabolic phenomena of Kentucky bluegrass under high temperature. Crop Sci. 12:87–90.
14. ———, ———, ———, and ———. 1973. Temperature influence on the physiology of selected cool-season turfgrasses and bermudagrass. Agron. J. 65: 591–594.
15. YOUNGNER, V. B., and F. J. NUDGE. 1968. Growth and carbohydrate storage of three *Poa pratensis* L. strains as influenced by temperature. Crop Sci. 8:455–457.

ABSTRACTS

Abstracts of all papers not published herein but presented at the Conference are included below to round off this Section. These abstracts, unlike the printed papers, have not been refereed.

SECTION 1 ABSTRACT—IDENTIFICATION OF VARIETIES OF KENTUCKY BLUEGRASS BY SEED CHARACTERISTICS

With the increasing number of varieties of Kentucky bluegrass (*Poa pratensis* L.) that appear on the market, it is important that each be identified by seed characteristics, particularly since certain varieties are more adapted to specific areas than others.

Several methods have been used to distinguish the different varieties. One method is to measure the length and width under 20X magnification and then classify the various varieties in different length and width groups. Once this has been done, other morphological seed characteristics such as distribution of color, straightness or arching of the dorsal profile, and the presence or absence of intermediate nerve, make final varietal separation possible.—D. E. Brown, Virginia Department of Agriculture and Commerce.

DISCUSSION

D. T. DUFF—Evaluations of bluegrasses for use in the United Kingdom are of special interest because of their extensive use in cool, humid sections of the United States. Is any attempt being made to select annual bluegrasses with perennial growth characteristics for use on football fields in the United Kingdom?

J. P. SHILDRICK—No attempt is being made in the United Kingdom to breed this type of annual bluegrass. We have become increasingly aware of differences between the true annual type and the perennial that tolerates close mowing and wear. Between these extremes of types that propagate from seed and are not very important in turf to types that develop much more by prostrate growth, there is a wide variation in plant type. It seems to us that the latter type would be more useful on football fields, but because of limited seed production of these spreading types, commercial seed supply is likely to be unavailable. Where annual bluegrass is used now the seed is obtained from the cleanings of other seed crops and this source provides a wide range of annual bluegrass types. In fact, it may be better to sow this broad-based material and depend on natural selection under existing conditions to increase dominance of superior types rather than try to develop cultivars specifically for particular situations.

J. P. VAN DER HORST—Could differences in the satisfactory performance of ryegrasses and bluegrasses observed in the United Kingdom, the United States, and the Netherlands be related to differences in height of cut of these grasses? On soccer fields in Holland a 3-cm cut produces high-quality, well-groomed turf that is wear resistant.

J. P. SHILDRICK—Yes, the height of cut will affect turf quality and wear tolerance ratings. Climatic variables will also influence response of the turf under these conditions. Any factor that creates stress within the turf will have an effect. Further, these differences in response are basic in making assumptions regarding use of these grasses. This information is not always available in published form. I would like to add a comment regarding the roller treatment. Our investigations have not produced the same results on turf that were obtained in the Netherlands. We feel that a more drastic treatment with a modified aerator is necessary to improve turf quality under our conditions.

C. Y. WARD—What minimum temperatures have been tolerated by 'Berlin' bermudagrass?

G. W. BURTON—This bermudagrass has survived in Lake City, Michigan, for a number of years. 'Midland' bermudagrass which we thought of as winter-hardy has not survived there. The Berlin bermudagrass has a good deep rhizome development that may be related to increased winter survival. I'm certain that there is more to winterhardiness than this, however. Certainly minimum temperatures have been lower than −20 C.

J. B. BEARD—Soil temperature is the critical factor, not air temperature. These soils are basically sands. A fair amount of snow cover is characteristic in this area.

J. B. BEARD—With regard to wear effects on turf, I think we must recognize that a communications problem exists. Studies on wear and effects of traffic on turf have two components—wear of the turf itself and changes in physical soil properties. Both can be detrimental to immediate and long-term survival of the turf. Thus, when evaluations are made of various species and cultivars, we must know whether overall traffic effects or wear effects or soil compaction effects are responsible for the results. The correct terminology must be used. When various types of apparatus are used to simulate wear, information on impact versus abrasive wear effects must be known. This point is in need of clarification. What type of evaluation is being used?

J. P. SHILDRICK—I agree that wear effects are partly related to soil type and that soil compaction can be a major problem, but more important, I believe for United Kingdom conditions, is the effect of abrasion on the grasses. The effects of players on the turf need further study. We must know what characteristics grass should have to be most resistant to wear, and we must know what soil conditions are affected least. With the studded roller alone on turf grown on a medium loam soil, very little effect from the studs was noted. On other fescue and ryegrass turf grown on sandy soil marked effects from the studded roller were obtained. These results may be similar to those referred to in the Netherlands. In general, we have felt that either a knocking type of action with the modified aerator or a scuffing action producing actual abrasion on the grass is the most important element in our trials.

R. W. SCHERY—What provision is the Netherlands and the European economic community making for the recognition of synthetic varieties embracing several clonal components?

H. VOS—At this time we do not have exact models to describe synthetic varieties that fail to fit a normal distribution. This matter is under discussion. Until recently we have had no synthetic varieties that could be used as an example. Now it appears that in some European countries inbreds are being described. Registration must follow the breeders work and then regulations must be developed that will improve the registration of synthetic varieties.

E. W. SCHWEIZER—Are hairs on bluegrass seed, specifically on 'Marion' bluegrass, a useful characteristic in seed identification?

D. E. BROWN—It is one of many useful characteristics that aid the analyst in seed identification. Seed control or enforcement agencies usually have a very short time to determine best ways for distinguishing between the many new cultivars as they come on the market. As many characteristics as possible are studied to determine which are most reliable for identification purposes.

R. C. O'KNEFSKI—What was the number of the U. S. Department of Agriculture handbook that describes seed characteristics useful in identification?

D. E. BROWN—USDA handbook number 219 serves as a valuable reference for seed analysts.

P. MC MAUGH—Is there any future for *Festuca arundinacea* X *Lolium perenne* crosses in view of wear differences reported in different countries?

R. E. SCHMIDT—These crosses might prove to be important.

Nutrition and fertilizers

Section II

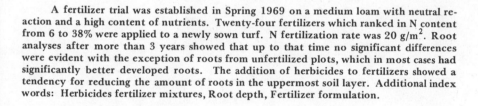

13

Influence of various fertilizers on root development in a turfgrass mixture[1]

P. BOEKER & W. OPITZ VON BOBERFELD

A fertilizer trial was established in Spring 1969 on a medium loam with neutral re-action and a high content of nutrients. Twenty-four fertilizers which ranked in N content from 6 to 38% were applied to a newly sown turf. N fertilization rate was 20 g/m². Root analyses after more than 3 years showed that up to that time no significant differences were evident with the exception of roots from unfertilized plots, which in most cases had significantly better developed roots. The addition of herbicides to fertilizers showed a tendency for reducing the amount of roots in the uppermost soil layer. Additional index words: Herbicides fertilizer mixtures, Root depth, Fertilizer formulation.

Grass roots, besides supplying water and nutrients to the plants, perform other functions such as erosion control. It is useful to know which factors influence root development. In this respect it is known that the intensity of management, for instance the intensity of cutting, has a great influence on the total amount and the vertical distribution of the roots (Klapp, 1971; Saglamtimur and Bogdan, 1970; Skirde, 1970, 1971).

Of equal importance are the level of fertilization, and the chemical formulation of fertilizers, the water supply, the soil texture, etc. Further, root development is to a certain degree determined by the choice of the turfgrass species and varieties (Boeker, 1971, 1973; van der Horst and Kappen, 1970; van der Horst, 1970; Skirde, 1971). The results discussed in this paper give evidence related to the question whether the application of various forms of fertilizers have a lasting effect on the root development of grasses in a turf.

MATERIALS AND METHODS

The trial was situated 15 km north of Bonn in the Rhine Valley. The mean annual precipitation is 669 mm, well distributed, but with a slight maximum in June, July, and August. The mean annual temperature is 9.9 C.

[1]Contribution from Institut fuer Pflanzenbau, Katzenburgweg, Bonn, West Germany.

Table 1—Sand- and ash-free root dry matter in g/1,000 cm^2.

Fertilizer, %			Layer, 0 to 5 cm		Layer, 5 to 10 cm	
N	P$_2$O$_5$	K$_2$O	Nov 1971	Jul 1972	Nov 1971	Jul 1972
6	1	2	126.359	101.531	2.202	4.442
6	3	2	84.779	126.903	1.524	6.630
7	2	2	71.831	118.501	1.695	4.125
7	3	4	101.267	107.896	2.022	5.593
9	2	4	89.793	135.891	2.271	7.936
10	3	5	118.309	116.646	1.877	6.148
10	4	6	100.686	136.959	1.467	5.857
10	4	6	84.073	95.239	2.701	5.116
10	4	6	108.663	121.954	2.016	7.034
12	12	20	99.836	115.298	2.732	4.421
15	9	5	98.260	151.286	4.027	6.214
15	9	15	78.045	98.013	1.412	4.147
16	5	12	99.225	112.980	2.244	5.318
18	3	3	100.819	79.263	2.370	5.225
20	4	4	88.231	95.016	2.104	6.671
20	5	5	108.083	98.815	2.208	5.386
20	5	5	96.125	113.437	1.918	5.593
20	5	10	95.259	145.346	7.314	6.344
21	7	14	113.428	127.204	1.672	6.541
21	17	50	103.638	90.682	2.743	5.769
26	8	8	105.968	113.769	3.089	10.735
26	8	8	98.954	106.056	2.494	7.117
34	5	5	117.521	107.616	1.970	5.101
38	--	--	97.778	115.303	3.172	7.143
--	--	--	135.736	129.236	3.318	8.366
LSD .05			34.9952	44.0941	2.5590	3.2561

The soil is a sandy loam which is of loess origin. The soil reaction was pH 7.1 (in KCl). The natural content of P and K is high and sufficient for medium yields.

The trial was established with three replicates for each fertilizer arranged in three blocks, the size of plots was 10 m^2. The mixture that was sown in Spring 1969 with 10 g/m^2 was composed of 45% *Poa pratensis*, 'Merion', 25% *Festuca rubra commutata*, 'Topie', 25% *Festuca rubra rubra*, 'Oase', and 5% *Agrostis tenuis*, 'Highland'. The grass was cut once a week to 3 cm.

The plots were fertilized at a rate of 20 g/m^2 N with the exception of the control which received no nitrogen. Twenty-four fertilizers were included; their composition is given in the Tables 1 and 2. According to the chemical formulation of the nitrogen the number of dressings varied from one to four. There were four fertilizers which contained herbicides. In order to prevent damage to the sward only one or two dressings in spring or summer were made with such fertilizers; the rest of the season the same fertilizer formulation without herbicides was used. Sulfate of ammonia was used as a standard fertilizer treatment.

The sampling for root analyses was done at two dates, in November 1971 and in July 1972. Two samples were taken per plot, or six replicates per fertilizer treatment. The techniques for sampling have been described by Opitz von Boberfeld (1972).

Table 2—Sand- and ash-free root dry matter in g/1,000 cm^2.

Fertilizer, %			Layer, 10 to 15 cm		Layer, 15 to 20 cm	
N	P$_2$O$_5$	K$_2$O	Nov 1971	Jul 1972	Nov 1971	Jul 1972
6	1	2	1.581	2.462	1.016	2.286
6	3	2	0.762	4.079	0.539	1.923
7	2	2	1.208	1.804	0.638	1.265
7	3	4	1.130	2.882	0.353	2.115
9	2	4	1.332	3.758	0.747	2.581
10	3	5	1.203	3.037	0.752	2.167
10	4	6	1.187	3.665	0.596	2.581
10	4	6	1.275	3.079	0.643	1.908
10	4	6	1.125	3.862	0.492	1.949
12	12	20	1.068	2.452	0.705	1.851
15	9	5	2.789	3.312	1.405	2.146
15	9	15	0.740	2.167	0.575	1.628
16	5	12	1.244	2.887	1.089	1.234
18	3	3	1.648	3.810	0.964	2.312
20	4	4	1.420	3.685	0.886	2.333
20	5	5	1.047	2.898	0.643	1.426
20	5	5	1.358	2.877	0.487	1.674
20	5	10	2.094	3.468	0.674	1.861
21	7	14	1.151	4.089	0.678	2.498
21	17	50	1.922	2.550	0.877	1.545
26	8	8	1.156	3.554	0.648	2.390
26	8	8	1.344	3.468	0.790	2.167
34	5	5	1.068	3.053	0.607	1.970
38	--	--	1.623	3.986	0.798	2.276
--	--	--	2.504	6.443	1.700	4.551
LDS .05			0.8602	1.3677	0.6472	1.0230

RESULTS

The amount of roots was determined as sand- and ash-free dry matter. Table 1 and 2 show data from two dates and four layers examined. The figures are grouped according to the kind of fertilizers applied. The first nine fertilizers contained small amounts of nitrogen (6 to 10%); they were mostly of organic origin either from plant material or from animals. Group 2 composed of nine fertilizers contained materials of mixed origin, partly organic or synthetic organic or pure mineral fertilizers with a N content between 12 to 20%. The last group of six fertilizers with a N content between 21 to 38% comprised materials of synthetic organic origin.

The results of the root analyses indicate that the differences between the various fertilizer treatments are significant only in a few cases, and mostly only for one date of sampling. Only the amount of roots in the unfertilized plots were significantly higher in most instances. The main reason for this is probably modification in the composition of the sward.

There is disagreement over the question whether there is a relation between fertilization and the depth and amount of roots. Some argue (Mitscherlich, 1912) that roots of unfertilized plants on the "search" for nutrients will penetrate deeper in the soil; others are in opposition to this argument and stress the point that roots of fertilized plants are more vigorous

Table 3—Sand- and ash-free root dry matter in g/1,000 cm^2 as influenced by application of fertilizers with and without herbicides.

	Layer							
	0 to 5 cm		5 to 10 cm		10 to 15 cm		15 to 20 cm	
Date of sampling	Nov 1971 1	Jul 1972 2	Nov 1971 1	Jul 1972 2	Nov 1971 1	Jul 1972 2	Nov 1971 1	Jul 1972 2
Dry matter:								
With herbicides	94.993	98.499	2.371	5.763	1.406	3.309	0.721	2.015
Without herbicides	100.348	116.880	2.488	6.078	1.343	3.183	0.736	2.001

and therefore better able to grow deeper into the soil (Gliemeroth, 1951). The results of this trial favor the first premise, especially with regard to the deeper layers of the soil.

A significant difference could not be found among the three groups of fertilizers; variation between values was considerable. But this may have been because the duration of the trial was only 3 years.

The results for root analyses on plots which received fertilizers with or without herbicides are shown in Table 3. The last group is comprised of four fertilizers in which the active ingredients were 2,4-D [(2,4-dichlorophenoxy) acetic acid], CMPP, and dicamba (3,6-dichloro-o-anisic acid). Although the differences are not significant, there is a trend toward the reduction of roots in the uppermost layer when herbicides were applied. This was to be expected since all plots which received fertilizers were completely free of weeds and there were no large variations in the composition of the swards. Similar observations have been made following the application of certain herbicides to cereals (Hafner, 1963; Maas, 1971).

Table 4—Composition of the sward.

	Fertilization		
Species	Sulfate of ammonia	Other N-fertilizers	Without N
		% ground cover	
Agrostis tenuis	33	35	20
Festuca rubra	19	14	46
Lolium perenne		+	
Poa annua	3	3	3
Poa pratensis	43	45	28
Poa trivialis	2	3	2
Trifolium repens	0		1
Achillea millefolium	0		+
Cirsium arvense	0	+	
Plantago maior	0	+	+
Ranuculus repens	0		+
Stellaria media	0	+	
Taraxacum officinale	0	+	+
Veronica serpyllifolia	0		+

The composition of the turf was examined yearly. The results from September 1972 are given in Table 4. Considerable differences between the fertilized and unfertilized plot are noted. In those receiving fertilizers *Poa pratensis* and *Agrostis tenuis* increased while in the others *Festuca rubra* was the main component of the sward. This is considered the most important reason why the soil under the unfertilized plots had a relatively large amount of roots. According to other investigations (Boeker, 1973) *Festuca rubra* has the greatest amount of roots of all turfgrass species.

REFERENCES

1. BOEKER, P. 1971. Wurzelmassenentwicklung unter einigen Rasengraeserarten und -sorten. Protokollheft, DLG.:25–35.

2. ———. 1974. Root development of selected turfgrass species and cultivars. p. 55–61. *In* E. C. Roberts (ed.) Proc. Second Int. Turfgrass Res. Conf. Amer. Soc. Agron., Madison, Wis.

3. GLIEMEROTH, G. 1951. Der Einfluss von Duengung auf den Wasserentzug der Pflanzen aus dem Unterboden. Z. Pflanzenernaehr., Duengung, Bodenkunde 52(97): 21–41.

4. HAFNER, K. 1963. Einfluss einiger wichtiger Wuchsstoffherbizide und Triazin-verbindungen auf das Getreide bei vorhandener und fehlender Unkrautkonkurrenz. Diss. Hohenheim.

5. KLAPP, E. 1971. Wiesen und Weiden. 4 Aufl. P. Parcy, Berlin.

6. MAAS, G. 1971. Zur unterschiedlichen Sortenempfindlichkeit von Kulturpflanzen gegenueber Bodenherbiziden. Nachrichtenbl. Deutsch. Pflanzenschutzd. 23:161–164.

7. MITSCHERLICH, E. A. 1912. Das Wasser als Vegetationsfaktor. Landw. Jahrb. 42:701–707.

8. OPITZ VON BOBERFELD, W. 1972. Zur Problematik des Stichprobenumfanges bei Wurzelgewichtsfeststellungen von Rasengraesern. Rasen-Turf-Gazon 3:51–53.

9. SAGLAMTIMUR, T., and G. BOGDAN. 1970. Untersuchungen ueber den Einfluss von Nutzungschaeufigkeit und Stickstoffduengung auf Sorten vom Deutschen Weidelgras (Lolium perenne L.) Z. Acker-u. Pflbau 132:16–35.

10. SKIRDE, W. 1970. Reaktionen von Rasenmischungen auf physiologisch saure und physiologisch alkalische Duengung. Rasen-Turf-Gazon 1:58–60.

11. ———. 1971. Bewurzelung der Rasendecke mit Beispielen fuer Abhaenigigkeit und Beeinflussung. Rasen-Turf-Gazon 2:112–115.

12. VAN DER HORST, J. P. 1970. Die Pruefung von Sportrasengraesern in den Niederlanden. Rasen-Turf-Gazon 1:88–90.

13. ———, and L. M. KAPPEN. 1970. Bewurzelung von Rasengraesern. Rasen-Turf-Gazon 1:15–16.

14

Influence of nitrogen fertilization on species dominance in turfgrass mixtures[1]

R. E. ENGEL

Influence of nitrogen fertilization on increase or decrease of individual species composing turfgrass mixtures is of continuing concern to the turf manager. When such population shifts occur, total growth response to N is considered part of the mechanism. Also, N has indirect effects that influence a plant's competitiveness. Disease susceptibility, drought tolerance, and temperature tolerances are good examples. In some of these situations with most severe conditions, sudden kill of a turfgrass species can occur. At such time, survival of one of the competitive species gives a sudden and large shift in turfgrass species composition.

The amount of N fertilizer applied, the season of N application, the season N becomes available from the soil, and various forms of N carriers are expected to produce slow shifts in grass population on turf sites. The degree of species change should vary with the aggregate of dissimilarities of the competing species that effect the N response. Kentucky bluegrass-bentgrass and bentgrass-annual bluegrass mixtures which are rather similar in temperature and moisture requirements do not show a great shift toward complete dominance of one species with varied N use. Major shifts in turfgrass population from N fertilization developed with a mixture of zoysiagrass (*Zoysia japonica* Steud.) and Kentucky bluegrass (*Poa pratensis* L.). A good supply of available N is expected to favor the more aggressive, weedy, or colonizing grasses.

Nitrogen fertilization has an important influence on turfgrass species populations in a mixture. The potential of this influence from N fertilization will vary with temperature and moisture. In most cases shifts in species content of mixed turf will occur rather slowly and subtly. As turfgrass production becomes more efficient and single species or cultivars are grown, the influence of N fertilization on species population changes will need more study. Additional index words: Turfgrass mixtures, Nitrogen fertilization, Kentucky bluegrass, Red fescue, Annual bluegrass, Bermudagrass, Zoysiagrass, Bentgrass, Turfgrass species balance, Growth temperature limits, *Zoysia japonica* Steud., *Poa pratensis* L.

Nitrogen is known for its ability to make turf greener or grow more rapidly. Also, N has other influences on the plant. These effects may cause two grass species to react differently to N application. Aside from nitrogen's effect on growth rate and quality, its influence on turf failure is accepted. If

---

[1] Paper of the Journal Series, New Jersey Agricultural Experiment Station, Department of Soils and Crops, Cook College, Rutgers University, The State University of New Jersey, New Brunswick, NJ 08903.

knowledge related to ability of N to encourage growth or destroy a turfgrass is utilized, it may be possible to manipulate the relative abundance of a species in a turfgrass mixture. Species manipulation has greater importance than formerly because of the desire to maintain a monoculture or a balance of two or more species. The rather subtle influence of N on species content of a turfgrass mixture is not well understood and is often overlooked in management of turf.

It is the purpose of this paper to consider some of the theory, review literature, and report data that pertains to N fertilization and its influence on species populations in turfgrass mixtures.

THEORY ON EFFECT OF N ON MIXED TURFGRASS

Man has known for ages that high or low soil fertility may determine the plant species on a site. Nitrogen is a major ingredient of soil fertility. While N fertilization is considered important in turf growing, turfgrass science at times fails to appreciate the use of N except as it encourages growth. With regard to grass populations, little specific data has been developed on the balance of two species in the turf sward. A theoretical mechanism for N influencing the balance of turf species involves several factors. First, some plants make a greater total growth response to a given amount of N (14). This might result from species differing in determinate growth, range of size potential, and/or a physiological efficiency such as the differential photosynthetic response as illustrated by bentgrass and bermudagrass subjected to cool and warm growing temperatures as reported by Miller (10). Also, growth stage of the plant is a factor. Kentucky bluegrass (*Poa pratensis* L.) and bentgrass (*Agrostis* spp.) initiated growth at lower temperatures than annual bluegrass (*Poa annua* L.), according to Bogart and Beard (1). Temperature at the time N is available to the grass will influence net growth.

In addition to the direct effect of N on relative growth response of two different species, there are a large number of indirect N effects that influence the success of the individual grass species in a mixture. Since generous N fertilization results in a lower carbohydrate plant (6), it increases the grass plant's susceptibility to most forms of stress. Lowering the carbohydrates weakens root development (7, 12). This causes a higher top-to-root ratio (7) which, combined with the greater water requirements of the high N plant (15), accentuates drought injury (4, 5).

Conceivably, N use might function to destroy one grass species during heat-drought or cold stress and still allow the more hardy and desired species to survive. For example, unhardened, high N plants are far more susceptible to winterkill (2, 16); and, in theory, the least winter-hardy species in the mixture could be destroyed by use of this principle. Disease resistance is influenced by the amounts and types of N carriers (3, 8, 13) and it is theorized that this principle might be used by man or nature to destroy a susceptible species in a mixture. Thus, the N level available to turf has diverse influences on the growth and survival of the individual grass species. If both the growth-encouraging and the plant-destroying effects of nitrogen fertilizer are considered, this nutrient has potential for causing great changes in the month-to-month population of grass shoots of a given species. How great a force is the N influence in terms of grass population shifts? Such answers will come largely from research.

METHODS USED IN STUDIES ON N RATE AND SEASON OF APPLICATION ON SPECIES DOMINANCE IN MIXED TURFGRASS IN NEW JERSEY

Turfgrass mixtures were used in field-type studies in New Jersey to determine the influence of nitrogen rate and season of nitrogen application on turfgrass species balance. Outdoor studies were established on well-drained loam soils with a pH ranging from 6.0 to 6.5. Treatments were continued for 4 to 12 years for the several tests on grass species populations.

New Jersey has a humid climate with 110 to 113 cm average yearly rainfall. Drought occurs once to twice per year and necessitates irrigation for good-quality turf. Also, 1- to 3-week periods with temperature highs of 32–35 C are sufficient to cause serious attacks from *Fusarium roseum, Pythium* spp, and *Rhizoctonia solani*. Details of the several tests are given in Table 1. Results of the tests are presented in the following section and discussed in relation to the respective combinations of grasses.

Table 1—A summation of methods used to study rate and seasonal influence of nitrogen on turfgrass species balance in a humid, temperate climate (New Jersey).

Data reported in table	Grasses	Soil and irrigation*	Height of cut, cm	No. years treatment	Evaluation method
2	Mixture of Kentucky bluegrasses, bentgrasses, and red fescues	Loam, 1–2/year	3.8	4	Point quadrat 300 identifications per treatment (3 replications)
3	Merion Kentucky bluegrass and Pennlawn red fescue	Loam, 1–2/year	3.8	4	Point quadrat 300 identifications per treatment (3 replications)
4	Pennlawn red fescue	Loam, 1–2/year	3.8	4	Point quadrat 300 identifications per treatment (3 replications
5	Seaside and Penn-cross creeping bentgrass	Loam 3/week	0.64	11	Estimates
6	Meyer zoysia and Merion Kentucky bluegrass	Loam, 1–2/year	1.3 and 2.2	12	Estimates

Note: The first 3 tests were mowed once per 5 to 7 days during the growing season. The fourth (Table 5) was mowed 3 times per week at 0.64 cm. The fifth study (Table 6) was mowed 3 times per week in summer and once per week in spring and fall.
* Watering "1–2/year" indicates 3.7 to 5 cm were applied on an average of 1 to 2 times/year. The 3/week procedure was 1.25 cm, 3 times/week in dry warm periods.

Table 2—The effect of September to October versus late May to June fertilization with 4-3-2 ratio of N-P-K at 145 kg N/ha on Kentucky bluegrass-bentgrass content of turf cut to 3.8 cm.

Grass species*	Month fertilized	Grass species content, %					
		1964		1965		1966	
				145 kg N/ha			
Kentucky bluegrass	Sept–Oct	42	--	31	--	33	--
Kentucky bluegrass	May–Jun	40	--	32	--	20	--
Bentgrass	Sept–Oct	--	43	--	60	--	56
Bentgrass	May–Jun	--	54	--	63	--	75
				No nitrogen			
Kentucky bluegrass	–	29	--	18	--	23	--
Bentgrass	–	--	53	--	56	--	56
LSD .05	–	17	--	13	--	N.S.	17

* Mixed cultivars of Kentucky bluegrass and mixed cultivars and species of bentgrass.

RESULTS AND DISCUSSION ON THE RESPONSE OF TURFGRASS COMBINATIONS TO N FERTILIZATION

Kentucky bluegrass-bentgrass population balance

Kentucky bluegrass and bentgrass, two cool-season grasses, are both favored by a generous supply of N which would minimize expectation of a species shift from N fertilization of this mixture. Some leverage on species balance might be expected from such features as the cold hardiness of the Kentucky bluegrass and the broad-spectrum disease susceptibility of the bentgrasses. Data reported in Table 2 show that September-October fertilization in New Jersey was more encouraging to Kentucky bluegrass than May-June fertilization. Optimum growth response of Kentucky bluegrass to fall-applied N is supported by good growth characteristics as reported by Hanson and Juska (7). However, in this report, it was observed that season of fertilization did not maintain a shift of 5% significance in species content of the turf during a 4-year period.

Kentucky bluegrass-red fescue (*Festuca rubra* L.) population balance

Historically, it has been accepted that generous availability of N increases the Kentucky bluegrass population and lowers the red fescue content of turf containing these two species. A common theoretical explanation of this result has been greater N response by Kentucky bluegrass. Again research data on comparative response of the two species are rather limited. As a result of N fertilization, red fescue types grown in competition with Kentucky bluegrass decreased significantly in population over a period of several years (Table 3). Similarly, the weedy encroachment of Kentucky bluegrass was encouraged in red fescue turf in the New Jersey climate (Table 4) with comparatively low rates of N. Also, these tables show that application of N in August (commonly a warm, dry month in New Jersey) is least favorable to the red fescue population.

Table 3—Influence of 3 years of varied rate and season of fertilization with a 3-1-2 ratio of N-P-K on Merion Kentucky bluegrass competitiveness to Pennlawn red fescue cut to 3.8 cm.

Month	No. applications	Kentucky bluegrass, %	
		24 kg N/ha	48 kg N/ha
August	1	36	--
September	1	18	29
October	1	15	30
November	1	23	30
March	1	28	33
May	1	24	--
		48 kg N/ha	96 kg N/ha
August–September	2	47	61
September–October	2	35	40
September–March	2	38	41
October–November	2	31	38
		72 kg N/ha	144 kg N/ha
September–October–November	3	28	57
LSD .05		13.1	

Table 4—Kentucky bluegrass encroachment into 3.8 cm Pennlawn red fescue turf with 4 years of fertilization at varied rate and season of application of 3-1-2 ratio of N-P-K in 1972.

Month	No. applications	Kentucky bluegrass, %	
		24 kg N/ha	48 kg N/ha
August	1	19	--
September	1	15	9
October	1	6	5
November	1	3	11
March	1	2	7
May	1	12	--
		48 kg N/ha	96 kg N/ha
August–September	2	27	28
September–October	2	13	19
September–March	2	16	17
October–November	2	15	17
		72 kg N/ha	144 kg N/ha
September–October–November	3	9	24
LSD .05		13.7	

Table 5—Effect of rate and season of applying N fertilizer for 11 years on annual blue-grass content of creeping bentgrass turf cut to 0.64 cm with favorable levels of water and disease control (New Jersey).

Nitrogen carrier	Nitrogen, kg/ha	Season of application	Annual bluegrass, %, June 1972	Summer injury, August 1972
Urea	194	Steady	18	15
Urea	387	Steady	18	30
Urea	194	Cold	30	15
Urea	387	Cold	37	17
Act S.S.*	194	Steady	28	1
Act S.S.	387	Steady	28	11
Act S.S.	194	Cold	40	5
Act S.S.	387	Cold	34	30
Act S.S.	194	Warm	13	>1
Act S.S.	387	Warm	15	0
LSD .05			11.5	--

* Activated sewage sludge (6% N) sold as Milorganite by Milwaukee Sewage Co., Milwaukee, Wisconsin.

Bentgrass-annual bluegrass population balance

Annual bluegrass is commonly considered a weed in bentgrass turf. In attempts to combat this species, many turf growers in the United States have theorized that fertilization could be a major factor in its control. Some delay N application in the early spring because they consider annual bluegrass more aggressive than bentgrass when N is high and growing temperatures are lower. The research information available is too sparse to answer the question. Work by Bogart and Beard (1) showed bentgrass initiated spring growth at lower temperatures than annual bluegrass. Some growers and research studies (9, 11) from milder temperature latitudes suggest late fall or early winter fertilization of bentgrass because of the good turf quality that develops through winter and the forepart of the next growing season. Long-term influence of this practice on the annual bluegrass population has not been established. In a New Jersey test of 12 years, this weedy grass increased with cold weather use of N (Table 5), as compared with amounts of this grass developing from steady use of N or use of N in the warmer months of the growing season. However, the data suggest that none of the N procedures used were likely to be the major cause of the common encroachment of annual bluegrass into bentgrass turf in New Jersey.

Bermudagrass (Cynodon spp.)—Kentucky bluegrass population balance

In the middle latitudes of the United States, the two major turfgrasses, bermudagrass and the Kentucky bluegrasses, meet and intermingle on many turf sites. No published research was found on nitrogen's influence on the relative populations of these two species in mixtures. Many growers in the region where both of these grasses occur would agree that increasing incre-ments of N fertilization favors the bermudagrass. This is logical in view of

Table 6—Zoysiagrass population when grown in mixture with Merion Kentucky bluegrass with a 4–3–2 ratio fertilizer applied for 12 years at rate of 73 kg N/ha at different months. New Jersey, 1964.

Month fertilized	Zoysia grass content, %	
	1.3-cm cut	2.2-cm cut
No fertilizer	55	48
April	77	32
June	75	63
August	77	32
September	33	12
October	27	5
LSD .05	22	27

the great capacity of this species to use and tolerate this nutrient. Yet, it would seem logical that the net effect of N on the population balance of these grasses would be influenced greatly by the season of applying N because of their difference in temperature response. Bermudagrass will fail to grow in cooler weather when Kentucky bluegrass will make good N response and growth and it becomes more susceptible to winter injury with generous nitrogen supply.

Zoysia (*Zoysia japonica* Steud.) population as influenced by N use

The *Zoysia* species, like bermudagrass, require higher temperatures for optimum growth. By comparison with other turf types, they are very slow-growing grasses. When this grass is growing with bermudagrass, it is recognized that increased N fertilization favors the bermudagrass population. In the middle latitudes of the United States, *Zoysia japonica* has been introduced into Kentucky bluegrass turf areas. Whereas some might attempt to grow balanced populations of these grasses, others might wish to discourage one or the other. In the temperate climate of New Jersey, varied seasonal N fertilization procedures on a mixed 'Merion' Kentucky bluegrass and 'Meyer' zoysiagrass turf produced great shifts in population of the two species (Table 6). With a closer cut of 1.3 cm, zoysiagrass was dominant after 12 years with moderate amounts of N in June (late spring) while at a higher cut of 2.2 cm, the zoysiagrass stand was decimated with the same amount of N in October. This study shows the greater influence of nitrogen on species content of turf with larger differences in their growth temperature limits.

CONCLUSIONS

Nitrogen fertilization is an important factor in determining the aggressiveness and survival of the individual turfgrass species. Temperature and moisture will have greater influence on relative species abundance in mixtures. Nitrogen's influence on this characteristic will vary according to the species involved. The amount of shift in species balance caused by N fertilization will increase with the dissimilarity of the species involved. For ex-

ample, Kentucky bluegrass and zoysiagrass differ greatly in growth temperatures and response to available nitrogen. As a result of this, great shifts in
population of the two species can result from N fertilization procedures.
Kentucky bluegrass-bentgrass and bentgrass-annual bluegrass mixtures differ
less in response to temperature; and N procedure has less influence on the
abundance of these species. Turfgrass population shifts arising from N fertilization appear to occur slowly over a period of years on most sites. When N
fertilization is used generously, as compared with low and moderate N use,
the weedy, aggressive, and colonizing types appear to increase at the expense
of the less vigorous species. As more knowledge is obtained on N fertilization
effects on turfgrass species competition and turfgrass growing becomes more
specialized, N fertilizer procedures will be more precisely planned and managed to control species content of turf.

REFERENCES

1. BOGART, J. E. (J. B. Beard, Advisor). 1972. Factors influencing competition of
annual bluegrass (*Poa annua* L.) within established turfgrass communities and seedling stands. M.S. Thesis, Michigan State University, East Lansing.
2. CARROLL, J. C., and F. A. WELTON. 1939. Winter survival-nitrogen. Effect of
heavy and late applications of nitrogenous fertilizer on the cold resistance of
Kentucky bluegrass. Plant Physiol. 14:297-308.
3. COOK, R. N., R. E. ENGEL, and S. BACHELDER. 1964. A study of the effect of
nitrogen carriers on turfgrass disease. Plant Dis. Rep. 48(4):254-255.
4. FUNK, C. R., R. E. ENGEL, and P. M. HALISKY. 1966. Performance of Kentucky
bluegrass varieties as influenced by fertility level and cutting height. New Jersey
Agr. Exp. Sta. Bull. 816. p. 7-21.
5. ———, ———, and ———. 1967. Summer survival of turfgrass species as influenced by variety, fertility level, and disease incidence. New Jersey Agr. Exp. Sta.
Bull. 818. p. 71-76.
6. GREEN, D. G., and J. B. BEARD. 1969. Seasonal relationship between nitrogen
nutrition and soluble carbohydrates in the leaves of *Agrostis palustris*. Agron. J. 61:
107-111.
7. HANSON, A. A., and F. V. JUSKA. 1961. Winter root activity in Kentucky bluegrass (*Poa pratensis* L.). Agron. J. 53:372-376.
8. JUSKA, F. V., and A. A. HANSON. 1961. Nitrogen species and variety. N variable
in testing Kentucky bluegrass varieties for turf. Agron. J. 53:409-410.
9. LEDEBOER, F. B., and C. R. SKOGLEY. 1973. Effects of various nitrogen sources,
timing and rates on quality and growth rate of cool-season turfgrasses. Agron. J. 65:
243-246.
10. MILLER, J. D. 1960. Temperature effect on the rate of apparent photosynthesis of
seaside bentgrass and bermudagrass. Proc. Amer. Soc. Hort. Sci. 75:700-703.
11. POWELL, A. J., R. E. BLASER, and R. E. SCHMIDT. 1967a. Physiological and
color aspects of turfgrasses with fall and winter nitrogen. Agron. J. 59:303-307.
12. ———, ———, and ———. 1967b. Effect of nitrogen on winter root growth
of bentgrass. Agron. J. 59:529-530.
13. ROBERTS, E. C., and F. E. MARKLAND. 1966. Dollarspot tests yield tips.
Golfdom 40:38-48.
14. SKOGLEY, C. R., and F. B. LEDEBOER. 1968. Evaluation of several Kentucky
bluegrass and red fescue strains maintained as lawn turf under three levels of fertility.
Agron. J. 60:47-49.
15. SMIKA, D. E., H. J. HAAS, and J. F. POWER. 1965. Effects of moisture and nitrogen fertilizer on growth and water use by native grass. Agron. J. 57:483-487.
16. WILKINSON, J. F., and D. T. DUFF. 1972. Effects of fall fertilization on cold resistance, color, and growth of Kentucky bluegrass. Agron. J. 64:345-348.

15

Influence of fall nitrogenous fertilization on the carbohydrates of Kentucky bluegrass[1]

D. T. DUFF

Ten grams of nitrogen per square meter were applied October 1 and 15, November 1 and 15, December 1 and 15 to separate plots. Sample tissue was removed from the plots at 2-week intervals throughout the autumn, winter, and spring. Basal culm, lower leaf sheath, and apical meristem tissue were analyzed for carbohydrate content after extraction with a graded ethanol-water series.

There was a rapid increase in all soluble carbohydrate components studied during November, the period of hardening in Rhode Island, followed by a more gradual increase during winter. The levels of total long-chain and short-chain carbohydrates found appeared to be adequate for energy to support new growth at the end of the dormant season regardless of the time of N application the previous autumn. The levels of short-chain polymers were little effected by N treatments. The amount of long-chain polymers may account for reduced cold tolerance caused by fall nitrogen application found in a companion study. Additional index words: Carbohydrate polymers, Cold tolerance, Acclimation, *Poa pratensis*.

Recent investigations have shown that applications of nitrogenous fertilizers in the fall provide extended turf color into the winter (Hanson and Juska, 1961; Powell, Blaser, and Schmidt, 1967a). Additional benefits include increased root and rhizome growth without promotion of excessive top growth (Hanson and Juska, 1961; Powell, Blaser, and Schmidt, 1967b).

The principle has been stated that any management practice which tends to increase growth during the hardening period will reduce the cold tolerance of plants (Beard, 1966; Dexter, 1933). Application of nitrogenous fertilizer during the fall season has been shown to reduce the cold tolerance of turfgrasses (Carrol and Welton, 1939). In contrast, late fall applications of nitrogen have been made to turf in the field with no visual deleterious effects (Ferguson, 1966; Daniel and Goetze, 1960).

Changes in the carbohydrate status of grass plants during hardening have been studied (Powell, Blaser, and Schmidt, 1967a; Voblikova, 1965; Trunova, 1965). Some workers assign a central role to carbohydrates in

---

[1]Contribution no. 1504 of the Rhode Island Agricultural Experiment Station, Kingston, RI 02881.

determining hardiness levels (Koloska, 1965; Turnova, 1953). Others (Weiser, 1970; Sakai, 1963) concluded that although changes in carbohydrate status are requisite to low temperature acclimation, their mechanism of action is secondary.

Although the mechanism of the carbohydrate role during cold acclimation is poorly understood, evidence indicates that an accumulation of photosynthate is requisite to the hardening process in plants. This study was initiated to determine the effect of fall nitrogenous fertilizer application upon the carbohydrate status of a turf during the dormant season.

METHODS AND MATERIALS

Fall fertilization treatments were applied to a uniform turf of Kentucky bluegrass (*Poa pratensis* L.). Plots were arranged in a randomized complete block design with three replications. Each plot, exclusive of the check, received nitrogen at 5 g/m^2 on June 1, July 20, and September 1. Treatments of 10 g of N/m^2 were applied October 1 and 15, November 1 and 15, and December 1 and 15 to separate plots. An additional treatment, the combination, received 5 g of N/m^2 on each date. All nitrogen was applied as NH_4NO_3. Nitrogen treatments were initiated in the autumn and the plots fertilized as described for 1 year before samples were taken during the autumn, winter, and spring seasons. The turf was mown regularly at 3.8 cm and irrigated as needed during the summer months.

Plugs removed from the turf with a standard golf course cup cutter were separated into individual plants. Leaf blade and root tissue was removed and discarded, leaving the crown, lower leaf sheath, and apical meristem tissue for analysis. Samples were dried in a forced-draft oven at 70 C and ground in a Wiley mill through a 40-mesh screen. Prior to extraction and analysis, particle size was further reduced using a hand mortar and pestle.

Ground tissue was extracted overnight with aqueous ethanol solutions following methods developed in the laboratory of Smith (Grotelueschen and Smith, 1968; Smith, 1967; Smith and Grotelueschen, 1966). The carbohydrate content of the extracting solution was ascertained by the anthrone method (Yemm and Willis, 1954).

It was found to be impractical to extract the same samples with the various ethanolic solutions, therefore, separate samples were extracted with each solution making the data acquired additive in nature as the relative amount of water increased.

All data are reported as percentage of the sample's oven-dry weight. Data for each sampling date were subjected to analysis of variance and significant differences between treatment means ascertained by Duncan's range test at the 0.05 level of significance.

RESULTS

Typical curves for carbohydrate extracted with the graded series of ethanol solutions are presented in Fig. 1 and 2. In these curves, each data point represents the mean value obtained from all treatments and all replica-

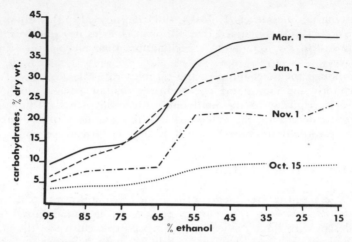

Fig. 1—Carbohydrates extracted with a graded ethanol-water series (March–October).

tions on the date indicated. In early autumn (Fig. 1), the curve is smooth and continuous, indicating a population of fructose polymers of steadily increasing chain length. In contrast, on November 1 there was a sharp increase in the content of longer chain fructose polymers as indicated by the sharp rise in the curve between 65% and 55% ethanol with a constant content thereafter. In Rhode Island, bluegrass begins hardening approximately November 1. At later dates, through the winter, the curves indicate a high level of carbohydrate content with a rather discrete segregation of the amount of short-chain and long-chain polymers (Fig. 1 and 2). On June 15 (Fig. 2), when the turf was again growing rapidly, the curve returned to a

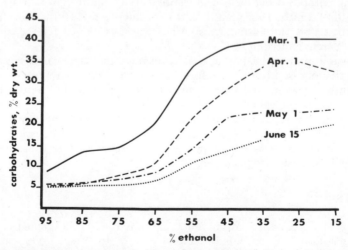

Fig. 2—Carbohydrates extracted with a graded ethanol-water series (March–June).

more continuous increase in carbohydrate content with decreasing ethanol, similar to the October 15 date.

To compare better the influence of nitrogen applications upon the different carbohydrate components, the mean of the content at 85 and 75% ethanol was calculated and defined as the short-chain carbohydrate. Similarily, the mean of the content at 25 and 15% ethanol was calculated and defined as the total soluble carbohydrate content. The difference between the total and short-chain content was calculated and defined as the long-chain content. The ratio between long-chain and total content was defined as the percent polymerization.

The total carbohydrate content increased from early autumn until it reached a maximum in late winter (Table 1), then gradually decreased throughout the spring period. Nitrogenous fertilization decreased the total carbohydrate content soon after application in the fall. This influence generally lasted through the autumn and early winter. On February 1, all treatments had a lower total carbohydrate content than the check. During the spring season, nitrogen applied in early fall had little influence upon the total carbohydrate content, indicating that nitrogen applied early was metabolized to the point where it no longer influenced carbohydrate levels. Conversely, nitrogen applied late in the fall or in early winter had more influence upon the total carbohydrate content the following spring.

The short-chain carbohydrate content increased from early autumn until it reached a maximum in late winter (Table 2). There were few occasions when the application of nitrogen through the autumn influenced the level of the short-chain component. The paucity of these occasions and their non-repetitive occurrence indicated that the few instances may have been artifacts of the analytical methods.

Table 1—Total carbohydrate content of crown tissue.

Treatment date	Harvest date								
	Sep 15	Oct 1	Oct 15	Nov 1	Nov 15	Dec 1	Dec 15	Jan 1	Feb 1
					% dry weight				
Check	16.6 a*	16.8 a	11.4 a	26.1 a	23.6 a	34.6 a	36.4 a	36.5 a	37.5 a
October 1	11.5 b	11.1 b	7.7 a	20.9 bcd	23.5 a	29.7 ab	34.8 ab	35.6 a	34.3 b
October 15	11.5 b	12.9 ab	12.1 a	20.4 cd	16.7 c	30.3 ab	31.9 bc	34.1 ab	32.6 bc
November 1	10.1 b	13.7 ab	7.5 a	21.3 bcd	17.7 bc	26.0 bc	34.2 ab	31.9 bc	33.8 b
November 15	10.8 b	13.3 ab	9.5 a	24.7 ab	21.9 ab	27.3 bc	29.9 cd	31.9 bc	32.4 bc
December 1	11.7 b	14.2 ab	7.9 a	23.5 abc	25.0 a	31.5 ab	31.8 bc	30.7 c	30.6 c
December 15	12.1 ab	10.5 b	11.8 a	26.4 a	23.5 a	31.7 ab	34.9 ab	35.0 a	34.4 b
Combination	14.2 ab	12.9 ab	7.3 a	18.4 d	15.8 c	23.8 c	27.5 d	30.9 c	30.5 c

	Mar 1	Mar 15	Apr 1	Apr 15	May 1	May 15	Jun 1	Jun 15	
Check	45.2 a	43.4 a	38.1 a	31.9 ab	27.8 a	20.4 ab	29.5 a	28.2 a	
October 1	41.3 bc	40.9 ab	35.1 ab	32.9 a	26.5 a	22.6 a	25.1 a	18.9 bc	
October 15	41.5 abc	43.0 a	37.3 ab	29.9 ab	26.6 a	21.5 ab	27.3 a	20.3 bc	
November 1	43.3 ab	41.0 ab	36.5 ab	30.1 ab	22.4 b	20.6 ab	25.9 a	19.0 bc	
November 15	39.6 bcd	41.7 a	34.9 ab	29.3 ab	23.2 b	19.1 ab	28.1 a	19.8 bc	
December 1	40.3 bcd	39.3 ab	33.3 bc	28.4 ab	21.6 bc	22.2 a	22.2 a	16.9 cd	
December 15	38.8 cd	37.5 bc	29.5 cd	27.8 ab	22.0 b	20.5 ab	23.3 a	21.7 b	
Combination	36.9 d	34.9 c	28.7 d	25.9 b	19.1 c	17.0 b	20.7 a	14.0 d	

* Means followed by the same letter within a column are not significantly different at the .05 level.

Table 2—Short-chain carbohydrate content of crown tissue.

Treatment date	Sep 15	Oct 1	Oct 15	Nov 1	Nov 15	Dec 1	Dec 15	Jan 1	Feb 1
					Harvest date				
					% dry weight				
Check	5.3 bc*	4.9 a	4.4 a	8.5 a	5.1 a	11.5 a	9.2 a	11.6 c	14.6 a
October 1	5.3 bc	4.3 a	3.8 a	8.6 a	4.9 ab	12.6 a	10.0 a	13.0 ab	14.9 a
October 15	6.2 ab	5.3 a	3.9 a	8.1 a	4.2 bc	11.9 a	9.8 a	12.3 abc	14.2 a
November 1	5.1 c	4.9 a	3.5 a	8.0 a	3.9 c	11.3 a	9.8 a	13.3 a	15.3 a
November 15	4.7 c	4.9 a	4.4 a	8.2 a	5.2 a	10.7 a	9.1 a	12.6 abc	15.4 a
December 1	5.5 abc	4.7 a	3.7 a	8.9 a	5.3 a	10.9 a	11.5 a	12.1 bc	14.5 a
December 15	6.4 a	4.2 a	4.9 a	8.6 a	5.2 a	11.9 a	9.9 a	12.5 abc	13.4 a
Combination	6.3 ab	4.1 a	3.4 a	8.5 a	4.0 c	10.9 a	8.9 a	12.3 abc	13.5 a

Treatment date	Mar 1	Mar 15	Apr 1	Apr 15	May 1	May 15	Jun 1	Jun 15
Check	13.8 a*	9.5 a	7.5 a	8.6 a	6.9 bc	5.5 a	4.4 a	5.6 ab
October 1	14.6 a	9.2 a	6.9 a	8.2 a	7.4 ab	5.5 a	5.1 a	5.7 ab
October 15	13.8 a	10.1 a	7.6 a	8.2 a	7.4 ab	6.2 a	4.8 a	6.3 a
November 1	13.8 a	9.3 a	7.7 a	8.7 a	7.0 bc	5.6 a	4.6 a	5.4 b
November 15	13.9 a	9.6 a	7.6 a	8.1 a	7.2 abc	5.9 a	5.3 a	5.7 ab
December 1	14.1 a	9.9 a	7.6 a	8.2 a	7.0 bc	6.0 a	4.7 a	5.7 ab
December 15	14.2 a	9.6 a	7.7 a	8.6 a	7.7 a	6.2 a	5.2 a	5.8 ab
Combination	14.1 a	9.5 a	7.2 a	8.8 a	6.8 c	5.6 a	4.4 a	5.2 b

* Means followed by the same letter within a column are not significantly different at the .05 level.

The long-chain carbohydrate component followed a seasonal trend similar to that of the total and short chain. In contrast with the few differences found in the short-chain content, nitrogenous fertilization decreased the long-chain content soon after application in the fall (Table 3). In

Table 3—Long-chain carbohydrate content of crown tissue.

Treatment date	Sep 15	Oct 1	Oct 15	Nov 1	Nov 15	Dec 1	Dec 15	Jan 1	Feb 1
					Harvest date				
					% dry weight				
Check	11.4 a*	11.9 a	6.9 a	17.9 a	18.4 ab	23.1 a	27.1 a	24.9 a	22.9 a
October 1	6.3 b	6.8 b	3.7 a	12.3 cd	18.6 ab	17.2 bc	24.8 ab	22.6 ab	19.4 bc
October 15	5.4 b	7.7 ab	8.1 a	12.3 cd	12.5 c	18.4 bc	22.1 bc	21.7 bc	18.4 cd
November 1	5.1 b	8.7 ab	4.0 a	13.3 bc	13.8 bc	14.7 cd	24.4 ab	18.6 d	18.5 cd
November 15	6.2 b	8.3 ab	5.1 a	16.6 ab	16.8 abc	16.6 bcd	20.9 bc	19.4 cd	17.1 cd
December 1	6.2 b	9.4 ab	4.3 a	14.6 abc	19.7 a	20.5 ab	20.3 bc	18.6 d	16.1 d
December 15	5.7 b	6.3 b	6.9 a	17.8 a	18.3 ab	19.7 ab	24.9 ab	22.6 ab	20.9 ab
Combination	7.9 b	8.8 ab	3.9 a	10.6 d	11.8 c	12.9 d	18.6 c	18.6 d	16.9 d

Treatment date	Mar 1	Mar 15	Apr 1	Apr 15	May 1	May 15	Jun 1	Jun 15
Check	31.4 a	33.7 a	30.3 a	23.4 ab	20.8 a	14.9 ab	25.1 a	22.6 a
October 1	26.7 bcd	31.4 abc	28.2 ab	24.8 a	19.0 a	17.1 a	19.9 ab	13.2 bc
October 15	27.7 abc	32.7 ab	29.7 a	21.7 ab	19.2 a	15.3 ab	22.4 ab	14.0 bc
November 1	29.5 ab	31.6 ab	28.8 ab	21.4 ab	15.4 b	14.9 ab	21.3 ab	13.6 bc
November 15	25.7 bcd	32.0 ab	27.3 ab	20.9 ab	15.9 b	13.2 ab	22.8 ab	14.2 bc
December 1	26.2 bcd	29.1 bcd	25.7 b	20.2 ab	14.6 bc	16.2 a	17.5 ab	11.1 cd
December 15	24.5 cd	27.6 cd	21.8 c	19.2 ab	14.4 bc	14.4 ab	18.1 ab	15.9 b
Combination	22.8 d	25.1 d	21.5 c	17.2 b	12.4 c	11.4 b	16.4 b	8.9 d

* Means followed by the same letter within a column are not significantly different at the .05 level

Table 4—Carbohydrate polymerization of crown tissue.

Treatment date	Harvest date								
	Sep 15	Oct 1	Oct 15	Nov 1	Nov 15	Dec 1	Dec 15	Jan 1	Feb 1
	%								
Check	66.6 a*	71.2 a	59.5 a	67.3 a	77.9 ab	66.4 a	74.5 a	69.6 a	61.1 a
October 1	53.9 b	60.2 ab	49.4 a	58.4 ab	79.6 a	57.7 bc	71.1 a	63.5 b	56.4 ab
October 15	46.4 b	59.9 ab	63.1 a	60.1 ab	74.7 ab	60.5 ab	69.3 a	63.8 b	56.4 ab
November 1	49.8 b	62.7 ab	53.4 a	62.2 ab	76.8 ab	56.6 bc	71.3 a	58.2 c	54.8 b
November 15	56.3 ab	62.3 ab	53.0 a	66.7 a	76.4 ab	60.3 ab	69.6 a	60.7 bc	52.6 b
December 1	52.2 b	65.9 ab	47.4 a	62.0 ab	78.4 ab	65.1 a	63.8 a	60.6 bc	52.7 b
December 15	45.9 b	56.9 b	56.6 a	66.9 a	78.8 ab	62.0 ab	71.5 a	64.3 b	60.9 a
Combination	55.3 ab	67.7 ab	52.8 a	57.5 b	74.5 b	53.7 c	67.5 a	60.2 bc	55.6 ab

	Mar 1	Mar 15	Apr 1	Apr 15	May 1	May 15	Jun 1	Jun 15	
Check	69.5 a	77.6 a	79.4 a	79.2 a	74.9 a	73.1 ab	84.6 a	79.9 a	
October 1	64.7 abc	76.5 ab	80.4 a	74.4 a	71.9 ab	75.4 a	78.3 b	69.6 bc	
October 15	66.6 abc	75.7 abc	79.7 a	72.5 a	72.0 ab	71.1 ab	82.2 ab	68.9 bc	
November 1	68.0 ab	77.1 ab	78.8 a	70.9 ab	68.6 bc	72.7 ab	81.9 ab	71.2 bc	
November 15	64.8 abc	76.7 ab	78.2 ab	71.1 ab	68.9 bc	69.2 ab	81.1 ab	71.3 bc	
December 1	65.0 abc	73.8 abc	77.2 ab	71.1 ab	65.5 cd	71.6 ab	78.8 b	65.8 cd	
December 15	63.1 bc	73.5 bc	73.7 c	69.1 ab	65.3 cd	69.9 ab	77.6 b	73.1 b	
Combination	61.8 c	71.9 c	75.0 bc	66.2 b	64.6 d	67.2 b	78.8 b	62.9 d	

* Means followed by the same letter within a column are not significantly different at the .05 level.

general, the long-chain polymer content was influenced in a manner similar to the total carbohydrate content.

The ratio between the long-chain and total components ranged from about 60% in autumn to 85% in late spring (Table 4). The time of application of nitrogenous fertilizer in the autumn had only sporadic effect upon the degree of polymerization.

DISCUSSION AND CONCLUSIONS

There was a rapid increase in all soluble carbohydrate components of crown tissue during November, the period of hardening in Rhode Island, followed by a more gradual increase in winter. They may have arisen as photosynthate produced during the period or may have been translocated from other organs to the crown area. Photosynthesis has been found to occur during low temperature periods in wheat (Bohenko, 1967), conifers (Freeland, 1944), and turf (Powell et al., 1967a). The conclusion that the accumulated carbohydrate found in this study was produced throughout the low temperature season has support.

The levels of short-chain, long-chain, and therefore total carbohydrate found appeared to be adequate to support renewed spring growth. In mid-May, the total carbohydrate content was 20% of the dry weight. This level would appear adequate for energy to support new growth after the end of the dormant season.

In a companion study (Wilkinson and Duff, 1971), similar fertilizer treatments reduced the cold hardiness of bluegrass crown tissue in a manner paralleling the reduction in the long-chain fructose carbohydrate component of this study. Direct evidence of the interference of long chain polymers upon freezing has been reported (Olien, 1965). Reduction in the long-chain component found here would account for reduced inherent cold tolerance of crown tissue.

REFERENCES

1. BEARD, J. B. 1966. Winter injury. Golf Superintendent 34(1):24–30.
2. BOHENKO, V. I. 1968. Peculiarities of metabolism of soluble carbohydrates and free amino acids in winter wheat induced by negative temperatures. Soviet Plant Physiol. 15:710–715.
3. CARROL, J. C., and F. A. WELTON. 1939. Effect of heavy and late applications of nitrogenous fertilizer on the cold resistance of Kentucky bluegrass. Plant Physiol. 14:297–308.
4. DANIEL, W. H., and N. R. GOETZE. 1960. Heavy nitrogen fertilization of cool season turfgrass. Agron. Abst.
5. DEXTER, S. T. 1933. Effect of several environmental factors on the hardening of plants. Plant Physiol. 8:123–140.
6. FERGUSON, A. C. 1966. Winter injury north of the 49th. Golf Superintendent 34(8):38–39.
7. FREELAND, R. O. 1944. Apparent photosynthesis in some conifers during winter. Plant Physiol. 19:179–185.
8. GROTELEUSCHEN, R. D., and D. SMITH. 1968. Carbohydrates in grasses. III. Estimations of the degree of polymerization of the fructosans in the stem bases of timothy and bromegrass near seed maturity. Crop Sci. 8:210–212.
9. HANSON, A. A., and F. V. JUSKA. 1961. Winter root activity in Kentucky bluegrass (*Poa pratensis* L.) Agron. J. 53:372–374.
10. KOLOSKI, O. I. 1965. Peculiarities of the carbohydrate and nitrogen metabolism of frost resistant varieties of wheat and rye. Soviet Plant Physiol. 12:935–939.
11. OLIEN, C. R. 1965. Interference of cereal polymers and related compounds with freezing. Cryobiology 2:47–54.
12. POWELL, A. J., R. E. BLASER, and R. E. SCHMIDT. 1967a. Physiological and color aspects of turfgrasses with fall and winter nitrogen. Agron. J. 59:303–307.
13. ———, ———, and ———. 1967b. Effect of nitrogen on winter root growth of bentgrass. Agron. J. 59:529–530.
14. SAKAI, A. 1963. Relation of internal and external factors on the increase of frost hardiness in woody plants. p. 20–22. *In* C. L. Prosser (ed.) The cell and environmental temperature. Pergamon Press, New York.
15. SMITH, D. 1967. Carbohydrates in grasses. II. Sugar and fructosan composition of the stem bases of bromegrass and timothy at several growth stages and in different plant parts at authesis. Crop Sci. 7:62–67.
16. ———, and R. D. GROTELEUSCHEN. 1966. Carbohydrates in grasses. I. Sugar and fructosan composition of the stem bases of several northern adapted grasses at seed maturity. Crop Sci. 6:263–266.
17. TRUNOVA, T. I. 1963. The first phase of frost-hardiness of winter crop plants in darkness on sugar solutions. p. 70–71. *In* C. L. Prosser (ed.) The cell and environmental temperature. Pergamon Press, New York.
18. ———. 1965. Light and temperature systems in the hardening of winter wheat and the significance of oligosaccharides for frost resistance. Soviet Plant Physiol. 12:70–77.
19. VOBLIKOVA, T. V. 1965. Cold resistance of winter wheat. Soviet Plant Physiol. 12:63–69.
20. WEISER, C. J. 1970. Cold resistance and injury in woody plants. Sci. 169:1269–1278.

21. WILKINSON, J. F., and D. T. DUFF. 1972. Effects of fall fertilization on cold resistance, color and growth of Kentucky bluegrass. Agron. J. 64:345–348.

22. YEMM, E. W., and A. J. WILLIS. 1954. The estimation of carbohydrates in plant extracts by anthrone. Biochem. J. 57:508–514.

16

Effects of nitrogen fertilization on nitrate movements under turfgrass[1]

P. E. RIEKE & B. G. ELLIS

Several nitrogen treatments were applied to 'Merion' Kentucky bluegrass (*Poa pratensis* L.) on two sites: a fine sandy loam and a heavily irrigated sand. Soil NO_3-N content was determined every 2 weeks during the 1970 and 1971 growing seasons at depths of 0 to 15, 15 to 30, 30 to 45, and 45 to 60 cm. On the fine sandy loam site there was some movement of NO_3-N downward when 2.9 kg N/100 m^2 was applied as NH_4NO_3 in one application in the spring. However, NO_3-N was not increased due to treatment in the 45 to 60-cm depth during either season. Significant leaching occurred on the sandy site from the excessive treatment of 3.9 kg N/100 m^2 applied in the spring as NH_4NO_3. Leaching of NO_3-N in the sand soil was markedly reduced when the 3.9 kg/100 m^2 treatment was divided into three applications during the season.

Slow-release N carriers (activated sewage sludge, ureaformaldehyde, isobutylidenediurea) seldom resulted in soil NO_3-N levels greater than the untreated plot. When reasonable N fertilizer programs are followed on turf there is not a significant potential for NO_3-N leaching except on heavily irrigated sands. Careful application of both N and water will reduce leaching of NO_3-N on such sites. Additional index words: Nitrogen carriers, Nitrate leaching, Irrigation, Turfgrass quality, *Poa pratensis.*

Considerable effort has been devoted to determination of the optimum N needs of turfgrasses with emphasis on top growth, root growth, and other physiological effects (3, 8, 14, 17). Little attention, however, has been given to that portion of the applied N which the turf does not utilize. With increased concern for environmental quality, it is important to consider the effects of turfgrass fertilization programs on the environment, particularly the potential for leaching of NO_3-N into groundwaters. The high N rates applied to some turfs and the liberal use of irrigation, especially on sandy soils, can result in increased leaching of NO_3-N.

Factors affecting losses of NO_3-N from soils include rate of N applied, N carrier, soil profile characteristics, rate of water passing through the soil profile, environmental conditions, N immobilized by plants and soil organism, and gaseous losses (12, 15, 18, 19).

In a comparison of nitrogen carriers, Benson and Barnette (4) observed that a NO_3-N source leached most rapidly through a sandy soil, NH_4-N was

---

[1]Michigan Agr. Exp. Sta. Journal Article No. 6756. Research supported in part by the Michigan Turfgrass Foundation and the Regional Technical Committee NC-98.

intermediate, and an organic N source was slowest. In a study of N sources used on turfgrasses, Bredakis and Steckel (6) reported that the N found in the leachate from a fine sandy loam soil during a 3-week incubation period resulted in the order: $(NH_4)_2SO_4$ = urea > Milorganite > ureaformaldehyde. Most of the $(NH_4)_2SO_4$ and urea were leached during the 3-week period. After 15 weeks of incubation, the total amount of N leached through the soil resulted in the same order of N carriers, indicating the organic carriers were not completely nitrified during the study.

Attempts to determine gains and losses of N in soil-plant systems (2) have left many unanswered questions. The possibility of extensive losses of N through denitrification has been suggested, especially in soils having a high water table, varying textural layers, or receiving heavy irrigation (1, 5, 16). In addition, N can be lost through volatilization (20). The presence of the thatch layer in turf and the accompanying microorganism populations can have marked effects on N transformations.

The objective of this study was to evaluate the movement of NO_3-N in two soils under turf treated with soluble and slow-response nitrogen sources. The treatments selected provided significant potential for leaching of NO_3-N.

MATERIALS AND METHODS

'Merion' Kentucky bluegrass (*Poa pratensis* L.) field plots at two sites in Michigan were utilized for this study. At East Lansing, plots were established in August 1965. The soil was Hodunk fine sandy loam (68% sand, 15% silt, 17% clay) with well-developed sandy clay loam subsoil. A series of nitrogen fertility treatments (Table 1) with three replications was initiated in April 1966 on 1.5 × 2.1 m plots. The turf was mowed at 4.4 cm twice weekly with all clippings removed. The activated sewage sludge (Milorganite) was provided by the Milwaukee, Wis. Sewerage Commission, the ureaformaldehyde (Uramite) by the E. I. DuPont Company.

Table 1—Nitrogen treatments selected for nitrate movement study.

Treatment no.	Annual N rate, kg/100 m²	Carrier	Application date 1970	1971
East Lansing-Hodunk fine sandy loam				
1	0	---	---	---
2	2.9	ammonium nitrate	May 1	Ap 18
3	2.9*	ammonium nitrate	May 1, 29, Aug 6	Ap 18, May 16, Aug 18
4	2.9	activated sewage sludge	May 1	Ap 18
5	2.9	ureaformaldehyde	May 1	Ap 18
Traverse City- Rubicon sand				
6	0	---	---	---
7	3.9	ammonium nitrate	May 6	Ap 16
8	3.9*	ammonium nitrate	May 6, June 19, Aug 6	Ap 16, June 16, Aug 15
9	3.9	activated sewage sludge	May 6	Ap 16
10	3.9	ureaformaldehyde	May 6	Ap 16
11	3.9	isobutylidenediurea	May 6	Ap 16

* N applied in three equal applications.

The second site was located in northwestern lower Michigan on the Traverse City Country Club grounds at Traverse City. The soil was Rubicon sand with 91% sand, 6% silt, and 3% clay. There was very little organic matter in the surface soil and little development of a B horizon in the sand subsoil. Plots had been established by J. Beard in May 1963. Nitrogen fertility treatments (two replications) were initiated in April 1964 on 1.5 × 2.1 m plots. Five of the existing treatments were selected for this study (Table 1). The isobutylidenediurea (IBDU provided by the Swift Agricultural Chemicals Corporation) treatment was initiated in April 1970. The IBDU particle size range was 0.7 to 1.4 mm. The turf was mowed twice weekly at 3.8 cm with all clippings returned to the plots.

The soil profile in each plot was sampled approximately every 2 weeks during the 1970 and 1971 growing seasons at depths of 0 to 15, 15 to 30, 30 to 45, and 45 to 60 cm. When soil sampling and fertilization dates coincided, samples were obtained before fertilizer application. Two soil cores, 1.9 cm in diameter, were removed from each plot and combined. The living plant tissue and the thatch layer were discarded. Soil samples were placed in plastic bags, transported in an insulated container cooled with dry ice, and stored in a 4 C chamber until analysis. Most of the samples were analyzed within 2 to 24 hours after sampling.

Nitrates were extracted from field moist samples with a saturated $CaSO_4$ solution. Duplicate analyses were made in each sample. In 1970, NO_3-N was determined by the method of Lowe and Hamilton (13). The NO_3 electrode method (7) was used in 1971 since this method was found to be more rapid and the accuracy compared favorably with the previous method at concentrations greater than 5 ppm N in solution.

Table 2—Monthly rainfall, irrigation, and mean temperature data for the 1970 and 1971 growing seasons.

Month	1970			1971		
	Rainfall	Irrigation	Temperature	Rainfall	Irrigation	Temperature
	—cm—		C	—cm—		C
East Lansing						
April	8.0(2.6)*	5.1	8.1	3.8(1.5)*	1.9	6.8
May	6.6(1.7)	8.9	14.8	4.9(3.3)	2.5	12.8
June	10.2(2.8)	5.1	18.6	13.0(4.2)	1.3	21.3
July	8.6(2.0)	6.4	21.2	12.2(4.3)	1.3	19.6
August	6.0(3.3)	7.6	20.1	6.4(2.2)	3.8	19.4
September	11.3(3.0)	5.1	16.4	13.3(2.7)	0.5	17.9
October	8.7(3.2)	2.5	11.0	5.8(2.6)	0.0	14.6
Total	59.4	40.7	---	59.4	11.3	---
Traverse City						
April	2.5(0.6)	9.5	7.8	3.4(1.3)	6.4	4.9
May	5.4(1.4)	11.4	12.3	7.4(1.8)	6.4	10.7
June	3.1(1.7)	12.7	18.6	3.0(0.7)	8.3	20.7
July	9.4(2.8)	10.2	22.2	10.2(2.1)	5.7	20.3
August	2.4(0.8)	14.2	20.6	7.8(4.8)	4.4	19.2
September	23.0(7.8)	3.8	16.1	4.9(1.3)	7.6	17.7
October	4.0(1.2)	10.2	11.5	3.4(0.9)	4.4	14.3
Total	49.8	72.0	---	40.1	43.2	---

* Figure in parenthesis is the largest single rainfall recorded for 1 day during the month.

Monthly rainfall, irrigation, and mean temperature data for the 1970 and 1971 growing seasons are summarized for both locations in Table 2. Liberal, frequent irrigation was practiced at Traverse City, especially in 1970, while more moderate irrigation was applied in East Lansing. Visual turfgrass quality ratings were taken each month on the basis of 1 = high quality turf, 10 = very poor turf.

Statistical analysis was performed separately for each date on the soil NO_3-N levels. When a significant treatment effect ($P < .05$) was obtained, the means were compared using the Duncan's Multiple Range Test.

RESULTS

East Lansing—1970

At East Lansing the N treatments were applied May 1, 1970. On May 15 (Table 3) there was a marked increase in soil NO_3-N at the 0- to 15- and 15- to 30-cm depths for treatment 2 (2.9 kg N/100 m² applied as ammonium nitrate) compared to the untreated plots. The high NO_3-N levels continued through June 12 in the 0- to 15-cm depth with some indication that there was movement into the 15- to 30-cm and 30- to 45-cm depths through June 24. On May 29, there was significant increase in NO_3-N at the 30- to 45-cm depth for treatment 3 (NH_4NO_3, three applications).

There were no further differences observed until the August 6 applica-

Table 3—Soil NO_3-N concentrations at East Lansing, Mich. in 1970.†

Treatment no.	Depth	Date of sampling										
		May 1	May 15	May 29	Jun 12	Jun 24	Jul 11	Jul 24	Aug 6	Aug 23	Sep 9	Oct 8
	cm							ppm				
1	0–15	5.5NS*	8.4c-e	6.5e	7.1bc	9.4c	13.9NS	12.4NS	13.3NS	6.3b	7.2NS	8.8a-c
	15–30	6.9	4.6e	6.6e	7.6bc	8.3c	11.2	11.8	13.0	8.6b	6.8	9.8a-c
	30–45	8.3	5.7de	8.9e	4.6c	8.5c	10.3	12.9	15.5	9.7b	5.5	9.0a-c
	45–60	6.4	7.3c-e	8.2e	4.1c	8.7c	12.7	11.9	17.5	12.2b	7.4	9.7a-c
2	0–15	5.4	44.2a	41.1a	31.0a	10.2bc	14.1	16.6	18.2	13.8b	9.4	13.7a
	15–30	3.8	16.4b	32.1b	11.3bc	14.7a	14.2	13.6	15.3	12.2b	6.8	9.2a-c
	30–45	6.1	10.2b-e	15.0cd	5.7bc	13.7ab	13.0	14.0	15.6	13.9b	7.6	10.2a-c
	45–60	5.8	7.9c-e	10.3c-e	4.6bc	10.9a-c	13.9	18.3	17.6	13.0b	7.4	9.9a-c
3	0–15	5.0	14.2bc	9.4de	14.5b	10.2bc	14.2	14.7	16.2	66.3a	8.1	14.1a
	15–30	5.7	9.3b-e	9.4de	5.2bc	8.7c	13.9	12.8	13.3	11.5b	8.2	13.3a
	30–45	5.4	6.5c-e	16.8c	7.8bc	8.7c	14.0	14.4	14.0	9.2b	6.0	12.7ab
	45–60	4.9	7.5c-e	8.8e	7.2bc	12.1a-c	11.5	13.0	19.1	12.3b	7.9	13.2a
4	0–15	4.2	8.9b-e	10.2c-e	6.6bc	9.1c	15.1	14.6	15.3	9.3b	7.1	9.2a-c
	15–30	6.1	7.1c-e	10.8c-e	3.6c	9.2c	13.0	20.4	15.6	14.9b	7.6	9.3a-c
	30–45	4.7	5.0e	10.9c-e	5.2bc	10.0bc	12.4	12.1	21.9	10.4b	6.0	14.4a
	45–60	5.7	5.7de	6.9e	5.7bc	9.4c	12.5	12.6	19.4	10.7b	6.5	12.6ab
5	0–15	5.5	13.6b-d	10.0c-e	4.7bc	9.8bc	14.2	17.8	16.5	13.2b	8.4	5.9c
	15–30	6.1	4.5e	8.1e	5.4bc	9.9bc	14.1	12.2	16.3	10.2b	9.0	6.8bc
	30–45	6.6	7.1c-e	10.4c-e	5.6bc	8.4c	13.9	13.3	16.8	10.1b	7.8	15.0a
	45–60	5.0	5.8de	8.1e	6.1bc	10.3bc	12.0	13.2	18.4	20.7b	6.8	12.2a-c

* Means within columns followed by the same letter are not significantly different at the .05 level according to Duncan's Multiple Range Test. NS = no significant difference. † Each value is an average of three replications.

tion of NH_4NO_3 (treatment 3) resulted in a marked increase in NO_3-N in the 0- to 15-cm depth on August 23. The 66 ppm NO_3-N found for this treatment was the highest observed at East Lansing in both years of the study. No further differences occurred during the remainder of the growing season except for small differences on October 8. There was a general trend for soil NO_3-N to increase throughout the profile for all treatments during July and August. In September, NO_3-N decreased to levels observed during the spring.

East Lansing—1971

The NO_3-N levels at East Lansing in 1971 (Table 4) were generally lower than in 1970. The initial N treatments were applied April 18. Although significant differences were detected among treatments, appreciable NO_3-N was not observed until May 16 in the 0- to 15-cm depth for treatment 2. The NO_3-N remained in the 0- to 15-cm depth for this treatment through the July 5 sampling date, then moved into the 15 to 30-cm depth on August 4. When the NH_4NO_3 treatment was divided into three equal applications (treatment 3), appreciable NO_3-N was found only in the surface layer 2 weeks after the second application on May 16. A small, but significant increase was also found in the surface layer 2 weeks after the third application on August 18.

Table 4—Soil NO_3-N concentrations at East Lansing, Mich. in 1971.†

Treatment no.	Depth	Apr 18	May 6	May 16	May 29	Jun 14	Jul 5	Jul 18	Aug 4	Aug 18	Sep 3	Sep 21
	cm						ppm					
1	0–15	0.4d*	1.0c	1.3b	1.3c	0.6c	0.7c	1.0NS	0.6b	0.6NS	0.2b	2.0NS
	15–30	0.1d	0.8c	1.2b	1.1c	0.8c	0.9bc	1.0	0.4b	0.3	0.2b	1.8
	30–45	0.2d	1.1c	2.3b	1.3c	1.4c	1.1bc	0.7	0.9b	0.4	0.2b	1.7
	45–60	0.0d	1.0c	1.3b	1.5c	1.2c	0.9bc	0.7	0.5b	0.3	1.7b	1.8
2	0–15	3.0bc	3.5ab	24.2a	29.0a	26.8a	29.0a	6.2	2.9b	3.5	0.5b	2.9
	15–30	0.8d	1.4c	2.0b	5.7c	2.9c	7.6b	2.7	10.4a	4.3	0.7b	1.6
	30–45	1.0d	3.8a	2.0b	3.6c	4.8c	3.3bc	1.5	1.0b	1.5	0.3b	2.2
	45–60	0.5d	1.4c	1.6b	2.0c	1.9c	2.8bc	0.8	1.6b	0.5	0.2b	1.9
3	0–15	4.8a	2.7b	2.6b	20.5b	11.9b	5.0bc	1.4	1.5b	1.7	9.9a	2.6
	15–30	1.1d	1.3c	1.5b	3.8c	3.8c	1.5bc	1.0	1.3b	0.3	2.0b	2.0
	30–45	1.3cd	1.3c	2.0b	4.5c	1.8c	1.9bc	0.8	0.7b	0.4	1.0b	2.0
	45–60	1.6cd	1.5c	1.7b	2.9c	1.8c	1.5bc	2.1	1.1b	0.2	0.3b	1.3
4	0–15	3.4ab	1.5c	2.2b	1.8c	1.3c	2.0bc	0.8	1.6b	1.0	0.5b	2.1
	15–30	1.2d	1.1c	1.3b	1.3c	0.8c	1.7bc	1.0	0.8b	0.4	0.2b	2.0
	30–45	0.6d	0.9c	1.3b	1.4c	8.0bc	1.3bc	0.9	0.7b	0.4	0.2b	2.0
	45–60	0.3d	1.4c	1.5b	1.9c	2.0c	1.2bc	0.8	0.8b	0.3	0.2b	2.3
5	0–15	4.9a	1.1c	2.1b	1.6c	1.2c	2.0bc	1.2	1.5b	1.7	0.6b	2.1
	15–30	1.5cd	0.9c	1.2b	1.2c	1.2c	1.1bc	0.6	0.7b	0.4	0.2b	1.8
	30–45	0.9d	1.1c	1.4b	1.3c	1.2c	1.3bc	0.9	0.6b	0.4	0.4b	2.2
	45–60	0.4d	1.3c	1.6b	1.6c	1.6c	1.1bc	1.1	0.8b	2.2	0.3b	2.0

* Means within columns followed by the same letter are not significantly different at the .05 level according to Duncan's Multiple Range Test. NS = no significant difference. † Each value is an average of three replications.

Traverse City—1970

Table 5 gives the NO_3-N levels observed at Traverse City for 1970. Treatments applied on May 6 resulted in significant increases in NO_3-N in the 0- to 15-cm and 15- to 30-cm depths on May 22 for both treatments 7 and 8 (NH_4NO_3 applied at the rate of 3.9 kg N/100 m^2 in one and three applications, respectively). Rapid downward movement of NO_3-N occurred under treatment 7 with high levels in the 15- to 30-cm depth on June 5 and in the 45- to 60-cm depth on June 19. On July 10 there were increased NO_3-N levels for treatment 8 at the 15- to 30-cm and 30- to 45-cm depths, apparently reflecting the June 19 fertilization with NH_4NO_3. Variability in the NO_3-N results caused a lack of statistical significance among certain treatments, especially on May 22, June 5, and August 6. Small, but significant increases in NO_3-N were detected on June 19 and July 3 for the Milorganite and urea-formaldehyde treatments (9 and 10, respectively) when compared to untreated plots. There were no significant treatment effects after the July 20 sampling date. The increase in NO_3-N in untreated plots during July and August was even more marked than was found at East Lansing in 1970.

Table 5—Soil NO_3-N concentrations at Traverse City, Mich. in 1970.†

Treatment no.	Depth	Date of sampling									
		May 1	May 22	Jun 5	Jun 19	Jul 3	Jul 20	Jul 31	Aug 6	Aug 24	Sep 16
	cm					ppm					
6	0–15	4.5NS*	5.5e	0.5c	6.2cd	12.2b-d	11.1b-d	7.6NS	18.5NS	19.4NS	7.0NS
	15–30	4.2	4.5e	2.7bc	6.4cd	8.9d	7.4d	7.4	21.0	12.5	7.4
	30–45	5.2	3.5e	3.0bc	5.6cd	9.1d	7.4d	6.0	16.2	14.7	5.8
	45–60	5.8	4.1e	2.9bc	5.8cd	10.2cd	8.9cd	7.4	16.4	12.2	5.5
7	0–15	6.1	46.0a	8.4bc	9.8b-d	12.7a-d	10.5b-d	12.7	14.4	14.7	8.6
	15–30	6.1	37.1ab	30.1a	7.2cd	11.2b-d	9.8b-d	5.7	20.0	14.7	7.8
	30–45	5.3	15.8c-e	19.0ab	8.2b-d	11.4b-d	9.0cd	7.2	13.9	17.5	7.4
	45–60	5.7	7.9de	2.1bc	16.0a	10.4cd	9.2cd	6.8	21.5	13.6	6.8
8	0–15	6.3	27.2bc	8.5bc	7.2cd	14.0a-c	9.5b-d	9.2	21.8	16.6	9.3
	15–20	6.0	22 9b-d	7.2bc	5.2d	12.1b-d	18.9a	5.9	15.6	13.7	6.4
	30–45	6.4	8.8de	15.5a-c	7.0cd	12.6a-d	12.8bc	6.9	13.8	10.2	5.9
	45–60	5.6	5.1c	9.1bc	8.6b-d	10.2cd	9.0cd	9.4	28.4	21.5	7.9
9	0–15	5.2	14.2c-e	6.4bc	9.7b-d	16.7a	9.4b-d	7.2	27.4	12.9	8.8
	15–30	6.1	7.6de	10.5bc	12.5ab	11.5b-d	7.8d	7.2	13.3	11.6	7.1
	30–45	6.4	4.4e	8.6bc	10.7bc	15.1ab	10.3b-d	6.1	15.9	11.8	8.7
	45–60	5.5	3.2e	6.4bc	9.5b-d	13.4a-d	8.9cd	5.4	18.0	9.5	5.1
10	0–15	7.5	7.7de	7.1bc	6.0cd	12.6a-d	9.1cd	13.5	14.2	18.9	8.9
	15–30	5.7	6.5de	9.8bc	6.1cd	14.0a-c	7.5d	7.0	17.8	12.3	7.7
	30–45	6.9	4.0e	8.4bc	4.4d	11.0b-d	8.3d	7.6	29.4	12.5	6.2
	45–60	5.0	3.6e	8.0bc	6.9cd	9.8cd	8.0d	7.8	22.5	13.4	7.4
11	0–15	6.5	9.8de	5.0bc	7.2cd	12.1b-d	13.7b	9.3	34.0	15.2	7.7
	15–30	6.3	4.5e	2.7bc	6.6cd	10.5cd	9.6b-d	6.7	21.9	19.1	8.8
	30–45	5.1	6.1de	5.2bc	7.9b-d	10.2cd	9.5b-d	10.5	27.9	18.6	7.6
	45–60	6.4	4.4e	1.6bc	6.9cd	11.2b-d	8.3d	6.3	20.5	17.2	7.0

* Means within columns followed by the same letter are not significantly different at the .05 level according to Duncan's Multiple Range Test. NS = no significant difference. † Each value is an average of two replications.

Table 6—Soil NO$_3$-N concentrations at Traverse City, Mich. in 1971.†

Treatment no.	Depth cm	Apr 16	Apr 30	May 18	Jun 1	Jun 16	Jun 30	Jul 17	Aug 1	Aug 15	Sep 1	Sep 23
							ppm					
6	0–15	2.4NS*	1.3c	1.3d	1.0c	0.9d	2.1c	0.9ab	0.7gh	0.7ef	0.7ef	2.1c
	15–30	1.4	0.8c	1.6d	1.0c	0.5d	1.9c	0.7ab	0.5h	0.5f	0.4f	1.9c
	30–45	1.3	0.9c	1.6d	1.1c	0.9d	2.0c	0.6ab	0.7gh	0.4f	0.4f	2.0c
	45–60	0.6	0.8c	1.2d	0.7c	0.6d	1.5c	0.5b	0.5h	0.3f	0.4f	1.6c
7	0–15	3.4	111.4a	27.1a	11.8b	11.9a	16.4a-c	1.7ab	2.4c-e	1.4d-f	1.3c-f	3.9bc
	15–30	1.5	43.9b	12.7b	18.3a	8.7ab	5.4bc	1.3ab	0.9gh	0.8d-f	0.7ef	2.1c
	30–45	5.0	6.3c	13.6b	17.3ab	8.2a-c	5.2bc	2.2ab	2.1d-f	1.5a-f	0.6ef	2.1c
	45–60	1.0	3.9c	7.5c	15.5ab	7.5a-d	3.9bc	3.1ab	0.8gh	0.8d-f	0.5ef	2.0c
8	0–15	3.6	17.2c	5.0cd	2.8c	3.0b-d	4.9bc	1.3ab	2.2d-f	1.2c-f	1.9bc	3.9bc
	15–30	2.7	1.4c	2.4d	4.7c	1.8b-d	9.5a-c	1.0ab	0.5h	0.6f	0.8d-f	2.0c
	30–45	2.9	4.0c	2.1d	5.1c	3.4b-d	11.7a-c	0.8ab	0.7gh	1.0df	1.2c-f	3.1bc
	45–60	1.7	1.3c	2.2d	4.8c	1.0cd	21.4a	0.8ab	0.6h	0.5f	1.7b-d	2.1c
9	0–15	3.6	1.6c	2.2d	4.7c	11.6a	19.2ab	2.2ab	1.4e-h	1.9a-d	1.8bc	4.1bc
	15–30	1.4	1.1c	1.6d	1.5c	7.6a-d	11.3a-c	1.7ab	1.4e-h	1.1df	0.7ef	1.8c
	30–45	3.0	1.2c	1.7d	2.4c	10.3a	12.8a-c	3.5a	1.3f-h	1.3b-f	1.0d-f	2.4bc
	45–60	1.2	0.9c	1.2d	0.9c	5.1a-d	5.5bc	3.4ab	1.2gh	1.5a-f	0.6ef	1.8c
10	0–15	4.1	2.8c	3.0d	1.3c	4.0b-d	7.8a-c	4.0a	4.3ab	2.6a	3.6a	14.9a
	15–30	2.7	1.6c	1.6d	1.2c	1.6b-d	5.1bc	1.9ab	1.7e-g	1.2c-f	1.3c-f	3.6bc
	30–45	4.0	1.4c	1.9d	1.3c	3.1b-d	6.2a-c	1.6ab	2.4c-e	2.3a-c	2.3b	7.3b
	45–60	1.5	1.2c	1.5d	1.4c	1.4cd	4.4bc	2.1ab	1.4e-h	1.5a-f	1.4b-e	2.8bc
11	0–15	2.4	1.6c	2.4d	1.3c	6.9a-d	6.4a-c	3.7a	4.8a	2.4ab	1.2c-f	5.8bc
	15–30	2.1	1.2c	2.3d	1.0c	3.6b-d	8.0a-c	2.9ab	3.4bc	1.0d-f	1.3c-f	2.6bc
	30–45	2.9	1.3c	2.2d	1.2c	4.1b-d	7.7a-c	3.1ab	2.8b-d	1.8a-e	1.4b-e	4.2bc
	45–60	1.2	1.0c	1.7d	1.2c	2.3b-d	8.7a-c	2.6ab	2.1d-f	0.9d-f	1.1c-f	2.6bc

* Means within columns followed by the same letter are not significantly different at the .05 level according to Duncan's Multiple Range Test. NS = no significant difference. † Each value is an average of two replications.

Traverse City—1971

As was observed at East Lansing, the soil NO$_3$-N levels at Traverse City were generally lower in 1971 than in 1970 (Table 6). However, treatment 7 had very high levels on April 30, 2 weeks after application. The 111 ppm NO$_3$-N level was the highest recorded over the 2-year study at either site. There was obvious leaching of NO$_3$-N under treatment 7 with marked increases over the check at all depths through June 16. When the NH$_4$NO$_3$ was divided into three applications (treatment 8) there was rapid movement into the lower depths within 2 weeks after the June 16 application. Increased NO$_3$-N also occurred with the Milorganite treatment, especially in June. Small, but significant increases in soil NO$_3$-N occurred with ureaformaldehyde (treatment 10) in August and September and for IBDU (treatment 11) in August. In 1971 there was not the increase in NO$_3$-N in the check plot during the summer months that was observed in 1970.

Turfgrass quality

Visual turfgrass quality ratings (based on density and color of the turf) were obtained monthly and are reported in Table 7. The heavy N rate ap-

Table 7—Visual turfgrass quality ratings for Merion Kentucky bluegrass.

Treatment no. *	Monthly quality rating†						Average
	April	May	June	July	August	September	
East Lansing							
1	7.4	7.8	6.8	7.7	7.1	7.6	7.4
2	5.3	2.0	1.8	2.2	2.6	3.7	2.9
3	4.5	2.3	1.8	2.3	2.8	2.3	2.7
4	4.6	3.4	2.4	3.1	3.4	4.0	3.5
5	4.6	3.5	3.7	3.1	3.0	3.3	3.5
Traverse City							
6	3.9	3.6	4.1	2.3	3.9	3.8	3.6
7	3.6	1.8	2.0	1.5	1.8	2.5	2.2
8	2.8	1.8	2.4	2.0	1.8	1.8	2.1
9	3.1	1.4	1.5	1.6	1.9	2.0	1.9
10	3.0	1.9	1.8	1.5	1.6	2.5	2.0
11	3.4	2.5	2.1	1.3	1.9	1.8	2.2

* Each value is an average over the 1970 and 1971 growing seasons.   † 1 = high quality turf, 10 = very poor turf.

plied as NH_4NO_3 in spring (treatments 2 and 7) resulted in excessive turf growth. Quality ratings were very good until late in the season indicating there was no apparent injury to the turf under the conditions of these studies.

When no N was applied (treatments 1 and 6), clipping return at Traverse City resulted in better quality turf than at East Lansing. Turf response to IBDU (treatment 11) was slow in the spring but resulted in very good quality turf during the June through September period.

DISCUSSION

There was very little NO_3-N observed in the soil on the first sampling date in spring indicating little residual influence from N treatments the previous year. Others have reported the loss of soluble N over the winter (10, 11). Turfgrass quality ratings in April indicated there were differences among treatments, in spite of the lack of variation in soil NO_3-N levels.

The heavy N treatments applied as NH_4NO_3 in the spring resulted in highly significant increases in soil NO_3-N levels at both locations. At East Lansing, in spite of this extreme N treatment (2.9 kg N/100 m^2) in April there was no time during either season when NO_3-N in the 45- to 60-cm depth was higher in the treated plot than in the untreated plot. When the NH_4NO_3 was applied in three applications at East Lansing (treatment 3), limited NO_3 movement was evident even though appreciable levels were found in the 0- to 15-cm depth for 2 to 4 weeks after treatment.

At Traverse City, leaching was much more apparent with one heavy annual application of NH_4NO_3. The higher N rate, the return of clippings to the turf, the porous nature of the sandy soil profile, and the liberal to excessive irrigation practiced were contributing factors. Some leaching also occurred with the split application of NH_4NO_3 (treatment 8).

The rate of NO_3 movement at both sites was slower in 1971 than in 1970. Pan evaporation data for East Lansing for the May through July period in 1970 were 44.1 cm water compared to 56.1 cm for the same period in 1971. Similar, but slightly lower moisture losses occurred at Traverse City during the 2 years. The combination of greater evapotranspiration and lower precipitation and irrigation resulted in less leaching in 1971. This is especially noticeable for the heavy NH_4NO_3 treatment at Traverse City (treatment 7). In 1970, NO_3-N was leached rapidly into the lower depths and out of the soil profile. In contrast, the NO_3-N levels were more evenly distributed to the 60-cm depth for the May 18 through June 16 sampling dates in 1971. The irrigation rate at the Traverse City site was reduced in 1971 because of the rapid NO_3 leaching observed the first year.

The sampling technique utilized may have contributed to the lower NO_3-N values observed early in the 1971 season when somewhat lower rainfall and irrigation were received. The live top growth and the thatch layer were discarded during sampling. It is likely that N fertilizer particles were discarded with the thatch where the N was not washed into the root zone. Since low NO_3-N levels were found in the untreated plots at both East Lansing and Traverse City in 1971, N loss by other means, such as denitrification or volatilization, may have occurred.

The slow-release N carriers resulted in reduced soil NO_3-N levels at both sites compared to NH_4NO_3. This was especially noticeable soon after application in spring when NO_3-N was quite susceptible to leaching during periods of extensive rainfall.

Although the increases were small, there was a tendency for NO_3-N to increase in the late summer under the slow-release N carriers at Traverse City, indicating that careful utilization of these carriers should also be practiced.

There did not appear to be a good correlation between visual turfgrass quality ratings and soil NO_3-N levels. Although turfgrass quality was acceptable when the very high N rates were applied at one time in this study, this rate of N application is not practical nor recommended. It was under these conditions that NO_3-N leached most readily. The NO_3-N levels at Traverse City late in the growing season resulting from the IBDU application (treatment 11) were not appreciably higher than on the untreated plot, yet the quality of the turf was much better. Thus soil NO_3-N level could not be used as a means to determine the adequacy of N in the soil for turf. This concurs with the observations of English (9) who reported that soil NO_3-N level could not be used effectively as a means of predicting optimum N needs for Kentucky bluegrass sod production on organic soil.

Although the treatments evaluated in this study were somewhat extreme, several points concerning leaching of NO_3-N were substantiated. The tendency to leach NO_3-N is greatest under conditions of 1) high annual N rates, 2) infrequent, heavy applications of water soluble N carriers, 3) intensive irrigation and/or rainfall, and 4) porous, sandy soils. There was no appreciable residual NO_3-N in the soil in the spring following treatment the previous year.

The leaching of NO_3-N observed on the sandy soil points out the importance of careful N fertilization programs for turf on such soils. On sites where there is a possibility of contamination of groundwaters as a result of turf fertilization, the following practices are suggested: reduced annual N rates, lighter and more frequent N applications, proper selection of N carriers, applying N only to actively growing turf, judicious irrigation, and utilization of lower N-requiring turfgrasses. When lower annual nitrogen rates or smaller amounts of nitrogen than were reported in this study are applied at one time, the potential for appreciable leaching of NO_3-N would appear to be limited under most turfgrass conditions. For example, seldom is more than 0.5 kg N/100 m^2 necessary in any one application when soluble N carriers are used. Some of the slower release N carriers may be needed at somewhat higher rates in spring applications for adequate response. Normally, a minimum of two or three applications of N annually is suggested under most conditions even with the slow-release carriers.

REFERENCES

1. ADRIANO, D. C., P. F. PRATT, and F. H. TAKATORI. 1972. Nitrate in unsaturated zone of an alluvial soil in relation to fertilizer nitrogen rate and irrigation level. J. Environ. Qual. 1:418–422.
2. ALLISON, F. E. 1955. The enigma of soil nitrogen balance sheets. Advan. Agron. 7:213–250.
3. BEARD, James B. 1973. Turfgrass: Science and culture. Prentice-Hall, Inc., Englewood Cliffs, N. J. 658 p.
4. BENSON, Nels, and R. M. BARNETTE. 1939. Leaching studies with various sources of nitrogen. J. Amer. Soc. Agron. 31:44–54.
5. BINGHAM, F. T., S. DAVIS, and E. SHADE. 1971. Water relations, salt balance and nitrate leaching losses of a 960-acre citrus watershed. Soil Sci. 112:410–418.
6. BREDAKIS, E. J., and J. E. STECKEL. 1963. Leachable nitrogen from soils incubated with turfgrass fertilizers. Agron. J. 55:145–147.
7. DAHNKE, W. C. 1971. Use of the nitrate specific ion electrode in soil testing. Comm. in Soil Sci. Plant Anal. 2:73–84.
8. DE FRANCE, J. A. 1938. The effect of different fertilizer ratios on colonial, creeping and velvet bent grasses. Proc. Amer. Soc. Hort. Sci. 36:773–780.
9. ENGLISH, Kendall R. 1971. Effects of nitrogen fertilization on the sod development of Kentucky bluegrass (*Poa pratensis* L. 'Merion') on Houghton mick as measured by several nitrogen responses. M.S. Thesis. Michigan State Univ. 70 p.
10. GASSER, J. K. R. 1961. Transformation, leaching and uptake of fertilizer nitrogen applied in autumn and spring to winter wheat on a heavy soil. J. Sci. Food Agr. 12:375–380.
11. HARDING, R. B., T. W. EMBLETON, W. W. JONES, and T. M. RYAN. 1963. Leaching and gaseous losses of nitrogen from some non-tilled California soils. Agron. J. 55:515–518.
12. JONES, Randall J. 1942. Nitrogen losses from Alabama soils in lysimeters as influenced by various systems of green manure crop management. J. Amer. Soc. Agron. 34:574–585.
13. LOWE, R. H., and J. L. HAMILTON. 1967. Rapid method for determination of nitrate in plant and soil extract. J. Agr. Food Chem. 15:359–361.
14. MADISON, John H. 1962. Turfgrass ecology. Effects of mowing, irrigation and nitrogen treatments of *Agrostis palustris* Huds., 'Seaside' and *Agrostis tenuis* Sibth., 'Highland' on population, yield, rooting and cover. Agron. J. 54:407–412.
15. MORGAN, M. F., and O. E. STREET. 1939. Seasonal water and nitrate leachings in relation to soil and source of fertilizer nitrogen. Connecticut Agr. Exp. Sta. Bull. 429.
16. OWENS, L. D. 1960. Nitrogen movement and transformations in soils as evaluated by a lysimeter study utilizing isotopic nitrogen. Soil Sci. Soc. Amer. Proc. 24:372–376.
17. POWELL, A. J., R. E. BLASER, and R. E. SCHMIDT. 1967. Physiological and color aspects of turfgrasses with fall and winter nitrogen. Agron. J. 59:303–307.
18. THOMAS, Grant W. 1970. Soil and climatic factors which affect nutrient mobility. p. 1–20. *In* O. P. Engelstad (ed.) Nutrient mobility in soils: Accumulation and

losses. SSSA Spec. Publ. No. 4. Soil Sci. Soc. Amer., Madison, Wis.

19. VIETS, Frank G., Jr., and Richard H. HAGEMAN. 1971. Factors affecting the accumulation of nitrate in soil, water and plants. USDA Agr. Handbook No. 413. Washington, D. C.

20. VOLK, Gaylord M. 1961. Gaseous loss of ammonia from surface-applied nitrogenous fertilizers. J. Agr. Food Chem. 9:280–283.

17

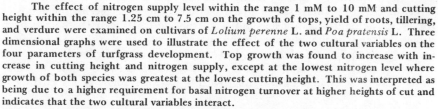

Effects of cutting height and nitrogen nutrition on growth pattern of turfgrasses

W. A. ADAMS, P.J. BRYAN, G. E. WALKER

The effect of nitrogen supply level within the range 1 mM to 10 mM and cutting height within the range 1.25 cm to 7.5 cm on the growth of tops, yield of roots, tillering, and verdure were examined on cultivars of *Lolium perenne* L. and *Poa pratensis* L. Three dimensional graphs were used to illustrate the effect of the two cultural variables on the four parameters of turfgrass development. Top growth was found to increase with increase in cutting height and nitrogen supply, except at the lowest nitrogen level where growth of both species was greatest at the lowest cutting height. This was interpreted as being due to a higher requirement for basal nitrogen turnover at higher heights of cut and indicates that the two cultural variables interact.

Root yields increased with cutting height but decreased with increase in nitrogen supply; the latter being opposite to the behavior of top growth. In both species, tillering was stimulated by increasing nitrogen supply between 1 mM and 4 mM at all but the lowest height of cut in *Lolium perenne* 'S.23' where it was depressed. Above 4 mM nitrogen there was either very little stimulation or a depression of tillering. No stimulation of tillering was recorded because of closer cutting except at the 1 mM nitrogen level in *Lolium perenne* S.23 where reducing the cutting height from 2.5 cm to 1.25 cm resulted in increased tiller numbers.

Examination of the total nonstructural carbohydrates (TNC) of *Lolium perenne* S.23 confirmed that stem bases are the main sites for fructosan storage. At higher nitrogen levels there was a more rapid turnover of carbohydrate for growth and therefore less TNC stored compared with low nitrogen levels where shortage of nitrogen prohibited carbohydrate utilization for top growth. Stored TNC was rapidly utilized for regrowth provided nitrogen was adequate. Even when large quantities were stored, substantial depletion was found to occur after 14 days regrowth in the dark.

On the basis of the experimental observations, two hypotheses were made to explain the growth responses of turfgrasses to nitrogen supply level and cutting height.

1) Top growth takes precedence over root growth when nitrogen is nonlimiting.

2) At low nitrogen supply levels, roots are relatively less nitrogen deficient than the tops to which little nitrogen is translocated. This is expressed in a change in root/shoot growth pattern. Additional index words: Total nonstructural carbohydrate, Basal nitrogen turnover, Verdure, *Lolium perenne* L., *Poa pratensis* L.

Cutting height and fertilizer use are fundamental factors in turfgrass culture. Cutting height is to a large extent dictated by the use of the turf; however, a range in height of cut is tolerable. It is vital that the consequences of altering cutting height are appreciated. Investigations (5, 10, 12) have shown the general relationship of the lower the cutting height the lower the top growth and the smaller the root system maintained, although frequency of cutting may have a modifying effect (8).

The quantity and balance of fertilizers used on turf should be manipulated to obtain the most desirable playing surface. Any essential plant nutrient may control growth and development, but nitrogen is the most important nutrient in the majority of cases and it is upon this nutrient that most work has centered. In general, elevating nitrogen supply increases top growth and depresses root growth (5, 10, 11, 13). But under circumstances where roots have been pruned in transplanting turf, nitrogen can have an initial stimulatory effect on root development (3).

Although both cutting height and nitrogen supply have been investigated, the clear recognition that the two interact has not been expressed. On the basis of this preliminary observation, an experiment was designed to examine this interrelationship on two cultivars of *Lolium perenne* L. and three cultivars of *Poa pratensis* L. Parameters of plant development examined were top growth, quantity of roots, tiller production, and verdure (10).

The response to cutting height and nitrogen level must be explicable in terms of environmental and/or plant factors acting as triggering mechanisms for a physiological response. Both cutting and nitrogen level have been shown to modify the carbohydrate content of plants (4, 6, 7). An experiment was set up using *Lolium perenne* 'S.23' to examine the level of the nonstructural carbohydrates (TNC) at different levels of nitrogen supply and also to see how these changed during regrowth following a single severe cutting.

MATERIALS AND METHODS

Experiment 1

The experiment was carried out in a greenhouse where temperatures were within the range 15 to 25 C. Seeds of the cultivars S.23 and 'Barenza' *Lolium perenne* L. and of the cultivars 'Merion', 'Nugget', and 'Fylking' *Poa pratensis* L. were soaked for 24 hours in aerated water. Seeds were planted into wooden boxes (20 cm × 15 cm × 15 cm deep) containing acid washed sand (silica sand purified by washing with hot 5M HCl). Nutrient solution was applied every third day and had the composition given below.

Element	Level (mM)
Nitrogen	1,4,10
Potassium	2.0
Calcium	1.5
Phosphorus	1.0
Sulfur	1.0
Magnesium	1.0
Iron	0.1
Boron	0.03
Manganese	0.01
Copper	0.001
Zinc	0.001
Molybdenum	0.0002

Three nutrient regimes varying only in nitrogen level were used. Seedling plants were thinned to leave 40 per box.

Clipping was carried out every third day and began 30 days after sowing the seed. Clipping heights were 1.25 cm, 2.5 cm, and 7.5 cm. Clippings were collected, dried, weighed, and a running total kept of top yield. The nine clipping height-nitrogen level treatments were replicated three times.

The grass was harvested 3 months from sowing. The number of tillers and verdure was recorded as described by Madison (10). Roots were washed from the sand and their dry weight recorded.

Experiment 2

Only the cultivar S.23 *Lolium perenne* was examined in the second experiment. The same cultural conditions were employed as those in the first experiment except that plants were grown in 300-ml polystyrene pots (3 per pot) and that since the experiment extended over a winter period the day length was maintained at 14 hours by the use of fluorescent lights. All plants of the three nitrogen treatments were maintained at a height of 3.75 cm by clipping every third day.

At 6 months of age, half of the plants were harvested; root weights and root lengths recorded; and leaves, stem bases, and roots analyzed for fructosan, sucrose, and hexoses. Plants were harvested immediately before a light period.

Leaf and stem base pigments were extracted by immersion for 1 week in diethyl ether (1). Monosaccharides and sucrose were extracted with 80% ethanol, the solution filtered, and deionized on anion and cation exchange columns. The sugars were separated by descending paper chromatography (9), diluted with distilled water, and estimated colorimetrically using the phenol-sulfuric acid method (2). Fructosan present in the ethanol extracted residue was hydrolyzed by refluxing with 1% oxalic acid, deionized, and estimated as fructose by the same colorimetric method.

The effect of nitrogen availability on the rate of regrowth and on changes in carbohydrate reserves was carried out on the remainder of the plants grown at either 1 mM or 10 mM nitrogen. Plants grown at each nitrogen level and maintained at the 3.75-cm cutting height throughout were clipped to 1.25 cm and transferred to the dark so that regrowth depended upon mobilization of plant carbohydrate and was not confounded by new photosynthate production. At this time half the plants maintained at the low nitrogen level were transferred to the high nitrogen level and the converse for half the plants grown at the high nitrogen level. Regrowth height was recorded and plants harvested at 0, 7, and 14 days to examine changes in carbohydrate concentrations.

RESULTS AND DISCUSSION

Variation within the species *Lolium perenne* L. and *Poa pratensis* L. was far less than that between, and for this reason Fig. 1, 2, and 3 incorporate mean values. Tillering response varied markedly between cultivars

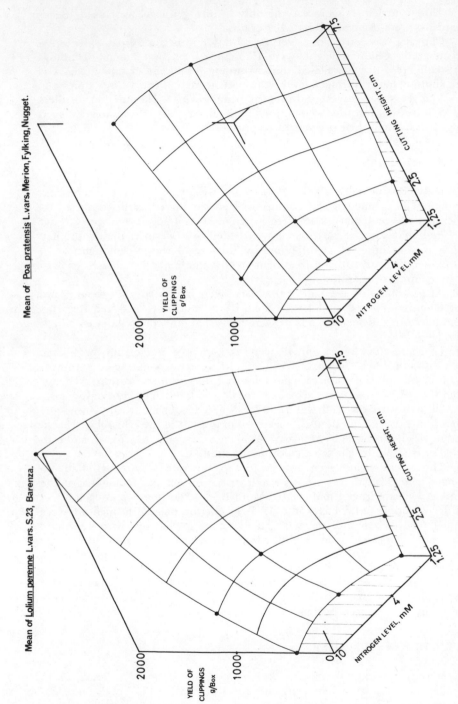

Fig. 1—Effect of nitrogen supply level and cutting height on the yield of clippings up to 3 months of age of *Lolium perenne* and *Poa pratensis*.

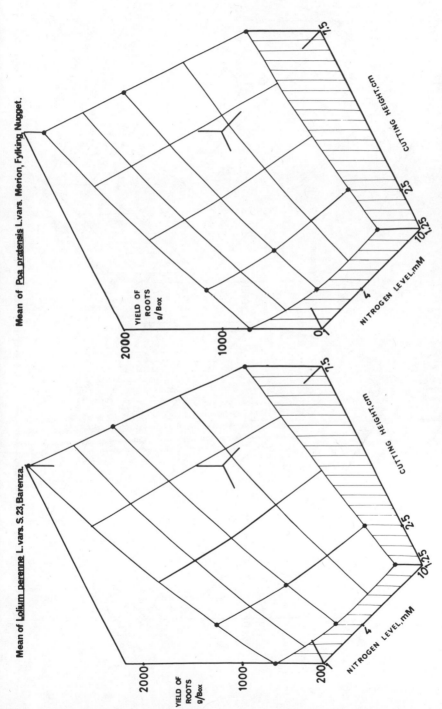

Fig. 2—Effect of nitrogen supply level and cutting height on root dry weight of 3-month-old *Lolium perenne* and *Poa pratensis*.

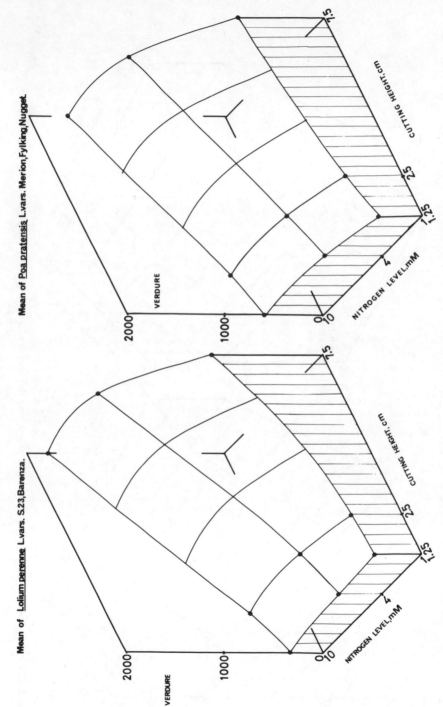

Mean of **Poa pratensis** L.vars. Merion, Fylking, Nugget.

VERDURE

2000

1000

NITROGEN LEVEL, mM

0·10

4

1·25

2·5

7·5

CUTTING HEIGHT, cm

Mean of **Lolium perenne** L.vars. S.23, Barenza.

VERDURE

2000

1000

NITROGEN LEVEL, mM

0·10

4

1·25

2·5

7·5

CUTTING HEIGHT, cm

Fig. 3—The effect of nitrogen supply level and cutting height on verdure at 3 months in *Lolium perenne* and *Poa pratensis*.

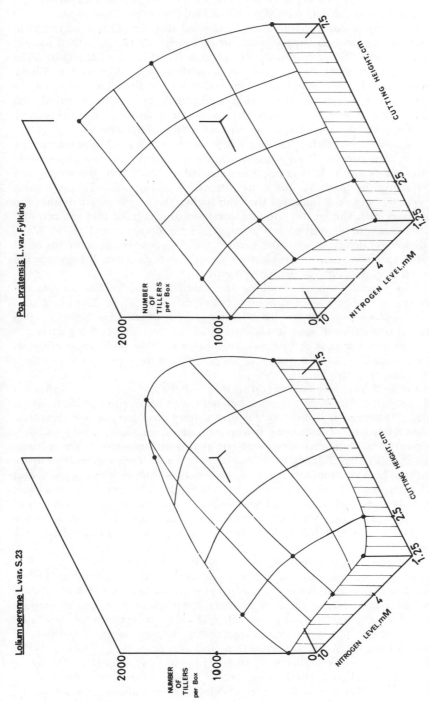

Fig. 4—The effect of nitrogen supply level and cutting height on the number of tillers at 3 months in *Lolium perenne* S.23 and *Poa pratensis* 'Fylking'.

and thus S.23 and Fylking were selected for Fig. 4. The authors justify this crystallization of the data with the goal of simplifying interpretation.

Three-dimensional graphs have been used to express the effects of the two variables, nitrogen supply and cutting height, on the measured parameters of growth. Observations at a large number of levels of the controlled variables are necessary to construct an accurate surface. Figures 1 to 4 have observations at nine points and the surfaces have been created from six smooth curves connecting these points. Extra lines have been introduced on the surfaces only to reinforce the visual appreciation of the contour of the surfaces and do not intersect at experimentally derived points.

As pointed out earlier, cutting height and nitrogen level have interacting effects on top growth. Even visual observation made this obvious, for whereas all cultivars cut at 1.25 cm and maintained at 1 mM nitrogen were green and healthy, the plants on the same nitrogen level but cut at 7.5 were weak and yellow. Figure 1 indicates that the higher the height of cut within the range examined, the greater the nitrogen level to which the turf will respond and the absolute amount of top growth. At the opposite end of the scale, the higher the height of cut, the greater the nitrogen requirement for basal nitrogen turnover, i.e., survival but no growth, and therefore the greater the nitrogen level necessary to permit top growth.

The general form of the three-dimensional graphs for *Lolium perenne* and *Poa pratensis* are similar; however they differ in detail. The key points are that *Lolium perenne* showed a higher growth potential at higher heights of cut and higher nitrogen levels, but that *Poa pratensis* had a greater potential growth response at lower cutting heights. The results suggest that at a given height of cut *Poa pratensis* has a higher nitrogen requirement for a given rate of top growth.

Figure 2 illustrates the general reciprocal behavior of rooting to nitrogen level compared with tops. Rooting behavior with respect to cutting height is similar. However, it is noteworthy that whereas top growth was greater at the lowest height of cut at the lowest nitrogen level, the quantity of roots was greater at the highest height of cut at this nitrogen level. The authors consider this to be evidence for the existence of a difference in relative nitrogen status between top and roots at low nitrogen supply levels, a point that will be discussed later. In the data presented, the rhizomes of *Poa pratensis* were bulked as part of the total root system. Comparison between the rooting responses of the two species indicates remarkable similarity, although there is a suggestion that *Lolium perenne* has a greater potential for root growth.

The effect of the two variables on verdure is expressed in Fig. 3. It is interesting to compare this with Fig. 1 and 4, for both top growth and tillering may be expected to influence this parameter. In *Lolium perenne*, verdure increased with cutting height at all nitrogen levels although maximum verdure occurred at a nitrogen level below 10 mM. Figure 4 refers to only S.23 *Lolium perenne* but it strongly suggests that verdure summarizes the combined influences of tiller production and top growth. Verdure in *Poa pratensis* followed a similar pattern to clipping yield except at the lower nitrogen levels where again tillering seemed to have a major influence.

Tiller production in Fig. 4 refers only to one cultivar of each species and substantial differences are discernible. The form of the graph for S.23 indicates that there is an optimum nitrogen level for tillering within the cutting heights examined and that tillering is relatively insensitive to cutting height. The notion that closer mowing within the examined range stimulates tillering is upheld only for S.23 at very low nitrogen levels. In all instances the turf was visibly nitrogen deficient at the highest cutting height. Fylking showed a tillering response with increase in cutting height and increase in nitrogen level over the range examined, but stimulation by nitrogen declined considerably above 4 mM.

The general effect of increasing nitrogen supply is to stimulate both tillering and top growth. However, the stimulation of tillering begins to decline with increasing nitrogen before overall top yield. Increasing nitrogen supply has the reverse effect, within the range examined, on the quantity of roots supported. This observation has implications in turfgrass culture since it indicates that compromises need to be made in the use of nitrogenous fertilizers. For example, the British winter games of soccer and rugby subject turf to a considerable wear stress. Wear tolerance is improved by both a tight turf and a dense root system. Overeagerness to produce a lush, quick-growing turf by excessive nitrogen applications may result in a turf whose underground development is inferior to turf receiving moderate nitrogen applications. Moreover, this effect of excessive nitrogen on the root system would be accentuated were the cutting height reduced.

Figures 1, 2, 3, and 4 show an overall similarity in the behavior of *Lolium perenne* and *Poa pratensis* to variations in nitrogen level and cutting height, but highlight notable differences in potential top growth and tillering. The similarity in behavior suggests that biochemical analysis of one may be generally applicable and help account for the characteristic behavior of roots and tops.

Table 1 confirms the data in Fig. 2, namely that the quantity of roots decreases the increase in nitrogen level but goes further to show that depth of rooting is substantially reduced.

The data in Table 2 are expressed as both total content of carbohydrate and concentration in the dry plant tissues. The root systems of plants grown with a 1 mM nitrogen supply contained much higher quantities of TNC. principally in the forms of fructosan and sucrose. However, this higher quantity was related to the size of the root system and the concentrations of TNC in the roots of all nitrogen treatments was similar. This suggests that carbohydrate utilization was not impaired in the roots of plants grown at the lowest nitrogen level.

Table 1—Mean root lengths and root weights per plant of 6-month-old *Lolium perenne* S.23 grown at three nitrogen levels and maintained at a 3.75-cm cutting height.

	Nitrogen level, mM		
	10	4	1
Root length,* cm	8	14	23
Root weight,* mg	119	360	500

* Root length LSD (0.05) = 4; root weight LSD (0.05) = 60.

Table 2—Total quantities and concentrations of fructosan, sucrose, and hexoses in the leaves, stem bases, and roots of 6-month-old *Lolium perenne* S.23 plants grown at three nitrogen levels and maintained at a 3.75-cm cutting height.

Tissue	Nitrogen level	Fructosan		Sucrose		Hexoses		Total nonstructural carbohydrate	
	mM	mg	%*	mg	%*	mg	%*	mg	%
Leaves	10	6.6	3.3	8.0	3.6	17.0	8.5	31.6	15.8
	4	9.3	4.7	9.0	5.0	10.2	5.1	28.5	14.2
	1	4.0	4.0	8.0	8.0	9.0	9.0	21.0	21.0
Stem bases	10	10.4	5.0	4.6	2.1	9.8	4.6	24.8	11.7
	4	14.6	6.5	3.3	1.4	12.6	5.4	30.5	13.3
	1	54.6	19.8	10.0	3.9	16.4	6.5	81.0	30.2
Roots	10	7.7	6.5	10.0	8.6	2.2	1.3	19.9	16.4
	4	24.2	7.5	19.8	7.0	3.4	1.2	47.4	15.7
	1	34.6	7.6	27.1	5.5	5.9	1.3	67.6	14.4

* % dry matter.

The stem bases present a different situation. Here again there were much higher quantities of both fructosan and sucrose in the plants of the 1 mM nitrogen treatment, but in this case it was due to a two- to threefold increase in the concentration in the tissue. The leaves of the 1 mM nitrogen plants also contained higher concentrations of TNC although the increase was less marked than in the stem bases. The data indicate a build-up of carbohydrate in the aerial parts, particularly the stem bases of plants suffering nitrogen deficiency. It is reasonable to suggest that this is because lack of nitrogen impairs carbohydrate utilization for top growth. Conversely, in plants grown at high nitrogen levels, carbohydrate turnover is rapid, there being no restriction of anabolic growth processes from nitrogen supply.

Although carbohydrate utilization and storage are affected by nitrogen supply, it is recognized that other factors, for example, seasonal changes in environmental conditions, may be of major importance in controlling carbohydrate levels in the field.

If nitrogen supply controls carbohydrate utilization then a sudden increase or decrease in nitrogen supply to plants varying in the amount of stored carbohydrate could be reflected in the regrowth pattern following clipping. Regrowth was examined when S.23 plants maintained on either 1 mM or 10 mM nitrogen and clipped at 3.75 cm were clipped to 1.25 cm and transferred to the dark at either the same or alternative nitrogen level.

The results of the regrowth experiment in Fig. 5 indicate that reserve TNC is used up quite rapidly and that plants grown on low nitrogen and transferred to high nitrogen have a more sustained capacity for regrowth. The data also indicate that a sudden depletion in nitrogen supply has a marked effect in reducing the plants' ability to regrow. The reason for this inability to regrow is indicated in Fig. 6 and 7 to be due to an inability to mobilize stored TNC. When plants grown at high nitrogen or at low nitrogen and transferred to high nitrogen are allowed to regrow in the dark, there is a rapid decrease in the concentration of all components of

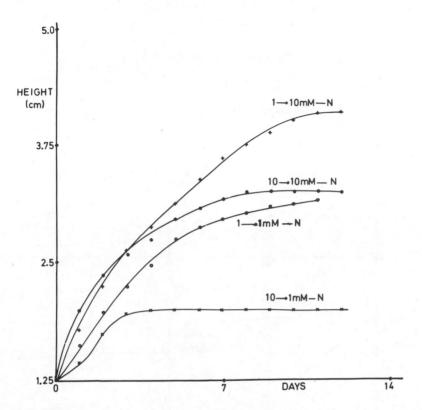

Fig. 5—Regrowth of *Lolium perenne* S.23 maintained at a 3.75-cm cutting height and then cut to 1.25 cm. Original nutrient treatments were 10 mM or 1 mM nitrogen and a 14-hour day. Transferred at time = 0 to the dark and either maintained at the same nitrogen level or the alternative.

the TNC in stem bases and roots. This is particularly noticeable in the roots and stem bases of plants grown initially at 10 mM nitrogen where reserves of TNC are small.

Metabolism in the dark involves a substantial catabolic component and it would seem from the fructosan depletion in the stem bases of plants maintained at low nitrogen that respiration is a substantial component and possibly is less inhibited by low nitrogen than the production of new tissue (Fig. 6). Figures 5, 6, and 7 studied together strongly suggest that nitrogen status holds the key to the utilization of carbohydrate for growth processes.

Two hypotheses seem to agree with experimental observations. These will enable an interpretation to be made of the responses in top growth and root development to variations in nitrogen supply level and cutting height. The first is that top growth has precedence over root growth. The second is that under conditions of low nitrogen availability, roots, being the absorbing organs, are relatively less deficient than the areial parts.

On the basis of these hypotheses we can examine the situation of low nitrogen availability. Under these circumstances the tops cannot utilize

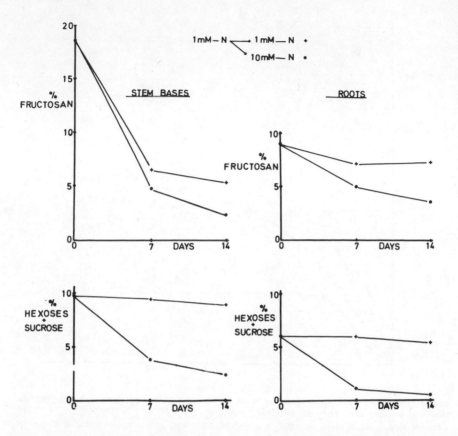

Fig. 6—Changes with time in the concentrations of fructosan and sucrose plus hexoses in the stem bases and roots of *Lolium perenne* S.23 when changed at time = 0 from a regime of 1 mM nitrogen and a 14-hour day to either 10 mM nitrogen in the dark or 1 mM nitrogen in the dark.

photosynthate for growth because of lack of nitrogen. However, the roots having a relatively higher nitrogen status are able to utilize some translocated carbohydrate for regrowth, the remainder accumulating mainly as fructosan in the stem bases of S.23 *Lolium perenne*. As the nitrogen supply is increased, more nitrogen is translocated to the tops; and since top growth takes precedence, less photosynthate will be translocated to the roots and therefore less root growth will occur.

Cutting height is an added complication but may be explicable in terms of photosynthate available for growth and therefore nitrogen may be required for its utilization. Figure 1 indicates that there is a maximum nitrogen supply level to which top growth can respond that depends upon cutting height. The lower the cutting height the lower the amount of top growth and the lower the nitrogen level necessary to achieve this maximum top growth. This suggests that closer mowing reduces the carbohydrate available for

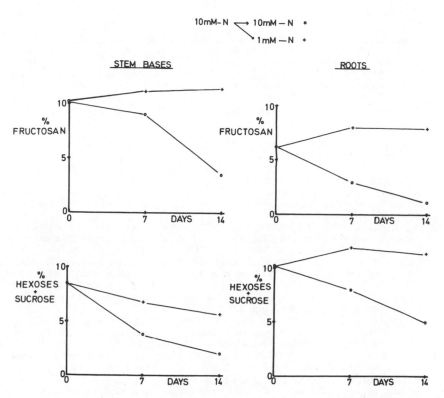

Fig. 7—Changes with time in the concentrations of fructosan and sucrose plus hexoses in the stem bases and roots of *Lolium perenne* S.23 when changed at time = 0 from a regime of 10 mM nitrogen and a 14-hour day to either 10 mM nitrogen in the dark or 1 mM nitrogen in the dark.

growth thereby decreasing the nitrogen supply level for its utilization. It has been proposed that top growth takes precedence over root growth. If so, then when nitrogen is restricted the lower the cutting height the less nitrogen necessary for the carbohydrate available for growth to be used by the tops; thus root growth is reduced. As cutting height is reduced, it would be expected that the quantity of roots relative to top growth would decrease if the nitrogen supply remained constant and low. This is clearly in agreement with the data in Fig. 1 and 2 obtained for the 1 mM nitrogen supply level.

The ultimate control of the distribution of growth between tops and roots is hormonal. However, it is suggested that both nitrogen supply level and cutting height affect the internal nitrogen status of the plant relative to carbohydrate available for growth and that the latter constitutes a key triggering mechanism.

ACKNOWLEDGMENT

P. J. Bryan is grateful for a grant provided by the Sports Council.

REFERENCES

1. BAKER, H. K. 1957. Studies on the root development of herbage plants. III. The influence of cutting treatments on the roots, stubble and herbage production of a perennial ryegrass sward. J. Brit. Grassl. Soc. 12:197-208.

2. DUBOIS, M., K. GILLES, J. K. HAMILTON, P. A. REBERS, and F. SMITH. 1951. A colorimetric method for the determination of sugars. Nature 168:167.

3. DUNN, J. H., and R. E. ENGEL. 1970. Root response to 'Merion' Kentucky bluegrass sods to various nitrogen applications near the time of transplanting. Agron. J. 62:623-625.

4. EVERS, G. W., and E. C. HOLT. 1972. Effects of defoliation treatments on morphological character and carbohydrate reserves in kleingrass (*Panicum coloratum* L.) Agron. J. 64:17-19.

5. GOSS, R. L., and A. G. LAW. 1967. Performance of bluegrass varieties at two cutting heights and two nitrogen levels. Agron. J. 59:516-518.

6. GREEN, D. G., and J. B. BEARD. 1969. Seasonal relationships between nitrogen nutrition and soluble carbohydrates in the leaves of *Agrostis palustris* Huds. and *Poa pratensis* L. Agron. J. 61:107-111.

7. JONES, D. I., G. ap GRIFFITH, and R. J. K. WALTERS. 1961. The effect of nitrogen fertilizer on the water soluble carbohydrate content of perennial ryegrass and cocksfoot. J. Brit. Grassl. Soc. 16:272-275.

8. JUSKA, F. V., and A. A. HANSON. 1961. Effects of interval and height of mowing on the growth of 'Merion' and common Kentucky bluegrass (*Poa pratensis* L.) Agron. J. 53:385-388.

9. LAIDLAW, R. A., and S. G. REID. 1951. Analytical studies on the carbohydrates of grasses and clovers. J. Sci. Food Agr. 3:19-25.

10. MADISON, J. H. 1962. Turfgrass ecology. Effects of mowing, irrigation and nitrogen treatments of *Agrostis tenuis* Huds. 'Seaside' and *Agrostis tenuis* Sibth. 'Highland' on population, yield, rooting, and cover. Agron. J. 54:407-412.

11. OSWALLT, D., A. R. BERTRAND, and M. R. TEEL. 1959. Influence of nitrogen fertilization and clipping on grass roots. Soil Sci. Soc. Amer. Proc. 23:228-230.

12. SULLIVAN, E. F. 1962. Effects of soil reaction, clipping height and nitrogen fertilization on the productivity of Kentucky bluegrass sod transplants in pot culture. Agron. J. 54:261-263.

13. WEINMANN, H. 1948. Underground development and reserves of grasses. A review. J. Brit. Grassl. Soc. 3:111-140.

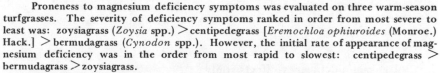

18

Magnesium deficiency in zoysiagrass

Y. KAMON

Proneness to magnesium deficiency symptoms was evaluated on three warm-season turfgrasses. The severity of deficiency symptoms ranked in order from most severe to least was: zoysiagrass (*Zoysia* spp.) > centipedegrass [*Eremochloa ophiuroides* (Monroe.) Hack.] > bermudagrass (*Cynodon* spp.). However, the initial rate of appearance of magnesium deficiency was in the order from most rapid to slowest: centipedegrass > bermudagrass > zoysiagrass.

Six levels of magnesium oxide were utilized to investigate magnesium deficiencies in zoysiagrass. The levels used were 0, 5, 10, 20, 30, and 40 ppm. The plant characteristics evaluated included leaf color, leaf length, leaf width, node number, shoot length, shoot weight, root length, and root weight. In this experiment zoysiagrass showed magnesium deficiency symptoms at levels below 20 ppm. Leaf length was increased up to 10 ppm, while shoot length and shoot weight were increased up to 20 ppm. The number of nodes increased up to 40 ppm. Leaf width, root length, and root weight were not affected by the magnesium level. Additional index words: Bermudagrass, Centipedegrass, Shoot growth, Root growth, *Zoysia* spp., *Cynodon* spp.

Zoysiagrass has been widely used for turfgrass purposes in Japan with the improved bermudagrass being introduced more recently. Fundamental research concerning mineral element nutrition of these warm-season species is needed in Japan. Objectives of this investigation were 1) to assess the relative magnesium requirements in zoysiagrass, bermudagrass, and centipedegrass, and 2) to evaluate the growth and morphological responses of zoysiagrass to various magnesium oxide levels.

MATERIALS AND METHODS

Warm-season species studies

Included in the study were two zoysiagrasses, Japanese lawngrass (*Zoysia Japonica* Steud.) and Emerald zoysiagrass (*Z. Japonica* X *Z. tenuifolia*); two bermudagrass cultivars, 'Tifgreen' and 'Tifdwarf' bermudagrass (*Cyndon dactylon* X *C. transvaalensis*); and centipedegrass [*Eremochloa ophiuroides* (Munro.) Hack.]. The zoysiagrasses and bermudagrasses were

Table 1—Influence of two MgO levels on the shoot and root growth of five warm-season turfgrasses.

Turfgrass	Shoot weight			Root weight		
	40 ppm	0 ppm	Rate*%	40 ppm	0 ppm	Rate*%
	────────────────── g dry weight ──────────────────					
Zoysia Japonica	20.36	2.84	13.95	9.11	0.22	2.41
Emerald Zoysiagrass	11.03	0.42	3.81	1.85	0.01	0.54
Tifgreen bermudagrass	30.80	3.85	12.50	4.41	1.27	28.80
Tifdwarf bermudagrass	18.42	3.20	17.37	3.89	1.40	35.99
Centipedegrass	32.39	2.44	7.53	7.27	0.60	8.25

* (Weight of 0 ppm/weight of 40 ppm) X 100 = rate.

established from seedlings containing three nodes whereas centipedegrass was established from seedlings that were in the three-leaf stage. A sand culture system involving a Hoagland's nutrient solution was utilized in this experiment. A washed quartz sand was used. The solution was added at a rate of 300 cc/pot two times a week. Two magnesium levels were established, 0 and 40 ppm of magnesium oxide. The data taken included observations as to the rate and types of magnesium deficiency symptoms that developed on these five turfgrasses.

Magnesium deficiency effects study

Emerald zoysiagrass was selected for more extensive magnesium deficiency studies. Seedlings containing a node and roots were excised and propagated in a quartz sand bed with moisture provided by the daily addition of distilled water. When the seedlings attained a root length of 5 cm, they were transferred to 1/8,000—are Wagner pots in the greenhouse. A water culture system involving a Hoagland's solution was utilized during the experiment. The culture solution was supplied at a rate of 150 cc/pot every other day with all solutions being changed every other week. Magnesium levels were established at 0, 5, 10, 20, 30, and 40 ppm magnesium oxide by means of magnesium sulfate ($MgSO_4$). The duration of the experimental period was 90 days, from April 1 to June 30. The plant responses evaluated were leaf color, leaf length, leaf width, node number, shoot length, shoot weight, root length, and root weight.

RESULTS

Warm-season species study

Typical magnesium deficiency symptoms were observed on zoysiagrass. These initially included a general, yellowish discoloration of leaf tissue followed by the appearance of tortulous (sic.) yellow spots on the leaves. Bermudagrass did not exhibit these typical symptoms. Numerous small, yellow spots were observed over the entire leaf surface. In the case of centipedegrass,

Table 2—Influence of six MgO levels on the growth and morphological responses of Emerald zoysiagrass.

MgO Level	Average of three pots							
	Leaf length	Leaf width	Node no.	Stolon no.	Shoot length	Dry shoot wt.	Root length	Dry root wt.
ppm	cm	mm			cm	mg	cm	mg
0	2.91	2.29	4.0	3	4.63	0.08	14.46	0.0083
5	2.76	2.05	16.0	5	15.03	0.26	9.06	0.0070
10	4.96	2.26	22.0	6	28.93	0.59	12.60	0.017
20	5.93	2.35	33.3	9	42.80	1.14	17.20	0.018
30	6.16	2.32	45.0	9	34.10	1.23	13.40	0.035
40	5.16	2.30	53.3	12	39.06	1.32	17.83	0.020
LSD 5%	0.62	NS	17.93		13.28	0.50	NS	NS
1%	0.81	NS	25.14		18.60	0.70	NS	NS

the spotting characteristic did not appear on the leaves but the lower older leaves became distinctly red in color.

The effects of two magnesium levels on the root and shoot growth of five warm-season turfgrass species are shown in Table 1. Growth was more adversely affected in the case of centipedegrass and zoysiagrass than for bermudagrass at deficient magnesium levels. Root growth was reduced more by magnesium deficiencies than shoot growth.

The rate of appearance of magnesium deficiency symptoms occurred in the order from most rapid to slowest as: centipedegrass > bermudagrass > zoysiagrass. However, in the order from greatest to least, the symptoms were most severe in: zoysiagrass > centipedegrass > bermudagrass.

Magnesium deficiency effects study

Zoysiagrass leaves exhibited distinct magnesium deficiencies at the 0, 5, and 10 ppm magnesium oxide levels. At the termination of the experimental 90-day period there was also a light green to slightly yellowish appearance on the leaves of zoysiagrass grown at 20 ppm, while the 30 and 40 ppm treatments were distinctly darker green.

Characterization of leaf dimensions revealed that leaf lengths declined with reductions of magnesium oxide below 20 ppm while leaf width measurements on the same leaves showed no effects from the six magnesium levels (Table 2).

Counts of the number of nodes showed that there is a direct relationship to the magnesium oxide level, as well as to the number of stolons. That is, as the magnesium oxide level increased there was a proportional increase in the number of stolons. This means that magnesium deficiencies can have a strong influence on the rate at which a zoysiagrass turf is established from stolons.

Shoot length measurements were made based on the length of the longest stolon in each pot solution culture. The maximum shoot length occurred at the 20 ppm magnesium oxide level and decreased with decreasing magnesium levels.

Shoot growth measured on a dry weight basis showed proportional increases with increased magnesium oxide levels. The deficiency effects as measured by this parameter were greatest at magnesium oxide levels of below 20 ppm. In contrast to the shoot growth responses, the root length and total root growth as measured on a dry weight basis were not affected by these six magnesium oxide levels. It is concluded that zoysiagrass growth will respond to magnesium up to levels of 30 ppm magnesium oxide.

19

Performance of bermudagrasses in the transition zone as affected by potassium and nitrogen[1]

F.V. JUSKA & J.J. MURRAY

The effects of K and N on winter survival, recovery, disease reaction, and turf quality of bermudagrasses (*Cynodon* spp.) were studied in 1971 and 1972. Applications of K decreased winter injury on Arizona common and 'Tufcote' but had little effect on the more winter-hardy cultivar 'Midiron.' "High" potassium and higher rates of NH_4NO_3 significantly increased bermudagrass recovery from winter injury and increased turf quality. Damage caused by a *Helminthosporium* sp. (leaf spot) was less pronounced on plots of Arizona common and Tufcote which had been treated with K. Midiron and 'Tifgreen' were resistant to this pathogen. *Sclerotinia homoeocarpa* F. T. Bennett (dollar spot) infestation was less severe on plots treated with K. Dollar spot infestation was greater on plots treated with ureaformaldehyde and 1.5 kg/100 m^2 of NH_4NO_3 than on plots treated with 4.3 or 2.9 kg of NH_4NO_3. Additional index words: Nitrogen, Potassium, *Helminthosporium*, *Sclerotinia*, *Cynodon* spp.

Many bermudagrass (*Cynodon* spp.) cultivars are subject to severe winter damage in the transition zone that separates the regions of best adaptation for cool- and warm-season grasses. Observations made over several years at the USDA-ARS Center at Beltsville, Maryland (4) have provided comparative data on the winterhardiness of specific cultivars and accessions. Relative winter injury scores of bermudagrasses vary greatly with tests and years. Much of this variation can be attributed to management practices other than soil fertility and to environmental variables. In addition, there is evidence that soil fertility, especially levels of available K and N, contribute substantially to the degree of variation encountered in evaluating the winterhardiness of bermudagrass cultivars.

Although K is the most active of the essential plant nutrients, its role in plant growth is not clearly understood (2). Much of the K in plants appears in a soluble form, and it may be leached from leaves by rain or irrigation (5). The leaching loss of K from soils is well established. Potassium may influence the reaction of grasses to certain diseases and the recovery of grasses from disease damage, as well as the overall hardiness of grasses under adverse conditions (3).

[1]Contribution from Turfgrass Laboratory, Plant Genetics and Germplasm Institute, Agricultural Research Service, U. S. Dept. of Agriculture, Beltsville, MD 20705.

The contribution of K and N to winter survival, recovery, disease reaction, and turf quality of bermudagrasses was studied in 1971 and 1972. The experiment was designed to measure the magnitude of the differences that may be encountered in adaptation studies and in growing cultivars selected for use in the transition zone.

MATERIALS AND METHODS

Four bermudagrasses (Arizona common, 'Midiron,' 'Tufcote,' and 'Tifgreen') selected to represent a wide range in tolerance to winter injury, were planted in June 1970 on Chewacla silt loam soil. The soil pH was approximately 6.0 and tested high in Mg and P and low in K using Dual acid, extract procedure, North Carolina tests (6). The bermudagrasses were established in replicated plots, 7.3 m X 12.2 m, separated by a 1.5-m border which had been seeded to tall fescue. Cores 5.0 cm in diameter of Midiron, Tufcote, and Tifgreen were set on 45-cm centers and hulled seed of Arizona common was sown at 97 kg/ha. Ammonium nitrate was applied uniformly at a rate of 0.48 kg of elemental N/100 m^2 after planting on June 17 and at approximately 3-week intervals until October 25, 1970, for a total of 2.9 kg N/100 m^2. In 1970, bermudagrass plots were mowed once a week at a height of 2.5 cm. Throughout the rest of the experimental period the plots were mowed twice a week. Clippings were removed at each mowing.

Potassium was not applied on plots that tested low (70 kg/ha) in K. Elemental K at 336 kg/ha was applied on one-half the bermudagrass plots in 1970. Muriate of potash (0-0-60) was applied in three equal increments on August 3, September 9, and September 25, 1970, for the "high" total level of 336 kg/ha. The same rates of K were applied in June, August, and October of 1971 and 1972.

In Spring 1971, four N treatments were applied in duplicate within each of the two K levels. Each nitrogen plot was 3.0 m X 3.6 m. Elemental N treatments included 1.5 kg, 2.9 kg, and 4.3 kg as NH_4NO_3 and 4.3 kg as ureaformaldehyde/100 m^2 per year. Nitrogen as NH_4NO_3 was applied at 0.48-kg or 0.96-kg increments during the growing season in order to avoid burning the grass. Ureaformaldehyde was applied as a single application in the spring. The schedule of nitrogen applications was similar in 1971 and 1972.

The percentage of winter damage was estimated visually except for plant counts taken within Arizona common on May 20, 1971. Plant counts were taken by placing a 30.5 cm X 30.5 cm grid at random at six locations within each of the nitrogen subplots. Quality scores were based on a visual estimate of overall density, disease, color, and general appearance of the turf; a score of 10 indicated the best combination of the four criteria.

RESULTS AND DISCUSSION

By Fall 1970, a cover of 95% or better had been obtained on both seeded and vegetatively planted bermudagrass plots. Plant counts taken May 20, 1971 on the Arizona common plots showed more winter injury on plots

Fig. 1—Arizona common bermudagrass. Left, high K; right, low K. Extensive winterkill on the right.

that were not treated with K than on plots treated with K (Fig. 1). The average number of plants in plots treated with K was 53/9.3 dm^2, whereas the average number for plots not treated with K was 16. Visual estimates of winterkilling taken in Spring 1971 for the three cultivars and Arizona common averaged 8% for plots treated with K and 27% for plots not treated with K.

Results obtained in June 1972 were similar to those in 1971, with an average winterkill of 7% for plots treated with K and 27% for the low K (Table 1). Winter damage of bermudagrasses differed greatly as anticipated on the basis of previous performance data. The interaction of bermudagrasses and K was highly significant, with the poorly adapted Arizona common and Tufcote responding more effectively to K than the more winter-hardy

Table 1—Percentage of winterkill of bermudagrasses as affected by K fertilization, June 27, 1972.

Bermudagrasses	Low K	High K	Average
Arizona common	70.8	18.3	44.5
Tifgreen	10.0	6.5	8.3
Midiron	2.5	1.3	1.9
Tufcote	22.8	1.8	12.3
Average	26.5	7.0	---

LSD .05 for bermudagrasses = 3.2; K = 4.0; bermudagrasses and K interaction = 8.0.

Fig. 2—Midiron bermudagrass. Left, low K; right, high K. Very little winterkill with this more winter-hardy cultivar.

Midiron (Fig. 2). Although Midiron, Tufcote, and Tifgreen all had low damage scores in the plots treated with K, scores for Tufcote were significantly better than those for Tifgreen. Part of the overall damage to Arizona common may be attributed to less rhizome development than in the vegetatively propagated cultivars.

Nitrogen alone and the interaction of N and K did not significantly affect winter survival. In Spring 1971 and 1972 Arizona common and Tufcote became green 10 to 14 days earlier with high K than with low K. Color differences taken during a drought period in August 1972 showed highly significant differences for N treatments and the interaction of bermudagrasses and N. Application of NH_4NO_3 N at the 4.3 kg rate produced a darker green color for all cultivars. Arizona common and Tifgreen plots that received ureaformaldehyde were lighter green than plots that received NH_4NO_3 N at 2.9-kg or 4.3-kg rate. The color of Midiron and Tufcote plots that received ureaformaldehyde were approximately the same as plots that received 2.9 kg of N as NH_4NO_3.

Recovery from winter damage is reflected in the highly significant increase in bermudagrass quality in September 1972 (Table 2). Differences in recovery among bermudagrasses were highly significant, with the rate of recovery from best to poorest as follows: Tifgreen, Midiron, Tufcote, and Arizona common. All bermudagrasses showed the best recovery with higher rates of N in combination with high K. Ammonium nitrate increased recovery more rapidly than ureaformaldehyde at the same rate of application.

Table 2—Quality (10 = best) ratings of bermudagrasses as affected by K and N fertilization, September 1972.

Fertilizers, kg N/100 m²	Bermudagrasses								
	A. common		Tifgreen		Midiron		Tufcote		
	Low K	High K	Low K	High K	Low K	High K	Low K	High K	Avg
Ureaformaldehyde, 4.3	2	4	5	6	4	5	2	4	4.0
NH₄NO₃ 4.3	5	6	8	8	7	8	5	6	6.6
2.9	4	6	7	8	7	8	5	7	6.5
1.5	4	3	6	6	6	7	5	7	5.5
Avg	3.8	4.8	6.5	7.0	6.0	7.0	4.3	6.0	---
		4.3		6.8		6.5		5.1	

LSD .05 for bermudagrasses = 1.1; N = 0.5; bermudagrasses and N interaction = 1.0.

Table 3—Resistance (10 = most resistant) of bermudagrasses to *Helminthosporium* sp. (leaf spot) as affected by rates of K and N fertilization, August 1972.

Fertilizers, kg N/100 m²	Bermudagrasses								
	A. common		Tifgreen		Midiron		Tufcote		
	Low K	High K	Low K	High K	Low K	High K	Low K	High K	Avg
Ureaformaldehyde, 4.3	4	8	10	10	7	8	3	7	7.1
NH₄NO₃ 4.3	5	10	10	10	9	9	4	9	8.3
2.9	5	10	10	10	9	9	5	9	8.4
1.5	5	10	10	10	9	9	6	9	8.5
Avg	4.8	9.5	10	10	8.5	8.8	4.5	8.5	---
		7.1		10.0		8.6		6.5	

LSD .05 for bermudagrasses = 0.2; N = 0.4; bermudagrasses and K interaction = 0.8; bermudagrasses, N, and K interaction = 0.7.

A *Helminthosporium* spp., tentatively identified as *H. cynodontis* Marig. (leaf spot), damaged plots of Tufcote and Arizona common in August 1971. Tufcote and Arizona common with low K received average scores of 6 and 2 (10 = most resistant), respectively, whereas potassium-treated plots average 8 and 9. Midiron and Tifgreen were not damaged appreciably by leaf spot.

Leaf spot data for 1972 are shown in Table 3. Again, plots of Tifgreen and Midiron with low K were more resistant to leaf spot than plots of Arizona common and Tufcote but high K reduced damage to Tufcote and Arizona common. Rates of NH₄NO₃ did not affect resistance to leaf spot, but there was significantly more damage in plots treated with ureaformaldehyde.

Visual scores obtained for resistance to dollar spot *Sclerotinia homoeocarpa* showed a trend toward increase in susceptibility on plots with low K (Table 4). Associations of dollar spot with low N have been reported previously in the literature (1). Ureaformaldehyde releases N slowly, which might explain the greater susceptibility to dollar spot on ureaformaldehyde-treated plots. Tifgreen and Arizona common were most susceptible to dollar spot. Tufcote and Midiron were the most resistant.

Table 4—Resistance (10 = most resistant) of bermudagrasses to dollar spot as affected by K and N fertilization, September 1972.

Fertilizers, kg N/100 m²	Bermudagrasses								
	A. common		Tifgreen		Midiron		Tufcote		
	Low K	High K	Low K	High K	Low K	High K	Low K	High K	Avg
Ureaformaldehyde, 4.3	6	6	4	5	7	8	8	8	6.5
NH₄NO₃ 4.3	8	9	5	6	9	9	9	9	8.0
2.9	8	9	5	6	9	9	9	9	8.0
1.5	7	8	3	4	8	8	6	8	6.5
Avg	7.3	8.0	4.3	5.3	8.3	8.5	8.0	8.5	
	7.6		4.8		8.4		8.3		

LSD .05 for bermudagrasses = 1.9; N = 0.3; bermudagrasses and K interaction = 0.3; bermudagrasses, K, and N interaction = 0.8.

A highly significant increase in bermudagrass quality was obtained with high K and higher rates of N (Table 2). Differences in bermudagrasses and bermudagrass and N interaction were significant, with the higher rates of NH_4NO_3 producing better quality turf than ureaformaldehyde.

Results show that the apparent winterhardiness of bermudagrasses is influenced by K. Less winter-hardy cultivars can be expected to show a greater response to K than more winter-hardy cultivars. K, N, and source of N affected rate of recovery from winter injury, damage from leaf spot, and turf quality. Under the conditions of these experiments, K and N did not have a pronounced effect on the relative cultivar response to dollar spot.

REFERENCES

1. COUCH, H. B. 1962. Diseases of turfgrasses. Reinhold Publishing Co., New York. 289 p
2. DAVIS, R. R. 1970. Nutrition and fertilizers. In A. A. Hanson and F. V. Juska (ed.) Turfgrass science. Agronomy 14:130–145. Amer. Soc. Agron., Madison, Wis.
3. GOSS, R. L., and C. J. GOULD. 1968. Turfgrass diseases—the relationship of potassium. USGA Green Section Record. Vol. 5(5).
4. JUSKA, F. V., and A. A. HANSON. 1964. Evaluation of bermudagrass varieties for general purpose turf. U. S. Dept. Agr. Handbook 270. 54 p.
5. KNOOP, W. E. 1972. Turf nutrition. Weeds, Trees, and Turf 11(4):36–38.
6. UNIVERSITY OF MARYLAND. 1969. Soil testing methods. Soil Testing Lab. Agron. mimeo No. 37.

20

Effect of phosphorus, season, and method of sampling on foliar analysis of Kentucky bluegrass[1]

J.R. HALL & R.W. MILLER

Determination of the nutrient needs of turfgrass with foliar analysis has been hampered by the lack of a basic understanding of the effect of major element deficiency, the season, and the method of sampling on nutrient concentrations. The objectives of this study were: 1) to observe the seasonal effects of phosphorus on yield, overall desirability, and chemical composition of 'Merion' Kentucky bluegrass, 2) to compare sampling methods to determine which provided the most reliable estimate of the relationship between phosphorus soil test values and phosphorus content of clippings, and 3) to compare the reliability of soil testing and foliar analysis to accurately determine soil fertility. The experiment was conducted in a controlled temperature greenhouse on a Caldwell silt loam with a Bray phosphorus (P_1) of 2.2 kg/ha. Levels of phosphorus incorporation ranged from 0 to 640 parts phosphorus/2 million parts soil (PP$_2$MP). Eight clipping dates were utilized for chemical analysis of tissue. Soil tests for P were taken on four of the eight dates. On these same four dates two methods of tissue sampling, first blade and general clipping, were compared to determine which provided a more accurate estimate of nutrient availability. Foliar concentrations of N, K, P, Ca, Mg, Mn, Fe, B, Cu, Zn, Al, Sr, Mo, Na, Si, and Ba were determined. It was concluded that: 1) P availability influenced foliar element concentrations, 2) seasonal fluctuations of foliar element concentrations are significant, 3) physiologically young tissue should be avoided in sampling, 4) correlations between tissue phosphorus content and yield were stronger than correlations between phosphorus soil test values and yield, and 5) further studies are needed to investigate the possibility of utilizing foliar analysis for determination of the nutrient requirements of turfgrass. Additional index words: Tissue testing, Nutrient concentration, Turfgrass, Nutrition, *Poa pratensis* L. 'Merion'.

The ability to determine turfgrass nutrient status with foliar analysis has been hampered by a lack of understanding of the effect of major element deficiency and the season and method of sampling on nutrient concentrations. The development of a system to determine the nutritional status of turfgrass is difficult because the desired objective is visual quality and not yield. The construction of a key of interpretation for determining the nutrient needs of turfgrass has been neglected and a mass of unrelated information has accumu-

[1]Contribution by the Ohio Agricultural Research and Development Center, Wooster, OH 44691 and The Ohio State University, Columbus, OH 43210. Part of a thesis submitted by the senior author in partial fulfillment of the requirements for the Ph.D. degree at the Ohio State University.

lated with regard to the mineral composition of turf (1, 3, 4, 11, 16, 17, 22, 23).

The origin of soils in the United States is sufficiently diversified to provide both acid- and alkaline-phosphorus deficient soils (18). The complex chemistry involved in the fixation of phosphorus has made the interpretation of phosphorus soil tests difficult (2, 13, 15, 21). The difficulty of interpreting phosphorus soil tests that have utilized one extracting solution to extract soils containing varying proportions of iron (Fe), aluminum (Al), and calcium (Ca) phosphates is known. The strength of the correlation between extractable Bray P_1 phosphorus and plant uptake on calcareous soils has been questioned (2). There is a strong likelihood that foliar analysis could strengthen our capability to determine the phosphorus status of turfgrass grown on phosphorus deficient calcareous soils.

Determination of the many factors influencing nutrient concentrations must be made before plant analysis can be successfully utilized as a guide to nutrient needs. The determination of where on a yield curve a particular plant population is located is a separate problem for each plant species and for every element. However, it is generally conceded that once a key of interpretation for a particular plant species and a particular element is constructed, the same system can be used over a wide range of soils and climatic conditions. In California the same critical nutrient concentration for nitrogen and phosphorus is used for sugar beets (*Beta vulgaris* L.) grown in a wide range of soils. These values have been used successfully for a period of more than 25 years (19).

Nutrient concentrations of plants may be affected by soil pH, cation exchange capacity, soil genesis, plant species or cultivar, moisture conditions, height and frequency of mowing, time of sampling, soil temperature, herbicide and fertility program, and possibly other factors (1, 3, 4, 5, 6, 7, 9, 11, 14, 16, 20, 22, 23).

The objectives of this reserach were: 1) to describe the seasonal fluctuations in the rate of growth and chemical compositions of 'Merion' Kentucky bluegrass (*Poa pratensis* L. 'Merion') as they are affected by varying levels of phosphorus availability, 2) to compare phosphorus content in the leaves of youngest physiological age with the leaves of the general clipping to determine which provides the most reliable estimate of the relationship between phosphorus content and yield, 3) to describe the relationship between phosphorus soil test values and phosphorus in the leaf tissue at different sampling dates, and 4) to compare the reliability of soil testing and foliar analysis to estimate phosphorus requirements of Merion Kentucky bluegrass under alkaline conditions.

MATERIALS AND METHODS

Merion Kentucky bluegrass was grown in the greenhouse on a Caldwell silt loam (73.4% silt, 20.9% clay, and 5.7% sand) contained in 38.1 cm $\times$ 50.8 cm $\times$ 7.6 cm wooden flats. The original soil test indicated a pH of 5.2, Bray phosphorus (P_1) of 2.2 kg/ha, and (1N NH$_4$OAc) exchangeable potassium of 307 kg/ha. Organic carbon content was 0.89%, organic matter 1.5%, and total nitrogen 0.08%. The exchangeable magnesium was 1,070 ± 274 kg/ha. The cation exchange capacity of the soil was 24.7 ± 5.2 meq/100 g and the available manganese was 76.6 ± 18.8 kg/ha. $Ca(OH)_2$ was incorporated 19 days before seeding at the rate of 3,730 parts calcium/million parts oven-dry soil. The soil was kept moist during this incubation period. The pH of the 32 flats was 7.88 ± 0.1 94 days after the incorporation of lime. The phosphorus treatments had no effect on soil pH in this experiment. Each flat contained 11,140 g of air-dry soil or the equivalent of 9,450 g of oven-dry soil (118 C for 24 hours). On April 26 and May 1, 1968, 85 parts nitrogen/million parts oven-dry soil (ppm) was applied as $Ca(NO_3)_2 \cdot 4H_2O$ and the flats were irrigated.

The phosphorus was applied as $Ca(H_2PO_4)_2 \cdot H_2O$ at rates of 0, 10, 20, 40, 80, 160, 320, and 640 parts P/2 million parts oven-dry soil (PP_2MP) and raked into the surface to 2.5 cm. The flats were seeded on May 16, 1968 at the rate of 2.9 kg/200 m^2 and brought to 19% moisture. The eight phosphorus treatments were replicated four times and a completely randomized factorial design was utilized.

The controlled temperature greenhouse was held within 3 C of the outside day temperature and was brought to 22 C in the evening. During the period of this study the outdoor shade temperature exceeded 27 C on June 24, 25, 30, July 1, 2, 9, 10, 12, 13, 14, 15, 16, 17, 18, 19, 21, 22, 26, 31, August 5, 6, 7, 8, 9, 14, 15, 16, 17, 18, 19, 20, 21, 22, 23, 24, September 3, 4, 15, 16, 21, 22, 23, and 24. The grass was clipped at 5 cm at approximately 14-day intervals. Samples from eight clipping dates were utilized for chemical analysis of tissue. On four of these eight dates two methods of sampling, first blade and general clipping, were imposed on each flat. Maintenance nitrogen as $Ca(NO_3)_2 \cdot 4H_2O$ was applied on July 26, August 23, and September 20 at the rate of 50, 50, and 100 parts nitrogen/million parts oven-dry soil, respectively (Table 1). On an area basis this is equivalent to 0.5, 0.5, and 1.0 kg of N/200 m^2, respectively.

At 57, 85, 113, and 142 days after seeding, random samples of leaf blades of the youngest physiological age (first blade sample) were removed from individual grass plants for analysis. Not all of these blades were fully expanded. A minimum 2.5 g (fresh weight) first blade sample was harvested from each flat. Each flat was then cut to a 5-cm height and this harvested sample was analyzed, corrected for mineral elements removed in the first

Table 1—Summary of the maintenance schedule.

Days after seeding	Date	First blade clipping	General clipping	Soil test	Nitrogen applied, ppm*
0	May 16				
57	July 12	X	X	X	
71	July 26		X		50
85	August 9	X	X	X	
99	August 23		X		50
113	September 6	X	X	X	
127	September 20		X		100
142	November 2		X		

* Based on oven-dry soil weight (118 C for 24 hours).

blade, and referred to as the general clipping sample. During early sampling dates, the low phosphorus treatments did not provide ample material for analysis. This created missing data necessitating least squares analysis of variance.

One 26-g soil sample was taken from each flat with a 1.25-cm diameter probe on the dates of first blade harvest (Table 1). Soil tests were conducted by The Ohio State University soil testing laboratory. The extracting solutions utilized were: phosphorus $0.03N$ NH_4F in $0.025N$ HCl; potassium, calcium, and magnesium in NH_4OAc, and manganese $1N$ H_3PO_4. Phosphorus soil analyses were conducted according to the procedure of R. H. Bray and L. T. Kurtz as utilized by R. W. Blancher and A. C. Caldwell (2) with a soil to solution ratio of 1:50.

Foliar nitrogen determinations were made with a nitrogen (N) Auto Analyzer System (Technicon Chemical Co., Ardsley, N. Y.). Potassium (K), phosphorus (P), calcium (Ca), magnesium (Mn), iron (Fe), boron (B), copper (Cu), zinc (Zn), aluminum (Al), strontium (Sr), molybdenum (Mo), sodium (Na), silicon (Si), and barium (Ba) concentrations were determined with a direct reading emission spectrograph. Each flat was rated for overall desirability as a turf throughout the season. The range of this rating was 0 to 10; 10 was given to a plot that displayed good density, color, disease resistance, heat tolerance, and general appearance. Ratings less than 6 are considered of less than desirable quality.

All analyses of variance were computed with least squares procedures. Curvilinear regression was computed with the omnitab polyfit program. All

Table 2—Summary of the least square means and level of significance illustrating the effect of phosphorus incorporation levels on 17 variables measured eight times over the growing season.

Ordinate variable	Phosphorus incorporated, PP$_2$MP								Polynomial fit
	0	10	20	40	80	160	320	640	
Rate†	0.22	0.54c*	0.60c	0.93	1.19b	1.24b	1.33ab	1.41a	Quardic
%									
N	3.63c	3.82b	3.75bc	3.75bc	3.40	3.17a	3.04a	3.06a	Quintic
P	0.27b	0.26b	0.28b	0.30b	0.34	0.39a	0.45a	0.45a	Quadratic
K	2.66c	2.58c	2.53c	2.33b	2.25b	2.25b	2.05a	1.94a	Quardic
Ca	1.11ab	1.07b	1.03b	1.06b	1.15ab	1.08b	1.14ab	1.21a	Linear
Mg	0.29e	0.32de	0.33cde	0.35bcd	0.38ab	0.37abc	0.39a	0.39a	Quardic
Na	0.08b	0.09b	0.09b	0.12a	0.12a	0.12a	0.13a	0.12a	Quardic
Si	0.45a	0.42a	0.37ab	0.32b	0.38ab	0.48a	0.48a	0.41ab	Quardic
ppm									
Mn	256a	240a	221ab	236a	240a	213b	226ab	245a	Quintic
Fe	208a	136a	168a	145a	136a	122a	123a	120a	No Fit
B	15a	14a	14a	15a	15a	17a	14a	14a	No Fit
Cu	21a	15bc	16abc	17ab	17ab	15bc	16abc	13c	Linear
Zn	50	43a	40ab	39b	40ab	35bc	35bc	33c	Cubic
Al	38a	34a	29a	40a	34a	41a	34a	28a	No Fit
Sr	43a	43a	44a	42a	45a	47a	51b	52b	Quadratic
Ba	32bc	31c	32bc	33bc	36ab	37a	33bc	32bc	Cubic
Mo	2.1a	2.0a	2.1a	2.2a	2.2a	2.2a	2.4a	2.5a	No Fit

* Horizontal means with the same letter are not significantly different at the 5% level of significance (Duncan's Multiple Range Test), means without letters are significantly different from all others (12).
† Rate of growth unit of measure is g dry weight meter^{-1} day^{-1}.

computer work was done on the IBM 360 at The Ohio State University. Mean comparisons were conducted with Kramers modification of the Duncan's Multiple Range Test (DMR) (12).

RESULTS AND DISCUSSION

Phosphorus

A summary of the effect of phosphorus incorporation levels on the seventeen variables measured is presented in Table 2. Nonorthogonal polynomials were computed to describe the phosphorus effect. The relationship between applied phosphorus (PP_2MP) and percent phosphorus concentration in the blades of the general clipping over the four sampling dates is described:

$$\% P = B_0 + B_1 (X - \bar{X}) - B_2 (X - \bar{X})^2$$
$$\% P = 0.3820 + 0.000591 (X - 158.75) - 0.0000009 (X - 158.75)^2.$$

Where X is applied phosphorus (PP_2MP) and cannot exceed 640 and $\bar{X}$ is always 158.75. B_0 is the zero order constant, B_1 is the first order coefficient, and B_2 is the second order coefficient.

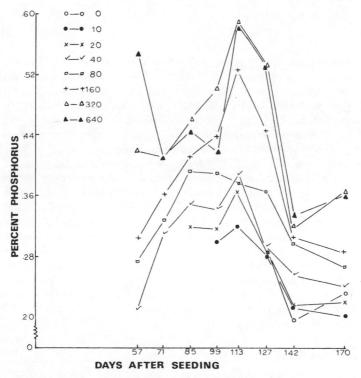

Fig. 1—Effect of phosphorus incorporation level (PP_2MP) and date of sampling on the phosphorus content of clippings.

A nonorthogonal single degree of freedom linear contrast was computed on all variables to determine if the difference between the control (OPP$_2$M phosphorus) and the other seven phosphorus incorporation treatments was significant. The increase in rate of growth and concentrations of P, Mg, and Na produced by increasing phosphorus availability was significant at the 1% level. The decrease in concentration of N with increasing phosphorus availability was significant at the 5% level. Increasing phosphorus availability decreased concentrations of K, Cu, and Zn at the 1% level of significance (Table 2). Failure to account for the effect of phosphorus availability on the concentrations of Mg, Na, N, K, Cu, and Zn when interpreting foliar analysis of Kentucky bluegrass tissue could lead to faulty recommendations.

The increase in rate of growth beyond the 80 PP$_2$MP level of phosphorus incorporation was of questionable significance (Table 2). The percent phosphorus in the tissue continued to increase to the 160 PP$_2$MP level of incorporation. This lag between the leveling off of the rate of growth at 80 PP$_2$MP and the phosphorus percent at 160 PP$_2$MP is interpreted as luxury consumption of phosphorus. This would also indicate phosphorus was not the factor limiting growth beyond the 80 PP$_2$MP level of incorporation. Study of the turfgrass quality, rate of growth, and foliar analysis data indicated that in Kentucky bluegrass tissue P contents less than 0.33% were associated with less than optimum rates of growth and overall desirability (Table 2, and Fig. 1).

Time

A summary of the effect of eight times of sampling on the seventeen variables measured is presented in Table 3. The complexity of the relationship between time of sampling and the variables measured was illustrated by the fact that attempts to fit nonorthogonal polynomials through quintic equations were unsuccessful. All time effects were significant at the 0.5% level. Time of harvest accounted for the largest portion of the variance for all 17 variables measured. Considerable variability occurred in the rate of growth of the newly established bluegrass turf over the first season. The maximum rate of growth occurred during the 15 days preceding the October 5 date of sampling. The large fluctuation in concentrations of N, K, and Ca at the August 23 date of sampling could only be ascribed to the fact that in 7 of the 10 days preceding August 23, 1968, the daily temperature exceeded 32 C. It is likely that some seasonal fluctuation in element concentration was caused by the variation in rate of growth. Trends in the concentrations of P, Mn, Fe, Ba, Zn, and B caused by time of sampling are extreme and should be taken into consideration when interpreting foliar concentrations of these elements. The seasonal fluctuations in P percent in the general clipping peaked at the September 6 sampling and then fell rapidly. This was previously noted by Brown (3).

Phosphorus × time

The interaction of phosphorus (P) and time of sampling (T) was significant at the 2.5% level for P and Mn, and significant at the 0.5% level for

Table 3—Summary of the least square means illustrating the effect of eight sampling dates averaged over all levels of phosphorus incorporation.

Variable	Jul 12	Jul 26	Aug 9	Aug 23	Sep 6	Sep 20	Oct 5	Nov 2
				Sampling Date				
Rate†	0.18*	0.65a	0.50a	0.68a	1.21	1.00	1.74	1.49
%								
N	3.40	No Data	2.94a	3.75	3.65a	3.66a	3.10a	4.24
P	0.31b	0.32b	0.37a	0.38a	0.44	0.38a	0.27c	0.27c
K	2.26c	2.03	2.59ab	1.83	2.50ab	2.64a	2.25c	2.49b
C	1.33a	1.47	0.89bc	1.20d	0.82c	0.87bc	0.96b	1.29ad
Mg	0.37	0.45a	0.30b	0.43a	2.9 b	0.24	0.28b	0.46a
Na	0.11b	0.10b	0.08c	0.08c	0.13	0.07c	0.15a	0.15a
Si	0.18bc	0.92	0.14c	0.63a	0.20bc	0.26b	0.27b	0.71a
ppm								
Mn	399	404	299a	215a	188	164	136b	139b
Fe	158abc	184ab	139abc	151abc	127bc	106c	108c	186a
B	27	19	11a	16	11a	11a	9a	14
Cu	13ab	15a	16a	11b	21	15a	25	16a
Zn	35c	34c	39bc	35c	46a	39bc	46a	42ab
Al	23bc	50a	26bc	35c	22b	21b	53a	50a
Sr	63a	64a	35c	50	41b	37bc	35c	41b
Ba	49	55	28ab	28ab	24bc	30a	24c	28ab
Mo	2.4a	3.1a	1.4b	2.8a	2.5a	1.2b	1.4b	2.8a

* Horizontal means with the same letter are significantly different at the 5% level of significance (Duncan's Multiple Range Test) means without letters are significantly different from all others (12).
† Rate of growth unit of measurement as g dry weight meter^{-2} day^{-1}.

N, Ca, and Si. The P X T interaction for P percent is illustrated in Fig. 1. The primary source of interaction appears to be the 640 PP_2MP treatment on August 23 (day 99) and the low PP_2MP levels after September 20 (day 127). These data indicate that the most reliable time to determine phosphorus nutrient status was at the September 6 sampling date (Table 4) when rates of growth were moderate (Table 3).

Soil phosphorus

Soil samples were removed from the flats for phosphorus and potassium analyses on July 12 (day 57), August 9 (day 85), September 6 (day 113), and October 5 (day 142). The effect of phosphorus incorporation levels upon phosphorus soil test values over all four sampling dates is summarized in

Table 4—Effect of phosphorus incorporation on percent phosphorus in clippings at September 6 and November 2 sampling dates.

Variable	0	10	20	40	80	160	320	640
	Phosphorus incorporation level, PP_2MP							
Percent P	No Data	0.322a*	0.366a	0.377a	0.390a	0.527b	0.570b	0.587b

* Means followed by the same letter are not significantly different at the 5% level of significance (Duncan's Multiple Range Test).

Table 5—Effect of eight phosphorus incorporation levels on phosphorus soil test values (kg of P/ha).

Phosphorus incorporation level, PP₂MP	Date of sampling			
	July 12	August 9	September 6	October 5
0	24.8	23.8	5.6	14.0a*
10	24.3	24.3	4.7	10.4a
20	24.3	22.6	5.7	9.6a
40	28.0	24.8	6.4	11.5a
80	59.4	30.5	8.1	10.1a
160	42.2	37.7	17.6	22.7a
320	64.4	83.1	48.7	37.4b
640	104.4	176.1	146.2	224.4c

* Means in this column followed by the same letter are not significantly different at the 5% level of significance (Duncan's Multiple Range Test) (12).

Table 5. Phosphorus treatment effects, time, and the P X T interaction were all significant at the 1% level. The Duncan's Multiple Range Test (DMR) conducted on the October 5 means indicated that after 170 days incorporation levels of 160 PP_2MP and less produced similar levels of soil phosphorus availability (Table 5). The only two treatments in which available phosphorus increased from July 12 to August 9 were the 320 and 640 PP_2MP treatments, indicating that during this period the phosphorus available was more than sufficient. The 640 PP_2MP level of incorporation was the only treatment in which the phosphorus available increased as the season progressed. Study of overall desirability ratings, rates of growth, and P availability indicated that P soil test values less than 30 kg of P/ha were associated with less than optimum overall desirability and rates of growth (Tables 2, 5, and 10).

A nonorthogonal polynomial quadratic equation described the relationship between phosphorus incorporated (PP_2MP) and phosphorus soil test values (kg of P/ha) over all four times of sampling. The equation is:

$$Y = B_0 + B_1 (X - \bar{X}) + B_2 (X - \bar{X})^2$$
$$Y = 30.4 - 0.134 (X - 158.7) + 0.003 (X - 158.7)^2$$

where: X = PP_2MP incorporated and cannot exceed 640,
$\bar{X}$ = 158.7 and
Y = Phosphorus soil test value (kg P/ha).

Sampling method

On July 12, August 9, September 6, and October 5, comparisons were made between the chemical composition of the first blade and the general clipping as described in materials and methods section. The only three element concentrations not significantly affected by method of sampling were N, Zn, and Al (Table 6). This implies that the method of sampling for foliar analysis of Kentucky bluegrass is critical and should be standardized.

The interaction of phosphorus and time of harvest for phosphorus percent was significant at the 0.5% level. Separate least squares analyses of

Table 6—Summary of the effect of sampling methods upon foliar analysis over four sampling dates and eight levels of phosphorus incorporation.

Variable	First blade mean	General clipping mean	First blade vs. general clipping level of significance
% N	3.48	3.55	n.s.
P	0.42	0.34	0.5%
K	2.99	2.42	0.5%
Ca	0.55	0.98	0.5%
Mg	0.22	0.30	0.5%
Na	0.106	0.116	5.0%
Si	0.26	0.20	0.5%
ppm			
Mn	191	233	0.5%
Fe	111	123	1.0%
B	23.8	13.9	0.5%
Cu	21.1	17.4	5.0%
Zn	43.4	41.3	n.s.
Sr	35.0	44.2	0.5%
Ba	24.2	31.3	0.5%
Mo	1.39	1.81	0.5%
Al	22.2	31.0	n.s.

variance were computed for the first blade data and the general clipping data to determine if one method contributed an unequal portion to the phosphorus $\times$ time interaction variance. The first blade P $\times$ T interaction variance (0.01435) was 43% larger than the general clipping P $\times$ T interaction variance (0.01007). The amount of the first blade sample used for analysis came from a greater area of the plot than the general clipping sample, therefore, sample size is not considered to have contributed to first blade variability. These observations support the contention that the first blade is less dependable than the general clipping as a means of describing the relationship between phosphorus incorporated and percent phosphorus in the tissue over time.

The interaction of time of harvest and method of sampling was significant for all variables measured except N, Fe, Cu, and Zn (Table 7). For these elements the concentration differences between first blade and general clippings did not vary with the time of sampling. Differences in the P, B, and Mn concentrations of the first blade and general clipping diminished as the season progressed. The differences between first blade and general clipping concentrations of K and Mo were generally unpredictable. Ca, an immobile element, displayed consistently higher concentrations in the older tissue of the general clipping as would be expected. Boron concentrations in young tissue were very high early in the season.

The interaction of phosphorus incorporation level and method of sampling for P percent was not significant. The differences in P percent caused by method of sampling occurred evenly over all levels of phosphorus availability.

This data substantiates the importance of knowing the physiological age of the tissue being analyzed. Severe errors in interpretation of phosphorus foliar analysis could occur as a result of not compensating for season of sampling or physiological age of the tissue.

Table 7—Summary of the time of sampling X method of sampling interaction for variables measured over all levels of phosphorus incorporation.

	Foliar concentration								
	Jul 12		Aug 9		Sep 6		Oct 5		Level of
Variable	1*	2	1	2	1	2	1	2	significance
%									
N	3.05	3.31	3.42	3.55	3.74	3.69	3.71	3.66	n.s.
P	0.41	0.31	0.48	0.37	0.46	0.44	0.32	0.27	2.5%
K	2.96	2.31	3.29	2.64	2.65	2.51	3.08	2.24	0.5%
Ca	0.80	1.31	0.55	0.87	0.35	0.81	0.55	0.96	2.5%
Mg	0.27	0.36	0.23	0.29	0.15	0.29	0.23	0.28	0.5%
Na	0.12	0.10	0.07	0.08	0.08	0.12	0.15	0.16	0.5%
Si	0.19	0.18	0.23	0.17	0.37	0.20	0.28	0.27	0.5%
ppm									
Mn	265	382	249	230	137	186	116	134	0.5%
Fe	140	141	117	129	90	117	97	107	n.s.
B	69	24	10	11	8	11	9	9	0.5%
Cu	19	11	18	13	24	21	23	25	n.s.
Zn	46	34	42	40	41	45	44	46	n.s.
Sr	59	64	27	36	24	41	30	35	0.5%
Ba	35	49	26	29	17	24	19	24	0.5%
Mo	2.63	2.21	1.49	1.19	0.45	2.45	0.99	1.39	0.5%
Al	33	22	29	26	29	21	28	52	0.5%

* 1 is first blade concentration, 2 is general clipping concentration.

Relationship between soil phosphorus and tissue phosphorus

First blade samples, general clipping samples, and soil tests were taken July 12, August 9, September 6, and October 5. Polynomial curvilinear regression through quartic equations was used to describe the relationship between phosphorus soil test values (kg of P/ha) and phosphorus percent in the tissue of both the first blade and the general clipping. With linear equations the proportion of the variance of Y that can be attributed to its linear regression on X is r^2. With quadratic and higher degree equations the fraction of the sum of squares of deviations of Y from its mean that is attributable to the regression on the x's is R^2. The general clipping provided the most significant R^2 or r^2 values at three of the four sampling dates (Table 8).

At the July 12 sampling date, during the early stages of development, the relationship between phosphorus soil test values (kg of P/ha) and percent phosphorus in the tissue was linear and at the August and September sampling dates the relationship became quadratic (Table 8 and Fig. 2), illustrating that there were periods during the growing season when phosphorus soil test values greater than 100 kg of P/ha did not increase the phosphorus concentration in the tissue.

The fact that the relationship between phosphorus soil test values and phosphorus percent could be fit at all four times of sampling indicate a fair amount of reliability can be placed in the Bray No. 1 phosphorus soil test method with a soil to solution ratio of 1:50. The data indicate that the assumption of linear relationships between phosphorus soil test values and phosphorus concentrations in the leaf tissue are subject to error (Fig. 2). The

Table 8—Relationship between phosphorus soil test values (kg P/ha) and percent phosphorus in the tissue of first blade and general clipping samples at four dates including squared simple and multiple correlation coefficients.

Date	First blade best fit	R^2	r^2	General clipping best fit	R^2	r^2
Jul 12	Linear		0.294*	Linear		0.459**
Aug 9	Quadratic	0.946**		Quadratic	0.982**	
Sep 6	Linear			Quadratic	0.980**	
Oct 5	Cubic	0.951**		Linear		0.223**

*, ** Significant at the 5 and 1% level of significance, respectively.

relationship between soil test values and plant uptake will vary with season and physiological age of the tissue sampled.

Relationship of soil testing and foliar analysis with yield

The relationship of phosphorus in the general clipping, phosphorus in the first blade, and phosphorus soil test values with percent of maximum

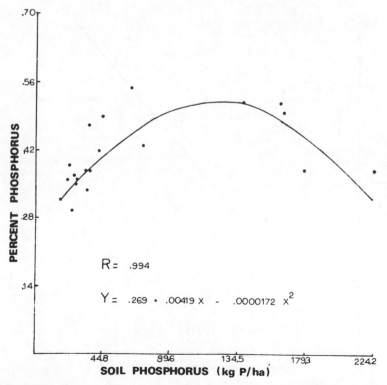

Fig. 2—Relationship between soil test values for phosphorus and phosphorus content of the general clipping on August 9 (day 85).

Table 9—Order of equations that describe the relationship between phosphorus in the general clipping, first blade, and soil, and percent maximum yield including simple and multiple correlation coefficients.

Date	General clipping			First blade			Soil test		
	Equation	R	r	Equation	R	r	Equation	R	r
Jul 12	Linear		0.861**	Linear		0.861**	Linear		0.604**
Jul 26	Linear		0.581*						
Aug 9	No Fit			No Fit			No Fit		
Aug 23	Quartic	0.962**							
Sep 6	No Fit			Linear		0.468**	No Fit		
Sep 20	Linear		0.639**						
Oct 5	Linear		0.732**	Quadratic	0.981**		Cubic	0.965**	
Nov 2	Linear		0.572**						

*, ** Significant at 5 and 1% level of significance, respectively.

yield was described with polynomial curvilinear regression through quartic equations on July 12, August 9, September 6, and October 5. Table 9 provides a summary of the order of the equations which fit the data and their respective r or R values.

General clipping phosphorus content provided a good linear relationship with percent yield over the greatest portion of the growing season. The strongest relationships occurred early in the season (Table 9). All methods

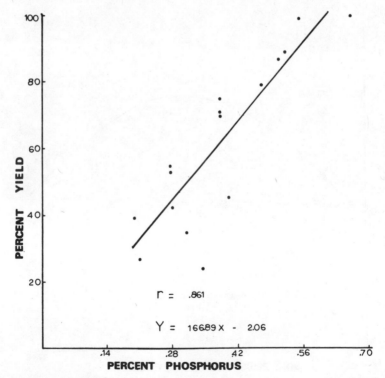

Fig. 3—Relationship between phosphorus content of the general clipping and percent of maximum yield on July 12 (day 57).

were inadequate during the periods of extreme heat stress which occurred at the August 9 sampling date. The data indicate that the relationship between phosphorus percent in the general clipping and percent of maximum yield could be fit six of the eight sampling times. The relationship between phosphorus soil test values and yield could be fit two of the four times and the October 5 relationship was an unexplainable cubic fit. The linear fit between phosphorus soil test values and yield on July 12 was approximately one half as strong ($r^2 = 0.364$) as the linear fit between phosphorus percent in the tissue and yield ($r^2 = 0.743$) for the same date. This greenhouse study on alkaline soil indicates there are periods during the year when foliar analysis can provide a better estimate of yield potential than soil testing with the Bray P_1 method. This high pH weakness of the Bray P_1 method of soil testing has been previously noted by R. W. Blanchar and A. C. Caldwell (2). To make a proper recommendation from foliar analysis data, however, it is necessary to have information about the soil that can be provided only by a soil test. In the final analysis the advantages of foliar analysis and soil testing need to be combined to provide the best estimate of the nutrient needs of Kentucky bluegrass turf.

Seventy-four percent of the Merion Kentucky bluegrass general clipping samples taken on days 57, 71, and 127 which had less than 0.36% phosphorus could be related to yields less than 50% of maximum (Fig. 3, 4, 5). Sixty

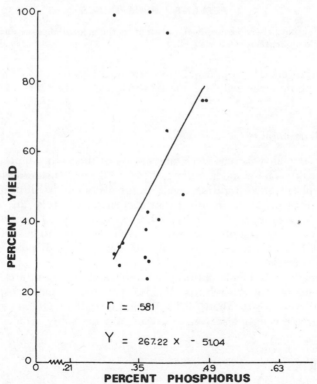

Fig. 4—Relationship between phosphorus content of the general clipping and percent of maximum yield on July 26 (day 71).

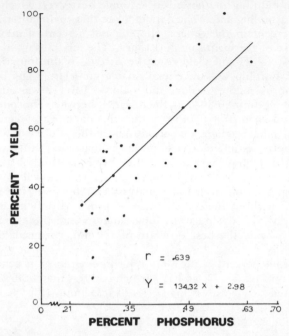

Fig. 5—Relationship between phosphorus content of the general clipping and percent of maximum yield on September 20 (day 127).

percent of the general clipping samples removed on day 142 which had less than 0.23% phosphorus could be related to yields less than 50% of maximum (Fig. 6).

Overall desirability

Turfgrass quality ratings were taken at six of the eight sampling dates to provide a quality factor independent of yield. Table 10 summarizes the effect of phosphorus incorporation levels on the overall desirability of the turf. The values presented are means of ratings made on July 26, August 9, August 23, September 6, September 20, and October 5. Overall desirability rating procedure is described in the materials and methods section. The 320 and 640 PP_2MP treatments provided significantly higher desirability ratings than the other treatments.

A comparison of the phosphorus incorporation effect on rates of growth (Table 2) and overall desirability (Table 1) indicates that phosphorus incorporation levels greater than 80 PP_2MP did not affect rates of growth significantly over the entire season, however, did favorably affect overall desirability.

CONCLUSIONS

These data support the following conclusions.
1) Interpretation of Kentucky bluegrass foliar analysis for many of the

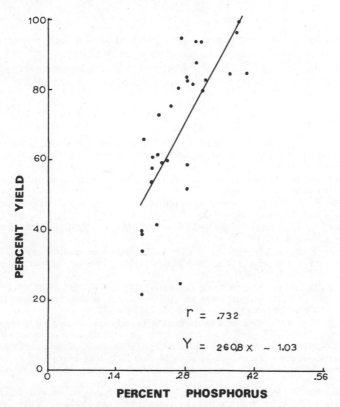

Fig. 6—Relationship between the phosphorus content of the general clipping and percent of maximum yield on October 5 (day 142).

elements measured in this study should take into consideration the effect of phosphorus availability, seasonal fluctuation, and method of sampling.

2) There are periods during the growing season when the relationship between available soil phosphorus and percent phosphorus in the tissue of Kentucky bluegrass is not linear.

3) Relationships between phosphorus soil test values, phosphorus percent in general clippings or first blades, and percent of maximum yield can be described with polynomial equations. The strength of the relationships vary with season. The lack of consistency in describing relationships between percent phosphorus in general clippings of Merion Kentucky bluegrass

Table 10—Effect of phosphorus incorporation on overall desirability ratings taken at 57, 71, 85, 99, 113, 127, and 142 days after seeding (10 was given to ideal turf).

Rating	PP$_2$MP incorporated							
	0	10	20	40	80	160	320	640
Overall desirability (rating)	2.4	4.7b*	4.6b	5.9c	7.1d	7.3d	8.0e	8.4e

* Means with same letter are not significantly different at the 5% level of significance. Means without a letter are significantly different from all others.

and percent maximum yield suggests that prediction of a yield response from a precise nutrient level is of questionable value at this time.

4) Further studies of the feasibility of utilizing foliar analysis for determination of the nutrient requirements of turfgrass are needed.

REFERENCES

1. BEARD, J. B., and W. H. DANIEL. 1967. Variations in the total nonprotein and amide nitrogen fractions of *Agrostis palustris* Huds. leaves in relation to certain environmental factors. Crop Sci. 7:111-115.
2. BLANCHER, R. W., and A. C. CALDWELL. 1964. Phosphorus uptake by plants and readily extractable phosphorus in soils. Agron. J. 56:218-221.
3. BROWN, E. M. 1943. Seasonal variation in the growth and chemical composition of Kentucky bluegrass. Missouri Agr. Exp. Sta. Bull. 360.
4. BUTLER, J. D., and T. K. HODGES. 1967. Mineral composition of turfgrass. Hort. Sci. 2:62-63.
5. COOPER, H. P., and W. H. GARMAN. 1942. Effect of applications of Na on the composition and yield of cotton on different levels of potash fertilization. Soil Sci. Soc. Amer. Proc. 7:331-338.
6. DOSS, B. D., D. A. ASHLEY, O. L. BENNETT, and R. M. PATTERSON. 1966. Interactions of soil moisture, nitrogen, and clipping frequency on yield and nitrogen content of Coastal bermudagrass. Agron. J. 58:510-512.
7. HALL, J. R. 1970. Problems in attempting to use tissue testing to determine fertilizer needs. p. 55-64. *In* Proceedings of the Ohio Turfgrass Foundation meetings.
8. ――――. 1971. The effect of phosphorus, season, and method of sampling on foliar analysis, mineral depletion, and yield of Merion Kentucky bluegrass. Ph.D. Thesis. The Ohio State University. Univ. Microfilms, Ann Arbor, Mich. (Diss. Abstr. 72-4510).
9. HOAGLAND, D. R., and T. C. BROYER. 1940. Hydrogen ion effect and the accumulation of salt by barley roots as influenced by metabolism. Amer. J. Bot. 27: 173-185.
10. HOPKINS, H. T., A. W. SPECKT, and S. B. HENDRICKS. 1950. Growth and nutrient accumulation as controlled by oxygen supply to plant roots. Plant Physiol. 25:193-209.
11. HYLTON, L. O., A. ULRICH, and D. R. CORNELIUS. 1967. Potassium and sodium interrelations in growth and mineral content of Italian ryegrass. Agron. J. 59:311-314.
12. KRAMER, C. Y. 1956. Extension of multiple range tests to group means with unequal numbers of replications. Biometrics 12:307-310.
13. LAVERTY, J. C., and E. O. MC LEAN. 1961. Factors affecting yileds and uptake of phosphorus by different crops: 3 kinds of phosphate—native, applied, and formed. Soil Sci. 91:166-171.
14. LETEY, J., L. H. STOLZY, N. VALERAS, and T. E. SZUSKIEWICZ. 1962. Influence of soil oxygen on growth and mineral concentrations of barley. Agron. J. 54:538-540.
15. MACK, A. R., and S. A. BARBER. 1960. Influence of temperature and moisture on soil phosphorus. I. Effect on soil phosphorus fractions. Soil Sci. Soc. Amer. Proc. 24:381-385.
16. MONROE, C. A., G. D. COORDTS, and C. R. SKOGLEY. 1969. Effects of nitrogen-potassium levels on the growth and chemical composition of Kentucky bluegrass. Agron. J. 61:294-296.
17. PELLETT, H. M., and E. C. ROBERTS. 1963. Effects of mineral nutrition on high temperature induced growth retardation of Kentucky bluegrass. -Agron. J. 55:473-476.
18. PRATT, P. F., N. HOLOWAYCHUK, and H. H. MORSE. 1955. Soluble phosphorus in soils of Ohio. Ohio Agr. Exp. Sta. Res. Circ. 27. 16 p.
19. ULRICH, A., D. RIRIE, F. J. HILLS, A. G. GEORGE, M. D. MORSE, and C. M.

JOHNSON. 1959. Plant Analysis. . .a guide for sugar beet fertilization. California Agr. Exp. Sta. Bull. 766. p. 78.

20. VICKERY, H. B. 1961. Chemical investigation of the tobacco plant. XI. Composition of the green leaf in relation to position on the stalk. Bull. 640. Connecticut Agr. Exp. Sta. New Haven. 41 p.

21. VOLK, V. V., and E. O. MC LEAN. 1963. The fate of applied phosphorus in four Ohio soils. Soil Sci. Soc. Amer. Proc. 27:53–58.

22. WADDINGTON, D. V., and J. H. BAKER. 1965. Influence of soil aeration on the growth and chemical composition of three grass species. Agron. J. 57:253–258.

23. WALKER, W. M., and W. J. PESEK. 1963. Chemical composition of Kentucky bluegrass as a function of applied nitrogen, phosphorus, and potassium. Agron. J. 55:247–250.

21

Effects of variable rates of sulfur on the quality of putting green bentgrass

R. L. GOSS

Sulfur deficiencies seriously retard the growth of plants, including turfgrasses. This element is important in many reactions, some of which are: 1) synthesis of certain vitamins, 2) synthesis of the amino acids cystine, cysteine, and methionine which are essential components of protein, 3) formation of nitrogenase enzyme, and 4) formation of ATP sulfurylase. Fertilization at high rates, especially with nitrogen, greatly increases the need for sulfur and may induce serious sulfur deficiencies. Research reported in this paper indicates that sulfur applied at 56 and 168 kg/ha per year at various N, P, and K levels greatly enhances color and certain quality factors of bentgrass turf. Phosphorus applied at 86 kg/ha per year significantly increased *Poa annua* invasion at all N levels. Sulfur applied at 168 kg/ha per year produced better turf with less *Poa annua* regardless of N and P levels. Sulfur applied at 56 kg/ha per year stimulated growth of both bentgrass and *Poa annua*. Additional index words: Cystine, Cysteine, Methionine, Nitrogenase enzyme, ATP sulfurylase, *Poa annua*.

The primary nutrients N, P, and K have received most of the attention in turfgrass fertilization programs. However, lack of any one of the essential plant nutrients will result in unsatisfactory growth. Sulfur deficiencies seriously retard the growth of plants since the element is required for synthesis of several amino acids which are essential components of protein; synthesis of certain vitamins; formation of nitrogenase enzyme; formation of ATP sulfurylase, an enzyme concerned with the metabolism of sulfur, and is required for many other reactions.

SULFUR REQUIREMENTS OF PLANTS

Crop plants differ in their requirements for sulfur (1). Sulfur levels of about 0.2% in the clippings appear to be adequate for forage grasses, and turfgrasses would be expected to respond similarly according to Ensminger (3). Love (6) reported concentrations of 0.04 and 0.08% S were found in S-deficient plants, while those receiving adequate nutrition contained 0.12 to 0.19%.

Similarities between sulfur and phosphorus content in leaf and stem

Table 1—Effects of N, P, K, and S on grass color and *Poa annua* invasion in bentgrass putting green plots.

Treatment no.	Fertilizer treatment				Mean visual ratings in March, 1973 Average of four replications	
	N	P	K	S	Color*	*Poa annua*†
	kg/ha per year					
1	974	0	325	0	5.0	4.3
2	974	86	325	0	6.8	4.5
3	974	0	325	56	7.5	8.8
4	974	86	325	56	6.8	10.0
5	0	0	0	0	4.0	7.0
6	974	0	325	168	10.0	1.5
7	974	86	325	168	9.5	4.0
8	584	0	325	0	6.5	4.3
9	584	86	325	0	6.8	3.0
10	584	0	325	56	8.3	5.3
11	584	86	325	56	7.8	7.8
12	584	0	325	168	8.8	1.8
13	584	86	325	168	8.8	3.8
14	292	0	325	0	6.3	5.5
15	292	86	325	0	7.3	4.3
16	292	0	325	56	5.0	8.0
17	292	86	325	56	5.3	10.0
18	292	0	325	168	5.5	3.0
19	292	86	325	168	5.8	4.0

* 10 = Deep green.   † 10 = *Poa annua* in every 7.5 cm square.

tissues are common in many agricultural crops (1, 5) and will be stressed further in this paper.

MATERIALS AND METHODS

In 1966 preliminary tests to determine the effect of S fertilization on *Ophiobolus graminis* Sacc. Var. *Avenae* E. M. Turner, *Ophiobolus* patch disease of turf, revealed significant color and growth responses on *Agrostis tenuis* Sibth. var. 'Astoria' managed as putting green turf. Trials were initiated in 1967 to assess the importance of sulfur fertilization to bentgrass turf in the Pacific Northwest. Combinations of nitrogen at 974, 584, 292 kg/ha, P at 0 and 86 kg/ha, K at 325 kg/ha, and S at 0, 56, and 168 kg/ha were applied in a randomized block design with one check plot and four replications. The results as evaluated in Spring 1973 are shown in Table 1. All N was applied in the form of urea, P in the form of phosphoric acid, K in the form of potassium chloride, and S in the form of wettable 98% pure elemental S. All fertilizer materials were applied by sprayer in an aqueous solution. N, P, and K were applied at 2-week intervals throughout the growing season to obtain the season totals shown in Table 1. Sulfur was applied in an aqueous suspension in three equal split applications in February and March each year.

DISCUSSION

The greatest color effect of sulfur was observed with 974 kg of N/ha per year and only slightly less at 584 kg N/ha per year. Color differences observed at the lowest N level of 292 kg/ha per year were small regardless of the S treatment. Fertilization at high rates, particularly with N, greatly increased the need for S and induced a serious sulfur deficiency on all plots. These observations are in agreement with Mortensen, Baker, and Dermanis (7) who observed that a sulfur deficiency restricted orchardgrass (*Dactylis glomerata* L.) response to N fertilization. They further reported the magnitude of response to S applications increased with the amount of N applied. Sulfur-deficient putting green bentgrass plots at the Puyallup, Washington station have not responded to color, growth, or density to high levels of N, P, and K.

Turfgrasses in western Washington State frequently develop an unsightly yellow mottled appearance in the spring when soils are cold and too wet. This condition usually disappears as soils warm up later in the season, however, sulfur fertilization can eliminate the mottling.

SULFUR EFFECT ON *POA ANNUA*

Table 1 shows vast differences in *Poa annua* invasion in relation to N, P, and S treatments. In general, more *Poa annua* was observed in plots with the highest N treatment. Sulfur applied at 56 kg/ha actually stimulated better growth of all turf, including *Poa annua*. When sulfur was increased to 168 kg/ha, regardless of N, P, and K treatment, there was a significant reduction in *Poa annua* and a concomitant increase in color of the bentgrass.

Phosphorus exerted a strong effect on *Poa annua* development, especially on plots that received 168 kg S/ha. *Poa annua* increased over 2.5 times between treatment 6 and 7, the only difference being the inclusion of P in treatment 7. The same trend occurred between treatment 12 and 13 and 18 and 19. P increased *Poa annua* development and 168 kg of S/ha helped suppress *Poa annua*. Escritt and Legg (4) reported that ammonium sulfate discouraged "annual meadow-grass" (*Poa annua* L.) as well as disease, weeds, earthworms, and produced firm, dry surface conditions. The sulfate sulfur contribution over the 39 years of continuous application may have caused these results. It is possible that sulfur decreases the surface pH and the availability of P to a point where shallow-rooted species such as *Poa annua* lose vigor and their ability to compete. Soil pH tests in the surface 1 inch indicate that sulfur has depressed the pH 0.6 of a point on the pH scale as compared to a mixed 3-inch sampling. The pH difference between applications of 56 and 168 kg of S/ha was found to be slight.

OTHER EFFECTS OF SULFUR

Plots that received S at either 56 or 168 kg/ha were free of algae. Blue-green algae usually develop in plots not receiving S during the warmer months of summer. This correlates with reports and local observations that multiple applications of the fungicide FORE (a coordination product of zinc ion and manganous ethlylenebisdithicarbamate; Mallinckrodt Chemical Works, St. Louis, Mo.) will suppress algae, probably due to its high level of residual S.

Earthworms were nonexistent in S-treated plots. Escritt and Legg (4) previously reported this phenomenon in England. Studies have not been conducted by the author to determine if this is an effect of pH, direct effect of S, or some other effect caused by S.

Sulfur apparently inhibits the development of *Ophiobolus* patch disease in bentgrass turfs. Davidson and Goss (2) reported that sulfur in the form of ammonium sulfate or elemental wettable sulfur eliminated *Ophiobolus* patch disease after 1 year of treatment. *Ophiobolus* patch has never occurred in any S-treated plot in any of these nutritional studies.

REFERENCES

1. BEATON, J. D. 1969. The importance of sulphur in plant nutrition. Agrichem. West. 12(1):4–6.
2. DAVIDSON, Roy M., Jr., and Roy L. GOSS. 1972. Effects of P, S, N, lime, chlordane, and fungicides on Ophiobolus patch disease of turf. Plant Dis. Rep. 56(7):565–567.
3. ENSMINGER, L. E. 1958. Sulfur in relation to soil fertility. Alabama Agr. Exp. Sta. Bull. 312. 19 p.
4. ESCRITT, J. E., and D. C. LEGG. 1970. Fertilizer trials at Bingley. p. 185–190. *In* Proc. First Int. Turfgrass Res. Conf. Sports Turf Research Institute, Bingley, England.
5. JORDAN, H. V. 1964. Sulfur as a plant nutrient in the Southern United States. USDA Tech. Bull. No. 1297. 45 p.
6. LOVE, J. R. 1970. Lime and fertilizer response on turf. p. 40–41. *In* L. M. Walsh (comp.) Proc. 1970 Wisconsin Fertilizer and Aglime Conf. University of Wisconsin College of Agriculture and Life Sciences, Madison, Wis.
7. MORTENSEN, W. P., A. S. BAKER, and P. DERMANIS. 1968. Sulphur deficiency of orchardgrass in Western Washington. Sulphur Inst. J. 4(2):9–11.

22

Nitrogen and iron fertilization of bentgrass[1]

V. SNYDER & R.E. SCHMIDT

Fall-winter applications of nitrogen increased spring clipping yields and root growth of creeping bentgrass (*Agrostis palustrus* Huds.), and improved turfgrass appearance. Applications of iron made in combination with nitrogen further enhanced appearance, chlorophyll content, and early spring shoot growth, and appeared to offset the injurious effects of heavy fall-winter nitrogen.

Root growth was influenced by rate and time of application of nitrogen and iron while differences due to iron sources were noted. Spring and summer applications of nitrogen were beneficial to turfgrass color and further enhanced turf vigor when coupled with iron fertilization. Additional index words: Iron chelate, Fall fertilization, Foliar application, Plant growth, Winter desiccation, *Agrostis palustrus* Huds.

Most research conducted on iron metabolism and deficiencies in plants has been on calcarious soils (2, 4, 14). Iron deficiencies in soils are seldom reported in the eastern states where availability is normally considered adequate (6).

Iron has been used for years in many sections of the country for maintaining an acceptable green color on bentgrass putting turf during the summer months (7, 10). This color improvement has been attributed to a temporary increase in leaf chlorophyll content and on bluegrass (*Poa* spp.) and was reported to last for 4 to 5 weeks after application to turf with slight differences still evident after 16 weeks (7).

The occurrence of Fe deficiencies in turf are often associated with factors which affect Fe availability in soils and the ability of plants to take up adequate amounts. Lessened Fe absorption and translocation in centipedegrass [*Eremochloa ophiuroides* (Munro.) Hack.] have been related to both high and low soil temperatures (8, 16). Low cation exchange capacity of roots and decreased soil Fe availability associated with increased temperatures were suggested as possible causes (16). Solubility of Fe in soils is highest when Fe is reduced (Fe^{2+}) (3), a condition often associated with poor aeration. The same conditions which increase Fe solubility may also decrease

[1]Contribution by the Department of Agronomy, Virginia Polytechnic Institute and State University, Blacksburg, VA 24061.

root growth and limit respiration and energy needed to reduce Fe in the root (1). Because of the limited root systems of putting green turf and the frequent shoot growth removal, plant uptake of soil applied Fe may not be adequate (10). Therefore, additional information regarding the effects and sources of foliar applied Fe on turfgrass growth is needed.

As the popularity of golf continues to increase and temperate species are used more often in warmer climates, improvement in turfgrass quality during the cooler seasons becomes more desirable. Fall and winter nitrogen (N) fertilization has been shown to enhance turfgrass color throughout the winter at Virginia latitudes without adversely affecting the physiology of the turf (12, 13). Further improvement in turfgrass color caused by Fe fertilization should be beneficial. Winter Fe applications may increase chlorophyll content and photosynthesis without stimulating shoot growth. Subsequently, root growth and carbohydrate storage may be enhanced which would benefit turfgrass growth and survival.

During Winter 1968, many nonirrigated golf course greens in southwest Virginia were injured by desiccation, including plots in a N source study. It was noted that turf which survived best had received fertilizer containing Fe and sulfur. A preliminary study the following year suggested that Fe nutrition aided in reducing winter desiccation while improving turfgrass color throughout the winter. The research reported here was conducted to study the effects of Fe and N applied to cool-season putting green turf at specific times of the year on color, root, and shoot growth, and tolerance to winter desiccation.

MATERIALS AND METHODS

This series of experiments was conducted at the Virginia Polytechnic Institute and State University Turfgrass Research Center, Blacksburg, Virginia. Unless stated otherwise, ammonium nitrate was the N source and Geigy's Sequestrene 330 Fe (10% Fe) was the chelated Fe source. Material amounts are specified for 200 m^2.

Turfs in all experiments were managed as putting greens. The grass was mowed three times a week at 0.63 cm until shoot growth ceased in late November and was resumed again in April.

Experiment I

In October 1969, 1.0 kg of N, 0.41 kg of P, and 0.83 kg of K/200 m^2 supplied by a commercial-grade fertilizer were applied to a 950 m^2 plot of 4-month-old 'Penncross' bentgrass (*Agrostis palustrus* Huds.). One kilogram of N was applied alone or in combination with 25.0 g of Fe to 2.4 m X 9.7 m plots as follows: 1) October; 2) October and November; 3) October, November, and December; 4) October, November, December, and February. Iron was also applied alone to separate plots at the following schedules: 1) October and December; 2) October and November; 3) October, November, and December; and 4) October, November, December, and February. Fertilizers were applied in solutions except for the October N application which was irrigated to prevent fertilizer burn.

Visual color observations were made periodically beginning in February. Fresh weight of clippings were sampled periodically from 4.25 m² of each plot. Fresh subsamples were obtained from the April 17 clippings and frozen within 1 hour for chlorophyll determination (11). Subsequently, chlorophyll was extracted for 24 hours at 21.1 C by an 80% ethanol-H_2O solution from 1,000 mg of thawed clippings, filtered, and chlorophyll content in micrograms per gram fresh weight of tissue was determined colorimetrically at 660 and 642.5 mμ (5).

In September, a Fredrick silt loam, obtained from 0 to 15-cm depth, was mixed with equal volumes of a coarse sand. This mix was placed and firmed to within 3.75 cm from the top of aluminum-painted steel cans (10.5 cm X 17.8 cm). Three weeks prior to fertilization the cans were embedded into each plot so that the top of the can was 1.25 cm below the soil surface. Turf plugs, removed from the plots to make the holes for the cans, were trimmed to a 5.0-cm thickness and placed firmly on top of the soil in the cans, flush with the soil surface.

Root weights were obtained by removing cans from plots in April and washing the roots free of the soil mixture. The roots were then excised from the 5.0-cm plug, dried, weighed, ashed at 450 C for 8 hours, and reweighed. Root yields were then determined by ignition loss.

One week after application of the February treatments, turf plugs 10.5 cm in diameter X 17.8 cm in depth were removed from each plot and placed into aluminum-painted steel cans. The cans were then placed in a metal box (0.91 m X 1.07 m X 2.08 m) and surrounded with a light weight aggregate to insulate and insure that only the grass tops would be exposed to natural ambient conditions. Subsequently, the desiccator was covered with a clear, 4-m plastic roof designed to prevent precipitation from reaching the plugs for 5 weeks. The plugs were then exposed to natural rainfall and supplemental irrigation during a 4-week recovery period, after which observations on percent live material were recorded. A randomized complete block design was utilized with treatments replicated three times.

Experiment II

On June 5, 10.0 kg of a 10–10–10 fertilizer/200 m² was broadcast over Experiment I. In addition, various frequencies of late spring and early summer applications of N (1.0 kg of N/200 m⁻²) and chelated Fe (25 g of Fe/ 200 m²) alone and in combination were applied in 2.44 m X 29.28 m strips across each of the 12 winter fertility treatments of Experiment I. Treatments were as follows: 1) N on June 5 (low N); 2) N on June 5 and Fe on May 9, June 5, and June 20 (low N + Fe); 3) N on May 9, June 5, and June 20 (high N); and 4) N plus Fe on May 9, June 5, and June 20 (high N + Fe). Except for the June 5 N application, all N treatments were applied as NH_4NO_3 in solution and watered in immediately after application but before Fe was applied. Visual color observations, shoot growth, and root growth were determined as described in Experiment I.

Experiment III

Two N regimes were applied to 1-year-old 'Cohansey' bentgrass (*Agrostis palustrus* Huds.) beginning in November 1971. The late fall N regime consisted of fertilizing with 1.0 kg of $N/200$ m^2 in November, December, January, May, and June. The early spring N regime was similar, but applications were made in March and April instead of December and January.

To each of these N regimes, chelated Fe at 25 g of $Fe/200$ m^2 was applied to separate plots as follows: 1) none; 2) November, December, January, March, April, May, and June; 3) November, December, January, May, and June; 4) November, December, and January; 5) March, April, May, and June; and 6) May and June.

Iron sulfate ($FeSO_4$) at 25 g of $Fe/200$ m^2 was also applied to separate plots to compare with chelated Fe treatments 2 and 5.

In addition, a treatment similar to the late fall N regime having seven chelated Fe applications was initiated with the exception that the January N + Fe application was delayed until February.

Treatments were arranged in a randomized block design and replicated four times. Clipping yields and visual ratings were taken at selected intervals. Two metal cans prepared for measuring roots as in Experiment I were placed into each plot in October 1971. On July 4, 1972, the soil was washed from the roots of one can from each plot. On the same date, the second can was placed in a desiccation chamber (Experiment I) and exposed to summer drought conditions for 2 weeks after which the soil was washed from the roots. The roots from both cans were processed as described in Experiment I to determine root development.

RESULTS

Experiment I

Turfgrass color enhancement from fall-winter N applications was slight in midwinter; however, in the spring, color improved significantly with each increment of N, especially when made in combination with Fe (Table 1). Applications of Fe alone generally improved color in February when compared to turf receiving only the single application of N in October. However, by April, turfgrass treated with Fe alone was inferior in color to plots receiving either N alone or in combination with Fe at the higher frequencies.

Chlorophyll content of leaves in April was not significantly increased by fall-winter application of Fe alone (Table 1). No differences in chlorophyll levels were noted among the Fe-alone treatments and levels were quite similar to plots receiving N alone or in combination with Fe in October. However, when Fe was applied in combination with N at the highest frequencies, chlorophyll levels were enhanced. Applications of N + Fe in October, November, and December and October, November, December, and February significantly increased chlorophyll contents of turf over treatments receiving Fe alone or N alone in October.

Spring foliage weights generally increased with N fertilization (Table 1). Iron applied in combinations with N tended to further increase shoot growth;

Table 1—Effects of fall-winter fertilization with combinations of nitrogen and chelated iron on turfgrass color, clipping yields, root weights, chlorophyll content, and recovery from desiccation of Penncross bentgrass.

Type of application	Application dates	Turfgrass color*‡			Chlorophyll content,* µg/g fresh wt	Clipping yield,* kg/200 m² fresh wt		Root weight,* g/can	Desiccation recovery,† % live material
		Feb 13	Mar 5	Apr 12	Apr 17	Apr 7	Apr 17	Apr 17	Apr 24
Iron, 25.0 g of Fe/100 m² per application	Oct, Dec	4.3c*	3.0bc	3.0b	1375abc	15.18a	9.61a	0.90ab	25abc
	Oct, Nov	4.0bc	4.3d	3.3b	1355abc	15.49a	9.69ab	1.33bcd	13ab
	Oct, Nov, Dec	5.7de	5.0d	4.7c	1256ab	18.87ab	10.79ab	1.56cd	75d
	Oct, Nov, Dec, Feb	6.3e	7.7e	5.0c	1191a	16.72a	10.53ab	1.19abcd	30abcd
Nitrogen, 1.0 kg of N/200 m² per application	Oct	3.0ab	1.3a	1.7a	1298ab	14.29a	10.81ab	0.85a	55 abcd
	Oct, Nov	3.7abc	4.0cd	5.0c	1647cde	24.42c	12.91b	1.29abcd	53abcd
	Oct, Nov, Dec	4.3c	5.3d	7.7de	1391abcd	33.42d	25.72d	1.65d	10a
	Oct, Nov, Dec, Feb	4.7cd	6.7e	9.7fg	1570bcde	50.58e	32.76e	1.14abc	10a
Nitrogen, 1.0 kg of N and iron 25.0 g of Fe/200 m² per application	Oct	2.7a	2.0ab	1.3a	1235ab	13.88a	9.88ab	1.01ab	20abc
	Oct, Nov	6.3e	5.0d	6.7d	1435abcd	23.35bc	11.43ab	1.18abcd	48abcd
	Oct, Nov, Dec	8.3f	8.7f	8.7ef	1701de	37.03d	23.29c	1.21abcd	68cd
	Oct, Nov, Dec, Feb	8.7f	10.0g	10.0g	1830e	59.71f	36.53f	1.00ab	60bcd

*,† Values having a letter in common do not significantly differ from each other at the 5% level.　　‡ Rated from 1-10; 10 = best.

however, only the highest frequency of the combination treatment gave consistently higher yields than comparable N alone treatments. Shoot growth was not affected by Fe alone when compared to the single October N treatment.

Root weights in April were lowest on turf receiving 1.0 kg of N in October and highest when N was applied in October, November, and December (Table 1). When additional N was applied in February, a significant reduction in root weight was noted. Roots from plots receiving Fe alone or in combination with N show similar trends. However, only applications of Fe alone in October and November and in October, November, and December caused significant increases in root weights when compared to turf receiving the single October N treatment.

Recovery of turf from winter desiccation was aided by frequent applications of N + Fe (Table 1). Three and four applications of N + Fe maintained 68 and 60% viable material, respectively, after 4 weeks compared to 10% live material for turf fertilized with N alone at the same frequencies. Highest recovery of all plots occurred on turf receiving three applications of Fe alone.

Experiment II

The interactions between winter and summer fertilizer applications for color, root development, and shoot growth were not significant and therefore are not presented (15). The influence of the late spring treatments masked the late fall-early winter fertilization effect by early June. The highest color ratings were obtained when frequent Fe applications were made with the heavy spring N fertilizer regime (Table 2). Turfgrass color was enhanced by applications of Fe alone under the low N spring regime, but by June 27 appearance was appreciably poorer than on those plots receiving additional N.

Clipping yields were highest for both sampling dates on plots receiving high N spring fertilization (Table 2). However, on June 29, shoot growth was reduced on plots receiving Fe applied in combination with high nitrogen. No such reduction in shoot growth occurred when Fe was applied under the low nitrogen regime.

Root yields obtained in July from the heavy N spring application plus iron treatment were significantly increased over all other spring treatments, which did not differ significantly among themselves (Table 2).

Table 2—Effects of spring fertilization with combinations of nitrogen and chelated iron on turfgrass color, shoot growth, and root growth of Penncross bentgrass. Data averaged over winter treatments.

Spring fertilization	Turf color†		Clipping yields, kg/200 m² fresh wt		Root wt, g/can
	June 10	June 27	May 28	June 29	July 1
Low N	2.08a*	4.08a	2.13a	2.55a	3.54a
High N	6.04b	8.25c	2.81b	5.36c	2.92a
Low N + Fe	5.64b	6.15b	2.15a	2.51a	3.28a
High N + Fe	8.94c	9.33d	2.55b	4.86b	4.36b

* Values having a letter in common do not differ significantly at the 5% level. † Rated from 1–10; 10 = best.

Table 3—Effect of various chelated iron applications as influenced by a heavy, late fall and a heavy spring nitrogen fertilizer regime on Cohansey bentgrass root dry weights (g/can) measured July 4, 1972.

Iron chelate application frequencies		Late fall heavy N	Early spring heavy N
Fall	Spring		
3	4	0.76d*	0.51abc
3	2	0.75d	0.51abc
3	0	0.68cd	0.64cd
0	4	0.69cd	0.50ab
0	2	0.57abcd	0.62bcd
0	0	0.61abcd	0.42a
Average		0.68	0.53

* Values having a letter in common do not differ significantly at the 5% level.

Experiment III

The 1971–72 study showed root development was enhanced with a heavy, late fall N regime compared to a early spring, heavy N regime (Table 3). Iron applications tended to increase rooting under both N regimes; however, when N was heavily applied in the winter, roots tended to be heavier with increased Fe applications. The seven Fe applications under the late fall N regime increased root weights 56% over the no Fe treatment for the early spring, heavy N regime.

Initial spring clipping yields were largest under the late fall, heavy nitrogen regime, especially when Fe was also applied (Table 4). Clipping yields for the various treatments were not significantly different after March.

Turfgrass appearance in March was best when fertilized with heavy N in late fall (Table 4). Under both N regimes, the addition of Fe in November,

Table 4—Effect of various chelated iron applications on clipping yields, appearance, and tolerance to summer desiccation of Cohansey bentgrass as influenced by heavy, late fall and heavy spring nitrogen fertilization regimes.

Iron chelate application frequencies		Clipping yields, kg/200 m^2 Fresh wt			Visual ratings†				Recovery from desiccation rating*
Fall	Spring	Mar 15	May 23	Jun 15	Mar 15	Apr 18	May 17	Jun 8	Jul 24
					Heavy, late fall N fertilization regime				
3	4	2.82c*	8.00a	3.76a	6.8c	7.8a	5.3abc	7.5a	6.0a
3	2	3.29c	10.82a	4.00a	7.8cd	8.0a	5.6abc	8.0a	7.8a
3	0	4.24d	8.94a	3.76a	8.5d	7.8a	4.0a	7.0a	6.2a
0	4	2.59b	9.65a	3.76a	7.6cd	8.3a	7.3bcde	7.5a	6.2a
0	2	2.35b	10.35a	3.29a	7.0c	8.0a	4.5ab	6.8a	5.8a
0	0	2.12b	9.41a	4.00a	6.8c	8.0a	5.3abcd	8.0a	6.5a
					Heavy, early spring N fertilization regime				
3	4	0.71a	8.71a	3.76a	4.3ab	7.3a	6.3bcde	7.0a	5.5a
3	2	0.71a	10.82a	3.29a	3.8ab	7.3a	7.0cde	8.5a	4.8a
3	0	0.71a	8.47a	3.29a	4.8b	6.8a	5.3abc	6.0a	6.0a
0	4	0.94a	13.41a	4.71a	3.5a	7.0a	7.8e	8.7a	4.5a
0	2	0.94a	9.65a	3.53a	3.6a	7.3a	6.3bcde	6.8a	6.0a
0	0	0.71a	9.41a	3.76a	3.3a	6.8a	7.3dc	6.3a	5.8a

* Values having a letter in common do not differ significantly at the 5% level. † Rated from 1–9; 9 = best.

December, and January further enhanced appearance. No significant differences were evident in April, but in May the spring-applied N gave turfgrass a somewhat better appearance than the fall N fertilization. By June, the early spring N regime showed no improved bentgrass appearance over the late fall N regime.

Applications of N on bentgrass in February enhanced shoot growth and appearance of bentgrass in March; but little difference in appearance was measured in May and June when compared to the January treatment (Table 5). The reduction in root growth and desiccation tolerance caused by the delayed February treatment was nonsignificant.

Better root systems were obtained with chelated Fe than with $FeSO_4$ when the late fall N regime was employed (Table 6). No significant difference was found between the Fe sources of the spring N regime.

DISCUSSION

Results reported by Powell et al. (12, 13), that frequent late fall-winter fertilization enhanced bentgrass root development and turf appearance, were confirmed by this series of experiments. The lack of statistical differences

Table 5—Effect of delaying nitrogen and iron fertilization from January to February on Cohansey bentgrass growth. (Other nitrogen and iron fertilization applications were made in November, December, May and June.)

Month of last winter fertilization	Root wts, mg Jul 4	Desiccation ratings*	Clipping yields, kg/200 m² Fresh wt Mar 5	May 23	Jun 15	Appearance ratings* Mar 15	Apr 18	May 17	Jun 8
Jan	0.76	6.0	2.71	9.13	3.84	6.8	7.8	5.3	7.5
Feb	0.65	4.3	4.47	8.66	4.71	9.0	8.0	5.3	6.8
LSD .05	0.21	3.0	1.08	3.74	1.51	1.2	1.1	1.5	2.3
LSD .10	0.17	2.5	0.89	3.11	1.27	1.0	0.9	1.2	1.9

* Rated from 1–9; 9 = best.

Table 6—Effect of iron chelate and sulfate applications in association with late fall and spring nitrogen fertilization regimes on Cohansey bentgrass root growth and recovery from summer desiccation (measured July 1972).

Iron application frequencies Fall	Spring	Root wt, g/can Chelate	Sulfate	Recovery from desiccation* Chelate	Sulfate
		———— Heavy late fall N fertilization regime ————			
3	4	0.76	0.59	6.0	4.5
0	4	0.69	0.56	6.2	4.5
		———— Heavy early spring N fertilization regime ————			
3	4	0.51	0.67	5.5	6.0
0	4	0.50	0.63	4.5	8.0
LSD .05		———— 0.21 ————		———— 3.0 ————	
LSD .10		———— 0.17 ————		———— 2.5 ————	

* Rated from 1–9; 9 = best.

between treatments in recovery from desiccation was influenced by the limited number of replications and sample size. Nevertheless, the data infer that the most frequent applications of N yielded the lowest recovery values of all treatments and that frequent applications of Fe appeared beneficial in offsetting this heavy N fertilization effect.

Although Fe alone appeared beneficial to spring root growth, winter color and spring vigor expressed as clipping yields were not satisfactory for putting quality turf. Deal and Engel (7) previously reported Fe to be beneficial to turfgrass quality when grown at low fertility levels. However, the combinations of frequent, late fall N and Fe applications not only provided superior winter color and improved recovery from desiccation over N alone, but also enhanced early spring chlorophyll content (Table 1).

Applications of N in combination with Fe in the late fall and winter tended to give higher early spring clipping yields than comparable N alone treatments and may reflect earlier spring regrowth (Tables 1 and 4). By late spring, however, the opposite was true. This reduction in shoot growth may have been a primary factor in the heavy root weights obtained with the frequently applied combination fertilizer treatment (Table 2).

Previous reports that a February N application coupled with a late fall N regime reduced root growth (13) are confirmed by results of this study. Spring clipping yields and appearance were enhanced when N was applied in February while increases in root yields sampled in April diminished (Table 1). It appears the N fertilization, with or without Fe after January and before mid-May, stimulates spring shoot growth at the expense of root development.

Although Fe chelate applications tended to enhance rooting under the spring N regime (which is the conventional N program for bentgrass), a significant increase of rootings occurred with the winter heavy N regime coupled with frequent Fe applications (Tables 2 and 3). High-maintenance temperate grasses fertilized in the late fall still need additional spring N fertilization (8). However, N should be judiciously applied only after mid-May to provide good bentgrass turf appearance without seriously reducing roots, since most roots are developed before mid-May.

Not only did the combination of Fe + N and the timing of application appear important in enhancing turf vigor, but the source of these elements was important. Nitrogen must be available to the plant under cold conditions to obtain effects from the late fall N regime. There are also indications that the N-Fe interaction is influenced by the N regime and source of Fe. Better results were obtained with chelated Fe then with $FeSO_4$ under the late fall N regime. The enhancement of root development and recovery from desiccation under the spring heavy N regime with $FeSO_4$ was not significant from the chelated iron treatment (Table 6).

The effect of N and iron fertilization on bentgrass is strongly influenced by the environment. Although data from these studies indicate that enhancement of turfgrass quality from iron fertilization may at times not differ statistically at the 5% level from grass not fertilized with iron, there generally were increases in color, density, and root development when iron was applied. These increases were largest during the years when the grass was under stress (unpublished data). Therefore, it may be good insurance to apply iron frequently to offset adverse conditions such as moisture stress.

ACKNOWLEDGMENT

This research was partially supported by funds from the Golf Course Superintendents Association of America, Ciba-Geigy Agricultural Chemicals, and the Virginia Turfgrass Council.

REFERENCES

1. BANIN, A., and J. NAVROT. 1972. Pattern of iron distribution in the soil-plant system and its possible relations to iron-chlorosis. Commun. Soil Sci. Plant Anal. 3:177–182.
2. BERGER, K. C. 1962. Micronutrient deficiencies in the United States. Agr. Food Chem. 10:178–181.
3. BLACK, C. A. 1968. Soil-plant relationships. J. Wiley and Sons, Inc., New York.
4. BROWN, J. C. 1961. Iron chlorosis in plants. Advan. Agron. 13:329–369.
5. COMAR, C. L., and F. P. ZSCHEILE. 1942. Analysis of plant extracts for chlorophylls a and b by a photoelectric spectrophotometric method. Plant Physiol. 17: 198–209.
6. DAVIS, R. R. 1969. Nutrition and fertilizers. In A. A. Hanson and F. V. Juska (ed.) Turfgrass science. Agronomy 14:130–150. Amer. Soc. Agron., Madison, Wis.
7. DEAL, E. E., and R. E. ENGEL. 1965. Iron, manganese, boron, and zinc: Effects on growth of Merion Kentucky bluegrass. Agron. J. 57:553–555.
8. HANSON, A. A., and F. V. JUSKA. 1961. Winter root activity in Kentucky bluegrass (Poa pratensis L.). Agron. J. 53:372–374.
9. HORN, G. C. 1963. Yellowing of turfgrasses. Florida Turfgrass Assoc. Bull. 10 (1). Reprinted in Calif. Turfgrass Cult. 13:22–24.
10. MADISON, J. H. 1971. Principles of turfgrass culture. Van Nostrand Reinhold Company, New York.
11. ———, and A. H. ANDERSON. 1963. A chlorophyll index to measure turfgrass response. Agron. J. 55:461–464.
12. POWELL, A. J., R. E. BLASER, and R. E. SCHMIDT. 1967. Physiological and color aspects of turfgrasses with fall and winter nitrogen. Agron. J. 59:303–307.
13. ———, ———, and ———. 1967. Effect of nitrogen on winter root growth of bentgrass. Agron. J. 59:529–530.
14. PRICE, C. A. 1968. Iron compounds and plant nutrition. Ann. Rev. Plant Physiol. 19:239–48.
15. SNYDER, V. 1972. Nitrogen and chelated iron fertilization on the growth and physiology of creeping bentgrass (Agrostis palustrus Huds.). M.S. Thesis, Virginia Polytechnic Institute and State University, Blacksburg, Va.
16. TENG, J. K., and W. L. PRITCHET. 1970. Effect of season, night temperature and potassium on the absorption and translocation of iron in centepedegrass (Eremochloa ophiuroides [Munro] Hack). Bot Gaz. 131:272–276.

23

Photosynthate translocation and metabolism in Kentucky bluegrass turf as a function of fertility[1]

R. J. HULL & L. M. SMITH

The influence of fertilizer practices on carbon transfer through bluegrass (*Poa pratensis* L.) turf was the subject of this investigation. 'Merion' Kentucky bluegrass plots were established in 1966 and subjected to four fertilizer ratios: N-O-O, N-P-O, N-O-K, and N-P-K. In 1970, the plots were subdivided and each ratio was applied at three rates: 2.5-1-1, 5-2-2, and 10-4-4 kg/200 m^2 per year. The test was replicated four times. Soil samples were analyzed for N, P, and K in early summer and midautumn of 1971 and 1972. Midsummer clippings were analyzed for the same elements each year.

Assimilate translocation and metabolism were measured by exposing 15-cm diameter circles of turf to $^{14}CO_2$ and harvesting the turf at selected times following exposure. Individual grass plants were separated into deep and shallow roots, stems, and leaves. Plant tissue was freeze-dried and the ^{14}C analyzed quantitatively and characterized biochemically.

Mineral analysis of soil and plant tissue indicated that the fertilizer treatments had produced marked differences in soil fertility and in the mineral content and yield of grass. During the growing season, carbon fixed by leaves was translocated into stems and roots within 2 hours. Roots received maximum photosynthate during early winter and spring, although translocation rates were slower during the cool seasons. During the warm seasons, photosynthate translocated more rapidly in low fertility grass than in heavily fertilized turf. Turf grown under high fertility maintained smaller carbohydrate pools, but the turnover rate of these pools was greater than in low fertility turf. Additional index words: Nitrogen, Phosphorus, Potassium, Carbon-14.

The effects of fertilization practices on turfgrass have been evaluated largely as a function of turf quality. While quality parameters are the measurements of greatest practical significance, they usually fail to provide reasons underlying poor turf response to management.

This study attempts to measure the influence of fertilization practices on the flow of energy through grass plants. Carbon dioxide assimilation, photosynthate translocation, and carbohydrate metabolism are processes so fundamental to grass growth that any effects of management on them must be reflected in the physiological condition of the turf. This paper reports

[1]Contribution from the Plant and Soil Science Department, University of Rhode Island. Journal Paper No. 1511 of the Rhode Island Agricultural Experiment Station, Kingston, RI 02881.

some preliminary findings on the impact of fertilizer rates and ratios on the energy relations of Kentucky bluegrass (*Poa pratensis* L.) turf.

MATERIALS AND METHODS

In 1966, 54 m^2 plots of 'Merion' Kentucky bluegrass were seeded and managed under four fertilizer ratios: N:O:O, N:P:O, N:O:K, and N:P:K. In 1970, these plots were divided into 18 m^2 subplots, so that each ratio was applied at three rates: 2.5-1-1, 5-2-2, and 10-4-4 kg of N, P_2O_5, and K_2O/ 200 m^2 per year. The experimental area was organized as a split-plot design with ratios comprising the main plots and rates the subplots. The test contained four replications. The grass was cut to a 4-cm height on Monday and Friday during each week of the growing season. Clippings were removed following mowing.

All fertilizer elements were applied in inorganic form: N as NH_4NO_3, P as superphosphate (20%), and K as muriate of potash. Half the P and K was applied in April and half in September. Nitrogen was applied as follows: 2.5 kg rate—1 kg in April and 1.5 kg in November, 5 kg rate—2 kg in April, 1 kg in September, and 2 kg in November, 10 kg rate—2 kg in April and November and 1 kg in each intervening month. The experimental area was located on a Bridgehampton silt loam at Kingston, Rhode Island.

Soil samples were collected in June and November of 1971 and 1972 and analyzed for N, P, and K using the Maryland method of soil analysis (6). Clippings were collected from a 1.4-m^2 area of each plot during midsummer of 1971 and 1972. Clippings were oven-dried, weighed, and analyzed for N, P, and K using methods described in Horwitz (5): determination sections 2.051, 3.019, and 7.098.

The distribution of assimilated CO_2 within turf plants was determined by a ^{14}C tracer technique. In this procedure, a 15-cm diameter circle of turf was exposed to 15 μCi of $^{14}CO_2$ for 10 to 15 min. The turf was covered by a 4.25-liter bell jar into which $^{14}CO_2$ was introduced by reacting a known amount of $Na_2{}^{14}CO_3$ with 85% lactic acid. A 10-cm plug was removed from the treated circle with a standard golf course cup cutter. The soil was washed from the roots, and the root mass divided into deep (> 2.5 cm) and shallow (< 2.5 cm) fractions. Shoots were processed as a single fraction except in a companion study where leaf blades were separated from leaf sheath and stem tissue. Blanched sheath and stem tissue was assumed to be photosynthetically inactive and to function as storage and transport organs. Few rhizomes were found in this turf, but those present were included with the stem fraction since such organs do not function as roots.

Turf was harvested at selected times following exposure to $^{14}CO_2$. After the turf was separated into tissue fractions, the samples were freeze-dried, weighed, and ground in a Wiley mill to pass a 40-mesh screen. Ground tissue samples were placed in metal planchets, tamped to form a uniform surface, and assayed for radioactivity in a Tracerlab FD-1 gas flow counter equipped with a thin aluminum coated Mono Mol resin window. Counting data were corrected for background and self-absorption using counting efficiency curves.

Distribution of ^{14}C among carbohydrate fractions was determined on selected samples. Shoot samples were used for this analysis because root tissue contained little radioactivity and was not expected to be a primary site of energy storage. Lipoidal material was removed from 500-mg samples of ground tissue by Soxhlet extraction with chloroform. The residue from chloroform extraction was Soxhlet extracted with 80% ethanol to remove simple sugars, organic acids, and amino acids. A final shaker extraction with water at room temperature removed water-soluble polymeric carbohydrates. Each extract and the final residue were analyzed for radioactivity by placing aliquot samples in planchets and counting as described for ground tissue. The ethanol and water extracts were assayed for carbohydrates using the phenol-sulfuric colormetric procedure (4). The water extract was analyzed for fructose using a modified Roes procedure (1).

All data collected from the complete experiment were subjected to analysis of variance for a split-plot design. Carbon-14 tests were applied to only one or two replications because of the time involved in sample processing. Data from these tests were not subjected to statistical analysis.

RESULTS AND DISCUSSION

Mineral analysis

Soil samples collected in Spring and Autumn of 1971 and 1972 were analyzed for N, P, and K (Tables 1 and 2). The application of P and K was reflected in significantly greater soil concentrations of these elements. Increasing the rate of fertilizer application was not always reflected in greater soil fertility (Table 2). Increased N fertilization generally resulted in higher soil N, but P and K did not always show the same trend. Available soil P usually was highest in plots receiving the high P rate, but only in June 1972, was this difference significant. Soil K showed little relationship to rates of fertilizer application. These results can be explained as a function of the

Table 1—Mineral analysis of soil from bluegrass turf plots receiving fertilizer in several ratios.

Fertilizer ratio	N	P	K	N	P	K
			— ppm† —			
		May 13, 1971			Nov 10, 1971	
N	3.1a*	15.2a	0.4a	2.3a	26.8a	3.1a
NP	3.0a	34.3b	1.2a	2.6a	39.8bc	1.7a
NK	2.3a	20.2a	62.3b	2.1a	29.2ab	75.2b
NPK	1.4a	39.9b	59.1b	2.8a	48.0c	80.6b
		Jun 13, 1972			Nov 22, 1972	
N	3.2a	36.6a	9.4a	7.0a	39.8a	19.2a
NP	1.6a	59.9b	12.2a	5.6a	55.1b	14.7a
NK	2.0a	27.8	37.9b	7.9a	41.8a	55.2c
NPK	1.8a	60.8b	36.1b	5.3a	61.8b	45.1b

* Means in the same column followed by the same letter are not significantly different at the 5% confidence level. † All values based on analysis of a weak acid extract.

Table 2—Mineral analysis of soil from bluegrass turf plots receiving fertilizer at various N-P-K rates.

N-P$_2$O$_5$-K$_2$O rate, kg/200 m^2	N	P	K	N	P	K
			ppm**			
	May 13, 1971			Nov 10, 1971		
2.5-1-1	1.6a*	28.9a	31.2a	0.8a	35.1a	42.1a
5-2-2	2.5ab	26.5a	29.4a	0.8a	35.4a	35.9a
10-4-4	3.3b	26.8a	31.7a	5.7b	37.3a	42.4a
	Jun 13, 1972			Nov 22, 1972		
2.5-1-1	2.2a	45.0a	26.7a	4.6a	48.0a	34.6b
5-2-2	1.9a	42.9a	23.2a	6.2ab	48.6a	28.7a
10-4-4	2.2a	50.9b	21.8a	8.6b	52.2a	37.3b

* Means in a column followed by the same letter are not significantly different at the 5% confidence level.   ** All values based on analysis of a weak acid extract.

grass yield removed from the plots with each mowing (Table 3). Midsummer yields increased directly with increased rates of fertilizer applied. With greater grass growth, more soil nutrients were removed from high fertility plots resulting in little net change in available soil nutrients. Throughout this study all clippings were removed from the plots following each mowing, and the mining effect of increased grass growth on soil nutrients was accentuated.

Although fertilizer ratios did cause changes in soil nutrient status, there was little effect on grass growth or the rate of nutrient removal from the soil (Table 4). While not statistically significant, the data suggest that including

Table 3—Dry matter yield and mineral content of clippings from bluegrass turf receiving fertilizer at various N-P-K rates.

N-P$_2$O$_5$-K$_2$O rate, kg/200 m^2	Aug 5, 1971				Jul 7, 1972			
	Yield	N	P	K	Yield	N	P	K
				g/m^2				
2.5-1-1	34.1a*	1.32a	0.20a	0.35a	8.9a	0.35a	0.046a	0.20a
5-2-2	41.3b	1.72b	0.23a	0.41a	11.8b	0.50b	0.054a	0.26b
10-4-4	54.6c	2.74c	0.29b	0.52b	18.9c	0.94c	0.083b	0.43c

* Means in a column followed by the same letter are not significantly different at the 5% confidence level.

Table 4—Dry matter yield and mineral content of clippings from bluegrass turf receiving fertilizer in several ratios.

Fertilizer ratio	Aug 5, 1971				Jul 7, 1972			
	Yield	N	P	K	Yield	N	P	K
				g/m^2				
N	42.3a*	1.96a	0.21a	0.42a	12.0a	0.53a	0.049a	0.23a
NP	41.3a	1.83a	0.24a	0.38a	12.6a	0.56a	0.063a	0.25a
NK	44.8a	1.99a	0.24a	0.45a	14.1a	0.64a	0.061a	0.35b
NPK	44.9a	1.91a	0.26a	0.45a	14.2a	0.64a	0.072a	0.36b

* Means in a column followed by the same letter are not significantly different at the 5% confidence level.

K in the fertilizer increased yields, as well as the amount of K removed from the soil. The inclusion of P had no effect on yield, and only slightly increased the rate of P removal from the soil, while causing an accumulation of available P in the soil (Table 1). The rate of P removal from plots that received only N and K was almost as great as from plots that received P. Continued removal of P under these conditions would result in a reduced P content in N–K plots. The data in Table 1 only suggest that this may be happening. These Bridgehampton soils have been managed under turf for many years and contain substantial quantities of fixed P.

Data collected in this study indicate that the fertility regimes employed have altered the growth rate and mineral content of the turf and the fertility level of the soil. We propose, therefore, that the differences in the energy relations of turfgrass reported below are at least partially a result of the fertilizer programs under which the grass was grown.

Assimilate distribution

Translocation of assimilates into the turf root system is summarized in Tables 5 through 7, and expressed as the percentage of total ^{14}C recovered from the turf that was found in the roots. Fertilizer ratio exerted little influence over the proportion of assimilated carbon migrating into the root system (Table 5). Assimilate translocation to roots was maximal during late autumn and spring with lesser movement recorded in mid- to late summer. This corresponds to the annual pattern of root growth in turfgrasses (10).

The rate of assimilate translocation into roots during midsummer and early autumn was more rapid in low fertility turf than in heavily fertilized grass (Table 6). During this time, the amount of photosynthate transported into high fertility roots was less than that entering the roots of low fertility turf, but the duration of translocation was longer in high fertility grass. During late autumn and spring, when root growth is most active (3, 10), little difference in assimilate movement into roots was noted among variously fertilized grass. Reduced assimilate movement into roots of heavily fertilized grass is even more apparent when we consider the amount of ^{14}C recovered from roots more than 2.5 cm below the soil surface (Table 7). The percentage of assimilated carbon that was transported to deep roots of low and moderately fertilized turf was similar, but in high fertility grass transport to

Table 5—Percent of the ^{14}C fixed by turf recovered from root tissue of bluegrass receiving fertilizer in several ratios.

Fertilizer ratio	Recovered ^{14}C					
	Jul 7, 1970*	Sep 1, 1970	Oct 27, 1970	Apr 13, 1971	Jun 22, 1971	Dec 13, 1971
	%					
N	9.5	6.5	8.1	12.0	12.8	11.4
NP	8.6	9.5	7.7	9.6	11.7	9.8
NK	9.6	8.3	7.8	13.0	17.3	10.2
NPK	10.1	8.0	8.5	14.2	11.0	9.6

* Date of exposure to 15 μCi ^{14}CO$_2$.

Table 6—Percent of the ^{14}C fixed by turf recovered from root tissue of bluegrass receiving fertilizer at various N–P–K rates.

Fertilizer rate	Hours after treatment	Recovered ^{14}C				
		Jul 7, 1970*	Sep 1, 1970	Oct 27, 1970	Jun 22, 1971	Dec 13, 1971
		%				
2.5-1-1	2	10.6	6.3			
	24	13.0	10.7	6.8	14.4	3.2
	48					10.6
	72	11.8	10.0	9.3	12.5	
	96					17.1
	144			10.0		
5-2-2	2	6.0	6.7			
	24	10.1	9.8	4.8	12.9	4.6
	48					10.4
	72	10.2	9.9	10.2	10.5	
	96					14.8
	144			11.4		
10-4-4	2	6.7	4.2			
	24	8.1	6.6	4.7	14.2	3.2
	48					11.2
	72	8.4	8.5	6.8	14.6	
	96					17.2
	144			8.2		

*Date of exposure of 15 μCi $^{14}CO_2$.

Table 7—Percent of the ^{14}C fixed by turf recovered from deep roots (>2.5 cm) of bluegrass receiving fertilizer at various N–P–K rates.

Fertilizer rate	Recovered ^{14}C					
	Jul 7, 1970*	Sep 1, 1970	Oct 27, 1970	Apr 13, 1971	Jun 22, 1971	Dec 13, 1971
	%					
2.5-1-1	3.0	2.0	1.4	4.6	3.5	1.6
5-2-2	2.4	1.8	1.6	5.2	2.8	1.1
10-4-4	1.6	0.9	0.8	4.4	3.4	0.7

* Date of exposure of 15 μCi $^{14}CO_2$.

deep roots was reduced by one half. Again, assimilate transport in spring seemed little affected by the fertility program.

In a companion study, distribution of assimilates between leaves, stems, and roots of high and low fertility turf was determined during 1972 (Table 8). In winter, most assimilated carbon remained in the leaves, with about one-third translocated to stems and roots within 72 hours. In spring, stems became a dominant sink accumulating almost 50% of the fixed carbon. During the summer, assimilate distribution reverted to the winter pattern except that roots were less active and the rate of transport was more rapid. Autumn exhibited a distribution pattern midway between that of spring and summer except that roots constituted a particularly weak sink in the mid-October test. During all seasons except winter, low fertility grass translocated more photosynthate to roots. The May and October tests suggest that the rate of photosynthate translocation may be slightly lower in high fertility grass.

Table 8—Percent of the ^{14}C fixed by turf recovered from leaves, stems, and roots of bluegrass fertilized at two rates.

Fertilizer rate	Hours after treatment	Plant part		
		Leaf	Stem	Root
		% of recovered ^{14}C*		
January 6, 1972				
2.5-1-1	24	83	11	6
	72	63	23	14
10-4-4	24	86	9	5
	72	63	23	14
May 24, 1972				
2.5-1-1	24	41	52	7
	72	47	45	8
10-4-4	24	62	34	4
	72	47	48	5
July 26, 1972				
2.5-1-1	24	64	27	9
	72	65	28	7
10-4-4	24	61	36	3
	72	67	30	3
October 17, 1972				
2.5-1-1	24	71	26	3
	72	57	39	4
10-4-4	24	72	27	1
	72	65	34	1

* Each value is the average of two plants.

Assimilate metabolism

Leaf and stem tissue of turf just described was analyzed for simple sugars and water-soluble polymeric carbohydrates (fructosans) (Table 9). The simple sugar content of leaves and stems of low fertility turf did not

Table 9—Simple and water soluble polymeric carbohydrate content of bluegrass turf fertilized at two rates.

Fertilizer rate	Hours after mowing	Plant part	Simple sugars			Fructosan		
			May 23*	Jul 25	Oct 16	May 23	Jul 25	Oct 16
			mg/g					
2.5-1-1	48	Leaf	76	85	125	36	82	108
		Stem	56	67	59	117	209	150
	96	Leaf	126	81	107	32	104	107
		Stem	77	59	58	100	246	218
10-4-4	48	Leaf	53	99	144	2	8	30
		Stem	38	91	66	38	74	165
	96	Leaf	101	106	138	4	15	20
		Stem	53	94	77	28	111	116

* Date of mowing.

vary consistently over the three test dates, whereas the fructosan content increased between May and July. Leaf tissue of high fertility turf showed a progressive increase in simple sugars as the season advanced from May to October. A similar trend was observed in the fructosan content of leaves and stems of high fertility turf. Generally high fertility turf contained less simple sugar than low fertility grass in May, but the reverse was indicated in July and October. Throughout the test period, the fructosan content of low fertility turf was consistently higher. Simple sugars were most abundant in leaf tissue, while fructosans were concentrated in stems.

The results generally follow the seasonal trend in carbohydrate levels reported for cool-season grasses (2, 10). However, the progressive increase in both simple and polymeric carbohydrates from spring to autumn in turf receiving 1 kg of N/200 m^2 per month seems inconsistent with much published work (7, 8, 9). The ability of turfgrass to accumulate carbohydrates while growth is being stimulated by abundant N might result from the greater net CO_2 assimilation rates observed in high fertility turf (7).

Carbon-14 distribution between carbohydrate fractions was determined and presented as specific activity values to show the dynamics of carbon flow through these metabolic components (Table 10). In this case, reference to simple sugars is actually to the ethanol soluble fraction which contains some organic and amino acids in addition to simple sugars. In leaf and stem tissue of low fertility grass, the amount of ^{14}C per miligram of simple sugar decreased between 24 and 72 hours after exposure to $^{14}CO_2$. In high fertility grass, this drop in specific activity was apparent in leaf tissue but not in stems. The specific activity of fructosans in leaf and stem tissue increased between 24 and 72 hours in both high and low fertility grass. A similar increase in specific activity was noted in the residue fraction of leaves and stems.

These ^{14}C tests can be described as pulse-chase experiments in which a pulse of labeled carbon was introduced photosynthetically into the plant at the time of exposure to $^{14}CO_2$. When the exposure chamber was removed, the grass resumed fixing unlabeled CO_2 which chased the ^{14}C through the

Table 10—Specific activity of ethanol and water soluble and residue fractions of bluegrass turf fertilized at two rates.

Fertilizer rate	Hours after treatment	Plant part	Ethanol			Polymeric			Residue		
			May 24*	Jul 26	Oct 17	May 24	Jul 26	Oct 17	May 24	Jul 26	Oct 17
			cpm/mg times 10^2								
2.5-1-1	24	Leaf	15.4	8.6	10.6	4.5	1.0	0.4	3.1	0.7	0.3
		Stem	11.3	7.4	7.6	8.0	1.9	1.6	6.6	3.0	0.6
	72	Leaf	8.0	5.3	6.3	7.5	1.8	0.6	3.8	1.8	0.4
		Stem	7.7	4.2	2.6	7.2	3.9	2.7	4.4	2.8	1.7
10-4-4	24	Leaf	13.6	4.3	11.5	9.4	1.5	4.2	3.1	1.1	0.7
		Stem	9.9	3.3	3.9	6.4	2.9	1.6	6.2	2.8	1.0
	72	Leaf	6.3	3.2	5.8	5.4	3.0	7.9	5.2	2.2	1.0
		Stem	13.5	2.4	3.9	6.4	3.5	5.0	6.7	2.3	1.7

* Date of exposure of 15 μCi $^{14}CO_2$.

metabolic sequence of assimilate utilization. Therefore, a loss in specific activity from a metabolic pool indicates that carbon in that pool is being lost to another fraction or unlabeled carbon is being added to the pool diluting the ^{14}C originally present or both.

In this study, the loss of specific activity from the simple sugar pool with a concomitant increase in the ^{14}C content of the fructosan and residue fractions indicates that the simple sugar pool is being partitioned between storage carbohydrates and the synthesis of new cells. The lower specific activity of the residue fraction obtained in October indicates that less carbon is being utilized in new growth during autumn and more is entering the fructosan pool. The October 17 test was conducted during a cold period when night temperatures were below freezing.

The exceptions to the above scheme can be of interest. The loss of specific activity in the fructosan fraction of high fertility leaf tissue in June probably indicates that when growth is rapid, leaf fructosans may be mobilized to support tissue development. Actually, the increase in specific activity of leaf fructosans between 24 and 72 hours following treatment argues against this being a transitory carbohydrate pool analogous to starch grains in the chloroplasts of starch-producing plants. The reduced specific activity of the stem residue fraction between 24 and 72 hours following ^{14}CO$_2$ fixation in July may reflect the emergence of leaf tissue from what we have been calling stem either by the unfolding of a new leaf or rapid intercalary meristematic growth.

The greater specific activity values of the fructosan fraction in high fertility turf, especially in October, coupled with the lower concentration of these polymeric carbohydrates indicates that the turnover of carbon through this fraction is accelerated by high fertility. This rapid turnover of carbon in heavily fertilized turf could explain the increased growth rate, stimulated CO$_2$ assimilation (7), retention of photosynthate in shoots, and other responses to high fertility. The significance of this to the capacity of grass to perform favorably as turf remains to be studied.

ACKNOWLEDGMENT

We extend our appreciation to Stuart H. Blackmar and Roland W. Gilbert of the Food and Resource Chemistry Department, University of Rhode Island for performing the soil and tissue analyses presented in this report. Financial support from Agway, Inc. is gratefully acknowledged.

REFERENCES

1. DAVIS, J. S., and J. E. GANDER. 1967. A reevaluation of the Roes procedure for determination of fructose. Anal. Biochem. 19:72-79.
2. DUFF, D. T. 1974. Influence of fall nitrogenous fertilization on the carbohydrates of Kentucky bluegrass. p. 112-119. In E. C. Roberts (ed.) Proc. Second Int. Turfgrass Res. Conf. Amer. Soc. Agron., Madison, Wis.
3. HANSON, A. A., and F. V. JUSKA. 1961. Winter root activity in Kentucky bluegrass (Poa pratensis L.). Agron. J. 53:372-374.
4. HODGE, J. E., and B. T. HOFREITER. 1962. Determination of reducing sugars and carbohydrates. p. 380-394. In R. L. Whistler and M. L. Wolfrum (ed.) Methods

in carbohydrate chemistry. Volume I Analysis and preparation of sugars. Academic Press, N. Y.

5. HORWITZ, W. 1970. Official methods of analysis of the Association of Official Analytical Chemists (Ed. 11). Assoc. Off. Anal. Chem., Washington, D. C.

6. MILLER, J. R., R. H. SEHER, and N. R. USHERWOOD. 1963. Methods used for testing soil samples at the University of Maryland Soil Testing Laboratory. Univ. Maryland Agronomy Mimeo No. 37.

7. POWELL, A. J., R. E. BLASER, and R. E. SCHMIDT. 1967. Physiological and color aspects of turfgrasses with fall and winter nitrogen. Agron. J. 59:303–307.

8. SCHMIDT, R. E., and R. E. BLASER. 1969. Ecology and turf management. *In* A. A. Hanson and F. V. Juska (ed.) Turfgrass science. Agronomy 14:217–239. Amer. Soc. Agron., Madison, Wis.

9. WATSCHKE, T. L., R. E. SCHMIDT, E. W. CARSON, and R. E. BLASER. 1972. Some metabolic phenomena of Kentucky bluegrass under high temperature. Crop Science. 12:87–90.

10. YOUNGNER, V. B. 1969. Physiology of growth and development. *In* A. A. Hanson and F. V. Juska (ed.) Turfgrass science. Agronomy 14:187–216. Amer. Soc. Agron., Madison, Wis.

24

Influence of N and K nutrition on net photosynthesis, dark respiration, and carbohydrates in centipedegrass[1]

R. H. WALKER & C.Y. WARD

A series of experiments was conducted to determine the influence of N and K fertilization on the rate of net photosynthesis, dark respiration, and nonstructural carbohydrate accumulation in centipedegrass (*Eremochloa ophiuroides* (Munro) Hack.). The response of centipedegrass to varying ratios of N to K fertilization was related to its ability to withstand low winter temperatures.

Centipedegrass under greenhouse and field conditions was fertilized with 0.98, 1.96, and 2.94 kg of N; and 0.82, 1.63, and 2.45 kg of K/100 m^2. Phosphorus was constant at 0.22 kg/100 m^2 for all treatments.

Net photosynthesis and dark respiration increased as N fertilization was increased. Conversely, increasing K fertilization generally decreased these parameters.

Starch accumulation in the stolons was enhanced by increased K fertilization, usually at the expense of a lower concentration of simple sugars. Additional index words: Carbon dioxide, Infrared, Light.

Centipedegrass (*Eremochloa ophiuroides* (Munro) Hack.) is becoming increasingly important as a home lawn turf in the southern United States. Although centipedegrass has emerged as an important turfgrass for home lawns, it has some major weaknesses. Presently its greatest weakness is inconsistent winter survival. Many management factors seem to be linked to the damage of centipedegrass caused by low temperatures during the dormant season. Among the least understood of these factors is the influence of soil fertility, especially nitrogen and potassium fertilization.

Since variable persistence of centipedegrass has been obtained where N and K fertilization was varied, it was hypothesized that the influence of these nutrients on photosynthesis and respiration might be linked to subsequent low temperature injury. A series of experiments was conducted to evaluate this hypothesis.

The initial study was begun on the turfgrass research plots located on the Plant Science Farm at Mississippi State, Mississippi during the summer of 1972. A plot consisted of a 200-liter drum which had been cut in half and

[1]Publication No. 2828. Agronomy Department, Mississippi Agricultural and Forestry Experiment Station. Mississippi State University, Mississippi State, MS 39762.

filled with a sand-soil mixture. The prepared sand-soil mixture had the following physical properties: 7.4% clay, 9.2% silt, and 82.3% sand, resulting in a loamy sand textural class. Chemically, the soil had an average pH of 4.9 and contained 239 ppm of N, 4.6 ppm of P, and 30.5 ppm of K, and had a magnesium base saturation of 5.1%. The plots were sodded with centipedegrass sod which had been washed free of native soil. The grass was allowed to grow for 2 weeks after a root system had developed before treatments were initiated.

Nitrogen at 0.98, 1.96, and 2.84 kg; P at 0.22 kg; and K at 0.82, 1.63, and 2.45 kg/100 m^2 were applied using ammonium nitrate, ordinary superphosphate, and muriate of potash as the souces. A completely random design with a 3 X 3 factorial arrangement replicated six times was chosen as the statistical design. Nitrogen and K fertilizer application was split into two equal applications, which were applied on July 3 and August 6. All P was applied on July 3.

Mowing height was maintained at approximately 7 cm until September 1, at which time the mowing was discontinued in order to provide sufficient leaf blade sizes to be used in the CO_2 leaf chamber for photosynthesis and respiration determinations.

A second study was initiated in the greenhouse during the summer of 1972. An individual plot consisted of a 15.24-cm dia plastic pot which contained 2.1 kg sterile sand. A 15-cm dia sod piece with all soil removed was placed on the sand and allowed to root. The pots were watered on a weight basis to bring the soil water content to approximately field capacity with demineralized water daily. After the root system had developed, the grass was allowed to grow for two additional weeks prior to fertilizer applications.

The variable fertility rates were the same as reported for the experiment in the field. The pots were fertilized with four different stock fertilizer solutions which were prepared from reagent grade chemicals. The stock nutrient solutions were stock N, stock K, stock P, and stock minor elements. Application of the nutrient solutions was split, as in the field study, into two equal applications. The minor element solution, which supplied nutrients other than N, P, and K, was applied three times (June 30, July 24, and August 2).

The pots were clipped at weekly intervals at a height of 7 cm with all clippings removed.

SYSTEM FOR PHOTOSYNTHESIS AND RESPIRATION DETERMINATIONS

An open system (Fig. 1) was used in these experiments. This system was predetermined to be the method best suited for the centipedegrass samples used. In one series of measurements (field experiment) each treatment was evaluated by placing 4 to 6 tillers in a water vial which was then placed in a Plexiglas chamber. In a second experiment (greenhouse), a Plexiglas chamber was constructed to fit over the pots and photosynthesis and respiration determined on the uniformly clipped sod (Fig. 2).

A Beckman Model IR215 infrared CO_2 analyzer was used to measure the differential CO_2 concentration between two flowing samples. The instru-

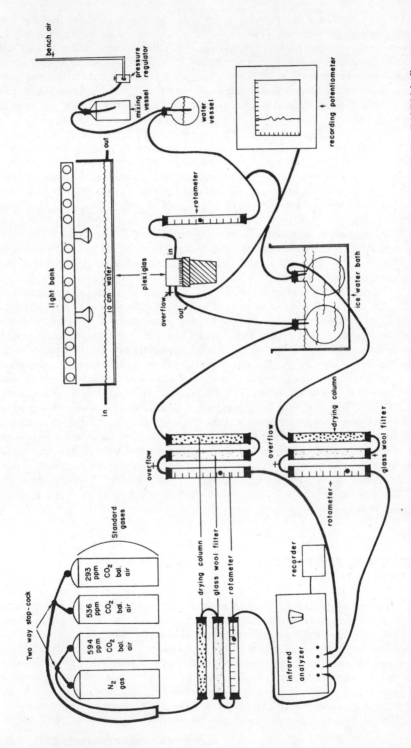

Fig. 1—Open system used for photosynthesis and respiration determinations. Light bank contained 12 Sylvania Lifeline-F48T11 bulbs, two 300W Westinghouse reflector flood bulbs, and four 150W bulbs (Amplex Corp., Division of Chrysler).

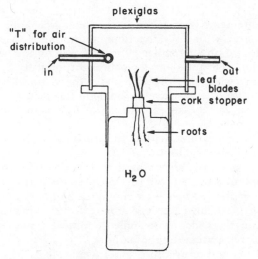

Chamber used for individual tillers

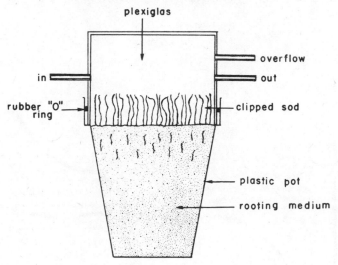

Chamber used for sod contained in plastic pots

Fig. 2—Plexiglas chambers used in both experiments.

ment was equipped with both sample and reference cells open. A Beckman Model 1005 linear-log 25.4-cm potentiometric recorder was used with the analyzer.

Temperatures were recorded with a Leeds-Northrup multipoint recording potentiometer. The sensing device was a thermocouple made of copper-constantan wire. Measurements were recorded at 30-sec intervals. Average leaf chamber temperatures for net photosynthesis determination were 33.5 C and 31.5 C for dark respiration measurements.

Light measurements were taken in the field, greenhouse, and under the artificial light source with a Weston Illumination meter, Model 603. Light intensity as measured on September 19 at 1:00 p.m. in the field at grass level averaged 0.81 klux. On the same day, the light intensity in the greenhouse averaged 0.52 klux while the intensity under the artificial light source averaged 0.39 klux at grass level. In addition, light quality between wavelengths of 400 to 700 mu was measured with an ISCO Spectro-radiometer, Model SR. These data are shown in Fig. 3.

Flow rates were measured with 0.40-cm dia rotameters. They were calibrated using a Brooks gas calibrator.

A 15-liter glass container was used as a mixing tank for the air source (bench air) in order to smooth out any possible fluctuations in CO_2 concentration. On the average the bench air contained 350 ppm CO_2.

Each sample was allowed to equalibrate for 20 min prior to net photosynthesis determinations. However, only 20 min were allowed for equalibration prior to dark respiration determinations.

Photosynthesis and respiration values were calculated according to the method used by Baker and Musgrave (2) and Hesketh and Musgrave (4).

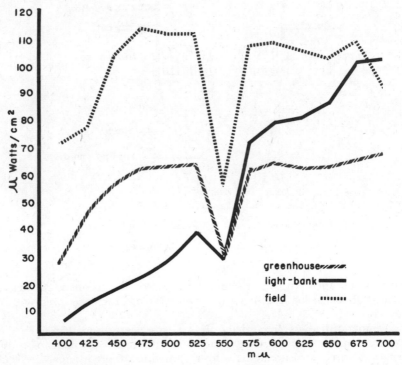

Fig. 3—Light quality measurements taken at Mississippi State, Miss. Greenhouse and field data were taken on September 19 at 1:00 p.m.

Total nonstructural carbohydrates (TNC)

Total nonstructural carbohydrates (TNC) were determined on a 150-mg sample of prepared centipedegrass stolons from each treatment according to the method of Weinman (11). Somogyi's (10) copper reagent and Nelson's (9) chromogenic reagent were used to detect reducing sugars.

Reducing and nonreducing sugars

Prepared samples of 0.5 g were extracted with 80 ml of 80% ethanol. The ethanol was added to the samples which were then placed on a shaker for 20 hours. The samples were then filtered, after which the ethanol was removed by evaporation in a steam bath. Following evaporation, the samples were quantitatively transferred to 100-ml volumetric flasks and brought to volume. Two 50-ml aliquots were removed from each sample, placed in separate 100-ml volumetrics, and brought to volume. One half of the samples was checked for neutralization, and the Somogyi and Nelson procedure was used to complete the test for actual reducing sugars. The remaining half of the samples was boiled for 30 min after 2.5 ml of 25% HCl was added to each sample. This was done to hydrolyze the nonreducing sugars into reducing sugars. This half of the samples contained actual reducing sugars plus reducing sugars which were hydrolyzed into the reduced form so that they could be detected colormetrically. Values for the first half of samples were subtracted from the second half to give actual values for nonreducing sugars. Likewise, reducing and nonreducing sugars were subtracted from TNC values to give starch concentrations.

Analysis of leaf blade tissue for potassium and magnesium

Potassium was determined on leaf blade tissue that had previously been used for net photosynthesis and dark respiration determinations. Triplicate samples of 0.5 g from each treatment were extracted according to Lancaster (5) and analyzed on a Coleman flame photometer, Model 21. Data are expressed as ppm of K.

The above tissue were also analyzed for Mg. Prepared samples of 0.5 g were extracted with $1N$ ammonium acetate and analyzed on a Perkin-Elmer atomic absorption spectrophotometer, Model 290. Data are expressed as ppm Mg (5).

RESULTS AND DISCUSSION

All data were analyzed using recognized statistical procedures. Analysis of variance was performed according to the general ANOV computer program, and Fisher's F-test was used to determine significance. Duncan's new multiple range test was used to separate means. All determinations were made at the 0.05 level of probability.

Net photosynthesis per standard land area

Net photosynthesis determined on the centipedegrass grown in the greenhouse showed that increased N fertilization significantly increased the amount of CO_2 fixed when expressed on a standard land area (Table 1). This particular response to increased N fertilization was anticipated since it is well known that increased N fertilization tends to maximize dry matter production. However, no significant values were observed for increased K fertilization when expressed on the same standard land area.

Table 2 shows the means of the various N × K treatments on the fixation rate of CO_2 by the centipedegrass turf when expressed on a standard land area. These means also suggest that N was the dominant factor causing differences in net photosynthetic rates of the greenhouse-grown grass. How-

Table 1—Effect of nitrogen and potassium fertilization on net photosynthesis of centipedegrass in a greenhouse experiment. Pots were clipped uniformly at a 7-cm mowing height.

Fertilization level, kg/100 m²	Rate, mg CO_2/dm² per hour
Nitrogen	
0.98	32.95 b*
1.96	34.77 ab
2.94	36.72 a
Potassium	
0.82	34.04 a
1.63	35.45 a
2.45	34.95 a
C. V. = 11.1%	

* Means within the column followed by different letters are significantly different at the 0.05 level according to Duncan's new multiple range test.

Table 2—Effect of nitrogen and potassium fertilization on net photosynthesis of centipedegrass in a greenhouse experiment. Pots were clipped uniformly at a 7-cm mowing height.

Fertilization level, kg/100 m²		Rate, mg CO_2/dm² per hour
N	P	
0.98	0.82	31.00 e*
0.98	1.63	32.87 bcde
0.98	2.45	34.99 abcde
1.96	0.82	34.63 abcde
1.96	1.63	35.41 abcd
1.96	2.45	34.26 bcde
2.94	0.82	36.50 ab
2.94	1.63	38.97 ab
2.94	2.45	35.59 abc
C. V. = 11.1%		

* Means within the column followed by different letters are significantly different at the 0.05 level according to Duncan's new multiple range test.

ever, some interesting trends for K fertilization can be seen from this table. Increased K fertilization increased net photosynthesis within each N level for all treatments except two. These two, K fertilization at 2.45 kg/100 m^2 with either 1.96 or 2.94 kg of N/100 m^2, decreased net photosynthesis when compared to the other K rates within the two N levels. Therefore, these data suggest no beneficial net photosynthetic effect(s) from K fertilization above 1.63 kg/100 m^2 with either 1.96 or 2.94 kg N/100 m^2.

Net photosynthesis per gram dry weight

These measurements were made in order to better determine the effect(s) of N and K fertilization on net photosynthesis of individual centipedegrass tillers and to eliminate possible turf density differences that could confound the data, as might have been the case when measurements were taken and expressed on a standard land area.

Increased N fertilization generally produced an increase in net photosynthetic rates but only the data from the field experiment yielded significant values. Conversely, increased K fertilization significantly decreased net photosynthesis in the centipedegrass from both experiments (Table 3).

To further gain insight into the increased K fertilization response, centipedegrass leaf blade tissue that had been used in the net photosynthesis and dark respiration determinations was analyzed for K and Mg content. These data show that increased K fertilization significantly increased the ppm of K in the grass tissue while a significant decrease was noted for ppm of Mg (Table 4). All treatments appeared to have had sufficient minimum K concentrations (2.1%) since Gallaher, Parks, and Josephson (3) reported that 1.5% was the critical level for most plant tissue. On the other hand, all analyzed tissue for Mg levels appeared to be in a range of borderline to suboptimum (0.215 to 0.098%) since the critical level for Mg in plant tissue for optimum growth is considered to be 0.25% (W. R. Thompson, Jr. 1972.

Table 3—Effect of nitrogen and potassium fertilization on net photosynthesis of centipedegrass.

Fertilization level, kg/100 m^2	mg CO$_2$/g dry wt per hour	
	Greenhouse	Field
Nitrogen		
0.98	26.20 a*	27.70 b
1.96	25.64 a	35.52 a
2.94	27.64 a	34.64 a
Potassium		
0.82	28.67 a	35.67 a
1.63	25.79 b	32.37 b
2.45	25.02 b	29.82 b
C. V. =	10.4%	15.7%

* Means within each column followed by different letters are significantly different at the 0.05 level according to Duncan's new multiple range test.

Table 4—Potassium and magnesium content of centipedegrass leaf blade tissue as influenced by nitrogen and potassium fertilization. Sample was composed of greenhouse and field blade tissue used for net photosynthesis and respiration determinations.

Fertilization level, kg/100 m^2		ppm K	ppm Mg
N	P		
0.98	0.82	22110 c*	1353 de
0.98	1.63	24860 b	1400 d
0.98	2.45	26840 a	980 g
1.96	0.82	23210 c	2147 a
1.96	1.63	24970 b	1680 c
1.96	2.45	25190 b	1727 c
2.94	0.82	21120 e	1913 b
2.94	1.63	25190 b	1213 f
2.94	2.45	27060 a	1260 ef
C. V. =		1.6%	4.0%

* Means within each column followed by different letters are significantly different at the 0.05 level according to Duncan's new multiple range test.

Personal communication). However, Mg concentrations were not low enough to produce deficiency symptoms since none were observed at anytime during the duration of the experiments. But, it is highly probable that the Mg concentrations were low enough to affect net photosynthesis. When the Mg concentration data are compared with net photosynthesis data, N × K means (Table 5), it is evident that a relationship exists. In general, as ppm of Mg declined so did the fixation rate of CO_2. Such response would not be out of the ordinary since Mg is an essential part of the chlorophyll molecule. In addition, Mg plays a role in the phosphate metabolism of plants and therefore, indirectly in the respiratory mechanism. Magnesium ions also appear to

Table 5—Effect of nitrogen and potassium fertilization on net photosynthesis of centipedegrass.

Fertilization level, kg/100 m^2		mg CO_2/g dry wt per hour	
N	P	Greenhouse	Field
0.98	0.82	28.92 ab*	32.90 a
0.98	1.63	25.00 abcde	26.07 b
0.98	2.45	24.69 bcde	24.14 b
1.96	0.82	27.60 abcd	37.85 a
1.96	1.63	26.60 abcde	35.91 a
1.96	2.45	22.72 e	32.80 a
2.94	0.82	29.50 a	36.27 a
2.94	1.63	25.78 abcde	35.13 a
2.94	2.45	27.65 abc	32.53 a
C. V. =		10.4%	15.7%

* Means within each column followed by different letters are significantly different at the 0.05 level according to Duncan's new multiple range test.

Table 6—Effect of nitrogen and potassium fertilization on the carbohydrate composition of centipedegrass.

| Fertilization level, kg/100 m² | | | mg/g dry wt. | | |
N	P	TNC	Reducing sugar	Nonreducing sugar	Starch*
0.98	0.82	195.80	7.10	74.93	113.77
0.98	1.63	198.00	4.43	91.53	102.04
0.98	2.45	213.80	4.20	82.87	126.73
1.96	0.82	179.50	6.10	75.93	97.47
1.96	1.63	210.50	6.80	51.47	152.23
1.96	2.45	179.30	4.60	47.27	127.43
2.94	0.82	205.80	7.10	62.27	136.43
2.94	1.63	169.30	6.40	65.60	97.30
2.94	2.45	194.00	3.90	55.07	135.03

* Starch content obtained by subtracting, reducing and nonreducing sugars from TNC.

be specific activators for a number of enzymes, including certain transphosphorylases, dehydrogenases, and carboxylases (6).

Other factors may also be involved with the decreased rate of photosynthesis with increased K fertilization. Several authors (1, 7, 8) have shown a stimulative effect from the K ion on the activity of granule-bound starch synthetase (ADPG-starch transglucosylase) which is involved in starch synthesis. These responses to the K ion have been demonstrated in several type plants. It appears that the particular enzyme(s) may be widely distributed in higher plants. Assuming this to be true, centipedegrass with high K could be expected to have higher starch concentrations in the stolons and leaves due to the stimulative effect of K on the starch synthesizing system. And indeed, starch concentrations were found to be higher with increased K fertilization in the grass stolons (Table 6), but were not measured in the grass leaves. Assuming that starch concentrations did increase in the grass leaves and that net photosynthesis was expressed as mg of CO_2/g dry weight, then erroneous conclusions may be drawn because of the increased dry weight due to increased starch synthesis. In addition, measurements were made at midday to early afternoon when starch concentrations are generally highest in plants. It can be seen that increased K fertilization could be inaccurately related to decreased net photosynthesis of centipedegrass.

Dark respiration per gram dry weight

Dark respiration rates of the centipedegrass were determined for each greenhouse and field treatment. Increased N fertilization increased the dark respiration rate, yet the only significant values were obtained from the field data. However, the intermediate rate of K fertilization produced the highest respiration rate in both experiments (Table 7).

A difference in degree of dark respiration occurred between experiments. The higher rate of dark respiration measured for the greenhouse turf was due to the added effect of the ecosystem (roots, stolons, microflora,

Table 7—Effect of nitrogen and potassium fertilization on dark respiration of centipedegrass.

Fertilization level, kg/100 m²	mg CO_2/g dry wt per hour	
	Greenhouse	Field
N		
0.98	9.43 a*	1.25 b
1.96	10.16 a	1.58 ab
2.94	11.16 a	1.89 a
P		
0.82	9.96 ab	1.63 a
1.63	11.83 a	2.03 a
2.45	8.97 b	1.07 b
C. V. =	25.7%	51.2%

* Means within each column followed by different letters are significantly different at the 0.05 level according to Duncan's new multiple range test.

microfauna) in the pots whereas the rates for the field-grown sod were taken on grass tillers with roots suspended in a soil-free solution and sealed outside the chamber.

Carbohydrates: Total nonstructural, reducing, and nonreducing sugars

Centipedegrass stolons were analyzed for total nonstructural carbohydrates (TNC). No real differences were detected among N and K fertilization rates for the greenhouse-grown grass. However, significant differences were found with N fertilization in the field experiment. Increased N fertilization reduced the level of TNC found in the stolons. As in the greenhouse, no real differences were detected among K fertilization rates on TNC levels (Table 8).

Reducing and nonreducing sugar analyses were also performed on the collected centipedegrass stolons. Reducing sugar content responded some-

Table 8—Effect of nitrogen and potassium fertilization on total nonstructural carbohydrates of centipedegrass.

Fertilization level, kg/100 m²	% TNC/g dry wt	
	Greenhouse	Field
N		
0.98	13.54 a*	20.25 a
1.96	13.98 a	18.98 b
2.94	12.11 a	18.97 b
P		
0.82	14.03 a	19.37 a
1.63	12.60 a	19.26 a
2.45	13.00 a	19.57 a
C. V. =	19.3%	7.1%

* Means within each column followed by different letters are significantly different at the 0.05 level according to Duncan's new multiple range test.

Table 9—Effect of nitrogen and potassium fertilization on the reducing sugar content of centipedegrass.

Fertilization level, kg/100 m²	Reducing sugar, mg/g dry wt.	
	Greenhouse	Field
N		
0.98	7.75 a *	5.24 b
1.96	7.81 a	5.83 a
2.94	6.88 b	5.80 a
P		
0.82	10.09 a	6.77 a
1.63	6.62 b	5.88 b
2.45	5.72 c	4.23 c
C. V. =	11.5%	6.0%

* Means within each column followed by different letters are significantly different at the 0.05 level according to Duncan's new multiple range test.

what differently between the two experiments to increased N fertilization. However, increased N fertilization significantly lowered the nonreducing sugar concentration in both experiments while increased K fertilization significantly reduced both reducing and nonreducing sugar concentrations (Tables 9 and 10).

Starch concentrations for each treatment were obtained by subtracting total soluble sugars (reducing and nonreducing) from TNC. Generally, increased K fertilization increased the starch content of centipedegrass stolons (Table 8).

CONCLUSIONS

Several general conclusions may be drawn from these experiments. 1) Net photosynthesis data indicate that 0.82 kg of available K/100 m² is suf-

Table 10—Effect of nitrogen and potassium fertilization on the nonreducing sugar content of centipedegrass.

Fertilization level, kg/100 m²	Nonreducing sugar, mg/g dry wt.	
	Greenhouse	Field
N		
0.98	55.15 a*	83.11 a
1.96	53.46 b	58.22 c
2.94	48.55 c	60.98 b
P		
0.82	61.23 a	71.04 a
1.63	52.22 b	69.53 a
2.45	43.70 c	61.73 b
C. V. =	3.5%	3.0%

* Means within each column followed by different letters are significantly different at the 0.05 level according to Duncan's new multiple range test.

ficient to provide optimum photosynthesis and TNC levels. However, if higher starch concentrations are needed, then K fertilization at either 1.63 of 2.45 kg/100 m^2 is required. 2) Determination of optimum Mg levels for centipedegrass is needed. If low Mg absorption is indeed responsible for decreased net photosynthesis with high K fertilization, then perhaps the problem could be lessened with concomitant Mg fertilization. Likewise, most of the Coastal Plain soils that centipedegrass is grown on are inherently low in Mg. 3) Net photosynthetic rates and total soluble sugar levels appear to be directly related. 4) Nitrogen fertilization above 1.96 kg/100 m^2 should be used cautiously since TNC levels are decreased by such rates. Sufficient turf quality can be maintained with the 1.96 kg/100 m^2 rate of N fertilization.

REFERENCES

1. AKATSUKA, T., and O. E. NELSON. 1967. Starch granule-brand adenosine diphosphate glucose-starch glucosyl-transferase of maize seeds. J. Biol. Chem. 241: 2280–2285.
2. BAKER, D. N., and R. B. MUSGRAVE. 1964. Photosynthesis under field conditions. V. Further plant chamber studies of the effect of light on corn (*Zea mays* L.). Crop Sci. 4:127–131.
3. GALLAHER, Raymond N., W. L. PARKS, and L. M. JOSEPHSON. 1972. Effect of levels of soil potassium, fertilizer potassium, and season on yield and ear leaf potassium content of corn inbreds and hybrids. Agron. J. 64:645–647.
4. HESKETH, J. D., and R. M. MUSGRAVE. 1962. Photosynthesis under field conditions. IV. Light studies with individual corn leaves. Crop Sci. 2:311–315.
5. LANCASTER, J. D. 1972. Chemical methods used in the extension soil testing department, Mississippi State, Mississippi. 31 p.
6. MEYER, B. S., D. B. ANDERSON, and R. H. BOHNING. 1960. Introduction to plant physiology. D. Van Nostrand Co., Princeton. 541 p.
7. MURATA, T., and Takashi AKAZAWA. 1964. The role of adenosine diphosphate glucose in leaf starch formation. Biochem. Biophys. Res. Comm. 16:6–11.
8. ——— and ———. 1961. Stimulative effect of potassium ion on starch synthetase of different plant origins. Plant Cell Physiol., 10:457–460.
9. NELSON, N. 1944. A photometric adaption of the Somogyi method for the determination of glucose. J. Biol. Chem. 153:375–380.
10. SOMOGYI, M. 1952. Notes on sugar determinations. J. Biol. Chem. 195:19–23.
11. WEINMANN, H. 1974. Determination of total available carbohydrates in plants. Plant Physiol. 22:279–290.

ABSTRACTS

Abstracts of all papers not published herein but presented at the Conference are included below to round off this Section. These abstracts, unlike the printed papers, have not been refereed.

SECTION 2 ABSTRACT–EFFECT OF DEFICIENT NUTRIENT SOLUTIONS ON THE CONCENTRATIONS OF 16 MINERAL ELEMENTS IN CLIPPINGS OF KENTUCKY 31 TALL FESCUE

In a greenhouse study, 'Kentucky 31' tall fescue (*Festuca arundinacea* Schreb) was seeded and grown for 8 weeks on a complete Hoagland's solution. Solutions were then modified to eliminate N, Ca, P, Mg, Fe, S, and K. Solutions were changed weekly and water was added between changes to maintain a constant solution level. Clippings were harvested and concentrations of 16 elements were determined with a direct reading emission spectrograph. Nitrogen concentrations ranged from a low of 2.56% to a high of 4.06%. The percentages of phosphorus, potassium, magnesium, and calcium, respectively, were 0.22 to 1.50, 1.58 to 6.25, 0.15 to 0.70, and 0.25 to 1.49. The uptake of 69 combinations of elements was significantly correlated; 20 were negative and 49 were positive. The uptake of K was positively correlated with N uptake. Ca and Mg uptakes were positively correlated with Mg, Na, Fe, Cu, Zn, Al, Sr, Ba, and Mo uptake. The uptake of K was negatively correlated with Ca, Mg, Na, Mn, Zn, and Mo in the tissue. The ranges of concentrations of microelements in ppm were Mn, 122 to 335; Fe, 123 to 169; Bo, 34 to 89; Cu, 11 to 17; Zn, 49 to 93; Al, 10 to 90; Sr, 40 to 59; Ba, 12 to 65 and Mo, 1 to 5. Differences among the treatments in the concentrations of all 16 elements were significant.—R. W. Miller, The Ohio State University.

DISCUSSION

F. J. WRAY—What form of nitrogen is recommended for use in nutrient solutions to develop deficiencies of other mineral elements? Where NH_4^+ is used pH would be influenced more than where NO_3^- is used. Would not the form of nitrogen have an effect on the proportions of cations and anions taken up by the turf?

R. W. MILLER —A combination of nitrate and ammonium sources of nitrogen such as in the standard Hoagland's solution is recommended.

R. E. ENGEL—Should not turfgrass quality readings be correlated with other data such as rooting, carbohydrate levels in the tissue, and respiration rates? It would seem that with modern methods of handling data, many different growth measurements and indicators could be correlated with turfgrass quality readings. More accurate interpretation of research results is possible where such correlations are made.

R. E. BLASER—Turf research results of fertilization with nitrogen are difficult to interpret. For example, we have found that soluble carbohydrates in tissue increase whenever photosynthesis exceeds respiration. Low nitrogen, cool temperatures, and drought depress photosynthesis less than cell division; hence, carbohydrates increase. The combined effect of cool temperatures and liberal nitrogen that occur during fall and winter nitrogen applications does not adversely depress soluble carbohydrates. Autumn and winter nitrogen fertilization has improved turf quality of cool-season grasses grown in the Blacksburg, Virginia region; it would be interesting to know how well these nitrogen fertilization results apply in more northern latitudes. Was temperature elevation monitored and photorespiration considered and were the data on photosynthesis corrected for the differential carbon dioxide evolution in work at Rhode Island?

R. J. HULL—Our measurements were of net carbon assimilation; no effort was made to determine gross photosynthesis, photorespiration, etc. I agree that gross photosynthesis was undoubtedly higher in summer than in winter. However, photosynthetic rates in winter were appreciable. In regard to monitoring of temperatures, readings were taken only during the first minute of turf enclosure within the bell jar. During this time we critically monitored the conditions in the jar although no attempt was made to modify them. During the first minute, with the highest out-of-doors temperatures with which we worked, the temperature increase within the jar was only between 3 to 4 degrees. We feel that any changes in either respiratory or other sources of carbon dioxide during this period would not be significantly greater than they would be under natural turf-growing conditions. We did not subtract or take into account photorespiration or other contributions which could reduce the net assimilation rate.

R. E. BLASER—Then, photosynthesis would actually be much higher with the high nitrogen in the summer as compared to the winter, because respiration was much higher.

W. H. BENGEYFIELD—Have correlations been made between sulfur applications to turf and changes in soil pH, especially in relation to the development of annual bluegrass?

R. L. GOSS—Yes, they have. Phosphorus, potassium, calcium, magnesium, and pH are monitored annually to determine pH shifts and the effect that this may have on other elements. At the present time the highest level of sulfur applied for the last 6 years has lowered the pH by about 0.6 in the surface 1 cm of soil. In the surface 7.5 cm pH has decreased less than 0.3.

R. E. ENGEL—Has any interaction between iron nutrition of turf and temperature been observed?

R. E. SCHMIDT—Temperature does have an effect on iron fertilization of bentgrass. At low temperatures bentgrasses tend to become off-color. At these times heavy iron applications produce a gray cast on the foliage. This color change usually does not last long. With either an increase in temperature or with mowing the normal color is enhanced.

Turfgrass environment

Section III

25

Heating turf by underground warm air

G.G. FISHER

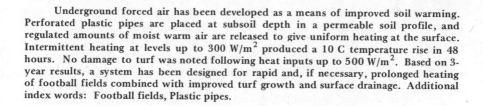

Underground forced air has been developed as a means of improved soil warming. Perforated plastic pipes are placed at subsoil depth in a permeable soil profile, and regulated amounts of moist warm air are released to give uniform heating at the surface. Intermittent heating at levels up to 300 W/m^2 produced a 10 C temperature rise in 48 hours. No damage to turf was noted following heat inputs up to 500 W/m^2. Based on 3-year results, a system has been designed for rapid and, if necessary, prolonged heating of football fields combined with improved turf growth and surface drainage. Additional index words: Football fields, Plastic pipes.

The specialized construction of soil for turf has long been standard practice on bowling greens and cricket squares. A sand:soil mix to match that found naturally on the first sand-dune golf links is now increasingly used for new golf greens.

Only recently has the same care been taken in providing correct conditions for growing turf for winter games such as football. Yet the game makes serious demands on standards of grass growth and playing surface, and a good game requires protection against adverse climatic conditions giving rise to excess wetness, frozen ground, and snow. Ede (2) cites a survey conducted among the top 44 clubs of the English Association Football League. It was found that during the 1968–69 and 1969–70 seasons there were 45 matches postponed, 29 because of frost and snow and 16 because of bad and poor drainage. In another 39 matches, play took place but was severely handicapped for the same reasons. The overall loss in reduced gate money was estimated at £200,000 (about $480,000) per season.

Playing conditions have been greatly improved by construction of an artificial soil profile. Careful regulation of soil textures and pore spaces provides rapid drainage to the subsoil and a surface which resists compaction. Further improvement of the turf environment by soil warming was described by Daniel (1), Escritt (3), Janson (4), and Langvad (6). In all the developed systems described, heat was supplied either by an underground system of pipes with circulating water or brine, or from buried electrical cables. The low thermal conductivity of soil, resulting in a steep temperature gradient, requires that the heat sources are close to each other and to the surface. Typical installations have heat sources spaced 23-cm apart and 15-cm deep, with power inputs normally between 60 and 110 W/m². These levels of power input are effective for continuous heating over substantial periods, especially when combined with plastic covers. They are not suitable for intermittent heating required for providing protection for occasional events on specific dates or against sudden spells of cold weather.

Successful systems depending on heat conduction are operating in a number of countries but the presence of wires or pipes at shallow depth can interfere with turf maintenance at critical periods, for example, when spiking is required, or in spring when cultivation is needed to break up a compacted soil. In a number of instances electrical systems for soil warming have been taken out of intensively used stadia in Britain because of interference with turf management.

Janson and Langvad (5) reported soil heating trials using warm air passed through standard 52-mm perforated plastic drainage pipes, but the method was abandoned because of the rapid fall of temperature along the underground pipes. It was found that temperatures dropped from 40 to 4 C in only 30 m, yet the high permeability of free-draining soil profiles to both air and water lends itself to a method of soil heating depending on air movement. Forced warm air from an underground source has the advantage that it does not rely on the thermal conductivity of the soil because the heat is transmitted by air circulated through the pores in the soil rather than through the solid material. The potential advantages include the use of high power inputs with cheaper fuels and the uniform spread of warmth throughout the root zone, thus allowing deeper and wider spacings of pipes and eliminating interference with other turf maintenance operations.

MATERIALS AND METHODS

Investigation of warm-air heating has been carried on at the laboratories of Land and Water Management at Cambridge since 1969. Early developments were concerned with the depth and spacing of pipes and obtaining uniform warming of the soil surface above the length of an underground pipe. Installation of the system in a natural soil has not been recommended so far; results to date have given uneven escape of air from the surface. This work has been described by Ede (2). The complete system, which evolved from further experiments at Cambridge, was later extended into turf under constant and severe wear.

A typical arrangement of the underground pipe system in a football field is for the supply main to traverse the field at the half-way line, with lateral pipes passing from the half-way line to the goal line. Warm, moist air from the large main pipe feeds into lateral pipes at spacings of 68.5 cm. Laterals are flexible-plastic drainage pipes of 70-mm internal dia, but with a special pattern of perforations. Optimum depth of laterals appears to be in the range 30 to 45 cm from the surface to invert; pipe depth affects speed of initial heating response.

A suitable soil profile is shown in Fig. 1. This type of profile gives

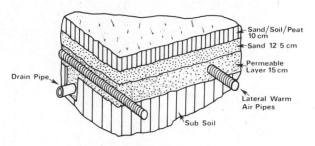

Fig. 1—Typical soil profile.

rapid drainage and resistance to surface compaction and a turf which will withstand intensive wear at all times of the year. The profile has a permeable layer of gravel, clinker, or artificial aggregate into which the warm air is introduced. An ample rooting zone for grasses is provided by the sand layer above and the topsoil mix of sand, soil, and peat.

Humidifying the air which is blown into the system increases the heat carrying capacity by a factor of approximately 4. Increased carrying capacity means that the working temperatures of air in the pipe systems need not be normally higher than 40 C. Warm, moist air escapes from the lateral pipes releasing heat and moisture to the soil profile as it cools in passing to the surface. The moisture in the warmed air reduces but does not eliminate the steep temperature gradient which occurs with unmoistened air. Full correction to uniform surface temperatures is obtained by varying the release of air along each lateral pipe. A computerized design is employed for the optimum spacing of perforations along the pipe to produce uniform heat at the soil surface. A prepared program enables a design to be arrived at for a new area on short notice.

Forced and saturated warm air is normally supplied from a source situated at the side of the area to be heated, for example, beneath a spectator

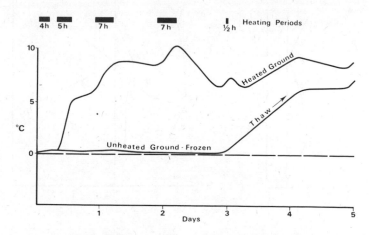

Fig. 2—Soil temperature at 2.5 cm below soil surface.

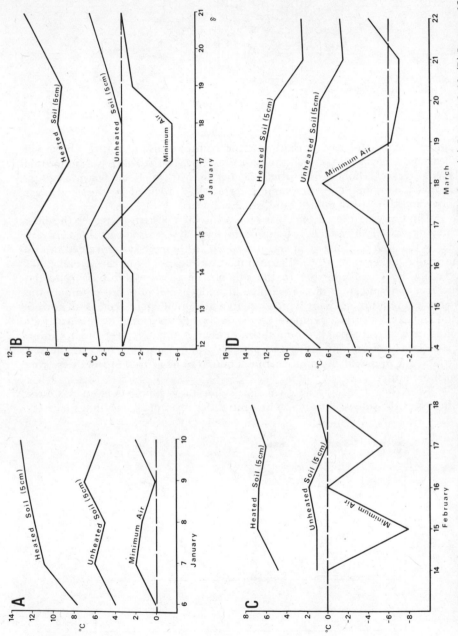

Fig. 3.—Heating system performance on a training ground at Liverpool, England, during 1973 from (A) January 6–10, (B) January 12–21, (C) February 12–18, (D) March 14–22.

Table 1—Forced-air heating system performance on a football training ground at Liverpool, England, Winter 1973.

Period	Days	Average soil temperature increase at 5 cm	Average power input
		°C	W/m²
Jan 7–10	4	6.7	155
Jan 12–21	10	5.6	138
Feb 15–18	4	5.8	158
Mar 14–22	9	5.2	139

stand. For a maximum heating rate of 300 W/m² on a normal-size football field, total power of up to 2.5 MW is required. The quantity of air is of the order of 27,000 cubic feet/min at a pressure of 61-cm water gauge, although each field must be subject to individual design.

Experiments with 46-m length pipes spaced 68.5 cm apart at a 34-cm depth to invert demonstrated rapid warming of frozen ground when air temperatures were considerably below freezing, as shown in Fig. 2. Starting in the cold, 9 hours of heating spread over 12 hours was required to start raising the temperature at the surface. Once the soil was warm over the full depth from pipes to surface there was immediate response of surface temperature to further inputs of heat, such that intermittent heating at 300 W/m² gave temperature differentials of up to 10 C between heated and unheated soil a little more than 48 hours after heating was started. No adverse effects on turf were noted following heating at rates up to 500 W/m².

The soil profile on part of the training ground of Everton Football Club in Liverpool was reconstructed for warm air heating in 1970. Heating pipes were installed by trenchless method in the following year with virtually no disturbance of the turf or soil profile.

The performance during four periods of the winter of 1972–73 is shown in Fig. 3 and summarized in Table 1.

Distribution of soil temperatures close to the surface away from the main air supply is shown in Fig. 4. For the first few days after starting to

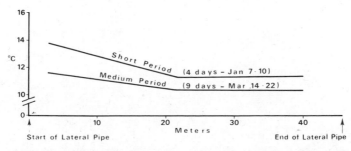

Fig. 4—Soil temperature decreases at distances from main heat supply (5-cm depth).

heat there was a tendency for temperatures to be higher close to the main supply. This tended to disappear with continued heating.

The effects of warm-air soil heating on turf and playing conditions have now been observed over several years. Under concentrated daily winter practice the turf has remained playable under all weather conditions and is consistently greener in the winter with spring growth starting some 6 weeks earlier than on unheated areas. Superior growth and drainage has reduced the need for renovation to a minimum. However, there have not been any restrictions on turf maintenance operations, including cultivations and deep spiking.

The fuel used so far has been propane, but natural gas, electricity, or oil could also be used. In Winter 1972-73 at Everton, fuel costs were £0.59/ m² (about $1.50/m²). In this case there was an unavoidable loss of warm air to the drainage system of the surrounding unheated field. This would not take place in a complete stadium installation. This and the choice of a more economic fuel should bring the annual running cost of a football field of 0.73 ha to an estimated £2,500 (about $6,475).

Underground warm air is an effective method of soil heating, assisting the growth, appearance, and drainage of turf with no interference to play or to turf maintenance. There is virtually no labor involvement. It controls many adverse environmental conditions affecting turf used for winter play, allowing more intensive use of natural turf without recourse to artificial playing surfaces.

REFERENCES

1. DANIEL, W. H. 1970. Soil warming in North America. p. 235–237. *In* Proc. First Int. Turfgrass Res. Conf. Sports Turf Research Institute, Bingley, England.
2. EDE, A. N. 1970. Soil heating system using warm air. J. Sports Turf Res. Inst. 46:76.
3. ESCRITT, J. R. 1970. Soil warming in the United Kingdom. p. 241–242. *In* Proc. First Int. Turfgrass Res. Conf. Sports Turf Research Institute, Bingley, England.
4. JANSON, L. E. 1970. Theoretical investigation of artificial heating of the topsoil. p. 243–251. *In* Proc. First Int. Turfgrass Res. Conf. Sports Turf Research Institute, Bingley, England.
5. ———, and B. LANGVAD. 1968. Prolongation of the growing season for sports turf grasses by means of artificial heating of the root zone. Weibulls Grästips 10, 1968.
6. LANGVAD, B. 1970. Soil heating under sports turf in Sweden. p. 252–257. *In* Proc. First Int. Turfgrass Res. Conf. Sports Turf Reserach Institute, Bingley, England.

26

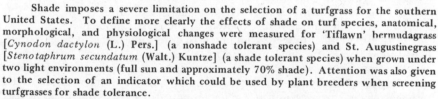

Persistence of southern turfgrasses in a shade environment [1]

C.W. WINSTEAD & C.Y. WARD

Shade imposes a severe limitation on the selection of a turfgrass for the southern United States. To define more clearly the effects of shade on turf species, anatomical, morphological, and physiological changes were measured for 'Tiflawn' bermudagrass [*Cynodon dactylon* (L.) Pers.] (a nonshade tolerant species) and St. Augustinegrass [*Stenotaphrum secundatum* (Walt.) Kuntze] (a shade tolerant species) when grown under two light environments (full sun and approximately 70% shade). Attention was also given to the selection of an indicator which could be used by plant breeders when screening turfgrasses for shade tolerance.

Although the anatomy of leaf blades of bermudagrass and St. Augustinegrass differ, shading caused only minor changes within a species. Leaf and internode lengths of both grasses generally increased when grown in a shade environment, while leaf width decreased in bermudagrass and increased in St. Augustinegrass with reduced light intensity. Total nonstructural carbohydrate reserves decreased in both species as a result of the shade environment. An increase in the total chlorophyll content of the grasses grown in the shade environment substantiated the observation that grasses grown under shaded conditions were darker green. Net photosynthesis and dark respiration decreased significantly in bermudagrass grown in the shade environment, but no difference was noted in St. Augustinegrass. No characteristic was found that could be used as a consistent indicator for shade tolerance of bermudagrass or St. Augustinegrass. Additional index words: Shade, Photosynthesis, Respiration, Chlorophyll, Carbohydrate.

Shade, whether from trees, buildings, or barriers, presents a problem in the selection and management of turfgrasses. It has been estimated that approximately 20% of all turf under intensive management is maintained under some degree of shade (5).

Numerous turfgrass shade studies have been reported, but the question of why one grass will grow under shaded conditions, while another will not, still remains to be resolved.

Burton and Deal (8) observed that shading increased succulence of southern turfgrasses, making them less resistant to wear, disease and insect damage, and water stress. Juska (12) reported that bentgrass (*Agrostis* spp.)

[1]Journal Article No. 2634. Agronomy Department, Mississippi Agricultural and Forestry Experiment Station, Starkville, Miss.

cultivars grown under shaded conditions were less dense and lighter green than when grown in full sun.

Although cool-season turfgrasses grown under reduced light intensity show a decrease in top, root, rhizome, and stolon growth, disease incidence is the major factor influencing the adaptation of cool-season grasses to shaded conditions (4).

McBee and Holt (14) reported that the density of St. Augustinegrass turf was not affected by decreasing light intensity, but bermudagrass turf became more open and upright in growth. These workers suggested that short internode length might be a useful guide in classifying bermudagrass for shade tolerance, and postulated that, as light intensity is reduced, a physiological system related to an enzyme which is light sensitive may be either inhibited or activated resulting in a reduction in stem diameter and an increase in stem elongation. Miller and Miller (16) suggested that blue light regulated cell elongation by regulating an auxin system. Beard (6) reviewed several articles and concluded that shading of grass typically resulted in a decrease in leaf width and an increase in leaf and internode length and plant height. Grasses grown under reduced light intensities had a thinner cutin layer, thinner cell walls, and the vascular and supporting tissues were poorly developed.

Turf grown in shade increased in chlorophyll content (6) and decreased in leaf longevity (22), net photosynthesis and respiration (1, 6, 7, 10, 22), and total available carbohydrate content of the grass stolons (17, 18).

These experiments were conducted to determine the effects of reduced light intensity on the anatomy and morphology of 'Tiflawn' bermudagrass and St. Augustinegrass; to determine the influence of shading on chlorophyll content, net photosynthesis, respiration, and carbohydrate reserves of the two grasses; and to ascertain if a reliable indicator exists which can be used when screening turfgrasses for shade tolerance.

MATERIALS AND METHODS

In order to obtain vegetative material for various phases of the experiment, 130 containers 18.5 cm in diameter were planted as solid sod to both St. Augustinegrass and Tiflawn bermudagrass. A 7-1-2 mixture by volume of sand, soil, and peat was used as the potting medium. Prior to planting, roots of the sod were washed free of all existing soil. Phosphorus was incorporated in the soil mixture at 1.08 kg/100 m^2. After the grasses were planted, they were watered several times daily until a new root system developed, thereafter they were watered every 2 days by flooding from the top. Nitrogen at 0.98 kg/100 m^2 was applied at 3-week intervals throughout the experiment.

To reduce disease and insect damage, rigid preventative plant protectant programs were maintained. Initially, 2,4,5,6-tetrachloroisophthalonitrile (Daconil 2787) was applied at 122 g/100 m^2 every 10 days, but since the pots were watered frequently, an additional treatment of dimethyl 4,4'-O-phenylenebis (3-thioallaphanate) (Topsin), a systemic fungicide, was applied every 30 days at 30.5 g/100 m^2. The insecticide 1-napthyl-N-methylcarbamate (50% Sevin wettable powder) was applied at 183 g/100 m^2 every 10 days.

The shade environment was obtained by covering a 2.2 × 5.2 × 1.9 m enclosure with green saran shade cloth to eliminate 75% of the incident sunlight. To facilitate adequate air movement within the enclosure, the shade cloth was raised approximately 23 cm from the ground on all sides. Air temperature and relative humidity were monitored with Belfort Hygro-Thermographs in both the shade and sun environments, while light intensity and quality measurements were made in both areas with a Weston Illumination Meter Model 603 and an ISCO Spectra-radiometer Model SR, respectively.[2]

Following an initial rooting period of 2 weeks in full sun, 65 pots of each grass were placed under the constructed shade enclosure, leaving an equal number to be used for the sun treatment. Each pot of grass served as a treatment unit and the sod or a portion thereof from each pot was subsequently sampled in various phases of the experiment.

Anatomy and morphology

To observe anatomical changes which occurred in the grasses as a result of shading, leaf blades were taken at random from each grass under each light intensity 5 weeks after the treatments were initiated. These leaf blades were killed and fixed with a formalin-acetic acid-alcohol mixture (11). Pieces 1 cm in length were sampled from the tip, middle, and base of each blade. These pieces were dehydrated in a tertiary-butyl alcohol series and embedded in parafin. Approximately 150 sections 15 μ in thickness were cut from each piece with a rotary microtome, mounted on slides, and subsequently stained in Safranin-O-fast green and observed under the microscope for anatomical changes.

Morphological changes as a result of reduced light intensity were determined by measuring leaf length and width and internode length. The third leaf and third internode from the tip of individual stolons were selected for a total of 45 random measurements from each grass under each treatment. Measurements were made with a caliper and ruler and expressed in millimeters.

Physiology

A simple switchback design was employed to determine total chlorophyll content of both grasses in both sun and shade environments. Ten pots of each grass under each light treatment were sampled 5 weeks after the treatments were imposed, with subsequent altering of treatments. All pots were sampled again at 10 weeks.

The third leaf from the tip of individual stolons was sampled to obtain leaves of approximately the same physiological age. One gram samples of St. Augustinegrass and 0.5 g samples of bermudagrass leaves were used. These samples were prepared for analysis following the method of MacKenney (13) as modified by Arnon (2). Photometric determinations were made using a Bausch and Lomb Spectronic 20 photometer and reported as milligrams total chlorophyll per gram of fresh weight.

---

[2]Mention of a trademark or proprietary product does not constitute a guarantee or warranty of the product by the Mississippi Agricultural and Forestry Experiment Station and does not imply its approval to the exclusion of other products that may be suitable.

A completely random design with ten replications was used to determine net photosynthesis and dark respiration of the two grasses under each light environment. The unit of study was an individual pot of each grass. The grass in these pots was clipped weekly to a height of 6.5 cm with all clippings being removed. Measurements were made 8 weeks after light treatments were initiated.

A Plexiglas chamber of sufficient size to fit within the lip of the 18.5-cm pot was constructed. A Beckman Model 215 differential infrared CO_2 analyzer was used to detect the change in CO_2 concentration due to photosynthesis or respiration. Analyzer output was recorded on a Beckman Model 1005 linear—log 25.40 cm potentiometric recorder. Bench air was used as the CO_2 source throughout the experiment with the flow rate being maintained at 9.5 dm^3/min.

A light intensity of 45.2 klux as measured under the Plexiglas chamber was from a 300 W Westinghouse reflector flood lamp bordered by 40 W Sylvania cool white fluorescent lamps. Light quality was also measured. A 10-cm water shield was placed between the light source and the chamber to reduce the temperature within the chamber.

Pots of grass were removed from the field in the early morning before each day's run. Each sample was placed under the light source for 30 min as a preconditioning treatment prior to being analyzed. Ten minutes were allowed for carbon fixation to reach a steady state after a sample was placed in the chamber.

In order to determine respiration, a green felt cover was placed over the chamber and pot. There was no deflection measured by the Weston light meter under this cover. The minutes were allowed for respiration to reach a steady state before measurements were made. All measurements were adjusted to standard pressure and temperature and net photosynthesis and dark respiration were calculated using the formula after the procedure of Baker and Musgrave (3).

Total nonstructural carbohydrate (TNC) content of stolons was determined by employing a completely random design. Stolons for TNC analysis were harvested from ten pots of each grass from each treatment 12 weeks after treatments were initiated. Stolons were washed free of foreign matter and oven-dried at 100 C before being ground in a micro-Wiley mill to pass a 40-mesh screen. Samples were stored in air-tight plastic bottles before being analyzed.

One hundred and fifty milligram samples were prepared for TNC analysis after the procedures of Weinmann (21), Somogyi (20), and Nelson (17). Photometric determinations were made using a Bausch and Lomb Spectronic 20 photometer.

RESULTS AND DISCUSSION

In general, there was little difference in the air temperature recorded between the sun and shade plots at any given time throughout the day. Air temperature averaged 32.2 C in the sun and 31.1 C in the shade environment during light periods, while an average temperature of 21.7 C was recorded in both environments at night. The maximum temperature recorded throughout the experiment was 35.0 C and the minimum was 16.7 C.

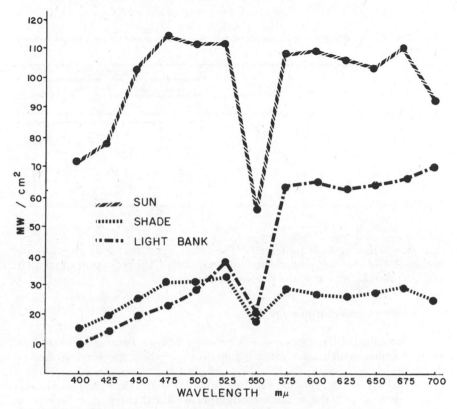

Fig. 1—Light quality in sun, shade, and under a light bank at Mississippi State, Starkville, Mississippi. Measurements taken September 19, 1972 at 1:00 p.m.

Values averaged over a 70-day period indicate that near 100% relative humidity was recorded in both light environments between 10:00 p.m. and 6:00 a.m. daily. The major diurnal differences between the two environments occurred at two periods: 1) in the early afternoon the relative humidity in the sun environment averaged approximately 4 percentage points lower (35 versus 39%), and 2) in midmorning there was an extended dew period of approximately 1 hour in the shade environment.

Light intensity values ranged from 12.90 klux at 9:00 a.m. to 33.36 klux at 1:00 p.m. and 10.76 klux at 5:00 p.m. in the shade, with values of 48.42, 88.23, and 43.04 klux recorded in the sun at these times. These values are above the 3.23 klux reported as being necessary to reach the compensation point of individual bermudagrass leaves, and approximate intensities which could light saturate individual leaves of bermudagrass throughout much of the day (1). It should be noted that due to self-shading and leaf angle, saturation of the turf under the shaded environment would be unlikely at the light intensities recorded during this experiment and would agree with reports in the literature (1, 6).

A comparison of light quality measured in sun, shade, and under the light bank is shown in Fig. 1. A uniform reduction of incident sunlight over

Table 1—Leaf size and internode length obtained on two grasses grown under two environments.

| Grass | Environment | Leaf blade | | Internode length |
		Width	Length	
		————mm————		
Bermudagrass	Sun	1.9	18.1	7.6
	Shade	1.6	59.5	32.9
	LSD .05	0.1	4.5	2.2
St. Augustinegrass	Sun	8.8	38.3	26.6
	Shade	9.7	96.8	44.8
	LDS .05	0.4	7.9	3.6

all visible wavelengths is indicated. The data suggest that light intensity and quality in the shade environment (approximately 70% reduction of incident sunlight) should not cause the demise of a turfgrass.

Anatomy and morphology

Anatomical differences existed between Tiflawn bermudagrass and St. Augustinegrass, which agree with the anatomy of these species described by Metcalfe (15).

Within a species, shading resulted in minor anatomical changes. Leaves of grasses grown in the shade were thinner with a thinner cutin layer than leaves grown in full sun, while no obvious difference was noted in the vascular bundles or general anatomy of shaded leaves as compared to leaves grown in full sunlight.

Shading changed the growth habit of both grasses. They appeared more succulent and darker green. Leaf blade and internode length increased significantly in both grasses when grown in a shade environment (Table 1). Shading of bermudagrass resulted in a 228% increase in leaf blade length, a 14% decrease in leaf blade width, and a 333% increase in internode length. Comparatively, shading of St. Augustinegrass resulted in a 153% increase in leaf blade length, a 10% increase in width, and only a 68% increase in internode length.

In the shade environment bermudagrass produced an open, upright sod, with little rooting at the nodes of stolons, while St. Augustinegrass stolons remained prostrate and rooted readily.

Since both grasses produced a less dense turf under shade, the increase in leaf width of St. Augustinegrass could possibly increase the photon-absorbing surface and thus enable this grass to be more adaptive than bermudagrass to reduced light intensities.

Other observations made in connection with morphology were specific leaf weight (SLW) and leaf longevity for each species in each light environment. Although St. Augustine grass leaves appeared to be thicker than Tiflawn bermudagrass leaves, there was no difference (4.01 and 4.04 mg dry wt/ cm^2, respectively) in SLW of these grasses. Shading resulted in an approxi-

Table 2—Chlorophyll content of two grasses when grown under two light environments.

| Environment | Chlorophyll content | |
	Bermudagrass	St. Augustinegrass
	mg/g fresh wt.	
Sun	1.04	0.65
Shade	1.58	0.86
LSD .05	0.21	0.09

mate 25% decrease in SLW (2.96 and 2.98 mg dry wt/cm^2, respectively) of both grasses.

Daily observations during a 55-day period for leaf longevity revealed no differences in the length of leaf life due to grass species or to light treatment. In spite of judicious use of preventive pesticides, disease and insect damage became evident after this 55-day period and caused the death of numerous test leaves. Because of this complication the continuation of these observations became impossible.

Observations before disease and insect damage occurred indicate that light intensities as low as 10.76 klux had little influence on the lifespan of leaves of the two test species. These observations suggest that the longevity of an individual leaf of both grasses is such that it would have little bearing on the appearance or the adaptability of a turfgrass to shaded environments. This is evidenced by the fact that even when dwarf species and/or growth regulators are used turfgrasses will, for appearance sake, likely require mowing more frequently than 40 to 60 days. In routine mowing of turfgrass, leaf blades are often partially removed or damaged thereby reducing their longevity and making their lifespan inconsequential.

Physiology

Bermudagrass had a higher total chlorophyll content than did St. Augustinegrass, while shading resulted in an increased chlorophyll concentration in both grass species (Table 2). These data suggest that the total chlorophyll content of grasses grown in shade environments had little, if any, effect on their adaptability to low light intensities.

Shading resulted in a 49% reduction in net photosynthesis of bermudagrass, while a 9% increase was noted for St. Augustinegrass (Table 3). In

Table 3—Rate of net photosynthesis and dark respiration of two grasses grown under two light environments.

Grass	Environment	Net photosynthesis	Dark respiration
		mg CO_2/dm^2 land area/hr	
Bermudagrass	Sun	57.94 a *	15.86 a
	Shade	29.42 b	5.95 b
St. Augustinegrass	Sun	31.41 b	6.87 b
	Shade	34.10 b	5.41 b

* Means tested by Duncan's New Multiple Range Test. Numbers followed by a different letter are significantly different.

drawing conclusions from these values it should be remembered that measurements were made under artificial light having an intensity above optimum for plants from the shade environment and below optimum for plants from the sun environment.

The decrease noted for net photosynthesis of bermudagrass grown in the shade environment is believed to be related to the difference in the density of the turf and not to reduced light intensity *per se*. Under full sun, bermudagrass produced a dense turf, while in the shade environment the turf was open and upright. This suggests that some system responsible for the growth habit of grasses may be triggered by light and may be significant in the adaptation of grasses to shaded habitats.

Values in Table 3 indicate a 62% reduction in dark respiration for Tiflawn bermudagrass and a 21% reduction for St. Augustinegrass. As in net photosynthesis, the reduction from shading may be due to the difference in density of the turf when grown in sun compared to shade environments. There was no significant difference in values obtained for any treatment with the exception of bermudagrass. Bermudagrass was grown in the sun environment which resulted in significantly higher values than all other treatments.

Total nonstructural carbohydrate (TNC) content of stolons was determined for each grass in each light environment. Data in Table 4 indicate that bermudagrass stores a higher percent TNC than does St. Augustinegrass, while both grasses grown in the shade environment contained a lower percent TNC compared to these grasses grown in full sunlight. These data agree with reports (9, 18, 19) that shading reduces TNC in plants.

With TNC reserves implicated in regrowth and persistence of perennial grasses and the assumption that St. Augustinegrass stores adequate quantities under shaded conditions, it appears that TNC reserves should not be considered a factor in the persistence and regrowth of bermudagrass due to the storage of a higher percent TNC than in St. Augustinegrass. If carbohydrate storage in a shaded environment is a factor in bermudagrass persistence, then this factor is likely involved with the rate of carbohydrate metabolism rather than the percent TNC storage.

No definite conclusions could be drawn from these experiments as to why a particular grass may be shade tolerant. Without a thorough study of the anatomy of a number of shade and nonshade tolerant species, anatomy cannot be implicated in shade tolerance. Indications are that SLW, leaf longevity, total chlorophyll content, and TNC reserves have little influence on the adaptation of a grass to shaded conditions. It is believed that a system

Table 4—Total nonstructural carbohydrate content of Tiflawn bermudagrass and St. Augustinegrass as affected by light environment.

Grass	Environment		Average
	Sun	Shade	
		% TNC	
Bermudagrass	21.27	14.65	18.94
St. Augustinegrass	16.61	10.32	12.48
Average	17.96	13.46	
LSD .05 Grass and environment =	1.09		

which is light sensitive and controls the growth habit and thus the density of a turf is primarily responsible for shade tolerance in turfgrasses. This control may be administered by growth substances such as auxins, but further research as to quantities and location would be necessary before any conclusions could be made to this effect.

No reliable indicator was found in studying any of the aforementioned parameters which could be used in screening turfgrasses for shade tolerance.

REFERENCES

1. ALEXANDER, C. W., and D. E. MC CLOUD. 1962. CO_2 (net photosynthesis) as influenced by light intensity of isolated bermudagrass leaves contrasted to that of swards under various clippings regimes. Crop Sci. 2:132-135.
2. ARNON, D. 1949. Copper enzymes in isolated chloroplasts. Polyphenoloxidase in *Beta vulgaris*. Plant Physiol. 24:1-15.
3. BAKER, D. N., and R. B. MUSGRAVE. 1964. Photosynthesis under field conditions. V. Further plant chamber studies of the effects of light on corn (*Zea mays* L.). Crop Sci. 4:127-131.
4. BEARD, J. B. 1965. Factors in the adaptation of turfgrass to shade. Agron. J. 57: 457-459.
5. ———. 1967. Shade grasses and maintenance. *In* Proc. Int. Turf Conf. and Show. 38:31 35. Golf Course Superintendent of America.
6. ———. 1973. Turfgrass: science and culture. Prentice-Hall, Inc., Englewood Cliffs, N. J. 658 p.
7. BURNSIDE, C. A., and R. H. BOHNING. 1957. The effect of prolonged shading on the light saturation curved of apparent photosynthesis in sun plants. Plant Physiol. 32:61-63.
8. BURTON, G. W., and E. E. DEAL. 1962. Shade studies on southern grasses. Golf Course Rep. 30(8):26-27.
9. ———, J. E. JACKSON, and F. E. KNOX. 1959. The influence of light reduction upon the production, persistence, and chemical composition of Coastal bermudagrass, *Cynodon dactylon*. Agron. J. 51:537-542.
10. HART, R. H., and D. R. LEE. 1971. Age vs. net CO_2 exchange rate of leaves of Coastal bermudagrass. Crop Sci. 11:598-599.
11. JOHANSEN, D. A. 1940. Plant microtechniques. McGraw-Hill Book Co., Inc. New York and London. 523 p.
12. JUSKA, F. V. 1963. Shade tolerance of bentgrasses. Golf Course Rep. 31(2):28-34.
13. MAC KINNEY, G. 1941. Absorption of light by chlorophyll solutions. J. Biol. Chem. 140:315-322.
14. MC BEE, G. G., and E. C. HOLT. 1966. Shade tolerance studies on bermudagrass and other turfgrasses. Agron. J. 58:523-525.
15. METCALFE, C. R. 1960. Anatomy of the monocotyledons. I. Graminea. Oxford University Press, London. 731 p.
16. MILLER, J. H., and P. M. MILLER. 1965. The relationship between the promotion of elongation of fern protonemata by light and growth substances. Amer. J. Bot. 52:871-876.
17. NELSON, N. 1944. A photometric adaptation of the Somogyi method for the determination of glucose. J. Biol. Chem. 153:375-381.
18. SCHMIDT, R. E., and R. E. BLASER. 1967. Effect of temperature, light and nitrogen on growth and metabolism of Cohansey bentgrass (*Agrostis palustris* Huds.). Crop Sci. 7:447-451.
19. ———, and ———. 1969. Effect of temperature, light and nitrogen on growth and metabolism of 'Tifgreen' bermudagrass (*Cynodon* spp.). Crop Sci. 9:5-9.
20. SOMOGYI, M. 1952. Notes on sugar determination. J. Biol. Chem. 195:19-23.

21. WEINMANN, H. 1947. Determination of total available carbohydrates in plants. Plant Physiol. 22:279–290.

22. WOLEDGE, J. 1972. The effect of shading on the photosynthetic rate and longevity of grass leaves. Ann. Bot. 36(146):551–560.

27

Morphological responses of *Poa pratensis* and *Festuca rubra* to reduced light intensity[1]

J.F. WILKINSON & J.B. BEARD

The objective of the study was to characterize the morphological responses of Kentucky bluegrass (*Poa pratensis*) and red fescue (*Festuca rubra*) to reduced light intensity. 'Merion' Kentucky bluegrass and 'Pennlawn' red fescue were grown in separate growth chambers under light intensities of 2,690, 5,380, 10,760, 21,530, and 43,060 lux. Light quality, soil moisture, and soil temperature were standardized among chambers. Plants were clipped weekly at 5 cm for 14 weeks.

Leaf length and width were determined prior to clipping. Leaf length of both species increased with decreasing light intensity to 10,760 lux. Length was reduced at intensities below 10,760 lux. Each species had narrower leaves with successive reductions in light intensity. Leaf angle was measured on plants grown singly. Both species displayed horizontal growth at high light intensities. Red fescue remained horizontal under low light intensities, while Kentucky bluegrass exhibited a vertical growth habit.

Clipping weight, percent moisture, leaf area, and chlorophyll content were determined after clipping. Both species responded similarly. Clipping weights decreased and percent moisture increased under lower light intensities. Clipping leaf area was greatest at 10,760 lux, and decreased at higher or lower light intensities. Chlorophyll per square decimeter decreased and chlorophyll per gram increased as light intensity was lowered. Kentucky bluegrass was comparable to red fescue under low light intensity in all four of the above categories.

Plant shoots and roots were separated following the final clipping. Shoot and root production decreased under lower light intensities. However, red fescue produced greater shoot weight than Kentucky bluegrass under the lowest intensity, while Kentucky bluegrass was superior at the highest light intensity. Kentucky bluegrass produced less leaf area, fewer shoots per square centimeter, and fewer tillers per plant with each decrement of lower light, while red fescue produced equal numbers in these categories through 5,380 lux. Thus, red fescue was superior to Kentucky bluegrass at low light intensities only in terms of shoot growth below the cutting height (verdure).

The superiority of red fescue under shade has been related to competition with tree roots, and the loss of Kentucky bluegrass has been credited to disease infestation. These factors were not present in this study. Since red fescue produced superior verdure under low light intensities, it must possess additional shade adaptation mechanisms. Additional index words: Chlorophyll content, Kentucky bluegrass, Leaf angle, Leaf area, Red fescue, Root growth, Shade, Shoot growth.

[1]Michigan Agricultural Experiment Station Journal Article No. 6425. This research was supported partially by the Michigan Turfgrass Foundation.

Both Kentucky bluegrass (*Poa pratensis* L.) and red fescue (*Festuca rubra* L.) form high-quality turfs in full sun, but red fescue is superior under shaded conditions (3, 8). Maintenance of turf in shade presents unique problems. A 1966 Pennsylvania survey of 326 golf courses indicated growing turf in shade to be the number one turf problem (4). It has been estimated 20% of the turf grown in the United States is subjected to some degree of shade (2).

The morphological responses of grasses associated with reduced light intensities include: decreased shoot, root, rhizome, and stolon growth; reduced shoot density and tillering; decreased root to shoot ratio; thinner leaves; longer internodes; increased leaf length; and upright growth habit (3). Lighter green leaves and increased succulence also have been found under low light intensities. A comprehensive study evaluating the morphological responses of Kentucky bluegrass and red fescue to reduced light intensity has not been made.

Wood (12) compared the growth of eight Kentucky bluegrass and eight red fescue cultivars in a controlled climate chamber study under light intensities from 2,480 to 32,290 lux. Shoot and root growth of both species was comparable at 16,150 and 32,390 lux. Red fescue cultivars generally outperformed Kentucky bluegrass cultivars at 2,480 and 5,380 lux. Wood reported both species responded to reduced light intensities by more flaccid, paler green, and narrower blades. A field study also showed red fescue superior to Kentucky bluegrass in the shade. Beard (1) grew several turfgrass species and mixtures beneath shade trees. Red fescue was superior to Kentucky bluegrass in terms of turfgrass quality ratings and shoot density counts. Red fescue-Kentucky bluegrass mixtures were predominantly red fescue after 2 years. Wilson (11) grew red fescue, orchardgrass (*Dactylis glomerata* L.), and white clover (*Trifolium repens* L.) at light intensities of 2,150, 6,460, and 19,380 lux. Growth of orchardgrass and clover was reduced with each decrement of reduced light intensity. Red fescue grew as well at 6,460 as at 19,380 lux, indicating greater tolerance to reduced light intensities than orchardgrass or clover, but was seriously impaired at 2,150 lux.

Many aspects of the shade environment in addition to reduced light intensity affect turfgrass growth: altered light quality, moderation of temperature extremes, increased disease incidence, decreased wind movement and evapotranspiration, increased soil moisture, and tree root competition. The adaptive mechanisms of shade-tolerant species may involve acclimation to these factors. Beard (1) showed that red fescue was more disease tolerant than Kentucky bluegrass under shaded conditions. Although the red fescue was thinned by *Helminthosporium* leafspot in its first year of growth, a more suitable turf resulted in subsequent years. Kentucky bluegrass was unable to survive due to powdery mildew. Whitcomb (9) compared the clipping yields of Kentucky bluegrass, red fescue, rough bluegrass (*Poa trivialis* L.), and perennial ryegrass (*Lolium perenne* L.) beneath shade trees, with and without tree root competition. Kentucky bluegrass shoot growth was impaired more by the tree roots than the other species. Whitcomb and Roberts (10) demonstrated Kentucky bluegrass rooting to be severely restricted by trees having shallow feeder roots.

The objective of this study was to characterize the morphological responses of 'Merion' Kentucky bluegrass and 'Pennlawn' red fescue to reduced light intensities. Other factors influencing turfgrass growth in shade (e.g., altered light quality, disease incidence, soil temperature and moisture levels, tree root competition) were eliminated. It was anticipated this information might give further insight into shade adaptation mechanisms of red fescue.

MATERIALS AND METHODS

Light

Light intensities of 2,690, 5,380, 10,760, 21,530, and 43,060 lux (1.1, 2.5, 4.3, 6.2, and 7.5 X 10^4 ergs/sec, respectively) were established in separate growth chambers. Preliminary studies indicated 2,690 lux was the lowest light intensity at which Merion Kentucky bluegrass could persist. A Weston Illumination Meter Model 765 and a YSI-Kettering Model 65 Radiometer were used for the light measurements.[2] A 14-hour photoperiod was used.

Light quality was first standardized among the chambers utilizing similar-make bulbs and the same proportion of fluorescent to incandescent bulbs. An ISCO Model SR Spectroradiometer indicated only slight variation in light quality among chambers. The variation in light quality within each chamber was not significant. The light was weak in the red and blue regions and strong in the green and infrared. A similar light quality has been found beneath deciduous tree canopies (7).

Light intensities were established by raising and lowering chamber shelves. Plant material at 43,060 lux was within 0.50 m of the bulbs. Leaf temperature, measured with a Stoll-Hardy Model HL4 Radiometer, and canopy temperature, measured with a copper/constantan thermocouple and potentiometer, were no more than 2 C above the soil temperature.

Separate growth chambers were used for each light intensity in order to establish uniform soil temperatures and to avoid the use of shading materials or screens which may significantly alter the turfgrass microenvironment.

Light intensity fluctuated markedly within each chamber, with variation increasing toward the chamber sides. All plant material was kept close to the center of the chamber and was rotated every other day.

Soil

A sandy loam soil mix was used. Soil temperatures were maintained at 20 C and were monitored using a bulb thermometer inserted 5 cm into the soil.

Uniform soil moisture was maintained utilizing 1.25-cm tensiometers (Irrometer Company, Riverside, California). The tensiometers were inserted into pots seeded with Kentucky bluegrass. Data were not taken from these

---

[2]Mention of trademark or proprietary product does not constitute a guarantee or warranty of the product by the Michigan Agricultural Experiment Station and does not imply its approval to the exclusion of other products that may be suitable.

pots. Soil moisture levels were monitored with the tensiometers, and all pots were watered accordingly. All pots were saturated weekly with a complete Hoagland's solution (5).

Plant material

Merion Kentucky bluegrass and Pennlawn red fescue were seeded in 10.2-cm dia plastic pots at 3.3 seeds/cm^2. Seeds were germinated in a greenhouse. Three replications of each species were placed under each light intensity when the seedlings were 1 cm in height. Additional pots were thinned to one seedling per pot for shoot angle determinations.

Parameters measured

After plants reached 5 cm in height, clippings above 5 cm were collected weekly using hand clippers with a collection pan attached. The following measurements were made prior to clipping:

1) Average leaf length above the 5-cm cutting height.
2) Leaf width was measured on the youngest fully expanded leaf, 1 cm from the leaf collar. Leaf widths were placed into classes of < 0.5, 0.5-1, 1-1.5, 1.5-2, and > 2 mm. Three measurements were taken for each replication.
3) Shoot angle. It was found difficult to estimate shoot angle on plants within an established turf. Pots with a single plant were included under each light intensity. Mean shoot angle (0°—vertical, 90°—horizontal) determinations were made prior to weekly clipping at 5 cm.

Leaf clippings were collected and placed in plastic bags to prevent desiccation. The following parameters were measured:

4) Total fresh weight.
5) Leaf area. A 10 to 20 leaf subsample was taken from the fresh clippings. Fresh weight was determined, the leaves taped to paper, and a photocopy made. Leaf area of the subsample was then estimated using a planimeter. The leaf area:leaf weight ratio established for the subsample was used to estimate the total clipping leaf area. The estimate included only one leaf surface.
6) Chlorophyll content. A second subsample (approximately 1 g) was removed from the fresh clipping sample, weighed, placed in a flask, and covered with 50 ml of methanol. The flasks were stoppered and left in a dark cabinet overnight. Samples were then ground for 2 minutes in a Virtis Mixer Model 45, filtered under vacuum, and brought to a volume equivalent to 1 liter. Absorbancy was measured at 650 and 665 nm with a Perkin-Elmer Model 27 Spectrophotometer. MacKinney's (6) formula for total chlorophyll in methanol solutions was utilized. Chlorophyll was expressed as milligrams per square decimeter and milligrams per gram of dry weight.
7) Dry weight. The remaining fresh clippings were weighed, dried at

70 C, and reweighed. Dry weight was determined including sub-samples taken for leaf area and chlorophyll estimations.

8) Percent moisture on a fresh weight basis was determined.

The final clipping was made 14 weeks after germination. All plants were cut off at the soil surface and the following parameters determined:

9) Total fresh weight.

10) Number of shoots per pot.

11) Number of tillers per plant.

12) Leaf area, determined using the same technique described for clipping leaf area.

13) Dry weight, determined as previously described.

14) Root dry weight. Four subsamples were removed from each pot, using a 1.5 cm circular soil sampling device. The soil and roots were dried at 70 C, ashed at 500 C, and reweighed. The loss in weight, corrected for the original soil organic matter content, was taken as root weight. The sides and bottom of the pots were avoided when the soil samples were taken.

Statistical analysis

A completely randomized block analysis of variance was made on the two species at each light intensity. The determined variances at each light intensity were pooled, and a single LDS value (0.05 level) was determined for each parameter measured.

RESULTS

Clippings were collected weekly between the 5th and 14th week following germination. Species responses to reduced light intensities were similar throughout this period. Results presented are those obtained during the 11th week.

Leaf length above the cutting height increased with decreasing light intensity to 10,760 lux (Fig. 1). Leaf length decreased at lower light intensities. Although both species responded similarly, red fescue leaf length was not as great as Kentucky bluegrass at any one light intensity. Leaf width (Fig. 1) decreased with each decrement of decreasing light. The response of the two species was similar.

Mean shoot angle measurements are shown in Table 1. The angle measured was the angle of the shoot from the vertical. Both species displayed a horizontal growth habit at the higher light intensities. Kentucky bluegrass had an upright growth habit under low light intensities, while red fescue remained horizontal.

Clipping dry weight and percent moisture are presented in Fig. 2. Both species responded similarly. Clipping dry weight was maintained under decreasing light intensity to 10,760 lux, but declined rapidly below 10,760 lux for both species. Kentucky bluegrass produced more leaf growth than red fescue at light intensities greater than 10,760 lux, while there was no difference below 10,760 lux. Percent moisture of both species increased with each

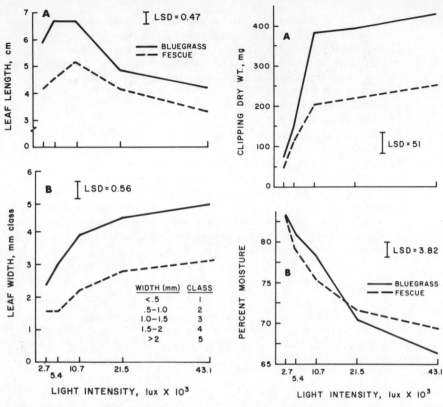

Fig. 1—(A) Average leaf length above cutting height, and (B) leaf width measured on the youngest, fully expanded leaf 1 cm from the collar prior to weekly clipping. Leaf widths are placed into classes.

Fig. 2—(A) Clipping dry weight (mg/pot) above 5 cm after 1 week's regrowth, and (B) clipping percent moisture on a fresh weight basis.

Table 1—Shoot angle of singly grown plants of Merion Kentucky bluegrass and Pennlawn red fescue at five light intensities. Vertical = 0°, horizontal = 90°. LSD .05 = 12.6.

Light intensity	Kentucky bluegrass	Red fescue
lux × 10³	Shoot angle, degrees	
2.7	20	38
5.4	25	55
10.7	30	60
21.5	70	70
32.1	75	80

decrement of reduced light, ranging from 68% at 43,060 lux, to 83% at 2,690 lux.

Clipping leaf area (Fig. 3) increased with decreasing intensities to 10,760

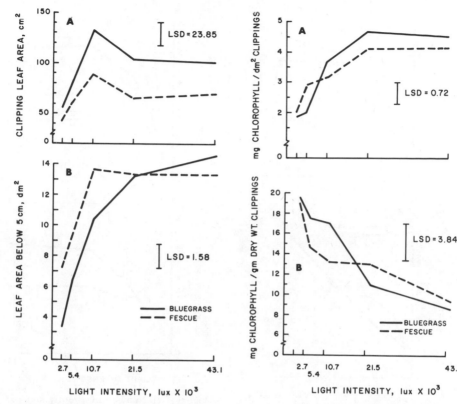

Fig. 3—(A) Leaf area of clippings collected above 5 cm after 1 week's regrowth, and (B) leaf area below 5 cm 14 weeks after germination.

Fig. 4—Amount of chlorophyll in clippings. (A) Chlorophyll per dm^2 and (B) chlorophyll per g dry weight of clippings.

lux, and then decreased under lower light intensities. The increased leaf area was due to the extended leaf length. Kentucky bluegrass had a greater clipping leaf area than red fescue above 10,760 lux, while the two species did not differ below 10,760 lux.

Both species responded similarly in terms of chlorophyll content (Fig. 4). Chlorophyll per square decimeter decreased with decreasing light intensities. This decrease corresponded to the lighter green of leaves observed at the lower light intensities. Chlorophyll per gram of dry weight increased with each decrement of decreasing light intensity.

Dry shoot weight below the cutting height and root weight are shown in Fig. 5. While shoot growth of Kentucky bluegrass was greater than red fescue at the highest light intensity, the fescue outperformed bluegrass at the lowest intensity. Root growth was reduced under low light (Fig. 5). No difference could be found in the root production between the two species. The most marked reduction in the root-shoot ratio occurred between 43,060 and 21,530 lux for both species.

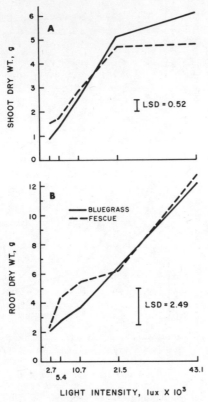

Fig. 5—(A) Shoot dry weight (g/pot) below 5 cm, and (B) root dry weight (g/pot) 14 weeks after germination.

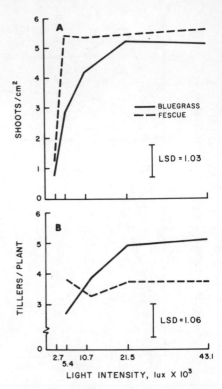

Fig. 6—(A) Number of shoots, and (B) average number of tillers 14 weeks after germination.

Kentucky bluegrass declined in leaf area below the cutting height with each decrement of reduced light intensity (Fig. 3). Red fescue maintained leaf area under decreasing light to 10,760 lux. Although leaf area of red fescue declined below 10,760 lux, the reduction was less for red fescue than Kentucky bluegrass at 2,690 and 5,380 lux.

The shoot density of Kentucky bluegrass declined below 21,530 lux, while shoot density of red fescue did not decline until the light intensity was lower than 5,380 lux (Fig. 6). Tillering of Kentucky bluegrass was severely restricted at light intensities below 21,530 lux (Fig. 6). Tillering of red fescue did not appear to be affected by light intensities as low as 5,380 lux.

DISCUSSION

Merion Kentucky bluegrass and Pennlawn red fescue responded differently to reduced light intensity only in terms of shoot weight and leaf area below the cutting height, tillers per plant, shoot density, and leaf angle. Red fescue produced superior verdure at the lower light intensities, thus providing a more suitable turf. Shoot density and tillering of red fescue did not decline until light intensities below 5,380 lux were reached. Perhaps more shade-tolerant ground cover species should be used at light intensities below 5,380 lux if there is no sunflecking.

Kentucky bluegrass displayed an upright growth habit under low light intensities, while red fescue remained horizontal. A shade-adaptive mechanism of red fescue may be involved. The more horizontal growth habit of red fescue shoots may enhance light interception within the shade environment. Also, less photosynthetically active, young leaf tissue will be removed by mowing.

The two species responded similarly to reduced light intensities in the following parameters: leaf length, leaf width, clipping area, clipping yield, percent moisture, chlorophyll content, and root growth. Kentucky bluegrass was superior at the higher light intensities in terms of leaf length, clipping weight, and clipping leaf area. Although red fescue provides a better turf than Kentucky bluegrass in shade, Kentucky bluegrass was comparable to red fescue at low light intensities in terms of vertical shoot growth above the cutting height and root production.

The marked increase in percent moisture of leaf tissue within the shade environment contributes to increased disease susceptibility. Plant factors besides succulence must be involved in disease susceptibility, since the response of both species was similar. Red fescue does possess more disease resistance in shade than Kentucky bluegrass (1).

Disease resistance and the ability to compete with tree roots have been studied as possible explanations for the favorable shade-adaptation characteristics of red fescue (1, 9, 10). Tree root competition was not a factor in this investigation, and disease was not observed at any time. Red fescue must possess additional shade adaptive mechanisms. These mechanisms may involve anatomical responses, photosynthetic efficiencies, and respiration rates.

It is recognized that this study was conducted on specific Kentucky bluegrass and red fescue cultivars. Cultivars may vary in their morphological responses to reduced light intensities.

REFERENCES

1. BEARD, J. B. 1965. Factors in the adaptation of turfgrasses to shade. Agron. J. 57:457–459.
2. ———. 1967. Shade tolerance and maintenance. Proc. 38th Int. Turfgrass Conf., Golf Course Superintendents' Association, Lawrence, Kansas.
3. ———. 1973. Turfgrass science and culture. Prentice-Hall, Inc., Englewood Cliffs, N. J. p. 181–209.
4. BOSTER, D. O. 1966. Pennsylvania turfgrass survey. 1966. Pennsylvania Crop Rep. Serv., Pennsylvania Dept. Agr., Harrisburg. 38 p.
5. HOAGLAND, C. R., and D. I. ARNON. 1950. The water culture method for growing plants without soil. California Agr. Exp. Sta. Circ. 374. 32 p.
6. MAC KINNEY, G. 1941. Absorption of light by chlorophyll solutions. J. Biol. Chem. 140:315–322.
7. VEZINA, P. E., and D. W. K. BOULTER. 1969. The spectral composition of near ultraviolet and visible radiation beneath forest canopies. Can. J. Bot. 44:1267–1284.

8. WARD, Coleman Y. 1969. Climate and adaptation. *In* A. A. Hanson and F. V. Juska (ed.) Turfgrass science. Agronomy 14:27–79. Amer. Soc. Agron., Madison, Wis.

9. WHITCOMB, C. E. 1972. Influence of tree root competition on growth response of cool-season turfgrasses. Agron. J. 64:355–359.

10. ———, and E. C. ROBERTS. 1973. Competition between established tree roots and newly seeded Kentucky bluegrass. Agron. J. 65:126–129.

11. WILSON, D. B. 1962. Effects of light intensity and clipping on herbage yields. Can. J. Plant Sci. 42:270–275.

12. WOOD, G. M. 1969. Evaluating turfgrasses for shade tolerance. Agron. J. 61:347–352.

28

Automatic irrigation systems for turfgrass[1]

J. R. WATSON

There has been marked progress in the development of automatic irrigation equipment during recent years. This equipment incorporated into a correctly designed system for a specific landscaped site permits the controlled application of precise amounts of water. Such systems are capable of delivering the water in accordance with the needs of various plants and in conformance with the infiltration and waterholding capacity of widely variable soils. Current automatic irrigation systems are economical to operate and are designed to conserve water. Automatic irrigation systems may be programmed to operate during "off peak" water use and play periods.

The mechanical components of an automatic irrigation system consist of a pumping station, pipe, valves, sprinklers, and controllers. The more advanced systems utilize a valve in or valve under each head and central controls which permit operation of individual heads. System design, installation, and programming are key factors in the successful performance of the various components. Additional index words: Watering, Infiltration, Water-holding capacity, Water conservation, Sprinklers, Design.

Turfgrass and landscape areas are irrigated to provide a more favorable environment for the plants. The application of supplemental water to these areas may be accomplished effectively and efficiently through the use of an automatic irrigation system. Automatic irrigation systems for turfgrass have evolved from the application of fixed sprinkler heads and automatic valves and controllers to the underground piping used for quick coupling systems. These latter systems, in turn, evolved from the various hose-end devices used to water turf areas.

During the past few years the replacement and automation of quick coupling systems and the installation of automatic systems on new turfgrass facilities have proceeded at a rapid rate. The reasons basically stem from a lack of qualified labor to handle the manual application of water, the need to conserve water, the need to apply water to landscaped areas in off-peak use periods, and the requirement for maximum utilization of the turf facility during daylight hours. The overall result has been a marked improvement in

---

[1]Contribution from The Toro Company in cooperation with its Irrigation Division. June, 1973.

turfgrass quality because automatic equipment presently available permits the controlled application of precise amounts of water. Water may be applied in accordance with the needs of the plants and in conformance with the infiltration and water-holding capacity of a given soil. Equally as important, automatic systems for turfgrass should function so as to assure conservation of water and minimal operating cost.

MECHANICAL COMPONENTS

The basic components of an automatic system are the sprinkler heads, the valves, the controllers, the piping, and pumps. All except the latter two components will be discussed in this review.

Sprinkler heads

The sprinkler head directs water to a specified area by forcing a stream or a spray from the head. If a spray is used, the area is continuously covered. If the stream method is used, the stream is rotated over the area to be covered and the distance water is thrown from the head is greatly increased and the application rate reduced.

Among the most common means of rotation are impulse, cam, and gear drive. Gear-driven heads are the smoothest operating and are usually more dependable because they have a constant force applied to them as they operate rather than a sporadic, high impact stress. Gear-driven heads are designed with variable speed ranges, thus producing more uniform coverage as shown in Fig. 1. Note that the arcs covered by the half-speed range receive double the amount of water received at the regular speed. Overlapping in the latter arcs produce uniform coverage.

The performance of a sprinkler head is often rated on the basis of the distance—radius or diameter—of throw. These are theoretical numbers usually derived from performance charts or from tests under ideal conditions. To use these numbers *per se* would result in over spacing and, subsequently, poor coverage. For effective watering of landscaped areas with an automatic irrigation system, the heads must be spaced in accordance with the actual conditions on the site. Spacing must take into account wind movement and rate and uniformity of application (distribution pattern and distribution

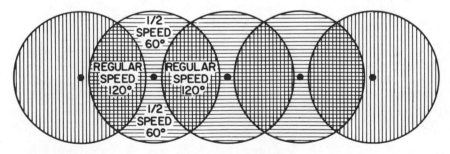

Fig. 1—Sprinkler heads.

curve) in pattern. This type of information is available from sprinkler manufacturers. The importance of wind is shown in the following table:

Wind velocity, km/hr	Maximum triangular spacing, % of dia.
0 – 4.827	70
4.827– 8.045	60
8.045–11.263	50
11.263–16.09	40

The number of heads required for effective watering goes up in inverse proportion to the square of the spacing.

Other factors that affect performance of sprinkler heads in an automatic system are:

1. Material of which it is constructed. Nonmetallic materials reduce corrosion problems and extend longevity.
2. Screen areas. Large screening areas prevent excessive wear, plugging of nozzle orifices, and jamming of the rotating mechanisms.
3. Isolation of drive or rotating mechanisms from the water stream. This avoids excessive wear and impairment of gears by waterborne abrasives like sand.
4. Ease of serviceability and interchangeability of major sprinkler components.

Valves

Valves used in automatic irrigation systems are usually of the globe type rather than the gate type. They are normally activated by the application of pressure against a diaphragm or piston. The pressure that opens or closes the diaphragm or piston may be exerted by an electrically activated solenoid in the electric valve or by water flowing through a tube in the hydraulic valve.

A valve may be used to control the flow of water through one or more sprinkler heads. However, the fewer the number of heads per valve the more precise the control of the water being applied will be. The most precise control results from use of a valve under or valve in each head as illustrated in Fig. 2. This greater degree of flexibility will permit water to be applied in accordance with the capability of the soil to accept and to store it, and commensurate with the water requirements of the grass or other plants.

Controllers

Controllers are electrically activated timing devices that initiate a signal—either electric or hydraulic—that causes a remote-controlled valve to either close or open and permit water flow to a sprinkler head. Controllers may be centrally placed in one location, located in the field near the heads they will control and operate, or a combination of these plans may be used. The num-

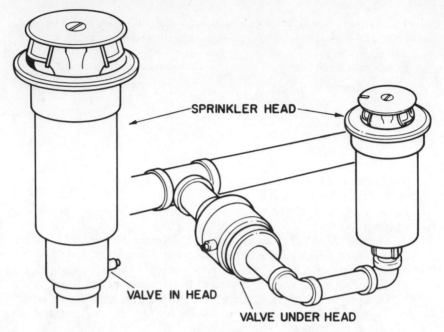

Fig. 2—Valves.

ber of "stations" or individual control elements will vary from 4 to 20 or more.

Controllers must be programmed to perform in accordance with the system design objectives. They also must be checked periodically to assure that they continue to operate as required by prevailing conditions and in accordance with design precepts.

The ability to cycle or to repeat the watering schedule is one of the major advantages of today's automatic irrigation system controllers. Applied for several short periods rather than for one extended period makes it possible to adequately water steep slopes as well as severely compacted soils. This method prevents incurring the severe run-off associated with these and similar areas with low infiltration capacities.

Flexible controller programs coupled with design and production of sprinkler heads with a wide range of capability permits changes in conventional water management programs for turfgrass. In fact, the proper utilization of automatic irrigation systems demands a reexamination of water management practices for turfgrass facilities

DESIGN

Basically, any system design is a compromise between cost and performance. Thus, the turfgrass manager must make certain basic decisions which revolve around obtaining the best performance for the costs involved. The turfgrass manager must answer such questions as area to be covered, hours available for watering, amount of water to be applied, type of system, precipitation rate, wind velocity, and service life of the equipment. Answers to these questions, once incorporated into the system design, are fixed and cannot be altered by simple programming procedures.

A system is purchased to water turf areas and to keep the plants green during the growing season. This often coincides with the driest time of the year. Failure to specify a system with the capacity to provide adequate water distribution and uniform coverage during these periods will produce unsatisfactory results.

SUMMARY

Automatic irrigation systems for turfgrass permit the development and the maintenance of optimum plant environments with maximum conservation of water. New ideas and new concepts in equipment and in system design are continually evolving. As these are incorporated into automatic irrigation systems for turfgrass, there is a need to continually reexamine conventional water management practices.

FURTHER READING

1. BEAN, Lee. 1969. Advancements in sprinkler irrigation. Paper presented at RCGA Conference. University of Saskatchewan, Saskatoon, Saskatchewan, Canada.
2. BEARD, J. B. 1973. Turfgrass science and culture. Prentice-Hall, Inc., Englewood Cliffs, N. J. p. 466–485.
3. DANIELSON, R. E. 1973. Factors affecting turfgrass irrigation. Western Landscaping News. 2:16–31.
4. HUNTER, E. J. 1968. Facts on automatic underground sprinkling. The Toro Company, Moist O'Matic Division, Minneapolis, Minn.
5. MADISON, J. H. 1971. Principles of turfgrass culture. Van Nostrand Reinhold Co., New York. p. 280–372.
6. MARSH, A. W. 1969. Soil water—irrigation and drainage. *In* Turfgrass science. Agronomy 14:151–186. Amer. Soc. Agron., Madison, Wis.
7. THE TORO COMPANY. 1972. Logic of sprinkler system planning. Moist O'Matic Division. Minneapolis, Minn.
8. WATSON, J. R. 1972. Planning to meet tomorrow's equipment needs. Proc. Eighth Annual Turfgrass Manage. Conf., Hawaii Turfgrass Assoc., Honolulu, Hawaii.

29

Applications of color infrared photography to turfgrass science[1]

G.M. WOOD

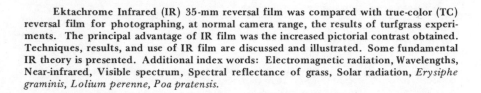

Ektachrome Infrared (IR) 35-mm reversal film was compared with true-color (TC) reversal film for photographing, at normal camera range, the results of turfgrass experiments. The principal advantage of IR film was the increased pictorial contrast obtained. Techniques, results, and use of IR film are discussed and illustrated. Some fundamental IR theory is presented. Additional index words: Electromagnetic radiation, Wavelengths, Near-infrared, Visible spectrum, Spectral reflectance of grass, Solar radiation, *Erysiphe graminis, Lolium perenne, Poa pratensis.*

Beyond the red portion of the visible light spectrum exists an invisible band of electromagnetic radiation called the near-infrared. This infrared (IR) radiation, like the visible spectrum, is actinic, or capable of image formation through chemical changes in sensitized photographic emulsions. Researchers have long been accustomed to thinking that infrared photography was the exclusive tool of the aerial photographer, but remote multispectral sensing that includes the IR is now a specialized area of research in the plant sciences.

Infrared photography is already recognized as a valuable tool in medicine, forestry, soil science, range management, geology, archaeology, and agriculture (1, 3, 4, 7, 8, 9, 10) and has recently been studied for use in turfgrass science (12, 13, 14). The turfgrass scientist need not be a technologist in this field. He can use IR photography at ground level in essentially the same manner as he does conventional photography. Infrared film has the advantage of emphasizing differences and can reveal information not attainable with conventional photographic techniques.

This paper is designed to introduce the turfgrass scientist to infrared photography, discuss some of the problems he may encounter, and demonstrate results that can be expected from its use.

All electromagnetic radiation can be classified according to wavelength, using the millimicron (mµ) as the unit of measure. The visible spectrum, generally considered to be in the 400 to 700 mµ range, which seen as white light, consists of several distinct color components, each distinguishable by its difference in wavelength. The near-infrared radiation most practical for

[1]Contribution 312. Vermont Agricultural Experiment Station, Burlington, VT 05401.

general photography exists in the 700 to 900 mμ range. This radiation can be recorded on both black and white and color IR-sensitized films, but is more interpretive and just as useful as color. Color IR-sensitized reversal film produces positive false-color transparencies which, when projected, result in images nearly identical to that from true-color (TC) film, except for the unusual colors. True-color film has three color-sensitive emulsion layers: blue, green, and red. Color IR film differs in that the blue-sensitive layer has been replaced by an IR-sensitive emulsion. Thus, with IR film both visible and invisible radiation play roles in image formation and color development. Since in addition to individual color sensitivities all layers of the IR film are sensitive to blue, a yellow (minus-blue) filter is needed to absorb the blue and produce the desired photograph. In TC film the yellow filter is incorporated into the film itself between the blue and underlying green and red sensitive emulsions. Elimination of the blue-sensitive layer and addition of the IR-sensitive layer result in an apparent shift in the colors. What is seen as blue becomes black, green becomes blue, visible red becomes green, and the invisible IR is recorded as visible red. Many other false-color combinations can result. These color shifts hold particularly for nonliving subjects. With plants and living systems other factors come into play, resulting in varied color effects.

The spectral response of grass and other plants to solar radiation depends on the reflection, transmission, and absorption of the incident radiation. Visible wavelengths, particularly in blue and red, are largely absorbed by chlorophyll and other leaf pigments (1, 2). Grass appears green because a small amount (up to 12%) of the green wavelength radiation is reflected back to the eye (10). The longer IR wavelengths remain largely unabsorbed and for the most part simply follow the physical laws of reflectance and transmission. Intensity of the infrared reflectance, which is high in both grasses . and dicotyledonous plants, is related to the sum of individual reflectances off of the internal cell wall surfaces, particularly in the area of the spongy mesophyll (2, 6). Figure 1 shows the spectral reflectance of healthy green grass compared to pine needles and green paint. The high IR reflectance of the grass (up to 87%) will be recorded predominantly as red or magenta; the pine needles, which have a lower IR reflectance than most plants (1), as a darker magenta or purple; and the green paint, also with a low IR reflectance, as bluish-purple or cyan. Thus, when photographed with color IR film, grass appears redder, or "more infrared," than it would green if TC film were used.

Diseased, injured, or otherwise stressed grass rapidly loses IR reflectance. This is one of the earliest symptoms of a loss in vigor and it appears due to a collapse of the leaf's spongy mesophyll tissues, induced when the damaging agent restricts the supply of water to the tissues (1). Loss of internal IR reflectance takes place long before there is any shift in the external visible-spectrum reflectance characteristics of the leaf, simply because chlorophyll has apparently not yet been affected. The plant will thus appear healthy even though the change in IR reflectance reveals internal difficulties (1). Under such conditions an entire series of gradations of IR colors result that can be more pronounced and informative than any changes in the shades of green in a TC photograph. As the loss in IR reflectance progresses, the bright

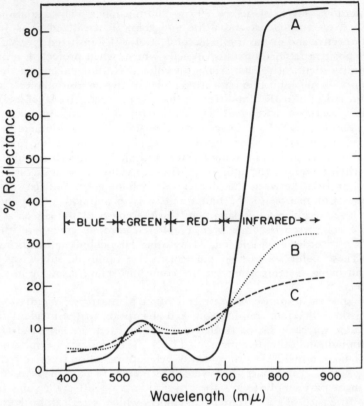

Fig. 1—Curves showing the spectral reflectance of (A) grass, (B) pine tree needles, and (C) green paint [after Fritz (5)].

red recorded for healthy turf grades away from magenta, into blue, green, and brown.

The principal advantage of recording with modified or false-color IR film in turfgrass work is the increased pictorial contrast that results. Yellow and brown colors tend to become lighter and contrast more sharply with the IR-produced red or magenta. For example, yellow dandelion (*Taraxacum officinale* Weber) in grass appears white in a red turf. Green, on the other hand, is much closer to yellow and brown in the spectrum of colors and therefore affords much less distinction when TC films are used. Similar results have been obtained in forestry (7, 8). The following discussion and results deal with some applications of IR photography in turfgrass research.

MATERIALS AND METHODS

A 35-mm Nikon camera with through-the-lens metering was used for all photographs. Any adjustable 35-mm camera with a reasonably good quality lens would be satisfactory. For the initial studies, which began in 1969, Kodak Ektachrome IR Aero film (Type 8443) was used. Since Eastman Kodak Company did not process this film, private laboratory processing was used. Shortly thereafter, Kodak released a new Ektachrome IR film (Type 2443) for which processing is provided. Directions for self-processing are also provided with the film. Both films are stated by Kodak to have virtually the same emulsion characteristics. Type 2443 now replaces the earlier film and was used for most of this research. Unless otherwise indicated, the IR refers interchangeably to infrared Ektachrome film of these two types.

All exposures were made with a yellow (minus-blue) filter (equivalent to No. 12 Wratten) attached to the camera, as recommended by Kodak, unless otherwise indicated. Dual cameras, loaded with either TC or IR film, were switched back and forth on a tripod in order to get exact comparisons. A number of TC films were compared with the IR film. A TC film with an ASA rating similar to the IR offers some advantage because like f/stops and shutter speeds can be selected. However, any TC film may be used according to preference. For most of the comparisons, Kodachrome II was used.

An ASA film speed rating of 125, instead of the 100 recommended by Kodak for trial with the IR film, was found to be more satisfactory for turf photography because of the slightly greater color saturation resulting. Because the ratio of IR to visible light varies, no exact ASA setting can be specified for all conditions. Also, the degree of color saturation desired will vary according to individual preference. The usual photographic light meter responds only to the visible portion of the spectrum and is useful only as a basis for trial. Bracketing of exposures one-half to one full stop below and above the visible light reading is desirable. According to Fritz (5), the range for acceptable results is only about one-half stop on either side of the optimum exposure.

Photographs of turf in the field with IR film are best made in bright sunlight when the sun is at a high angle, or between 10 a.m. and 3 p.m. Manzer and Cooper (9), working with potatoes (*Solanum* sp.) in both aerial and ground-level IR photography, also found that light quality, angle of incidence, and exposure were critical for good results. The darkening effect of cloud cover on the image was much greater with IR film than with TC film because shaded areas are illuminated by skylight which is nearly eliminated by a yellow filter (5). Electronic flash produces sufficient IR radiation to be useful for greenhouse and fill-in illumination.

Considerable variation in results was experienced between films that were not of the same lot number, age, and storage conditions. If possible, fresh film of the same origin should be obtained and stored in a freezer at −18 C or lower. Under some circumstances it may be desirable to age film at room temperature. This will result in changes in the relative speeds of the three component emulsion layers and a corresponding color balance shift (5). In aerial work, Houston (8) found subtle differences more apparent when fresh IR film was aged 90 days at room temperature. In the turf studies reported here only fresh or freezer-stored films were used. Fritz (5) described optimum methods for using infrared-sensitive color films.

No compensation was necessary or is recommended for the difference in focus that occurs between IR and TC wavelengths. Normally, sufficient depth of focus is present for acceptably sharp photographs, particularly if an aperture size of f/8 or smaller is used. Because of the penetration of the IR radiation into the turf itself, the image sometimes appears slightly more diffuse than when strictly visible light images are formed.

A stepladder, crane with boom, or other device may be used to elevate the camera above the area for plot photographs. Idaho workers (11) used helium-filled balloons to provide an aerial platform for photographing research plots with IR film. A wide-angle lens, used in conventional photography, is useful for photographing a greater area where working distance is small.

With IR photography, white signs tend to wash out and become less legible even though they remain quite readable when photographed with TC film (Fig. 2). Angling the sign so as to decrease the incident sunlight helped to avoid this difficulty. Probably, with a little experimentation, an appropriate combination of colored background and lettering could be found to improve sign readability.

WEAR STUDIES

A comparison of four films, Kodachrome II, Ektachrome IR, Kodak black and white IR (IR 135), and Kodak black and white Plus-X Pan, was made to record the effects of induced-wear treatments on turf cultivars cut at 1.3 and 2.5 cm (14). The Ektachrome IR film was judged better than TC film for demonstrating the effect of wear (Fig. 2). Black and white prints made from Kodachrome II and Plus-X Pan were about equal with IR 135 being least desirable.

POWDERY MILDEW STUDIES

Powdery mildew (*Erysiphe graminis* D. C.) infection in Kentucky bluegrass (*Poa pratensis* L.) was better demonstrated with IR than with TC (Kodachrome II) film (Fig. 3). In this greenhouse study, an electronic flash was used to adequately illuminate both IR and TC photographs. Light-colored foliage in Fig. 3 shows bluegrass cultivars infected with the mildew. Badly infected 'Pennstar,' center foreground in both pictures, is shown much more effectively with IR film. For all pictures the electronic flash (Honeywell Strobonar Model 65C-BCPS output 4000) was held above the photographer's head and aimed downward at an approximate 45° angle to the tripod-mounted camera.

FREEZING STUDIES

Artificial freezing studies with ryegrasses (*Lolium perenne* L.) and other turfgrasses were conducted. In these studies, potted, growth-chamber-hardened plants were frozen to –12 C in 14 hours in a freezer and then allowed to recover 2 weeks in the greenhouse. Figure 4, photographed in the greenhouse with natural light at 1 p.m. on July 11, 1972, shows the

Fig. 2—Comparison of IR (top) and TC (Kodachrome II) films for demonstrating effect of wear on 'Delta' Kentucky bluegrass when cut at 1.3 cm (foreground) and 2.5 cm (background). Black and white prints were made from color slides.

Fig. 3—Comparison of IR (top) and TC (Kodachrome II) films for demonstrating powdery mildew infection in Kentucky bluegrass cultivars. Black and white prints were made from color slides.

Fig. 4—Comparison of IR (top) and TC (Kodachrome II) films for detecting and illustrating injury in artificially frozen turfgrasses. Photos are black and white prints made from color slides.

relative effectiveness of IR film and TC (Kodachrome II). Although the resolving power of the TC film is definitely better, as demonstrated by the sharper detail, the ability to illustrate cold-injured tissue is superior in the IR film, as shown by the much greater contrast between living and dead tissue.

OTHER APPLICATIONS

In addition to the studies illustrated, IR film was observed in some instances to be more effective than TC film for demonstrating results in herbicide, seed identification, drought, and weed encroachment experiments, and other studies (12).

Since both broadleaf and grassy weeds differ from turfgrasses with respect to IR reflectance, their presence often can be demonstrated better with IR than with TC film in weed studies. This is particularly true when plants are in bloom, as in the case with dandelions.

Trial IR and TC aerial photographs of a golf course suggest that IR photographs taken of greens and fairways at regular intervals could be an effective method of monitoring the course and detecting potential trouble areas in time to alleviate critical situations. A valuable file for future reference might thus be developed. The use of IR film is no panacea or magic means of problem solving for the turfgrass scientist. In many situations IR photography may be no more, or even less, effective than conventional photography. The turfgrass photographer must be as familiar with its limitations as with its capabilities. Its usefulness to many fields of science cannot be questioned.

REFERENCES

1. COLWELL, Robert N. 1964. Aerial photography—a valuable sensor for the scientist. Amer. Sci. 52:16–49.
2. COULSON, K. L. 1966. Effects of reflection properties of natural surfaces in aerial reconnaissance. Appl. Optics 5:905–917.
3. EASTMAN KODAK CO. 1968. Applied infrared photography. Kodak Tech. Publ. M-28.
4. FRITZ, N. L. 1965. Film sees new world of color. Citrus World 2(2):11–12, 26.
5. ————. 1967. Optimum methods for using infrared-sensitive color films. Photogram. Eng. 33:1128–1138.
6. GATES, D. M., H. J. KEEGAN, J. C. SCHLETER, and V. R. WEIDNER. 1965. Spectral properties of plants. Appl. Optics 4:11–20.
7. HELLER, R. C. 1965. Aerial remote sensing research in forestry. Proc. Amer. Soc. Foresters. Amer. Soc. of Foresters, Washington, D. C. p. 162–168.
8. HOUSTON, D. R. 1972. The use of large-scale aerial color photography for assessing forestry tree diseases. 1. Basal canker of white pine: a case study. USDA Forest Serv. Res. Paper NE-230.
9. MANZER, F. E., and G. R. COOPER. 1967. Aerial photographic methods of potato disease detection. Maine Agr. Exp. Sta. Bull. 646.
10. SKAPTASON, J. B. 1969. Aerial infrared photos show plant diseases and insects. Croplife 16:8–9.
11. WATSON, R. D., W. L. MODEN, Jr., and R. N. MC GRAW. 1969. Platform for aerial photography. Down to Earth 25(1):3–4.
12. WOOD, G. M. 1971a. Color infrared photography: Technique and use in turfgrass research. p. 52. Agron. Abstr. 63rd Ann. Meeting, New York. Amer. Soc. Agron., Madison, Wis.

13. ———. 1971b. Photographing the invisible world of infrared. Vermont Farm Home Sci. 14(1):8-9. Univ. Vermont.
14. ———, and A. G. LAW. 1971. Evaluating Kentucky bluegrass cultivars for wear resistance. p. 65. Agron. Abstr. 64th Ann. Meeting, Miami Beach, Fla., Amer. Soc. Agron., Madison, Wis.

ABSTRACTS

Abstracts of all papers not published herein but presented at the Conference are included below to round off this Section. These abstracts, unlike the printed papers, have not been refereed.

SECTION 3 ABSTRACT—AMENDING WATER WITH SOIL-WETTING AGENTS

A review of the published and unpublished data on the use of wetting agents (surfactants) shows large differences in adsorptive characteristics of different types of wetting agents; improved wetting, infiltration, and drainage; reduced bulk density of compacted loam soil; reduced soil moisture tensions; more uniform distribution of soil moisture in the profile; and reduced evaporative losses (35%) for properly treated soils. Laboratory and field data indicate that 3 ppm of wetting agent is too little and that 15 to 30 ppm is required. Phytotoxicity data show large differences both between types of wetting agents and between wetting agents of a given type. The nonionic wetting agents were the safest. Greenhouse data indicate a 30 to 50% reduction in water required and an improved intercellular structure of grass plants.—R. A. Moore, Aquatrols Corp. of America.

DISCUSSION

H. H. WILLIAMS—In deference to the current emphasis on conservation of energy-producing natural resources (fuels), how can the use of tarps and/or plastic covers to reduce heat loss and other related benefits associated with soil warming under turf be justifiably de-emphasized?

G. G. FISHER—Generally, we are not using plastic covers in the United Kingdom for this form of soil heating. The additional cost of the tarp or plastic and the added labor cost are considered important in this regard. At the same time we realize that in particularly severe climates a plastic cover could be useful. The partial inflation of the cover by the underground air to help hold it above the turf is considered advantageous.

J. P. VAN DER HORST—How can the number of games played on sports fields be kept constant for all teams when not all playing fields are heated? In practice 24 teams may compete regularly. If half of these teams have heated sports facilities and half do not, some games will have to be cancelled because of frost or snow on the nonheated fields. After the playing season is over it would be expected that some teams played several games fewer than others, and this is certainly not desirable. Because of the high investment required for heating sports fields, wouldn't it be wise to start with the first division stadia and then determine how far improvements can be made from there? Also, with regard to loss of profit when games cannot be played, there will be times when the weather is so bad that spectators will not attend a game even when the facilities are heated. What experience has there been with attendance under these conditions?

G. G. FISHER—The installation of this type of heating in stadia is a process which should not unduly upset the playing characteristics of a field, but merely give the spectators a higher degree of certainty that the game will be played. We have not observed that this would upset a league program to any great extent.

J. P. VAN DER HORST—In wintertime, a nonheated facility may have to cancel from 7 to 10 games while a heated facility allows for play of all of its regularly scheduled games. In the Netherlands we do not want this situation to exist. It would seem that perhaps the best way to handle this type of situation would be to have heated fields installed by division. For example, each first division field must be heated.

P. BOEKER—In making comparisons between two species, one should use more than one cultivar per species, because within-species differences in behavior may be larger than differences between species.

J. F. WILKINSON —Yes, there is often great variation from one cultivar to the next. In our morphological studies we are attempting to learn as much as possible about Merion bluegrass and Pennlawn red fescue before going on with studies with other cultivars. Basically, we are looking for one shade adaptation mechanism that we can identify. Then we plan to screen other Kentucky bluegrasses and red fescues in the hope of finding cultivars which possess greater shade adaptation.

E. W. SCHWEIZER—We have found in Switzerland that grasses grown in shaded areas have less well-developed root systems. These restrictions in root development have been attributed to root competition by trees and also to physiological effects related to low light intensity. We have observed that foliar fertilization is more efficient in very shaded areas. Granular fertilizers are less efficient. Are these data in agreement with research conducted in Michigan?

J. F. WILKINSON —We have not considered foliar fertilization as a turfgrass treatment under shade. In our controlled studies a nutrient solution has been used at weekly intervals. This has been applied to the soil. Foliar application has not been attempted under these conditions.

R. W. SCHERY—Were there any morphological generalities that could be made following these studies with Merion bluegrass and Pennlawn red fescue?

J. F. WILKINSON —Leaf width response was the same in both red fescue and Kentucky bluegrass. Leaf width decreased and, from what I have seen, this was not a factor in terms of cool-season turfgrass adaptation to shade. C. W. Winstead working with St. Augustinegrass found that wider leaves were obtained at lower light intensities. This may be an example of a shade adaptive mechanism in St. Augustinegrass. We have not found this kind of morphological response with the grasses studied to date.

H. C. H. GHIJSEN—Have there been any studies on the change in chemical content of *Poa pratensis* leaves under lower light conditions that could be related to disease resistance? Perhaps sugars and other carbohydrates have been determined or other organic constituents of turfgrass foliage.

J. F. WILKINSON —We are investigating many different parameters and tissue has been prepared for analysis of carbohydrates and proteins. These could be important in disease resistance or susceptibility. Of course auxins and other growth regulators might well be important too.

H. C. H. GHIJSEN—What is the estimated cost of using infrared photography?

G. M. WOOD —Not appreciably more than the cost associated with high-quality color photography.

Turfgrass soils and their modification

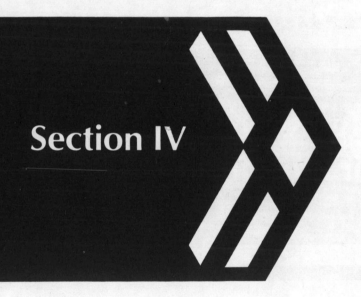

Section IV

30

Soil modification for athletic fields

W. SKIRDE

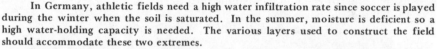

In Germany, athletic fields need a high water infiltration rate since soccer is played during the winter when the soil is saturated. In the summer, moisture is deficient so a high water-holding capacity is needed. The various layers used to construct the field should accommodate these two extremes.

Fertilization of a compact, stony, subsoil underlying a drainage layer and a surface rooting layer with calcium cyanamide increased turfgrass growth, improved appearance, and increased drought resistance with the effects continuing into the third year. A layer of peat, perlite, and vermiculite on the subsoil also improved turfgrass appearance and increased drought resistance.

Drainage layers constructed of lava or pumice had a higher water-holding capacity than gravel and therefore delayed the onset of wilt. Turfgrasses wilted 3 days later on lava and 8 days later on pumice as compared to gravel.

The composition of the surface rooting layer, based on the new German Norm DIN 18 035-4, should be as follows. Not more than 8% fine soil (0.02 mm), less than 4% organic matter (weight percentages), a water-holding capacity between 35 and 40% by volume, and an infiltration rate of more than 0.0015 cm/second.

If Hygromull (BASF, West Germany) is used in place of one-third of the peat in a high peat mix (40% by volume), the surface layer will be firmer and the Hygromull will supply additional nitrogen. An increase of the water-holding capacity of a surface layer without an effect on the infiltration rate is possible by substituting lava sand, pumice sand, or perlite for quartz sand.

The infiltration rate of a mixture containing well-decomposed peat was much lower than for a mixture using undecomposed fibrous peat. A high infiltration rate resulted in the improved quality of the turf, especially when inferior varieties of *Poa pratensis* were used. Additional index words: Calcium cyanamide, Fertilization, Hygromull, Peat, Perlite, Pumice, Sand, Water infiltration rate, Water-holding capacity.

In Germany the construction of athletic fields offers special problems for three reasons:

1) The major sport, soccer, is played in winter when the surface is soft from high-water content. The soft, excessively wet soil doesn't tolerate excessive wear.
2) In summer, when rainfall is usually deficient, a high water-holding capacity is needed.
3) It is necessary to install a drainage layer on impervious and compact soils, especially on slopes in the hill country.

In most regions of Germany, *Poa pratensis* is dormant during the winter so there is continuous wear of the turf cover without regrowth for a period of 2 to 5 months. Therefore, the construction of athletic fields regularly requires complete soil modification to produce a compromise between high infiltration rate and water-holding capacity. For this reason, every layer of the mixture used in athletic fields should contribute to turfgrass development, and root growth should not be limited to a 10- to 15-cm surface layer.

SUBSOIL IMPROVEMENT

Agricultural research has clarified the influence of various factors, especially fertilizers, on root growth. Drawing upon this knowledge, an experiment was started in April 1971, to test the ability of several materials to stimulate root growth in a compact, stony subsoil. The following materials were used:

500 g/m^2 of Agrosil (BASF, West Germany)

$1,000$ g/m^2 of calcium cyanamide fertilizer

$1,000$ g/m^2 of basic slag

20 liter/m^2 of Hygromull (BASF, West Germany)

20 liter/m^2 of peat

20 liter/m^2 of vermiculite

15 liter/m^2 of perlite.

The subsoil treated with these materials was overlaid with a drainage layer of 10 cm of gravel and a surface rooting layer of 10 cm consisting of (by volume) 5 parts of sand (0 to 3 mm), 1 part of peat, 1 part of Hygromull, and 1 part of perlite. The 10-cm surface layer and drainage layer were compared with a reference plot having a separate 15-cm layer of each of these materials (Fig. 1).

The first visible results, darker turfgrass color and increased growth, occurred in July of the seeding year where calcium cyanamide fertilizer had been applied. There was a 15% increase in turf growth the second year where calcium cyanamide had been applied and the appearance of the turf was better than that of the reference plot. This effect continued in the third year. All of the materials produced growth equal to the 15-cm layer of the control treatment, and they improved the appearance of the turf as well as increased drought resistance. The highest drought resistance resulted where the subsoil was treated with peat, calcium cyanamide, perlite, and vermiculite. The improvement of the turf is assumed to be due to a deeper root penetration caused by fertilizer nutrients and higher water-holding capacity.

DRAINAGE LAYER

The drainage layer, usually of gravel, has a different particle size than the surface layer and the subsoil and is presumed to improve root penetration. There appears to be no need, under normal circumstances, for the drainage layer to be thicker than 10 to 12 cm. The water-holding capacity of the drainage layer affects turfgrass. Water-holding capacity increased with the amount of fine and medium sand and is higher if a porous material is

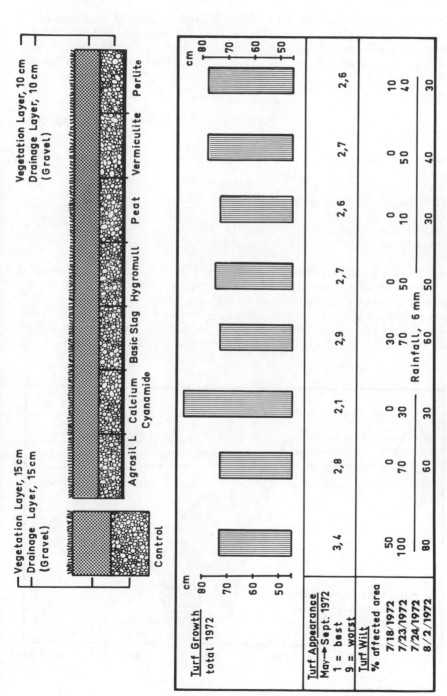

Fig. 1—Effect of substances for subsoil improvement on turf cover.

used. For example, pumice and lava with a particle size of 0 to 20 or 0 to 30 mm has a water-holding capacity under field conditions of 30% and 20% by volume, respectively. Gravel with the same particle size distribution shows a holding capacity of 12%, coarse gravel 5%, and broken whinstone (basalt) only 2 or 3% by volume. The water-absorbing capacity of materials for drainage layers is shown below.

Material	Particle size, mm	Water-holding capacity, % volume
Pumice	0–20	31%
Lava	0–30	20%
Lava	5–15	16%
Gravel (high amount of sand)	0–30	12%
Gravel	15–30	4%
Broken basalt	5–15	3%
Broken basalt	15–30	2%

A drainage layer is effective in reducing wilt of turfgrasses in proportion to its water-holding capacity. This fact is shown clearly in Fig. 2, where the turfgrass presented a much better appearance in the dry periods of 1972, with considerably higher wilt resistance on lava of 5 to 15 mm particle size when compared to gravel 0 to 30 mm in particle size. In another case, turf wilt occurred 8 to 10 days later on drainage layers of pumice 0 to 20 mm

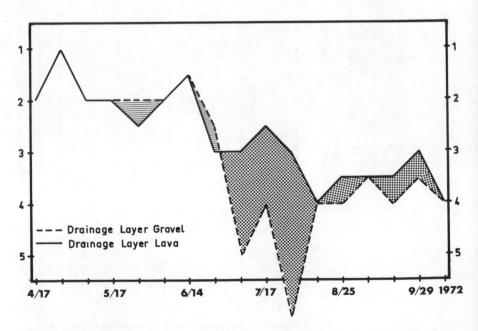

Fig. 2—Turf appearance caused by drainage layer form gravel on lava. 1 = best; 9 = worst.

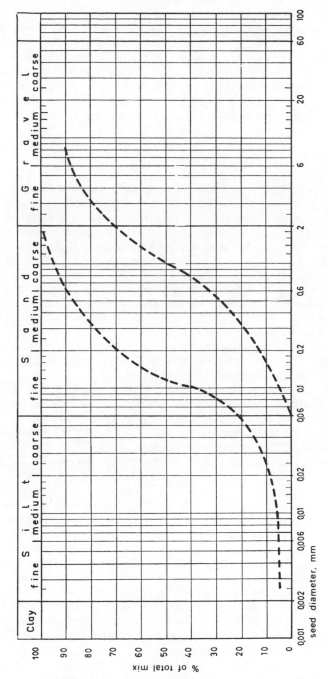

Fig. 3—Grain size distribution area for vegetation layers.

particle size with an overlying 6-mm surface layer than on a drainage layer of gravel 0 to 30 mm with an overlaying surface layer of 12 cm. The surface layer or root zone was composed of 50% sand, 38% peat, 12% soil, volume percentage.

Pumice and lava in Germany is available only in a small region west of the Rhine. Therefore, it is necessary to look for suitable materials for drainage layers for other sections of the country. Refuse slag looks promising because of its moisture-holding capacity and infiltration rate, providing the slag is free of phytotoxic substances and does not have a high salt content.

SURFACE LAYER OR ROOT ZONE MIX

The composition of the surface layer is important for tolerance to traffic and wear resistance of the turf cover, especially during wet winters. Therefore, the surface layer must have sufficient water permeability and stability to prevent a soft and soggy surface. Furthermore, it must permit a good bounce of the ball and provide good traction for the players. A good surface layer has four main characteristics based on the new German Norm DIN 18 035-4 "Sportfields—Turf Areas":

1) A particle size distribution with a maximum 8% of fine soil less than 0.02 mm, but a high rate of fine and medium sand combined (Fig. 3).
2) Less than 4% organic matter.
3) Between 35 and 40% water by volume at "field capacity".
4) An infiltration rate of 0.0015 cm/sec, or about 1 cm/7.5 min in an experimental compacted 10 cm surface layer.

Practically all soils in Germany have to be modified in order to meet specifications for the construction of athletic fields. The existing sandy soils are usually too fine and too uniform. Therefore, the mixture for the surface layer must usually be made from river or mine sand to which a small quantity of fine soil is added for binding. The incorporation of other substances to improve water-holding capacity is also important. Because of the winter playing season, the use of the LANGVAD mixture of 60% sand and 40% peat was found to be too soft and soggy for Germany. Furthermore, the surface layer needs to be more than 5 cm thick for drought resistance. An adequate water storage capacity is needed especially if the sand particles are large and no fine sand nor soil is used. In this case, substituting Hygromull for one-third of the peat has been proved satisfactory. Hygromull is easy to compress, decomposes faster than peat, and supplies the turfgrass with additional nitrogen. The nitrogen response is observed into the fourth year. If Hygromull was completely substituted for peat, water movement into the surface layer would be the same as for pure coarse textured sand. On the other hand, an increase in the water-holding capacity of the surface layer resulted without affecting tolerance to wear by substituting lava sand, pumice sand, or perlite for part of the quartz sand.

Lava sand increases the germination rate and results in better stability of the surface layer because of its rough surface. High rates of pumice sand expressed by K*mod. value, cm/sec.

	Sand-soil mix without peat		80% Sand-soil mix; 20% peat		70% Sand-soil mix; 30% peat		60% Sand-soil mix; 40% peat	
	Thickness of the compacted layer	K*mod.†	Thickness of the compacted layer	K*mod.	Thickness of the compacted layer	K*mod.	Thickness of the compacted layer	K*mod.
	cm	cm/sec	cm	cm/sec	cm	cm/sec	cm	cm/sec
Less decomposed, fibrous peat								
1. 100% River sand (0–5 mm)	10.7	0.0136	9.6	0.0175	9.2	0.0213	8.7	0.0222
2. 100% Lava sand (0–5 mm)	10.2	0.0458	9.5	0.0533	9.3	0.0369	8.8	0.0319
3. 100% River sand (0–3 mm)	10.3	0.0130	9.7	0.0150	9.3	0.0282	8.8	0.0299
4. 75% River sand, 25% Sandy soil	9.6	0.0047	9.1	0.0062	9.3	0.0107	8.8	0.0133
5. 70% River sand, 25% Sandy soil, 5% Loamy soil	10.0	0.0034	9.0	0.0031	9.0	0.0067	8.6	0.0109
6. 50% River sand, 40% Sandy soil, 10% Loamy soil	9.8	0.0021	9.5	0.0013	8.8	0.0029		
7. 30% River sand, 60% Sandy soil, 10% Loamy soil	9.4	0.0019	8.8	0.0007	8.6	0.0013		
8. 30% Lava sand, 60% Sandy soil, 10% Loamy soil	9.0	0.0017	8.9	0.0018	8.6	0.0015		
9. 100% Sandy soil	9.0	0.0039	8.6	0.0016	8.5	0.0017		
Well decomposed, fine textured peat								
1. 100% River sand (0–5 mm)	10.7	0.0136	9.5	0.0014	9.2	0.0014	9.1	0.0006
2. 100% Lava sand (0–5 mm)	10.2	0.0458	9.3	0.0021	9.1	0.0014	8.5	0.0009
3. 100% River sand (0–3 mm)	10.3	0.0130	9.1	0.0062	9.0	0.0015	8.8	0.0011
4. 75% River sand, 25% Sandy soil	9.6	0.0047	9.1	0.0038	8.7	0.0018	8.5	0.0004
5. 70% River sand, 25% Sandy soil, 5% Loamy soil	10.0	0.0034	9.0	0.0016	8.6	0.0015	8.3	0.0003
6. 50% River sand, 40% Sandy soil, 10% Loamy soil	9.8	0.0021	8.7	0.0016	8.6	0.0001		
7. 30% River sand, 60% Sandy soil, 10% Loamy soil	9.4	0.0019	8.4	0.0008	8.8	0.0004		
8. 30% Lava sand, 60% Sandy soil, 10% Loamy soil	9.0	0.0017	8.4	0.0011	8.0	0.0005		
9. 100% Sandy soil	9.0	0.0039	8.3	0.0025	8.8	0.0012		

†K*mod.-value is a modification of the K* value for the special purposes of turf sportfield construction.

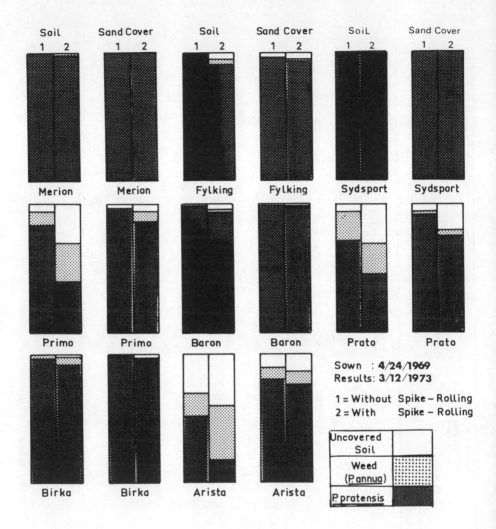

Fig. 4—Effect of soil and sand cover on sward density and weed invasion of *Poa pratensis*.

or perlite result in a loose surface layer that dries rapidly at the time of seeding and remains droughty until the turfgrass makes a complete cover.

The permeability of the surface layer depends on the particle size distribution and the nature of the organic matter. Hygromull, lava sand, pumice sand, or perlite have high mechanical strength and do not impair water permeability. However, different types of peat effect permeability. Because of particle migration, permeability is considerably reduced by a well-decomposed fine-textured peat called black peat, whereas a less decomposed fibrous peat called white peat promotes permeability (Table 1).

Water permeability and soil compaction are two important factors in-

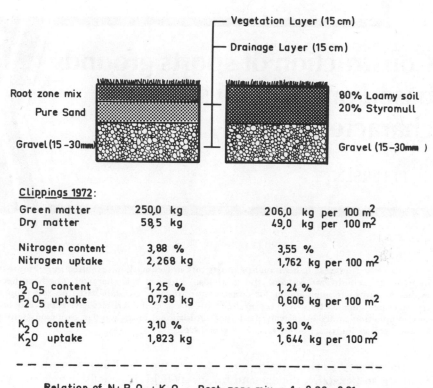

Vegetation Layer (15 cm)

Drainage Layer (15 cm)

Root zone mix

Pure Sand

Gravel (15 –30mm)

80% Loamy soil
20% Styromull

Gravel (15 –30mm)

<u>Clippings 1972</u>:

Green matter	250,0 kg	206,0 kg per 100 m^2	
Dry matter	58,5 kg	49,0 kg per 100 m^2	
Nitrogen content	3,88 %	3,55 %	
Nitrogen uptake	2,268 kg	1,762 kg per 100 m^2	
P_2O_5 content	1,25 %	1,24 %	
P_2O_5 uptake	0,738 kg	0,606 kg per 100 m^2	
K_2O content	3,10 %	3,30 %	
K_2O uptake	1,823 kg	1,644 kg per 100 m^2	

Relation of $N : P_2O_5 : K_2O$ – Root zone mix = 1 : 0,32 : 0,81

Soil/Styromull = 1 : 0,35 : 0,95

Fig. 5—Uptake of nutrients by a vegetation layer of sand and soil (1972).

fluencing the quality of a turf. When eight varieties of *Poa pratensis* grown on a 5-cm thick sand layer were compared with turf grown on a natural sandy loam for 4 years, it was found that the injurious effect of spike-rolling and invasion of weeds, primarily *Poa annua,* were reduced and the recovery by regrowth in the turf was improved on the synthetic medium (Fig. 4).

Turf grown on pure sand yielded 20% more clippings and a 9% higher nitrogen content than a vegetative layer grown on a loamy soil and Styromull (BASF, West Germany) (Fig. 5).

31

Construction of sports grounds based on physical soil characteristics

M. PETERSEN

Increased interest in high-quality sports turf in Denmark has resulted in attempts to improve soil conditions on new sports fields. Physical soil characteristics have been evaluated and recommendations for construction of these grounds based on soil properties have been made. Improved textural and structural characteristics have resulted in less soil compaction under intensively used turf. Additional index words: Soil compaction, Physical soil properties, Soil texture, Soil structure.

Because of greater wealth, more leisure time, and increasing interest in athletics and exercise, the demand for sports fields is steadily increasing. Because the new sports grounds will be intensively used, demands on their quality will increase.

It is sometimes impossible to choose the type of soil which will be most suitable for this purpose. The choice of field area is based mainly on proximity to urban centers and on economic considerations, whereas the suitability of the soil type for sports turf has often been considered to be of secondary importance. Usually, the construction of the sports grounds has consisted only of leveling and seeding. If the soil is initially unsuited and is further compacted by heavy machinery during leveling, the sports field will soon become unfit for use during rainy periods or intensive use.

Experiences in the past have stressed the necessity to establish suitable chemical and physical characteristics of soils to ensure good growth conditions and provide resistance to wear of the grass. With this end in view, a large number of sports fields in Denmark were examined in respect to structure and texture in order to gain information as a basis for construction of new and rehabilitation of old fields.

POOR GROUNDS

Fields with sparse growth of grass or with large patches without grass could be divided into 3 groups.

Group 1

The clay and silt content was higher than 20%. The higher the clay and silt content, the poorer the grounds. The volume weight was always very high, above 1.6 kg/liter. The porosity was low with a low content, 5 to 6 volume % on an average, of noncapillary pores.

The grounds were often waterlogged with up to 40 to 50 volume % water. The root system of the grass was weak and with few long roots.

Group 2

The clay and silt content was very low, ranging from 5 to 10%.

The volume weight was generally very low, rarely above 1.2 to 1.3 kg/liter, often less than 1.0 kg/liter.

Porosity was very high with a content of noncapillary pores often more than 20 volume %, particularly in cases where the content of coarse sand was high. Particle size of sand greatly affected porosity.

The turf was nearly always damaged because of water stress, and in many cases there were nutrient deficiencies. Often the grass was dislodged because the soil lacked cohesion. The root system was weakly developed.

Group 3

Soil amendments had been added, either as sand or spaghnum or both, to these grounds. Amendments had been added only to the upper 5- to 10-cm surface layer. In some cases, the soil below the amended soil layer was considerably compacted. In one instance a volume weight of almost 2.0 kg/liter resulted due to the use of heavy machinery when adding the amendments. The subsequent soil preparation had been very cursory. Sometimes top soil was added directly to a layer of sand of varying thickness without any mixing of the two layers.

The root system was not deeper than the depth of the top soil. In periods of precipitation these grounds were often waterlogged and in dry periods drought damage occurred frequently. The grass often suffered from nutrient deficiencies.

The humus content of the original top soils of the above groups was usually less than 3 volume %.

GOOD GROUNDS

A good sports field maintains a healthy turf under heavy use and under all weather conditions. Results of texture and structure analyses of soils from good grounds with best grass populations, even when maintained under heavy use and varying weather conditions, were similar. The soils were 4 to 5% organic matter (weight percentage), with 12 to 15% clay and silt, and 80 to 85% sand (about half coarse and half fine sand).

Volume weight ranged from 1.3 to 1.4 kg/liter. Porosity was about 50%, of which the noncapillary pores were about 15 volume %.

The depth of the root system depended on the physical conditions and the depth of the top soil. On good sports grounds the minimum depth was at least 30 to 35 cm.

Physical properties of soils, expressed in the parameters of texture and structure, are of importance for the growth and wear resistance of grass.

SOIL AMENDMENTS

In order to improve the physical qualities of soils it is usual to add soil amendments of either mineral and/or organic origin. Amendment effectiveness depends on the type and amount of amendment, on the original soil type, and the mixing procedure. The effects of soil amendments may be either to dilute clay particles or to aggregate sand particles and thus restore and stabilize soil structure. Systems consisting of a mixture of rigid and deformable particles are very sensitive to compaction, thus it can be difficult to predict the effects of such mixtures on permeability, compared with mixtures of rigid particles.

The percolation of water through a layer of soil depends on factors such as content of sand and size of grains, content of clay and silt, and content of organic matter.

SAND

Sand added in increasing amounts to various types of soil increases the porosity and the infiltration rate and decreases the field capacity.[1]

Sand can be divided into coarse sand, 2.0 to 0.2 mm, and fine sand, 0.2 to 0.02 mm. It is important for achieving good results that the appropriate size of sand, based on texture analysis of the soil, is chosen. Grass in pure sand is often stressed by drought and nutrient deficiencies. Grass roots in pure sand are short, rarely more than 10 cm long, and thick. This is probably caused by mechanical resistance to growth.

According to texture analysis, sand makes up to 80 to 85% of the total mixture, either as pure coarse or pure fine sand, or as half of each or about 30% fine and 50% coarse sand.

---

[1]Editor's note: This observation is not invariably true. When sand is added to certain soils, it may, in fact, decrease both the porosity and the infiltration rate. As the sand fraction approaches the condition of being the continuous phase of the soil matrix further increments of sand usually increase infiltration rates. Under these conditions total porosity is usually decreased somewhat although noncapillary pore space will probably increase.

CLAY AND SILT

Silt is defined as having particles ranging from 0.02 to 0.002 mm; clay particles are less than 0.002 mm in size.

One of the most important properties of clay minerals is their ability to absorb ions. By means of exchange these ions are available to plants during growth. In clay soil grass roots are often long and thin. Because of the large contents of capillary pores, clay soils retain considerable quantities of water against the influence of gravity. The risk of drought damage is considerably reduced, but the risk for soil compaction and puddling increases with rising clay content. In rainy weather clay soils become plastic, and when sports fields are used under these conditions the soil may become compacted and puddled to such a degree that gas exchange cannot take place. Because of this a total silt and clay content of more than 15% is not advantageous on sports grounds.

ORGANIC MATTER

Organic matter has colloidal qualities and, like clay, it is able to absorb and exchange nutrient ions. Applications of organic matter may improve pore size distribution and thereby the water supply to the plants. Grass roots in soil rich in organic matter and with high porosity will become sturdy and long, smooth and without root hairs.

Organic matter, which is generally applied as spaghnum, should never exceed 5% (weight basis) of the soil mixture.

CONSTRUCTION OF NEW SPORTS GROUNDS

On the basis of this information a number of trial plots were laid out to investigate the influence of the amendments sand and/or spaghnum on the resulting texture and structure of the soil mixtures. The method of adding and mixing the amendments with the soil was investigated with respect to the homogeneity of the resulting mixture.

Based on the results of these trials, it was possible to calculate the amounts of the amendments necessary for obtaining a top soil with a satisfactory texture and structure. The calculations were based on the assumption that a desirable top soil contained approximately (by weight) 5% organic matter, 15% clay and silt, and 80% fine and coarse sand.

Figure 1 and the information below show the results of soil analyses and compare calculated and determined values of soil texture and volumetric analyses after the addition of a 10-cm layer of sand. The figures are from a football field constructed in 1972.

Texture

	Depth, cm	Organic matter	Percent clay	Percent silt	Percent fine sand	Percent coarse sand	
Before construction	0–25	3.9	11.2	12.4	37.8	34.7	
Before construction	25–60	1.3	14.3	11.7	39.2	33.5	
Calculated	0–25	2.5	7.3	8.1	24.6	57.5	⎫ 10 cm
Determined	0–25	2.0	9.1	7.2	27.5	54.2	⎬ sand
Old grounds	0–20	4.8	14.2	15.8	36.5	29.6	⎭ added

Structure

	Depth, cm	Particle density	Volume weight	Volume and solid substances	Volume and pores	Volume and air	Volume and water
Before construction	0–25	2.60	1.40	54	46	--	--
Before construction	25–60	2.65	1.64	63	37	10	27
Determined	0–25	2.60	1.52	57	43	24	19
Determined	25–40	2.65	1.49	56	44	10	34
Old grounds	0–20	2.60	1.39	54	46	8	38

Before the soil was prepared, samples of soil for texture and structure analyses were taken. These analyses showed that the clay and silt content were too high. In order to reduce the clay and silt content a 10-cm layer of sand was added to the area. According to calculations, the resulting soil mixture should leave a clay and silt content of 15.4%.

Analyses 1 year after finishing the field showed that the soil contained 16.3% clay and silt and that the content of noncapillary pores was 24%. This was deemed satisfactory because compaction will take place when the field starts to be used. A homogenious mixture may be made when sand is added on top of a layer of spaghnum.

The depth of top soil and its content of capillary and noncapillary pores are very important factors. In trials, the greatest root development was found in a top soil with a depth of 30 to 35 cm and with a total pore space of 40 to 45%, of which noncapillary pores ought to be about 15% and not less than 10% or more than 20%.

In such soils the permeability of the top soil will generally be large enough to permit infiltration of rainfall having intensities of 10 to 20 mm

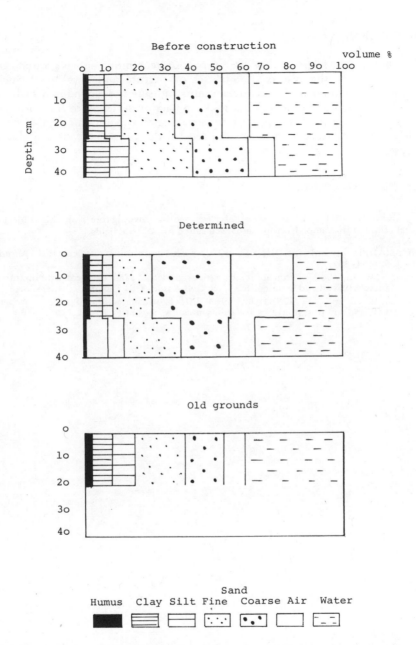

Fig. 1—Soil analyses on a football field before and after addition of a 10-cm layer of sand.

per hour. The supply of air and water in the root zone will be ensured. It is also necessary to provide adequate drainage when building up a soil suitable for sports.

CONCLUSION

The suitability of a soil for the purpose of becoming a sports ground can be predicted by the results of analyses of texture and structure. Such analyses can be used to determine amounts and types of amendments which should be applied in order to obtain soil compaction suitable for the purpose.

Heavy costs in connection with remaking and maintaining badly constructed sports grounds may be avoided by the proper use of the above analyses.

FURTHER READING

[Editor's note: The reader is referred to other investigations on this subject—several of which find amended fine sands well suited for athletic fields.]

BINGAMAN, D. E., and H. KOHNKE. 1970. Evaluating sands for athletic turf. Agron. J. 62:464–467.

GARMAN, W. L. 1952. Permeability of various grades of sand and peat with mixtures of these with soil and vermiculite. U. S. Golf Assoc. Turf Manage. 1(5):27–28.

SWARTZ, W. E., and L. T. KARDOS. 1963. Effects of compaction on physical properties of sand-soil-peat mixtures at various moisture contents. Agron. J. 55:7–10.

32

Prescription athletic turf system

W.H. DANIEL, R.P. FREEBORG, M.J. ROBEY

Many problems in designing, specifying, building, and maintaining athletic fields have been resolved by developing a system called the Prescription Athletic Turf System. This system uses a plastic barrier under a slitted drain pipe which is covered by a sand profile and a noncompacting surface top mix that stores much available water. Suction pumping for rapid drainage permits a level field. Soil moisture sensors, time clocks, and electric valves permit automatic subirrigation providing all-season automatic water control. Soil warming by electric cables permits extended turf growing, and keeps the surface ready for use in cold weather. Additional index words: Drainage, Plastic barrier, Sand profile, Slitted drain pipe, Soil warming, Subirrigation, Soil compaction.

In the past, outdoor athletic fields were built by grading the soil at the site, tilling the area, fertilizing, and planting seed. Sometimes imported topsoil was used, and often sand and peat were added. Tile drains were sometimes used. Further, fields may be crowned 30 to 60 cm to facilitate surface runoff. With rain, such fields become muddy and excessively wet at the surface so the turf tears and players slip.

Vertical trenching of sports areas for more rapid surface drainage has been developed in several countries. Some processes crack and loosen the soil with subsoiler-type machines and backfill the opening with calcined aggregates, sand, or fine gravel. Some processes, either during initial seeding or in renovation work, remove soil with narrow trenchers, place drains with numerous narrow slits then backfill to overflow with sand. However, the surface can become muddy because rain will still saturate the surface.

The "sand-bed" method is the result of work by Langvad (4) in Sweden. After the subgrade of the site is prepared, narrow, closely spaced (5 to 8 m) trenches of 15- to 20-cm depth are made. Slitted drain pipe is placed in these trenches, and they are backfilled with sand. A 10- to 15-cm layer of sand is spread over the area. About 30% peat by volume is mixed into the top 6 to 8 cm, and the field is compacted and planted. In many climates, such a system also needs automatic irrigation to maintain moisture for good playing conditions. In short, the sand-bed method provides a more porous upper layer to increase infiltration and minimize compaction. However, in demanding situations drainage may not be sufficiently rapid.

Artificial turf is expensive, but also has advantages and limitations. While its wear tolerance is obvious, replacement cost, maintenance problems, and players' dislike are disadvantages.

THE PRESCRIPTION ATHLETIC TURF (PAT) SYSTEM

Extremes of climate and wear create severe demands on turf and the root zone. Even under ideal weather and wear conditions, intense use may result in divots. The challenge is to counteract the effect of extremes on turf and root zones.

Suction pumps attached to the drain lines were first tested in turf research at Purdue University in 1971. Success of this concept permitted other practices to be incorporated so that a complete system evolved known as Prescription Athletic Turf (PAT). The system involves noncompacting surface soil mixes overlying a plastic barrier and drainage pipe. Vacuum pumps assure drainage. Automatic watering and soil heating can be incorporated. Principles pertaining to the system have been described in various publications (1, 2, 3, 5, 6).

THE ROOT ZONE

A flat subgrade is established with shallow, wide v-shaped trenches for collector drainage mains. The area is underlaid with heavy plastic sheeting (10 mil) allowing 30 cm for overlap. The upper edges are taped so that a watertight barrier under and around the root zone is achieved. Drainage tubing is installed which junctions into collector drains connected to pumps (Fig. 1). The minimum design uses dual diaphram pumps capable of removing 2.5 cm of rain/hour.

The plastic-lined field and drainage system are then covered with 30 to 50 cm of sand. Sands in which two-thirds or more of the material consists of medium and fine fractions (0.5 to 0.1 mm dia) work well. The primary consideration is that water infiltration be high (5 to 10 cm/hour with a 1-cm head), water retention at –50 millibars water potential be high, (about 15 to 30% volume percentage) and that air porosity at –50 millibars be adequate, i.e., about 10% by volume or more. The surface 5 to 10 cm may be modified by additives of peat and fertilizer plus some soil (if sod is used) so that the surface mixture gives good stability for players.

WATER MANAGEMENT

If rain falls during scheduled games, the pumps can be used to rapidly increase the hydraulic gradient so water does not accumulate at the surface. This procedure eliminates mud and slickness. Experience has shown that this procedure provides a firm footing and increases turf survival. Furthermore, before the game the exact root zone moisture desired for the best playable surface can be provided by adjusting the water potential with the pumps. Water potential is measured by sensing devices.

Fig. 1—Level subgrade, plastic barrier, trench, slitted drains, and collector mains as installed in model field at Grand Valley State College, Michigan, in August 1972.

Irrigation needs are met through automatic subirrigation. A preset resistance controller activates the subirrigation system at the selected value of the water potential. Thus, the most sensitive areas, the upper clean sand (at about 6 cm below the surface—where most turf roots are) will respond first. When root zone moisture is high, the moisture throughout the entire root zone adjusts. When the root zone dries to the predetermined level, the sensor will admit water to recharge to the desired limit.

If there is excess rain, an adjustable overflow standpipe will conserve moisture above the barrier to the level desired and permit the outflow of all excess water. The overflow includes a normally open electric valve which is double wired to close as irrigation is initiated or during induced suction when pumps are activated.

A standard drain outlet drains the system to minimize damage during severe winter freeze.

RESULTS

After 1 year of use, a model field was tested for suction. When 60 cm of suction (water) was measured in the pump pit, the four test locations throughout the field (at 15-cm depth) measured 40 to 50 cm of tension. Where double-ring infiltrometers were used at six locations with suction pumps operating, infiltration of 60 cm/hour was measured. Excessive surface water was pulled away within 10 min. Thus, the porous root zone proved responsive to vacuum pumping as evidenced by rapid water removal.

When use is scheduled in freezing weather, soil-warming cables (placed 15 cm deep and 30 to 60 cm apart, depending on climate and uses) can keep the root zone thawed, the footing firm, and reduce the loosening of sod caused by alternate freezing and thawing.

Alternatively, a clear plastic field cover with (5-mm) holes at 10 cm intervals (vented) will increase soil and sod temperatures by reducing soil heat losses and capture radiant energy when conditions permit. Use of field covers for extended periods may require extra care in management.

The PAT system attempts to anticipate the needs of players and coaches for dependable grounds. It permits management responses to the extremes of weather that may affect turf and root zones. It gives specific standards for building and allows for automatic water maintenance, while permitting maximum use of the area. Finally, it offers a definite alternative to artificial turf.

A patent is pending on the system, and a license for the United States and Canada has been assigned by the Purdue Research Foundation. The patent application is #355-263,434, dated June 16, 1972.

REFERENCES

1. BINGAMAN, D. E., and H. KOHNKE. 1970. Evaluating sands for athletic turf. Agron. J. 62:464–467.
2. DANIEL, W. H. 1970. Purr-Wick rootzone system for turf. Midwest Turf Bull. 40.
3. ———. 1972. Perscription for athletic turf—The PAT system. Grounds Maintenance 7(2):43–46.
4. LANGVAD, Bjerne. 1970. Soil heating under sports turf in Sweden. p. 252–257. *In* Proc. First Int. Turfgrass Res. Conf. Sports Turf Research Institute, Bingley, England.
5. RALSTON, D. S., and W. H. DANIEL. 1972. Effect of temperature on water table depth on the growth of creeping bedgrass roots. Agron. J. 64:709–713.
6. ———, and ———. 1973. Effect of porous rootzone material underlined with plastic on the growth of creeping bedgrass. Agron. J. 65:229–233.

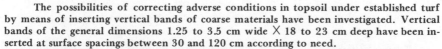

33

Vertical band soil additive methods for established turf

G.G. FISHER & A.N. EDE

The possibilities of correcting adverse conditions in topsoil under established turf by means of inserting vertical bands of coarse materials have been investigated. Vertical bands of the general dimensions 1.25 to 3.5 cm wide X 18 to 23 cm deep have been inserted at surface spacings between 30 and 120 cm according to need.

The effects on drainage, soil compaction, wear resistance, and grass vigor are described, and the hydraulic design of vertical drainage bands is considered. Closely spaced bands of compost or other soil-improving materials have been inserted into soils of low fertility. Machinery to carry out such operations with minimal disturbance of the surface is described. Additional index words: Drainage, French drain, Vertical mulch, Soil compaction.

Excessive soil compaction and impeded surface drainage can be avoided at the construction stage by attention to the permeability and compaction tolerance of the topsoil mix and related soil profile. Even under ideal constructions there can be deterioration with time due to the decomposition products of turf, aided in industrial areas by dust, soot, and other "fall-out."

Most of the playing fields in Britain, including many professional football stadia, have been laid out without improvement on the unmodified natural soils of the locality. The moist climate, long winter playing season for sports like football and golf, and a steadily increasing intensity of use make them highly susceptible to problems of soil compaction and surface drainage. Other problems such as soil infertility or susceptibility to drought are widespread, and with the scarcity of land on which to make new playing fields there is a general need to raise the standards on existing turf.

There have been strict limitations on the improvement of the soil profile of established turf. Remedial treatments such as spiking and slitting depend on a vertical penetration of the surface. Efficiency of this operation varies according to soil conditions, as well as the fiber and moisture content of the turf. These operations increase aeration nominally and may allow the introduction of soil ameliorants into hollow tine holes, but the process has limitations in the amount and penetration of the soil-conditioning material.

Most treatments applied to turf are limited to surface dressings, which unless soluble or translocated by grasses remain on the surface until they are overgrown at a peak rate of perhaps 0.5 cm per annum.

Lifting of turf, improvement or replacement of the soil below, relaying the turf, or reseeding deals effectively with all these problems, but this is expensive and drastically interferes with use.

Correction of poor surface drainage conditions by inserting vertical bands of soil-conditioning materials into turf has already been described by Clark (2), Werminghausen (4), Adams, Stewart, and Thornton (1), Daniel (3), and others. The dimensions of such drainage slits have generally been 25 to 38 cm deep × 5 to 10 cm wide, and spaced approximately 1 to 2 m apart. The dimensions have been fixed as much by the implements available as by an analysis of the physical requirements. The methods described include modified mole plows with hollow section blades and hopper attachments, or narrow trenchers for spoil removal followed by hoppers, sometimes with agitation, for refilling the trench with permeable material.

Mole plows may cause unacceptable ridging when pulled through turf and on bare soil the top section of the completed band may be destroyed by the reseeding which follows. Adapted narrow trenchers may typically require the handling of 300 to 600 metric tons of material for one football field, and special measures may be needed to restore the surface and the grass immediately above the trench.

Various means of reducing surface disturbance, material handling, the time required for renovation, and the possibility of using much narrower bands have been investigated in this program. The simplest form is a continuous vertical cut of constant depth made by a narrow-section vibrating blade. This was found to provide a sufficient, but short-term passage for air and water to improve aeration and drainage. Surface pressure may quickly close such a slit and terminate its usefulness.

A further step to improve the efficiency and life of such a vertical cut is accomplished by filling it with sand or other permeable material. We have found that a vibrating hollow-section blade can be made to insert vertical bands 1.27 cm wide × 23 cm deep with minimum disturbance of the surface contours. The method is being used with single-blade pedestrian operated machinery and with triple-bladed, tractor-drawn equipment (Fig. 1).

Vibration of the blade makes a clean cut through turf with the leading edge and improves the flow of bulky materials from the hopper to the slot below ground. Such materials have included damp sand and sand-peat mixtures of bulk densities as low as 1,085 kg/m^3.

In most soils seasonal timing is not critical. If the operation is done during the growing season the lateral growth of grass will cover the top of the slits within 2 to 4 weeks. The position of the slits may be visible for longer periods due to increased vigor of growth and the darker green grass. When clay soils, which are subject to severe shrinkage, have had sand slits inserted at the start of a dry spell, slits originally 1.25-cm wide have been known to open up to about 2.5 cm, leading to some collapse of the sand and the need for topping up. The remedy is to prevent drying out of the soil either by seasonal timing or by irrigation, until such time as the growth of new roots across the slit forms a matrix which holds up the material in the

Fig. 1—Triple-bladed, tractor-drawn equipment for inserting vertical bands of soil-conditioning materials.

slit. Such rooting can be very rapid, and as much as 20-cm vertical root growth in 18 days has been observed.

DRAINAGE

If the subsoil is already permeable, the injection of sand slits through a compacted surface soil can correct the surface drainage problem. More often it is necessary to provide a positive outlet for water which gathers in the slits, by ensuring that the surface slits connect frequently with the permeable fill overlaying the subsoil drains.

The spacing between slits will depend on soil factors, the pattern of subsoil drains, the demands of the sport being played, and other considerations. So far, the spacing has varied between 30 and 120 cm. When a new subsoil drainage scheme is installed, either at construction or later, the improved speed of drainage given by surface and slits may allow increased spacing between subsoil laterals.

With extremely free-draining profiles containing little, if any natural soil, there may be difficulty in satisfying demands for water and nutrients. Under these conditions, vertical banding with a finer textured soil may be used to increase water- and nutrient-holding capacity of the field. The zones of unmodified native sand would continue to provide rapid drainage.

HYDRAULIC DESIGN

In general, there is a single objective concerning water movement problems which, according to the situation, is achieved in one of two ways. The objective is to modify the hydrology of the situation so that the majority of the rainfall does not have to infiltrate the soil, but moves over the surface directly to a sand slit and is taken downward through the sand. At this stage in the water movement, the distance between slits is related to the roughness of the surface. The objective is to minimize water trapped in surface pockets.

Rainfall which does not enter the sand directly infiltrates the soil between the slits. When there is significant rainfall the amount tends at first to increase to a constant figure, regardless of the actual rainfall experienced. All excess water goes to the sand. After a period of satisfactory installation, the soil between the slits may show improved structural status, and its water-transmitting properties begin to be improved which is important in turf maintenance.

The objective of surface water control is only of value if internal drainage functions properly. There are two broad situations to be considered. 1) The subsoil is itself permeable and free draining, or there is a permeable and continuous, artificial drainage bed. 2) The subsoil is not sufficiently permeable to empty the sand slits.

In the first case, the sand slits drain entirely vertically. The rate of water movement needed can be calculated in relation to the rainfall to be controlled, by the selection of sand (e.g., high, fairly high, or moderate permeability) in categories determined by a laboratory test. An effective infiltration rate for the combined effect of the sand slit and the turf soil surface can be expressed on the following bases: effective width of sand slit, permeability of the sand used, spacing between slits, and permeability of the topsoil where appreciable.

In the second case the sand slits have the additional function of transmitting the received water horizontally along the slit to drainage outlet points, which in most cases are fixed by existing or new drains covered with granules or gravel. Lateral water movement through such a permeable system over an impermeable soil bed is well understood. Variables of concern include the depth of the sand, the width of the slit in which it is held, the permeability of the sand, and the distance between points of outlet draining the base of the slit. The flow equation is such that increases in any of the first three quantities are followed by corresponding increases in the effective infiltration quantities, but increased distance between outlets has a reducing effect. The effective infiltration rate of such a system is between one-fifth and one-tenth of that of a vertical draining system using sand of the same type. For this reason only sand in the higher categories of measured permeability is used, and the distance between drain outlets is adjusted to a classification which has been established by commercial usage.

APPLICATIONS

During the past 18 months the sand injection method for improving surface drainage has been employed on over 40.5 ha of turf, mainly on sports fields.

Football

Sand injection has been employed at three main periods: in late spring at the end of the playing season, prior to overseeding; in July and August on established or recently renovated turf; in the middle of the winter playing season as an emergency correction to drainage problems as they arise.

On soft ground the equipment operates on light wooden tracks. This slows down the rate of work, requiring about 3 days for completing a normal-size football field. Normal practice is to use 61-cm spacings, with 30-cm spacings down the intensively used center strip.

Cricket

A number of county grounds suffer from excessive fibrous mat in the outfield, which severely restricts the speed of drainage and causes delays in match resumption after rain. At the Lord's Ground of the Marylebone Cricket Club in London sand slits 1.25 cm wide have been injected to a depth of 23 cm at 61-cm spacings to an area adjoining the square. To ensure contact between the sand and the permeable fill over the drains, a narrow trench was made above each subsoil drain until clean fill was encountered at 30- to 35-cm depth, and then the trenches were backfilled with a permeable sand-peat mixture to within 5 cm from the surface.

Golf

Surface drainage of fairways has been improved by injecting vertical bands of sand at 61- to 122-cm spacings. Problem putting greens have also been sand injected at 61- or 30-cm spacings, the latter being preferable to avoid intermittent disturbance of the surface.

Sand, peat, and fertilizer mixtures have been successfully injected at 23-cm spacings to overcome grossly infertile fairway soil, as an alternative to turf lifting, soil replacement, and relaying.

CONCLUSION

The insertion of vertical bands of sand by vibrating hollow blades provides a rapid and effective means of improving surface drainage.

Other materials such as composts, fertilizers, and some pesticides can be placed in the soil by the same method. The technique adds a third dimension to many turf operations and opens up new possibilities for renovating and protecting turf, especially under conditions of heavy traffic or play.

REFERENCES

1. ADAMS, W. A., V. I. STEWART, and D. J. THORNTON. 1971. The assessment of sands suitable for use in sports fields. J. Sports Turf Res. Inst. 47:77–86.

2. CLARK, H. E. 1970. Drainage at Twickenham. J. Sports Turf Res. Inst. 46:14–16.
3. DANIEL, W. H. 1969. Vertical drainage for compacted turf areas. J. Sports Turf Res. Inst. 45:49–54.
4. WERMINGHAUSEN, B. 1970. Cellular polystyrene in the preparation of grass playing fields. p. 172–176. *In* Proc. First Int. Turfgrass Res. Conf. Sports Turf Research Institute, Bingley, England.

34

Refining green section specifications for putting green construction

A.M. RADKO

The U. S. Golf Association Green Section specifications for a method of putting green construction was first published in 1960. It was a departure from the norm in that it advocated use of a perched water table to insure a continuous supply of water and a physical analysis of the topsoil mixture with a specified micropore and macropore space capacity. The 1973 refinement adheres to these original specifications but offers several minor changes that combine the practical and scientific for ease of construction. Additional index words: Perched water, Topsoil mixture, Micropore space, Macropore space.

Since 1960, a substantial number of golf greens have been successfully constructed following specifications developed and published by the Green Section of the U. S. Golf Association. During this time new questions have arisen requiring additional research to further improve and refine the original technique. For example, construction men asked if the sand layer (D, Fig. 1) was necessary. Some found the original water infiltration rates inadequate for their part of the country. Others observed that greens built to these specifications were slow to provide playing resiliency. The Green Section responded by granting funds for research projects designed to help answer these questions. As a result of this research, areas of the original specifications have been modified as follows.

1. The minimum water transmission rates should be 5.0 or 7.6 cm/hour, for the bermudagrasses and 7.6 cm/hour for the bentgrasses, and ideally double this rate rather than the 1.3 to 3.8 cm/hour originally recommended.
2. Larger amounts of sand of a finer texture are now recommended. Sand of the brick or mason class is preferred. Silica sands are recommended. Other sands are acceptable only in rare cases where silica sand is unavailable. Ideal sand particle size would be as follows: 100% below 16 mesh (1.0 mm), 35% below 32 mesh (0.50 mm), 15% below 60 mesh (0.25 mm), 5% below 160 mesh (0.06 mm).

Permissible deviations from these specifications are discussed subsequently.

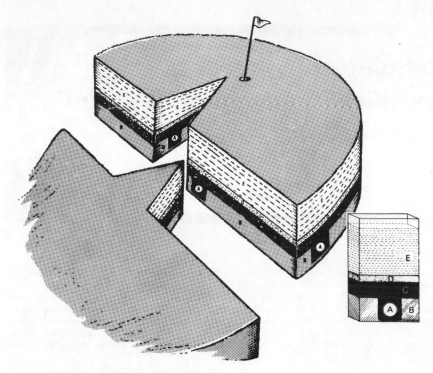

Fig. 1—Cross-section profile of putting green with trench and tile line. (A) tile 10 cm in diameter, (B) subgrade of native soil or fill material, (C) minimum 10-cm layer pea gravel, (D) Very coarse sand, 1 mm or greater in diameter, 3 to 5 cm in thickness, (E) topsoil mixture, minimum 30-cm layer.

3. The need for the 3.8 cm sand layer (D, Fig. 1) is still to be resolved through additional research. For the present we recommend it be retained.

4. The collar area preferably should be included as part of the putting green and should be constructed exactly like the green.

Table 1 summarizes the striking increase in the number of particles per gram in going from coarse sand to clay.

Seven steps in the construction procedure from the 1960 original specifications with undated refinements are presented herewith.

SUBGRADE

The contours of the subgrade should conform to those of the proposed finished grade, with a tolerance of 2.5 cm. The subgrade should be constructed at an elevation 35.5 cm below the proposed finished grade. The subgrade should be compacted sufficiently to prevent future settling which might create water-holding depressions in the subgrade surface and corresponding depressions in the putting surface.

Table 1—Characteristics of soil separates.

Name	Diameter*, m	No. particles per gram
Very coarse sand	2.00–1.00	90
Coarse sand	1.00–0.50	722
Medium sand	0.50–0.25	5,777
Fine sand	0.25–0.10	46,213
Very fine sand	0.10–0.05	722,074
Silt	0.05–0.002	5,776,674
Clay	below 0.002	90,260,853,860

* As established by the U. S. Department of Agriculture.

Where terrain permits, it is possible to build the subgrade into the existing grade or to cut it into the subsoil. It is not necessary to elevate or "build up" the green unless design considerations dictate the desirability of doing so.

It will be noted that layers of materials above the subgrade consist of 10 cm of gravel, 3.8 to 5.0 cm of coarse sand, and 30 cm of topsoil mixture (Fig. 1). Thus, the total depth will be 44.4 to 45.7 cm. However, this fill material will settle appreciably, and experience indicates that 35.5 cm will be the approximate depth of these combined materials after settling.

DRAINAGE

Tile lines of at least 10-cm dia should be so spaced that water will not have to travel more than 3.05 m to reach a tile drain. Any suitable pattern or tile line arrangement may be used, but the herringbone or the gridiron arrangements will fit most situations (Fig. 2).

Ditches or trenches should be cut into the subgrade so tile lines slope uniformly. Tile should not be placed deeper than is necessary to obtain the desired amount of slope. Tile lines should have a minimum fall of 0.5%. Steeper grades can be used but there will seldom be a need for tile line grades steeper than 3 to 4% on a putting green.

Tile may be agricultural clay tile, concrete, plastic, or perforated asphalt-paper composition. Agricultural tile joints should be butted together with no more than 6.4 mm of space between joints. The tops of tile joints should be covered with asphalt paper, fiber glass composition, or with plastic spacers or covers designed for this purpose. The covering prevents gravel from falling into the tile.

Tile should be laid on a firm bed of 1.27 to 2.54 cm of gravel to reduce possible wash of subgrade soil up into tile lines by rapid water flow. If the subgrade consists of undisturbed soil, so that washing is unlikely, it is permissible to lay tile directly on the bottom of the trench.

After the tile is laid, the trenches should be backfilled with gravel, and care should be taken not to displace the covering over the joints.

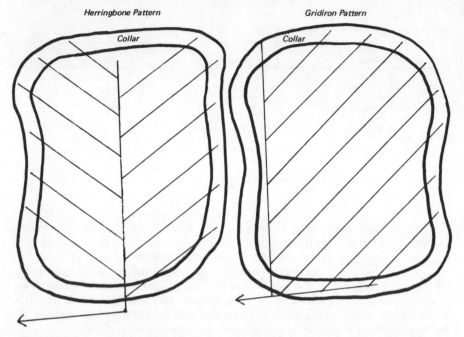

Herringbone Pattern   *Gridiron Pattern*

Collar   Collar

Fig. 2—Two most commonly used drainage patterns for putting greens. Tile 10-cm in diameter is spaced at 4.1 to 6.1 m intervals depending on slope. The collar is normally 1 to 2 m wide.

GRAVEL AND SAND BASE

The entire subgrade should be covered with a layer of clean washed gravel or crushed stone to a minimum thickness of 10 cm (Layer C, Fig. 1). The preferred material for this purpose is washed pea gravel of 6.4 to 9.5 mm dia particle size. If particles of any other size are included, they must be screened out. This is important to the proper functioning of the "perched water table". The maximum allowable discrepancy appears to be 5 to 7 diameters. In other words, if 6.4-mm pea gravel is used, then the particles of the overlying course sand should not be less than 1 mm in diameter.

The layer of coarse sand (Layer D, Fig. 1) used over the gravel base is for the sole purpose of preventing the soil particles from migrating downward into the gravel. We have evidence that under certain conditions the sand layer is not required, but the matter is under study at present. Pending further research, we feel it essential to continue with the sand layer.

"RINGING" THE GREEN

The earlier specifications recommended that the collar and apron soils should be put in place prior to placing the prepared top mixture on the green site. We are now changing this recommendation to state that the collar should be constructed to the same specifications as the green.

SOIL MIXTURE

The topsoil mixture used must have specific (known) soil physical characteristics which must be tested in the laboratory prior to green construction. Laboratory techniques are described by Ferguson, Howard, and Bloodworth (1). The topsoil mixture should be packed as described by the authors and then water allowed to flow through the mixture for 24 hours at a temperature of 20 C. The transmission rate at 24 hours should ideally be in the range of 10 to 15 cm/hour. The transmission rate should not exceed 25 cm/hour. After the water transmission rate measurements have been made the mixture should be drained at a tension of 40 cm. On a volume basis the mix then should have at least 15% air space and 20% water content. The total pore space volume of the mixture should be between 40 and 55%. Mixtures containing particle sizes within the range suggested below provide ideal soil physical conditions.

Particle size

The topsoil mixture ideally should contain no particle larger than 2 mm (9 mesh) in diameter. However, 3% particles larger than 2 mm are permissible if most of these are smaller than 3 mm. The total soil mixture should not contain more than 10% particles larger than 1 mm (16 mesh) and no more than 25% particles smaller than 0.25 mm (60 mesh). In addition, the mixture should contain less than 5% silt (0.05 to 0.002 mm) and less than 3% clay (smaller than 0.002 mm).

Topsoils having the above characteristics are almost nonexistent in nature; therefore, they must be compounded from available sand, soil, and organic amendments. Because of extreme local variations in these materials, a high degree of expertise is required in compounding topsoil blends with the desired properties. Different lots of sand vary considerably in particle size and shape. Native soils also vary greatly in particle size and shape, as well as in degree of aggregation, acidity, fertility, soluble salt content, and organic matter content. Perhaps the most variable of these materials are the organic amendments. They may differ in plant material origin, degree of decomposition, mineral impurities such as silt and clay, as well as in acidity and fertility. Manufactured or processed, organic materials also differ widely from natural materials.

It is unlikely that local golf course architects, builders, or superintendents can cope with the variability in construction materials when formulating topsoils and topdressing for greens. Therefore, since successful construction is dependent on the proper combination of physical and hydraulic properties in the topsoil, a soil analysis should be made of available construction materials before they are procurred. The supply of each material required to complete the job should also be assured, and representative samples tested.

Because of the narrow acceptable limits in the physical properties of the topsoil mixture, it is extremely important that recommendations based on laboratory analysis be followed carefully when mixing the components for the topsoil mixture. When it becomes necessary to substitute a new material for one of the original materials in the mixture, the mixture should be retested before proceeding with mixing.

Tables 2, 3, and 4 summarize data on the variability of sands and organic amendments used for various greens, and influence of soil content on the properties of topsoil mixes for greens.

The success of the method of construction herein described is dependent upon the proper physical characteristics of the soil and the relationship of that soil to the drainage bed underlaying the green. Therefore a physical analysis of soil should be made before the soil components are procured. When the proper proportions of the soil components have been determined, it becomes essential that they should be mixed in the proportions indicated. A small error in percentages in the case of high silt or plastic clay soils can lead to serious consequences. To insure thorough mixing and the accurate measurement of the soil components, "off site" mixing is advocated. During construction, quality control checks should be made periodically on all soil components as well as the final mix. At this time it is wise also to prepare and stockpile several hundred extra cubic meters of the topsoil mix for subsequent topdressing of greens.

SOIL COVERING, PLACEMENT, SMOOTHING AND FIRMING

Many implements are acceptable in spreading the soil at the green site. These include shovels, boards, and small equipment. A small crawler tractor suitably equipped with a blade, for example, is useful for pushing the soil mixture out onto the prepared base. If the tractor is always operated with its weight on the soil mixture that has been moved onto the site, the base of the green will not be disturbed.

Grade stakes spaced at frequent intervals on the green site will be helpful in indicating the finished depth of the soil mixture. Finishing the grade will likely require the use of a level or transit.

When the soil has been spread uniformly over the surface of the putting green it should be compacted or firmed uniformly. A roller is not satisfactory because it "bridges" the soft spots. "Footing" or trampling the surface will best eliminate the soft spots. Raking the surface and repeating the footing operation will result in having the seedbed uniformly firm. It is impossible to overemphasize the point that the raking and footing must be repeated until uniform firmness is obtained.

ESTABLISHMENT OF TURF

Let us reexamine the recommendations step by step and point out some of the opportunities for error.

The subgrade

When a new green is built there is a lot of fill to be moved away or onto the site as design and terrain dictate. In either case the builder must strive to compact the subgrade as thoroughly as possible. Only in this way will settling be prevented. If uniform layers of gravel, sand, and soil overlay the subgrade, it is obvious that any settling below will result in a corresponding

Table 2—Variability in sands selected for putting green construction from different locations.

Sand source	Particles 0.05 mm and larger	Particles, 0.002 to 0.05 mm	Particles less than 0.002 mm	Water transmission rate cm/hour
Whispering Pines, N. C.	99.0	1.0	0.0	79.2
Birmingham, Ala. #1	97.6	2.4	0.0	42.2
Birmingham, Ala. #2	85.0*	13.2	1.8	0.3
Norcross, Ga.	99.4	0.6	0.0	67.6
Tuscon, Ariz.	88.4	8.8	2.8	18.3
San Diego, Calif.	98.0	2.0	0.0	45.0
San Diego, Calif.	99.5**	0.5	0.0	312.9
Concord, Mass.	98.7	0.0	1.3	22.9
Highland Park, Ill.	97.5	0.5	2.0	31.5
Buffalo, N. Y.	98.4	1.6	0.0	29.0
College Station, Texas	98.9	1.1	0.0	25.1

* Sand mostly below 0.25 mm.   ** Eighty-five percent from 0.5 to 1 mm.

Table 3—Variability encountered in organic amendments for topsoil mixtures.

Organic material and source	pH	Titratable acidity to pH 6.5, meq/100 g	Ash, %
Sewage Waste (Calif.)	7.3	0.0	67.3
Muck—peat (Ind.)	5.8	5.0	25.8
Muck—peat (N. C.)	3.8	5.6	73.2
Moss peat (Ore.)	4.0	30.7	3.9
Sedge peat (Wis.)	6.0	1.4	12.8
Moss peat (Ga.)	6.2	2.8	19.4
Lignified wood (Calif.)	5.6	1.5	1.0
Rice hulls (Tex.)	6.4	0.0	24.3
Cotton gin trash (Tex.)	8.3	0.0	43.3

Table 4—Influence of native soil on various properties of a sand-soil mixture.

Ratio of components Sand*	Soil†	Silt + Clay, %	Bulk density, g/cc	Pore space Capillary	Noncapillary	Water transmission rate, cm/hour
10	0	2.1	1.36	13	36	26.4
9	1	3.0	1.30	14	37	22.4
8	2	3.9	1.39	17	30	10.2
7	3	4.8	1.41	25	22	5.6
5	5	6.6	1.47	39	6	0.2

* Sand contained 22.7, 36.3, 30.0, 7.3, 1.6, 0.0, and 2.1% of very coarse, coarse, medium, fine, very fine, silt and clay, respectively.   † The soil contained 88.8% sand, 6.3% silt, and 4.9% clay.

settling of the top. Therefore, a thorough compaction of fill areas in the sub-grade is of paramount importance if the green is to maintain the character of contours built into it.

Tile drainage

It is commonly believed that the use of a gravel layer provides adequate drainage and that the installation of tile is a needless expense. No doubt there is good reason for this belief in some cases. However, when large amounts of water are moving through soil under conditions of heavy rain or rapid irrigation, and where the water must move a considerable distance to reach an outlet, tile lines aid in speedy removal of excess water. Excess water is efficiently and effectively removed from the approach area by tile whereas with only a gravel layer little control of directional removal of water is obtained. In addition, tile lines assist in removing water trapped in pockets if settling should occur. Putting greens are the most expensive golf turf commodity and require the most exacting standards for excellence. The small additional cost of adding tile is worth the insurance it provides.

Gravel and sand base

In a few cases builders have used tile and then assumed that there is no need for a gravel layer above the subsoil base (Layer C, Fig. 1). This assumption is erroneous. The gravel layer provides a medium whereby water can rapidly move laterally and very easily find its way into the tile lines. The gravel also provides a barrier between the top mixture and the soil below to prevent the dry subsoil from drawing water out of the top mixture. The tile and gravel function together to provide insurance against waterlogging of any kind within the putting green profile. Tile is normally placed at the bottom of the gravel layer and is spaced at intervals of 4.1 to 6.1 m, depending on the degree and direction of slope.

The collar (apron) area

Establishing a collar or so-called apron to the same specifications as the putting green itself is important to the performance of the total green area. The same kind of turf normally is grown on the collar as is grown on the putting surface except that it is maintained at a higher cut. The collar is subject to heavy traffic and the same management as the green area, therefore to realize the best from it, construction must meet the same specifications as prescribed for the putting green proper.

The soil at the outer edge of the collar will abut against the native soil which probably will be heavier than the prepared top mixture and may be far less permeable to water. For this reason there could be a decided difference in plant and soil performance in this area. Therefore, it is important to place a strip of polyethylene plastic sheeting vertically between the two soils to reduce chances for problems developing along this line of division between the natural and synthetic soil.[1]

---

[1] Editorial note: Some authorities question the value of the polyethylene barrier since it would only accentuate the interface between the two soils. It is not clear how it would simplify management at the interface.

Fig. 3—Water does not move from a loam soil until the soil becomes saturated.

The interface

Apparently one of the most puzzling of the principles involved in the Green Section specifications is the function of the textural barrier, the boundary between the top mixture and the gravel. Figure 3 shows that water does not move from a layer of fine soil into a lower layer of a coarser textured soil until the fine-textured soil becomes saturated. The reason for this failure of water to readily cross the textural barrier is a matter of surface tension. When sufficient gravitational force (weight) accumulates, the tension force is overcome and water then drains out through the sand and gravel.

The textural barrier then can be used to increase the water-holding capacity of a coarse-textured soil. If irrigation is stopped just before the soil reaches the saturation point, no drainage occurs. On the other hand, in the case of an excessive rainfall, the soil will not hold too much water. It is paradoxical that the soil overlaying such a textural barrier can be made to hold more water than it would without the gravel layer, but it cannot be made to hold enough water to be harmful to plants if the proper soil mix is used.

The topsoil mixture

The proper blend of soil components to use in the top mixture (E, Fig. 1) is accurately determined after extensive laboratory tests. Only in this way is it possible for soil scientists to advise what proportions of sand, soil, and organic matter are to be mixed to meet the infiltration and physical requirements specified. This is critically essential to the success of construction, and it allows the builder to make the best possible use of materials available within reasonable distance of the construction site. This has favorable bearing on total costs of materials used for construction.

A chemical analysis of the recommended top mixture should then be made for lime and nutrient requirements in turfgrass establishment.

Mixing the materials to the specified ratio is another important step in building. To insure thorough mixing and accurate measurements of the topsoil components (Layer E, Fig. 1), "off site" mixing is advocated. There are several recommended ways to metering the sand, soil, and organic matter to specification but in the final analysis the result depends on the competence of the worker on the mixing site. If the worker is not conscientious and informed, the field mixture will never be recognizable as the recommended laboratory soil mix. Whether the sand, soil, and organic material is metered onto a stockpile and tumbled two or three times, layered, sliced, and tumbled, or shoveled by hand it is imperative that a thorough mixing be done.

Moist sand mixes easier and more intimately than dry sand. Since the greater percentage of the mixture will comprise sand, moistening the sand at intervals during the mixing process is important. The organic material also should be slightly moistened for better adhesion in mixing.

All laboratory recommendations are specific and refer to parts in 10, by volume. An 8-1-1, for example, refers to a mixture of 8 parts sand, 1 part soil, and 1 part organic matter. Once this mixture is placed on the site it is important to cover the green, until planted, with a protective cover such as a polyethylene tarpaulin or similar cover to prevent heavy rains from altering the mixture, especially the upper fraction of the soil profile. A *light* mulch is recommended during the grass planting operation, except when stolons are used, to help stabilize the soil mixture. Possibilities include asphalt emulsions, sphagnum, wood cellulose, hydro-mulch, or salt hay *lightly* applied. This is also important to the speed of seed germination and turfgrass establishment. Once grass roots are established, better stability of individual particles within the soil profile is assured. This is important to the resiliency of the playing surface.

PROBLEMS IN ESTABLISHMENT OF TURF

Because of the fact that soil mixtures prescribed are quite porous, there has been a number of cases where greens have been rather slow in becoming established. Frequent, light fertilization of newly seeded or vegetatively planted greens appears to be one method of speeding establishment. Light watering several times daily is essential to rapid turf establishment of the newly planted surface. It is necessary to syringe the surface frequently to get germination and plant growth initiated. Once plants are established, the danger of soil particle migration is lessened and heavier waterings can safely be initiated.

In some cases greens built to Green Section specifications have been sodded. This is acceptable only if the sod is grown on exactly the same soil mixture as is used in the green. If the sod is grown on any other type of soil and is moved onto the porous putting green soil, failure is a certainty. Generally speaking, a seeded or stolonized new green more quickly results in a smoother finished surface than one that is sodded.

During the first year, the green must be topdressed frequently to promote smoothness. The topdressing soil must be mixed to the same specification as the original top mixture. A different top mixture should never be applied to any new green. This refers to all greens, not just greens built to Green Section specifications.

These steps for constructing putting greens will provide excellent results if followed exactly and completely. There are no short cuts to excellence in putting green construction.

COST

Some clubs have been deterred from building putting greens by this method because they have thought that the construction costs would be excessive. We contend any method that insures that the green will be built right is not expensive; only greens that are poorly built are expensive. It is obviously impossible to pinpoint costs in any given region because of variations in the cost of soil materials, gravel, and labor.

ACKNOWLEDGMENT

The author would like to thank Drs. Richard L. Duble and Kirk W. Brown, Texas A&M University; Rollin C. Glenn, University of Maine; Coleman Y. Ward, Mississippi State University; and U.S. Golf Association Green Section Agronomists William H. Bengeyfield, Holman M. Griffin, James B. Moncrief, F. Lee Record, William G. Buchanan, Stanley J. Zontek, and Carl Schwartzkopf for their help.

REFERENCES

1. FERGUSON, M. H., L. HOWARD, and M. E. BLOODWORTH. 1960. Laboratory methods for evaluation of putting green soil mixtures. US Golf Assoc. J. Turf Manage., September. p. 30-32.

ABSTRACTS

Abstracts of all papers not published herein but presented at the Conference are included below to round off this Section. These abstracts, unlike the printed papers, have not been refereed.

SECTION 4 ABSTRACT—REPORT OF SAND-ORGANIC MIXES FOR PUTTING GREEN CONSTRUCTION

Three organic amendments, shredded bark, composted redwood, and reedsedge peat, were blended with three grades of sand, washed concrete, nursery, and a finely graded, baked sand. There were three depths of profile: 30 cm of mix, 15 cm of mix over 15 cm of sand, and 7.5 cm of mix over 23 cm of sand. The lower strata were precompacted in each plot. A digested, centrifuged, and composted sewage sludge was blended into each mix at three different ratios: 60–20–20 (sand-amendment-sludge, respectively), 60–30–10, and 70–20–10. 'Old Orchard' creeping bentgrass (*Agrostis palustris*) was stolonized on the entire experimental area. After establishment and irrigation the area was compacted with a vibrating roller to simulate traffic. For the first 2 years, fertilization and irrigation were held at a minimum. During the last year, these two management practices were increased to optimum, similar to the golf greens on the accompanying course. The measurements included visual ratings for color and appearance, optical density measurements, water infiltration rates, and measurements of rooting depths and density.

Results indicate no significant differences between the bark-redwood or peat. The 60–20–20 mix received higher visual ratings than the other two mixes, and this mix resulted in a greater depth of rooting than the others. Under reduced irrigation and fertilization, the washed concrete sand with a wider range of particle sizes showed stress faster than the other sands, but differences were not apparent when irrigation and fertilization were increased. The very fine baked sand offers no advantages in root development. Although the full 30 cm of mix received slightly higher ratings for appearance and roots, it would not be of economic value compared with the 15 cm of mix over the 15 cm of sand. The 7.5 cm of mix over the 23 cm of sand performed the poorest, but was still quite acceptable when irrigation and fertilization were increased.—W. C. Morgan, Kellogg Supply, Inc.

SECTION 4 ABSTRACT—USE OF SHEAR STRENGTH AS A MEASUREMENT OF TRACTION IN SPORTS FIELDS

The term traction describes the resistance of a sports field surface to the tearing action of studded footwear. An apparatus was constructed which reproduces shearing action of the player's studs. By using this apparatus, it is possible to quantify the tractive efficiency of a given playing surface. From calculations of the shear forces necessary to resist stud tear wear one can predict the extent to which a playing surface is likely to suffer tear damage. Tractive efficiency, as recorded by the above apparatus, was correlated with values obtained using a vane shear. Thus, by using this relatively simple piece of standard soil mechanics equipment, traction can be assessed in terms of the well-defined soil physical parameter—undrained shear strength.

Laboratory studies investigated the relationship between particle size distribution and shear strength at various moisture tensions and compaction levels. These studies were related to the selection of materials used in the construction of "hard porous" surfaces, where the most favorable compromise between hydraulic conductivity and tractive efficiency is sought. Several commercially available, hard porous materials were examined and their potential evaluated.

Laboratory and field studies on various grass surfaces indicated the important contribution that grass roots make to traction. This contribution gained importance as the content of sand in the rooting medium increased. Many sports fields are now being constructed from topsoil mixes very high in sand content. The inherent tractive potential of these mixes may be very low, making the establishment of a strongly binding surface rooting system of paramount importance. These considerations would appear to have important implications in the selection and management of turfgrasses.—D. J. Thornton and W. A. Adams, University College of Wales.

DISCUSSION

H. PRUN—Two materials for soil modification for sports turf have been referred to briefly. Additional information concerning these two products may be of interest. Hygromull is a flaked organic ureaformaldehyde resin form with many open spaces. The water holding capacity is 50 to 70% by volume and 4,000% by weight. Decomposition depends on soil pH. Only 3 to 5% of the decomposition rate is attributed to microbiological activity. The available nitrogen at pH 7 is 0% while 15 to 20% is available at pH 4.1. Hygromull wets slowly at first, but with repeated wetting water enters the particles immediately.

The other material is Agrosil, a powdered silicate colloid amended with phosphorus and organic ingredients. When wet it develops a colloidal system in the soil. It has the effect of adsorption of water upon the colloid and between the soil particles and the colloid. Nutrient adsorption with favorable availability for plant roots without expenditure of high energy is important. Agrosil prevents phosphorus from changing to less available forms within the soil system. Deeper penetration of phosphorus (20 to 30 cm) may be expected with resultant better root growth at these lower depths. Excess salts such as are found under saline soil conditions are adsorbed by this material.

F. J. WRAY—What is the cost of the various types of apparatus used for adding sand to soil by use of the vibrating slit trencher? What is the cost comparison between the single- and three-unit machines?

G. G. FISHER—The apparatus we used was experimental and thus constructed for us to meet our specifications by the contractor. Other machines have been built and are in use but only on contract for custom operation.

W. H. DANIEL—In the United States we use these slit trenchers in the application of calcined clay aggregates. These can be used under adverse conditions since they are bagged and relatively light weight. For example, it might take eight bags to make a run the length of a football field (91.4 m). If the vertical trench is 1 to 2 cm wide and 20 to 25 cm deep results will be excellent without use of sand which is heavy. Of course, the cost for calcined clay is greater than that for sand.

E. W. SCHWEIZER—Has anyone in the United States or Canada had experience with sub-irrigation and resulting salt accumulation at the soil surface? We have found that the system can work quite well, but obviously there is a danger of salt accumulation at the soil surface which could be damaging to fine turf.

G. V. JOHNSON—In Arizona we installed a cell system about 2 years ago and later had to dismantle it because of leaks. Since then we have increased the scope of our subirrigation research by installing a 30-unit lysimeter. Over a 1-year period at Tucson salt content has increased from about 1.0 m mho/cm to 2.0 m mho/cm under subirrigation. We don't anticipate this to be a real problem even under conditions of very high evapotranspiration found in the southwestern United States.

W. C. MORGAN—We have had experience with subirrigation at the Los Angeles Dodger Stadium infield. A significant increase in salinity resulted from this method of irrigation and its use has been discontinued. Where it has been used, surface irrigation has been necessary in addition to the subirrigation. Thus, in California the results have not been very successful, but keep in mind that rainfall in southern California comes in "streaks." We probably get close to 36 cm of rainfall per year and this is concentrated within a narrow range of time.

P. BOEKER—Because of the conflicting data on the amount and type of organic matter to be applied to the soil, a list should be prepared of the various materials used that would include data on chemical and physical properties. Controversy has arisen about amount of organic matter used in the soil. Reports state amounts varying from 5 to 40% soil organic matter. Various materials have such different properties that comparisons of this type have little meaning. Some researchers have referred to peat, which may be old, dark or light, all with different properties. Bark or other materials may have been used in some instances. These references must be accompanied by specific data on chemical and physical properties in order for us to understand why such great differences in amount needed have been reported.

W. H. DANIEL—In addition to the need for information on chemical and physical properties of organic matter there is variation in relation to weight and volume designations. For example 5% organic matter is likely based on weight while 40% is based on volume. With most types of organic matter about 20% by volume is equivalent to about 5% by weight.

R. L. MORRIS—When the Prescription Athletic Turf System is used how does the turf manager determine when to use the pumps to either extract moisture or to push it back in again?

W. H. DANIEL—Our experience has indicated that we have a wider range of satisfactory soil moisture for players when the surface is about 25% moisture by volume. If rain is anticipated, the turf manager draws water from the system prior to the game. If rain starts during the game the pumps would be started at that time. Thus, the turf manager can either anticipate conditions and prepare for them or correct conditions as they develop. In general practice the pump is used infrequently, only when it's raining during a game or pregame. Most of the year the system is used to assure uniform distribution and actually to conserve the rainfall or the irrigation water applied. Monitoring or recording apparatus for water levels in the soil is not an essential part of this system.

I. GREENFIELD—How does the cost of the Prescription Athletic Turf (PAT) System compare with the United States Golf Association (USGA) specifications for golf greens? What would be the difference in cost of construction of a putting green under each system? With the PAT system requiring a plastic barrier, porous pipes, and a pumping system wouldn't installation costs be high?

W. H. DANIEL —Even allowing for the plastic sheeting, pipe, and pump, the cost of the PAT system falls very close to the cost for USGA specifications construction. Materials cost is about one-half of the total cost. Labor costs vary considerably depending on how this is contracted or whether it is accomplished with in-house crews. Our estimate in the United States varies from $1 to $2/30 cm^2. This cost is to produce the finished product ready to use. Of course, we would recommend bulk delivery which saves time and money. We are not involved with off-site mixing which is necessary with the USGA method. The pump and installation technique are specific for the PAT system. The installation technique for the USGA system is also specific. All in all the costs of construction for the two systems are comparable.

A. M. RADKO—The USGA Green Section specifications for golf greens cost from $1 to $2/30 cm^2 to construct. They are no more costly than others. We contend that only greens built improperly are costly because they have to be rebuilt. If improperly built greens are not rebuilt they are much more costly to maintain.

P. E. RIEKE—Do the USGA Green Section specifications establish any specific cation-exchange capacities in these soil mixtures? Also, what is the effect of these exchange capacities on potassium fertilization? I would assume that the cation-exchange capacity of these soils would be quite low. What changes in potassium fertilization would these very porous mixtures require?

A. M. RADKO—Cation-exchange capacity of soil mixtures is a high-priority parameter for further study. At the present time we attempt to see that just enough silt and clay is present in the soil mixture to establish a cation-exchange capacity. Differences in the various components of the soil mixture would make some exchange capacities higher than others. In general they are all low. This means that USGA specification greens usually require a little bit more fertilizer. We recommend frequent feeding and application of a little more of most essential nutrients.

R. P. FREEBORG—Are the revised USGA Green Section specifications going to eliminate the intermediate layer of sand between the gravel and the topsoil?

A. M. RADKO—No, not at the present time. There may, however, be instances where this is practical. There have been indications that this intermediate layer may not be needed under certain conditions. We test and evaluate soil samples from throughout the country and see all types of sand, soil, and organic matter. With most of the materials worked with, the sand layer is needed; therefore, at this time we plan to keep the sand layer in the specifications. Our continued research should help to provide additional data that may result in the possibility of removal of this layer sometime in the future.

H. W. INDYK—What is the importance of wear or compaction treatments on soil-organic matter mixtures for putting greens?

W. C. MORGAN—Compaction and wear treatments are very important. In our work a vibrating roller was used weekly for this purpose.

R. A. KEEN—In Kansas and in California good results are obtained on almost pure sand. Why bother to add organic materials when turfgrasses grow so well on unamended soil?

W. C. MORGAN—Our experience has indicated that unamended sand is not well suited for turfgrass establishment and growth. We have large areas that are without natural rainfall for long periods of time and thus we have to irrigate more frequently and fertilize more frequently. By using organic materials less water is needed and fertilizers last longer. The net result is a decrease in both irrigation and fertilizer requirements when organic materials are used.

R. P. FREEBORG—What is the importance of determining cation-exchange capacities on different organic sources used with sand in mixtures for putting greens?

W. C. MORGAN—Data on cation-exchange capacity are important and are readily available for most organic sources. In general, the sludges have a higher cation-exchange capacity and the barks and wood fibers a lower capacity. Peats are usually intermediate.

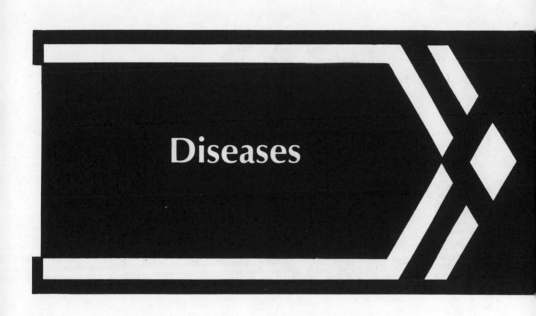

Diseases

Section V

35

Microclimate during wet periods on differently sheltered turfgrass swards[1]

T.J. GILLESPIE

Air temperature, leaf wetness duration, and wind were measured at the mown surface of three differently sheltered creeping bentgrass swards (*Agrostis palustris* Huds. 'Penncross') as an aid to understanding the higher incidence of fungal diseases on turf protected from sun and wind. The turfgrass was managed as a golf course putting green. One site was open to sun and wind, the second was artificially shaded from the morning sun by snowfencing until 11 a.m., while the third site was enclosed in all directions by a similar fence shelter.

All sites had similar temperatures during rainy periods. During dew periods the open site was slightly warmer than the shaded turf but cooler than the enclosed site. A wind speed of about 2 m/sec at 5 cm above the turf was found sufficient to prevent dew onset.

Dew periods on the open turf were of about 2½ hours shorter duration than on the shaded site, but about 2 hours longer than on the enclosed site. Despite a 100% difference between wind speeds at the two protected sites, morning drying after a night rain at both sites was about equally delayed until after the open turf dried. This implies that modification of the shelter around a green to provide increased direct sunlight will enhance rapid drying far more than will increasing wind flow alone. Additional index words: *Agrostis palastris* Huds. Penncross, Air temperature, Wind.

It is often observed that turf protected from sun and wind is susceptible to fungal diseases. One of the causal factors is thought to be that a microclimate more suitable for disease exists in such localities. The study reported here was intended to monitor the differences in temperature and leaf wetness duration occurring at the tops of three highly managed creeping bentgrass canopies; one unshaded and windswept, one partly protected from sun and wind, and the third surrounded completely by shelter. An assessment of the relative importance of sun versus wind in controlling the microclimate was also sought.

---

[1]Contribution from Department of Land Resource Science, University of Guelph, Guelph, Ontario, Canada.

MATERIALS AND METHODS

The experiments with differently sheltered bentgrass swards (*Agrostis palustris* Huds. 'Penncross') were carried out from August 26 to September 24, 1972, at the Cambridge Research farm about 20 km west of Guelph, Ontario. During these weeks, measurements were taken on 8 nights with mostly clear skies and appreciable dew deposition. Three wet periods caused by rain (August 27, August 31, and September 20) were also monitored. The turfgrass was managed as a golf course putting green.

A partly protected environment (hereafter called the shaded site) was provided by a length of 1.2 m tall, 50% open snowfencing erected to form an L-shape. The fence offered shade to the east and south of the point where measurements were taken, which was about 1 m from each arm of the L. Hence, at this site, the turf was shaded from the morning sun until about 11 a.m. A completely protected environment (hereafter called the enclosed site) was created by erecting snowfencing that formed a triangle when viewed from above. Measurements were made within this enclosure at a point whose perpendicular distance from each side of the triangle was about 1 m. These setups simulated a green having 50% porous natural shelters that are 0.6 times as high as the green is wide; for example, 15-m tall trees around a 25-m wide green. A third site, surrounded in all directions by at least 50 m of turfgrass (hereafter called the open site) was also established. Instrument limitations prevented the replication of any sites.

Air temperatures were measured at the turf top level with 0.36-mm diameter thermistors coated with highly reflecting white paint. Their small size and reflective paint reduced errors due to direct solar radiation on the sensors to less than 0.5 C without the need for artificial ventilation which would have destroyed the natural turf environment. The thermistors were connected to an electronic circuit utilizing an operational amplifier and a resistance bridge to produce pulses at a rate which was linearly related to temperature (1). The linear characteristics of the calibration allowed proper averaging of temperature fluctuations. The pulses were monitored with an Atmospheric Environment Service of Canada event recorder originally used to receive signals from an anemometer. Thus by simply counting the number of pulses emitted by the circuit in any desired time period, the average temperature during that period was immediately known.

Leaf wetness duration was measured with 1 X 6 cm printed circuit grids bonded to 1-mm thick epoxy-based board, similar to the devices described by Davis and Hughes (2). These grids of closely spaced interweaving copper fingers were coated with latex paint to make the electrical resistance of the unit very sensitive to the presence of liquid water. The color of the paint was adjusted until the sensors wetted and dried within 15 min of real leaves and one sensor was exposed within the turf canopy at each measurement site.

Wind speed was measured at each of the open, protected, and enclosed sites in addition to temperature and leaf wetness duration. The wind measurements were made with a very sensitive, propellor-type anemometer with a starting speed of less than 25 cm/sec (Weather Measure model W-131).

Some data concerning minimum windspeeds required to prevent dew formation on an open sward of turfgrass are also given in this report. These wetness data were obtained at the Elora Research Station (about 24 km north of Guelph, Ontario) using leaf wetness grids identical to those set out at the Cambridge Station. However, wind speed data at the Elora site were taken from a standard Atmospheric Environment Service of Canada anemometer located at the 10-m level.

RESULTS

Differences in wind speeds between sites

The snowfence barriers erected at the shaded and enclosed sites had considerable effect on wind speeds as measured about 5 cm above the turf. Wind speeds at the shaded site ranged from 0.30 to 0.44 of those in the open, with an average shaded-wind to open-wind ratio of 0.37. The average enclosed-wind to open-wind ratio was 0.18 with a range from 0.15 to 0.24. Hence the wind speeds at the shaded site were about twice those within the enclosure.

Temperature differences between sites during wet periods'

A comparison of temperatures at the shaded and open sites for a typical dew nite with mostly clear skies is shown in Fig. 1. During the night the

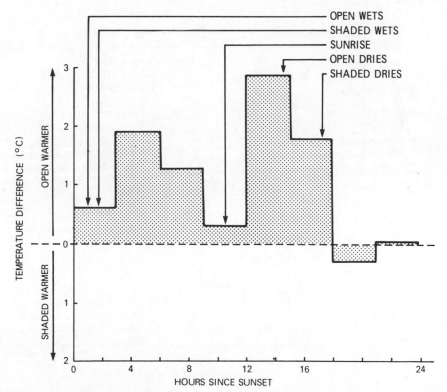

Fig. 1—Open and shaded sites 3-hour average temperature differences during a period with dew, Aug. 31–Sept. 1, 1972.

shaded site was always colder than the open site, with a maximum difference of about 2 C and an average difference near 1 C. Somewhat cooler nighttime temperatures were expected at the shaded site because it was still exposed to considerable amounts of cold sky and hence is quite freely losing radiant energy to space, but reduced wind speeds would allow a steeper temperature inversion to develop than at the open site. During the drying period after sunrise, protection from the solar beam kept the shaded site cooler than the open.

In contrast to the above results, during a clear night the enclosed site was typically warmer than the open site (Fig. 2). At the enclosed site the fencing blocked much of the turf's exposure to the sky and thus radiant energy losses were sufficiently reduced to keep temperatures higher than in the open. Shortly after sunrise, a deck of low clouds developed to block the direct solar beam during this drying period. Under these conditions, reduced evaporative cooling due to lower wind speeds in the enclosure was the likely mechanism for keeping temperatures at this site slightly warmer than in the open.

During periods of leaf wetness due to rain there were no measureable differences in 3-hour average temperatures between sites. This is to be expected because in cloudy, windy weather the atmosphere near the ground is virtually isothermal.

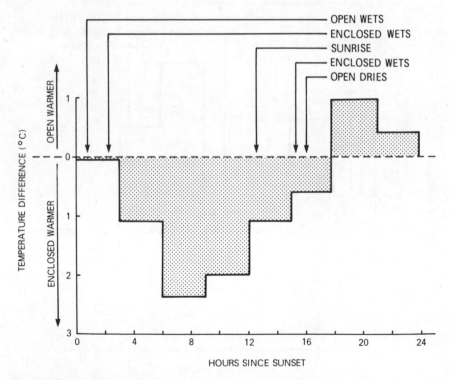

Fig. 2—Open and enclosed sites 3-hour average temperature differences during a period with dew, Sept. 20–21, 1972.

Differences in leaf wetness duration between sites

Leaves at the shaded site were typically wet longer than those in the open for cases of both rain and dew. With drying under sunny morning skies on August 29 (dew), August 31 (rain), and September 1 (dew), the shaded grass was wet 2½, 2¼, and 2 hours longer, respectively. With drying under cloudy skies on August 27 (rain) and August 28 (dew) the duration of wetness at the shaded site was extended 1¼ hours.

A comparison of the open and enclosed site revealed marked differences in wetness durations associated with rain as opposed to dew. On the morning of September 20, after a rain, the enclosed turf remained wet 2¼ hours longer than the open site. However, during the dew nights ending September 21 and 23, the durations of wetness were 2 and 2¼ hours shorter, respectively, within the enclosure than in the open. A likely explanation is that warmer nighttime temperatures noted at the enclosed site inhibit the dew formation process as is evidenced by late wetting and early drying of dew at the enclosed site (Fig. 2).

Minimum wind speeds required for dew prevention

The two primary weather elements controlling the onset of dew are cloud cover and wind speed. Under clear skies and light winds, liquid water typically begins to appear on turfgrass leaves within 1 hour of sunset (2). By simply noting the wind speeds at the time of dew onset during clear nights when dew fell later than 1 hour after sunset, an estimate of minimum wind speeds required for dew prevention may be obtained. The wind speeds at which dew begins vary on such nights (Table 1) because humidity and soil moisture have some influence on leaf wetness, but it can be seen that a wind speed of 4.5 m/sec at the 10-m level would have prevented dew formation during clear nights from May to August of 1973. Lower wind speeds would of course have been required on cloudier nights. According to the logarithmic relationship between height and wind speed (4) a 4.5 m/sec wind speed at the 10-m level implies about a 1.7 m/sec wind at 5 cm above a 1-cm tall turf surface.

Table 1—Wind speeds at dew onset during nights in 1972 when dew fell later than 1 hour after sunset.

Date	Time of dew onset, EST	Wind speed at 10-m level, m/sec	
		1 hour before dew	At dew onset
May 18	9:00 p.m.	3.1	2.2
May 19	9:00 p.m.	3.1	1.8
May 20	12:30 a.m.	3.6	3.1
May 22	9:30 p.m.	4.1	1.8
Jun 17	9:30 p.m.	3.1	2.7
Jul 22	9:30 p.m.	5.4	4.0
Aug 19	8:30 p.m.	2.7	2.7
Aug 20	9:00 p.m.	2.7	2.7
Aug 29	8:30 p.m.	3.1	1.8

DISCUSSION AND CONCLUSIONS

Recalling that the snowfencing used as shelter in this study was about 50% porous, the temperature and leaf wetness duration differences measured between sites probably represent minimum values encountered on variously shaded golf greens. Often natural shelters are less than 50% porous and this would be expected to enhance differences between open and shaded sites.

When both the shaded and enclosed sites were thoroughly wetted with night rain and then dried while sheltered from the clear morning sun (August 31 and September 20), they were both wet 2¼ hours longer than the open site. This occurred despite winds at the shaded site being double those within the enclosure. The implication is that winds have much less influence on the drying than does solar energy and so modification of the shelter around a green to provide increased direct sunlight will enhance rapid drying far more than will increasing wind flow alone.

Data on minimum wind speeds required to prevent dew onset may be used to assess the possibility of employing artificial ventilation to control fungal activity on a chronically diseased turf surface. A wind machine capable of creating a 2 m/sec air flow near the turf surface at night would appear adequate for this task.

An important aspect of disease development that should be investigated next is the survival of spores during periods when leaves are not wet. It is likely that the higher daytime humidities expected in sheltered areas allow significantly more spores to avoid death by dessication than at an open site. Such knowledge combined with studies of microclimate during wet periods, as reported here, could lead to optimum management of natural shelter around turf surfaces such that microclimates unfavorable for disease are purposefully created.

REFERENCES

1. BOOTSMA, A. 1972. Environmental factors affecting the development of yellow leaf blight (*Phyllosticta maydis*) in corn. M.Sc. thesis, University of Guelph, Guelph, Ontario.
2. DAVIS, D. R., and J. E. HUGHES. 1970. A new approach to recording the wetting parameter by the use of electrical resistance sensors. Plant Dis. Rep. 54:474–479.
3. MONTEITH, J. L. 1957. Dew. Quart. J. Royal Meteorol. Soc. 83:322–341.
4. MUNN, R. E. 1966. Descriptive micrometeorology. Academic Press, New York.

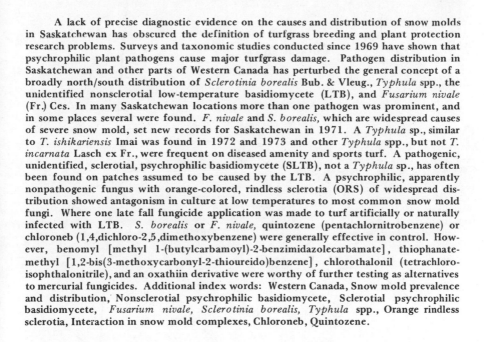

36

Snow molds of turfgrasses in Saskatchewan[1]

J.D. SMITH

A lack of precise diagnostic evidence on the causes and distribution of snow molds in Saskatchewan has obscured the definition of turfgrass breeding and plant protection research problems. Surveys and taxonomic studies conducted since 1969 have shown that psychrophilic plant pathogens cause major turfgrass damage. Pathogen distribution in Saskatchewan and other parts of Western Canada has perturbed the general concept of a broadly north/south distribution of *Sclerotinia borealis* Bub. & Vleug., *Typhula* spp., the unidentified nonsclerotial low-temperature basidiomycete (LTB), and *Fusarium nivale* (Fr.) Ces. In many Saskatchewan locations more than one pathogen was prominent, and in some places several were found. *F. nivale* and *S. borealis*, which are widespread causes of severe snow mold, set new records for Saskatchewan in 1971. A *Typhula* sp., similar to *T. ishikariensis* Imai was found in 1972 and 1973 and other *Typhula* spp., but not *T. incarnata* Lasch ex Fr., were frequent on diseased amenity and sports turf. A pathogenic, unidentified, sclerotial, psychrophilic basidiomycete (SLTB), not a *Typhula* sp., has often been found on patches assumed to be caused by the LTB. A psychrophilic, apparently nonpathogenic fungus with orange-colored, rindless sclerotia (ORS) of widespread distribution showed antagonism in culture at low temperatures to most common snow mold fungi. Where one late fall fungicide application was made to turf artificially or naturally infected with LTB, *S. borealis* or *F. nivale*, quintozene (pentachlornitrobenzene) or chloroneb (1,4,dichloro-2,5,dimethoxybenzene) were generally effective in control. However, benomyl [methyl 1-(butylcarbamoyl)-2-benzimidazolecarbamate], thiophanate-methyl [1,2-bis(3-methoxycarbonyl-2-thioureido)benzene], chlorothalonil (tetrachloro-isophthalonitrile), and an oxathiin derivative were worthy of further testing as alternatives to mercurial fungicides. Additional index words: Western Canada, Snow mold prevalence and distribution, Nonsclerotial psychrophilic basidiomycete, Sclerotial psychrophilic basidiomycete, *Fusarium nivale, Sclerotinia borealis, Typhula* spp., Orange rindless sclerotia, Interaction in snow mold complexes, Chloroneb, Quintozene.

Although winters are long and often severe in the prairies of Canada, until the start of this decade little attention had been paid to the overwintering diseases of turf and turfgrasses in Saskatchewan. Much more interest is now being shown in games played on turf and in its use to ameliorate the environment. There are now 35 golf courses with grass greens in play and several more under construction. The major cities of Regina and Saskatoon

---

[1]Contribution number 519, Agriculture Canada Research Station, Saskatoon, Saskatchewan, S7N OX2.

have several lawn bowling greens and amenity lawns of red fescue (*Festuca rubra* L.) and Kentucky bluegrass (*Poa pratensis* L.) are extensive. Turfgrass species are used in many roadsides. Recently, Kentucky bluegrass sod farms have been established. It is to be expected that, with an increased interest in sports and amenity turf, there will develop a better appreciation of the part played by overwintering and other diseases in turf quality and appearance.

Saskatchewan has a continental climate with hot summers and cold winters. It lies mainly in the southern part of the northern forest with a triangular section in the south and southwest in the prairie grassland region (Fig. 1). Between these is a parkland transition zone. The average annual rainfall is about 380 mm. The extreme southwest is semiarid with rainfall as low as 280 mm, but parts of the east receive an average 450 mm of precipita-

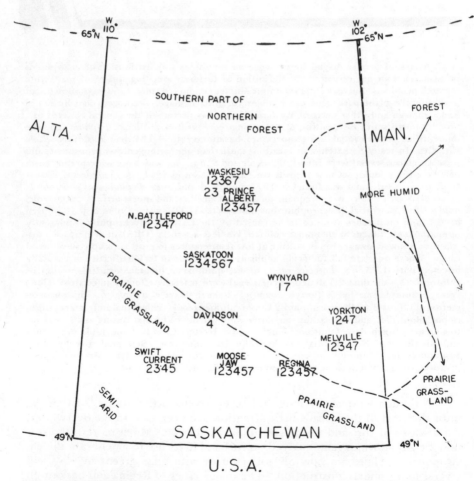

Fig. 1—Climatic regions and distribution of turfgrass snow molds in Saskatchewan, 1971–1973. 1 = ORS, 2 = *Sclerotinia borealis*, 3 = *Fusarium nivale*, 4 = SLTB, 5 = LTB, 6 = *Typhula*, 7 = *Typhula* sp.

tion. Average winter snowfall ranges from 635 mm in the southwest to nearly 1,380 mm in the north and east. Median snow depth in those regions ranges from 305 mm to 508 mm, respectively. Winter thaws during chinook periods frequently remove the snow pack in the southwest and turfgrass dessication may be severe. The median number of snow cover days ranges from about 120 to 180 in the settled regions in the southern part of the province (12, 19, 30).

Lebeau and Cormack (15) considered the distribution of snow mold pathogens on the Gramineae in Western Canada similar to that found by Ekstrand (5) in Scandinavia; *Sclerotinia borealis* Bub. & Vleug. was found in the extreme north, and *Typhula* spp. and *Fusarium nivale* (Fr.) Ces. further south. These were believed to be of minor or local importance in Western Canada compared with a sterile, nonsclerotial, psychrophilic basidiomycete, the so-called low-temperature basidiomycete (LTB) (1) not reported from other countries. The LTB was of widespread distribution and seriously damaged cereals, grasses, and forage legumes in Alaska and Western Canada (3). However, there are several anomalies in this distribution. Lebeau and Logsdon (16) isolated *S. borealis* and the LTB in Alaska and *Typhula ishikariensis* Imai in the Yukon; Vaartnou and Elliott found the latter to be the most prevalent snow mold pathogen on turfgrasses in the Peace River of Alberta and adjacent British Columbia, although *S. borealis, F. nivale,* and *T. incarnata* Lasch ex Fr. were recorded in successively decreasing frequency in Spring 1968 (31). After epidemics of snow mold on turf in southern Alberta caused by *F. nivale* in 1967 and 1968, Lebeau considered that a complex of the LTB and the latter fungus was probably involved in that region (14). In southern Manitoba, Platford et al. (18) reported that the LTB was the cause of the most serious turfgrass snow mold but an unidentified *Typhula* sp. and *F. nivale* caused damage to bentgrass (*Agrostis* spp.) golf greens.

In Saskatchewan the LTB appeared to be the cause of severe snow mold damage to many domestic red fescue/Kentucky bluegrass lawns surveyed in Saskatoon city in Spring 1969 (24). In Spring 1971, *F. nivale* and/or *S. borealis,* which had set two new provincial records, were isolated from golf green turf from Prince Albert in the north to Swift Current in the south; however, the LTB was rarely isolated (26). Vanterpool (32) found a sclerotia-producing *Typhula* sp. causing slight damage to a lawn in Saskatoon in 1943. In 1965 (23) a fungus with small black or dark brown sclerotia, then considered to be those of *Typhula* sp., was associated with severe snow mold on a bowling green in the city. This fungus, a sterile, sclerotial, psychrophilic basidiomycete (SLTB) was isolated in culture from some of these snow mold cases in Saskatoon in 1971 (26). Orange-colored, rindless sclerotia, superficially resembling those of a *Typhula* were found in leaves of dead *Poa annua* L. plants in golf turf in Regina, Saskatchewan in Spring 1971 (26).

One of the obvious deficiencies in the research effort to develop control measures for snow mold and other winter problems in turfgrasses by plant breeding and cultural and plant protection methods for this region is the lack of precise diagnostic evidence on the causes and distribution of disease. This paper summarizes the results of recent surveys, taxonomic studies, and field tests to find suitable fungicides for snow mold control.

SNOW MOLD ON DOMESTIC LAWNS

A survey of 900 Saskatoon lawns in early May 1969 showed that only 12% were free from symptoms of snow mold. Much of the damage appeared to have been caused by the LTB. Heavy shading by trees and "luxury land-scaping" were factors associated with high disease severity (24). In late April and early May 1971, a total of 1,200 lawns at seven centers in the province were surveyed. Snow mold damage was most severe at Swift Current in the southwestern "chinook" region of the province (26); only 18% were free from snow mold. In 1972, a total of 1,600 lawns at 14 centers were sur-veyed during the same period as in 1971. Although disease incidence was 56%, much lower overall, incidence and severity at Saskatoon was similar in 1969, 1971, 1972, and 1973. In early May 1973 the incidence of snow mold on 378 Saskatoon lawns was 86%. The LTB, SLTB, *F. nivale,* and *Typhula* spp. were found alone or in combination.

DISTRIBUTION OF PATHOGENS AND ASSOCIATED FUNGI ON ALL TURF TYPES

The unidentified low-temperature basidiomycete (LTB)

The pathogenicity, mode of action, or field control of the LTB or group of so-called unidentified, nonsporulating basidiomycetes has received con-siderable study (1, 15, 33). A reasonably accurate diagnosis of the LTB snow mold patches on turfgrass can be made by finding a white fungus with clamp connections, but no fruiting bodies or sclerotia, which grows rapidly on cul-ture media between 5 and 10 C. Many, but not all, isolates produce HCN which can be detected by the "benzidine-blue" reaction (6) of a steam dis-tillate of the culture substrate or the infested grass or sod. This test is labori-ous and does not lend itself to broad surveys. Fair reliance for routine diagnosis can be placed on the appearance of patches at snow melt when an abundant white fringe of mycelium is present. However, in some instances, little superficial mycelium is apparent yet considerable grass damage eventual-ly develops. This damaged turf frequently supports the growth of sapro-phytes, notably *Cladosporium herbarum* Fr. and a *Plenodomus* sp., which grow well at low temperatures and often "swamp" the LTB. Although the LTB is very common, there appear to be several other possible causes of snow mold, including other psychrophilic basidiomycetes; therefore it is difficult to ascertain the frequency of this fungus as a cause of snow mold in Saskatchewan. Vaartnou and Elliott did not report it on turfgrasses from the northwest of Canada in their 1968 survey (31). It has been isolated from several locations in Saskatchewan and typical mycelium and patches have been found elsewhere (Fig. 1). Turf of *P. pratensis,* especially var. 'Merion', *F. rubra,* and *Agrostis* spp., are all susceptible

Fusarium nivale

Although first officially recorded for Saskatchewan in 1971 (26), this pathogen is widespread on all turf species (Fig. 1). It was also found from the Peace River region to southern British Columbia in 1973. Positive and reliable diagnosis is based on the characteristic pink appearance of grass blades and mycelium on patches. This color persists after snow melt and often intensifies. Identification of the pathogen may be confirmed by finding typical spores on leaf fragments or by the production of abundant sporodochia and spores on isolates grown on culture media on a near-ultraviolet illuminated temperature gradient plate at 10 or 12 C. While this pathogen is common on Kentucky bluegrass and red fescue amenity turf receiving some heat from water pipes, sewers, and basements, it also develops on exposed sites under heavy drifts. It is an important factor in the winter-killing of *P. annua* on golf greens and is often isolated from such situations. Severe attacks occurred on many Saskatchewan golf greens in October 1972 before development of a permanent snow cover. The yellowish-brown areas typical of fusarium patch (27) developed rather than the pink snow mold symptoms which are characteristic of the same disease following snow melt. All common turf species were susceptible but bluegrass/fescue turf appeared to recover more rapidly from *F. nivale* attacks than from those of the LTB.

Sclerotinia borealis

Although unreported until 1971 from the province (26), this snow mold pathogen occurred on one or more *Agrostis* greens on every Saskatchewan golf course visited in Spring 1972 and 1973 (Fig. 1). It was also found on *F. rubra* and *P. pratensis* turf. In more extensive surveys in the Spring of 1972 and 1973, it was found from the Saskatchewan-Manitoba border to Beaver-lodge and Dawson Creek in the Peace River region of Alberta and British Columbia and as far south as Agassiz in southwestern British Columbia. Diagnosis is simple and reliable. Black sclerotia 0.5 to 7 mm in length are present in plant bases, leaf axils, and on leaves. On germination these give rise to apothecia which develop freely under near-ultraviolet light at 8 C, with a 4-hour day length. Abundant sclerotia can often be collected by maceration in water, sieving, and decanting of affected turf or leaf fragments collected by vacuum pickup from patches. In 1971 and 1972 the most severe outbreaks were associated with heavy snow drifts resulting from snow fences or branches placed on or around greens to prevent desiccation damage. 'Seaside' and 'Penncross' creeping bentgrass are apparently more susceptible than 'Colonial'.

Typhula spp.

T. incarnata Lasch ex Fr. [syn. *T. itoana* Imai (4, 6, 7, 22)] has not been isolated from infected snow mold turf in Saskatchewan although in the 1973 spring survey it was isolated from central and southern British Columbia. A fungus with sclerotia closely resembling those of *T. ishikariensis* Imai (8) [syn. *T. idahoensis* Remsberg (20) and *T. borealis* Ekstrand (5)] was isolated from snow mold patches in *P. pratensis* lawn turf in Saskatoon and from several *Agrostis* sp./*P. annua* golf greens in Prince Albert National Park in northern Saskatchewan in 1972 and 1973, respectively. A similar fungus was collected at several points in Alberta and British

Columbia. Sclerotia of an apparently undescribed *Typhula* sp. were collected in 1972 and 1973 from infected turf at all but one of the Saskatchewan centers (Fig. 1). The tawny to dark-brown, globular sclerotia measured 0.25 to 0.5 mm approximately in diameter when fresh, that is about half the diameter of *T. ishikariensis.* They were very loosely attached to the plants, sometimes being suspended in mycelial wefts. Germination and sporulation were induced and the filiform sporophores measured 0.82 to 2.85 mm X 0.16 to 0.54 mm. The pip-shaped basidiospores were 7.2 to 10.5 μ X 2.9 to 3.8 μ. Sporophore length and basidiospore length and width were smaller than given by Remsberg for *T. idahoensis* (20). Pathogenicity tests were inconclusive with this fungus. A further sclerotial fungus was isolated repeatedly from snow mold-damaged *P. pratensis* turf on the university campus at Saskatoon during a thaw in March 1973 and later at snow melt. It was also isolated from golf green turf at Penticton, British Columbia in April 1973. Mature sclerotia superficially resembled those of *T. ishikariensis* in color and in size when solitary, but they frequently were contorted, coalesced, or irregular in shape. Unlike *T. ishikariensis,* the mycelium of this fungus was coarse, rarely septate when young, and without clamp connections. Pathogenicity of this fungus has not been tested.

Sclerotial low-temperature basidiomycete (SLTB)

The SLTB was isolated from snow mold patches on golf, bowling, and domestic turf throughout Saskatchewan (Fig. 1) and in the Peace River region of Alberta and British Columbia from 1971 to 1973, and was frequently the dominant organism. The dark brown or black spherical, ovoid, irregular, or flake-like sclerotia, ranging from 0.25 to 1.5 mm in size, are formed on dead or senescent grass leaves and stems. The mycelium is sparse, white, and sometimes almost powdery and ephemeral. Clamp connections can be found on hyphae in culture and in sclerotial sections. Unlike *Typhula* spp., the sclerotia of the SLTB show no clear differentiation into medulla and cortex. In contrast with the LTB, no SLTB isolates produced HCN in tests. Isolation in culture is tedious and the success rate low, especially with mature sclerotia. The fungus grows at below 0 C in culture. SLTB isolates are pathogenic. No success has attended attempts to induce sporulation.

Fungus with Orange Rindless Sclerotia (ORS)

This fungus was found on snow mold patches, often associated with the SLTB, *S. borealis,* and the *Typhula* spp. from most of the survey points in Saskatchewan (Fig. 1) and from the Peace River region. It was also isolated from turf in Ottawa by Dr. L. Weresub. It was absent from snow mold material in southern British Columbia. The spherical or ovoid regular or flattened sclerotia, 0.25 to 2 mm in size, developed pink- to salmon-colored sporodochia after exposure to summer conditions in grass swards. Spores resemble those of a *Tubercularia* or *Gliocladium* and are approximately 1-2 X 4-10 μ but we are uncertain about the taxonomy of this fungus. Single spores yield typical orange sclerotia in culture. The fungus makes slow mycelial

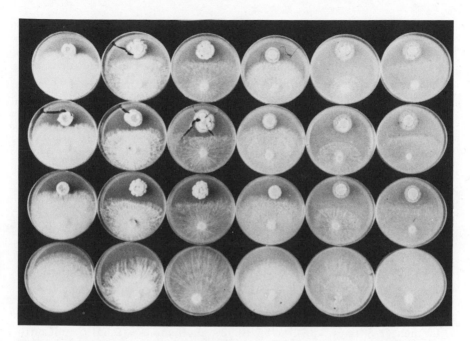

Fig. 2—Antagonism between three isolates of the ORS fungus (rows 1–3) and LTB isolate (columns 1 and 4), a *Typhula* sp. (columns 2 and 5), and an unnamed sclerotial fungus (columns 3 and 6) from snow mold patches grown at 5 C on malt, yeast extract, peptone medium (columns 1–3) and a cornmeal, malt, and yeast extract medium (columns 4–6). Row 4 is a check.

growth at all temperatures but sporulates and produces sclerotia below 0 C. Surveys in Spring 1973 in Saskatchewan, Alberta, and British Columbia suggested sclerotia developed and matured under snow and were produced in abundance on overwintered grasses of many species; they were also formed on alfalfa (*Medicago sativa* L.) and alsike clover (*Trifolium hybridum* L.) stems in deep snow or high humidity locations—in roadside ditches for example. Attempts to show pathogenicity have failed but the significance of this fungus may be in its antagonism to *F. nivale*, LTB, SLTB, *Typhula* spp., and *S. borealis* at low temperatures which has been demonstrated in culture (Fig. 2).

SNOW MOLDS—CONTROL WITH FUNGICIDES

Occasional *ad hoc* tests with fungicides have been made on domestic lawns in Saskatchewan since 1966. Inorganic and organic mercury compounds usually gave effective control of LTB snow mold. Some scientists consider it necessary, others expedient, and some workers think it fashionable to look for alternatives for mercury fungicides.

In 1971 in some domestic lawn tests with replicated 64.3 m^2 plots, quintozene (2.0),[2] chloroneb (1.9), phenyl mercuric acetate (0.15), and D735 (1.0) applied once in late fall considerably reduced snow mold caused by complexes of *F. nivale,* SLTB, and LTB. Erratic results with these materials in some other 1971 tests where the LTB and SLTB were dominant indicated the need for turf inoculation with specific pathogens or more precise diagnosis (26).

While inoculation with the LTB has been most effective, successful infections suitable for fungicide tests were also started by inoculation with *F. nivale, S. borealis,* and the SLTB grown on sterile grain. In all tests only one late fall application of fungicide was made.

LTB inoculated turf

At the end of 1971 and the start of 1972 (1971-1972), quintozene (1.96 & 3.92), mercurous + mercuric chlorides (0.78 & 1.56), phenyl mercuric acetate (0.13), chloroneb (1.39 & 2.80), thiram (1.63), and D735 (0.48 & 0.96) applied to inoculated, replicated creeping red fescue/Kentucky bluegrass plots (2.32 m^2) significantly reduced the percentage area affected. Benomyl, cadmium chloride, and thiophanate methyl were ineffective. In 1972-73, quintozene (0.98, 1.96, and 3.92), chlorothalonil (1.96 and 3.92), chloroneb (1.68 and 3.36), D735 (0.98), and benomyl (0.65) significantly reduced infection in one test; benomyl (0.33 and 1.29), thiophanate methyl (0.45 and 0.91), phenyl mercuric acetate (0.07 and 0.13), BAS 3460F (0.33), and CA 70203 (0.26) were ineffective; and BAS 3460F (0.65) and CA 70203 (0.13) were associated with significantly increased damage. A second test confirmed the effectiveness of chlorothalonil (1.96) and indicated effectiveness of thiobendazole (0.52) and the ineffectiveness of benomyl (0.65), thiophanate-methyl (0.91), phenyl mercuric acetate (0.13), BAS 3460F (0.33), CA 72003 (0.26), and TCMTB (0.43).

LTB—natural infection

On very heavy natural infection (82% average on check plots) in *P. pratensis* 'Merion', only mercurous/mercuric chloride (0.78) gave significant control (7.4% infection) from 15 materials tested.

S. borealis—artificial infection

In 1971-72, quintozene, (1.96 and 3.92) mercurous/mercuric chloride (0.74), phenyl mercuric acetate (0.06), thiram (1.86), D735 (0.48), benomyl (0.33), thiophanate-methyl (0.04), BAS 3201F (0.05), CA 70203 (0.02) were effective in significantly reducing a light artificial infection on Kentucky bluegrass-red fescue turf. BAS 3050 (0.08) was not effective.

---

[2]The numbers in parenthesis following the fungicide name are grams of active ingredient applied per m^2. Chemical names of fungicides may be found at the end of this chapter.

S. borealis—natural infection

In 1971-72 in one test in southern Saskatchewan on a 'Penncross' creeping bentgrass putting green, quintozene (2.08), chloroneb (1.86), and benomyl (0.33) were effective, mercurous/mercuric chloride (0.74) and phenyl mercuric acetate (0.06) were ineffective in significantly reducing percentage area of turf infected. In another test, on a golf green on the same course, quintozene at (0.98, 1.96, and 3.92) was most effective and phenyl mercuric acetate (0.07) was less effective in controlling a heavy infection (average of checks = 70.0%).

In 1972-73 on a very heavy infection (average of checks = 90%) on *Agrostis/P. annua* turf in northern Saskatchewan, quintozene (1.96) phenyl mercuric acetate (0.13), and chloroneb (1.69) provided outstanding control, and thiobendazole (0.52), benomyl (0.65), BAS 3460F (0.65), CA 70203 (0.26), and chlorothalonil (1.96), in descending order, also significantly reduced infection.

F. nivale—artificial infection

In 1971-72 in two tests with light infections, quintozene (2.09), mercurous/mercuric chloride (0.74), phenyl mercuric acetate (0.06), and chloroneb (1.61) significantly reduced disease.

F. nivale—natural infection

On a light infection which appeared on *P. annua* turf following a light snowfall in October 1972 phenyl mercuric acetate (0.13), quintozene (1.96), and chloroneb (1.69) were outstanding in preventing further disease development under a winter snow cover. Neither chlorothalonil (1.96), CA 70203 (0.26), thiobendazole (0.52), benomyl (0.65), thiophanate-methyl (0.91), nor BAS 3460F (0.65) provided significant control.

DISCUSSION

On the basis of present evidence, the geographic or climatic distribution of the main snow mold pathogens of turfgrasses is acceptable only as a very broad general principle. Probably local variations in microclimate are of more significance in determining pathogen prevalence than climate generally, even in a region as extensive as Saskatchewan. In 1971, 1972, and 1973 in the locations surveyed in Saskatchewan and elsewhere, more than one pathogen was prominent; in many locations there were several. This applied to the wider surveys in Western Canada also. In a previous paper, Smith (25) suggested that it was not possible to correlate the distribution of major snow mold pathogens to their cardinal temperatures. Nearly all will grow in culture at least at freezing point or below. Only when suitable climatic or cultural conditions present themselves do snow molds cause epidemics. This has been shown experimentally to be the case with *F. nivale* and the LTB by Lebeau (13) in relation to soil temperature. He found temperatures of 3 C and 6 C favored *F. nivale* and those at subzero were conducive to LTB attacks. However, the sappy conditions of the grass in a highly humid atmosphere under the snow at the higher temperatures may have been as important a factor as the temperature itself in favoring *F. nivale* snow mold. *T. incarnata* is sometimes found on winter cereals in Britain but only after the melting of the heaviest snowfall in living memory in March 1963 was it found as a common pathogen of turfgrass (9). Jackson noted that prolonged snow cover is necessary for this fungus to cause severe symptoms in Rhode Island (10). *F. nivale* and *Typhula* spp. can also cause severe damage in deep snow areas in Idaho, Washington, and Oregon (2, 27). The LTB often causes severe damage to turf where snow drifts melt slowly—yet its distribution is largely considered to be in a region of light to moderate snowfall (75 to 125 cm). The SLTB snow mold is often more severe on southeast shoulders of raised golf greens than slopes in other directions. It is uncertain whether this is related to prehibernal conditions, depth and duration of snow, or rate of snow melt. In those pathogens such as *S. borealis* and *Typhula* spp. (10, 11, 17) where mycelium or spores may be infective, conditions governing maturation, germination/spore discharge and prehibernal infection may be as significant in disease prevalence and severity as snow depth and snow cover duration. However there is considerable conflicting evidence about this in the case of *S. borealis* (11, 21, 28).

One factor which appears to have received little attention is the possible interaction of snow mold pathogens or other psychrophilic fungi in disease complexes. Exploratory studies have indicated that little antagonism exists between *F. nivale*, LTB, *S. borealis,* and *Typhula* spp. in pure culture. However, some isolates of ORS have shown antagonism towards all the last-mentioned pathogens at low temperatures. Since this is a widely distributed fungus its role in snow mold development requires further exploration.

Fungicide tests on turf inoculated with pure culture or where there was one dominant pathogen suggested that there were suitable alternatives to the mercurials for snow mold control. When one late fall application was made chloroneb and quintozene were generally effective; benomyl, thiophanate-methyl, chlorotholonil, an oxathiin derivative, and thiobendazole particularly, appear worthy of further testing. Since *F. nivale* may cause damage before winter, especially on *P. annua* turf, an additional fall application of fungicide may be justified where this disease is expected. Where multiple applications are used the range of effective fungicides may be extended.

Chemical names of fungicides.

BAS 3460F	not available
BAS 3201F	not available
Benomyl	= methyl 1-(butylcarbamoyl)-2-benzimidazolecarbamate
CA 70203	not available
Cadmium chloride	= cadmium chloride
Chloroneb	= 1,4,dichloro-2,5,dimethoxybenzene
Chlorothalonil	= tetrachloroisophthalonitrile
D 735 (DCMO)	= 5,6-dihydro-2-methyl-1,4-oxathiin-3-carboxanilide
Mercurous/mercuric chlorides	= mercurous chloride/mercuric chloride
Phenyl mercuric acetate (PMA)	= phenyl mercuric acetate
Quintozene (PCNB)	= pentachlornitrobenzene
Thiobendazole	= 2-(4'-(thiazolyl)-benzimidazole
Thiophanate-methyl	= 1,2-bis (3-methoxycarbonyl-2-thioureido)benzene
Thiram	= tetramethyl thiuramidisulfide

REFERENCES

1. BROADFOOT, W. C., and M. W. CORMACK. 1941. A low-temperature basidiomy-causing early spring killing of grasses and legumes in Alberta. Phytopathology 31: 1058-1059.
2. BRUEHL, G. W. 1967. Correlation of resistance to *Typhula idahoensis, T. incarnata* and *Fusarium nivale* in certain varieties of winter wheat. Phytopathology 57:308-310.
3. CONNERS, I. L. (Ed.). 1967. An annotated index of plant diseases in Canada. Can. Agr. Res. Br. Publ. 1251. 381 p.
4. CORNER, E. J. H. 1950. A monograph of Clavaria and allied genera. Oxford University Press. 740 p.
5. EKSTRAND, H. 1955. Höstsädens och vallgrasens övervintring. Statens Växtskyddsanstallt. 67:1-125.
6. FEIGL, F. 1958. Spot tests in inorganic analysis, 5th ed. Elsevier Publ. Co. p. 276-277.
7. IMAI, S. 1931. On some Typhula diseases of agricultural plants. Ann. Phytopathol. Soc. (Japan) 2:386.
8. ———. 1936. On the causal fungus of the Typhula blight of gramineous plants. Jap. J. Bot. 8:5.
9. JACKSON, N. 1962. Turf disease notes 1962. J. Sports Turf Res. Inst. 10:410-416.
10. ———, and J. M. FENSTERMACHER. 1969. Typhula blight: Its cause, epidemiology and control. J. Sports Turf Res. Inst. 45:67-73.
11. JAMALAINEN, E. A. 1949. Overwintering of Gramineae—plants and parasitic fungi. Maataloust. Aikakausk. 21:125-140.
12. KENDREW, W. G., and B. W. CURRIE. 1955. The climate of central Canada. Queen's Printer, Ottawa. 194 p.
13. LEBEAU, J. B. 1964. Control of snow mold by regulation of winter soil temperature. Phytopathology 54:693.
14. ———. 1968. Pink snow mold in southern Alberta. Can. Plant Dis. Surv. 48:130-131.
15. ———, and M. W. CORMACK. 1959. Development and nature of snow mold damage in Western Canada. IX Int. Bot. Congr. (Montreal) 1:544-549.
16. ———, and C. E. LOGSDON. 1955. Snow mold of forage crops in Alaska and Yukon. Phytopathology 48:148-150.
17. LEHMANN, H. 1965. Die *Typhula*—Fäule als Auswinterungs Krankheit des Getreides. Nachrichtenblatt für den Deutschen Pflanzenshutzdienst. 6:141-145.
18. PLATFORD, R. G., C. C. BERNIER, and A. C. FERGUSON. 1972. Lawn and turf diseases in the vicinity of Winnipeg, Manitoba. Can. Plant Dis. Surv. 52:108-109.
19. POTTER, J. G. 1965. Snow cover. Climatological studies no. 3. Can. Dep. Trans. Met. Br. Queen's Printer, Ottawa. 69 p.
20. REMSBERG, R. E. 1940. Studies in the genus *Typhula*. Mycologia 30:52-96.
21. RØED, H. 1960. *Sclerotinia borealis* Bub. & Vleug., a cause of winter injuries to winter cereals and grasses in Norway. Acta Agr. Scand. 10:74-82.
22. ———. 1969. Et bidrag til appklaring av forholdet Mellom *Typhula graminum* Karst. og *Typhula incarnata* Lasch ex Fr. Freesia 9:219-225.
23. SMITH, J. Drew. 1965. Snow mold on the lawn. Quart. Bull. Sask. Hort. Soc. Ass., Ext. Div. Univ. Saskatchewan 4:1, 3.
24. ———. 1969a. Snow mold on lawns in Saskatoon. Can. Plant Dis. Surv. 59:141.
25. ———. 1969b. Overwintering diseases of turfgrasses. N.W. Turf. Cong., Proc. 23rd (Hayden Lake, Idaho, Sept. 24-26). p. 65-78.
26. ———. 1972. Snow mold on turfgrass in Saskatchewan in 1971. Can. Plant Dis. Surv. 52:25-29.
27. ———, and N. JACKSON. 1965. Fungal diseases of turfgrasses, 2nd ed. Sports Turf Res. Inst. 86 p.
28. SPRAGUE, R. 1959. Epidemiology and control of snow mold of winter wheat and grasses in the Pacific Northwest of the United States. IX Int. Bot. Congr. (Montreal) 1:540-544.
29. TOMIYAMA, K. 1959. Snow blight of winter cereals in Japan. IX Int. Bot. Congr. (Montreal) 1:549-552.

30. UNIVERSITY OF SASKATCHEWAN, Extension Division. 1969. Guide to farm practice in Saskatchewan. 142 p.

31. VAARTNOU, H., and C. R. ELLIOTT. 1969. Snow molds on lawns and lawn grasses in Northwest Canada. Plant Dis. Rep. 53:891–894.

32. VANTERPOOL, T. C. 1943. Snow mold. *In* I. L. Conners and D. Ƅ. O. Savile (ed.) Cultivated grasses. 23rd Ann. Rep. Can. Plant Dis. Surv. 40 p. (mimeo).

33. WARD, E. W. B., and J. B. LEBEAU. 1962. Autolytic production of hydrogen cyanide by certain snow mold fungi. Can. J. Bot. 40:85–88.

37

Fusarium blight of Kentucky bluegrass in California

R.M. ENDO & P.F. COLBAUGH

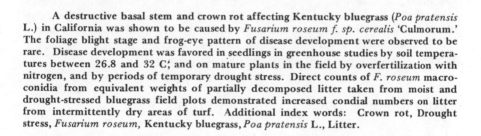

A destructive basal stem and crown rot affecting Kentucky bluegrass (*Poa pratensis* L.) in California was shown to be caused by *Fusarium roseum f. sp. cerealis* 'Culmorum.' The foliage blight stage and frog-eye pattern of disease development were observed to be rare. Disease development was favored in seedlings in greenhouse studies by soil temperatures between 26.8 and 32 C; and on mature plants in the field by overfertilization with nitrogen, and by periods of temporary drought stress. Direct counts of *F. roseum* macroconidia from equivalent weights of partially decomposed litter taken from moist and drought-stressed bluegrass field plots demonstrated increased condial numbers on litter from intermittently dry areas of turf. Additional index words: Crown rot, Drought stress, *Fusarium roseum*, Kentucky bluegrass, *Poa pratensis* L., Litter.

In California, Kentucky bluegrass is frequently affected with a destructive basal stem and crown rot. The cause of this disease was demonstrated to be *Fusarium roseum* (LK.) f. sp. *cerealis* (Cke.) Synd. & Hans. 'Culmorum', the same fungus that Couch and Bedford (4) established as the cause of the Fusarium blight disease of cool-season turfgrass in the northeastern United States. Couch and Bedford also demonstrated that *F. tricinctum* (Cda.) Snyd. & Hans. f. sp. *poae* (Pk.) Snyd. & Hans. was a second causal agent. However, to date we have not isolated this fungus from diseased bluegrass plants in California.

In the midwest and northeastern United States, Fusarium blight is usually manifested as a foliage blight; infections of the stem base and crown apparently occur infrequently (1, 2, 4). In California, this relationship is reversed: *F. roseum* usually infects the stem base and crown, but not the foliage. The foliage of infected plants dies following the death of the stem and crown which is affected with a dark brown to black, dry, firm rot; roots arising from the crown are often killed as well. The low incidence of foliage infection in southern California is presumed to be due to the low relative humidity and the lack of summer rainfall. In California, all plants within the blighted areas are usually infected, whereas, in the East and Midwest, plants within the center of the affected areas often mainfest little or no disease, which results in the typical frog-eye appearance (1, 2, 4).

Fusarium blight in California appears to be influenced by the same factors that affect the fungus and disease elsewhere (1, 2, 3, 4, 5). In greenhouse studies with bluegrass seedlings (*Poa pratensis* L. var. 'Park') the disease developed best in pasturized soil held at soil temperatures between 26.8 and 32 C; infection of the crown occurred at soil temperatures as low as 10 C, however, diseased plants transplanted from the field tended to recover at soil temperatures of 15 C and below. The disease was observed commonly in the field on bluegrass plants receiving high nitrogen fertilization and on plants that had been stressed for moisture.

IRRIGATION STUDIES

Irrigation experiments were conducted during the summer on 5-year-old 'Merion' bluegrass plots receiving 227 g $(NH_4)_2SO_4/929$ m^2 every 21 days. A direct relationship between the quantity of water applied to the plots and the incidence and severity of disease was observed. When a marginally adequate amount of water was applied, the disease involved approximately 40% of the plot area and the infected plants usually died. When an intermediate amount of water was applied, 13% of the plot area was affected and when abundant water was applied, less than 1% of the plot area was affected.

CONIDIAL POPULATION STUDIES ON LITTER

Samples of partially decomposed litter were taken from the irrigation plots receiving the least and highest amounts of water in order to determine the population of *Fusarium* macroconidia present in each area. A 50 g (dry weight) sample of litter was placed in a Waring Blendor with 200 ml sterile water and blended for 3 min. The number of *Fusarium* macroconidia in aliquots of the resulting suspension was determined with a hemocytometer and expressed as the total of macroconidia per gram dry weight of tissue. On moist litter there were 2.0×10^4/g of macroconidia and on the dry litter there were 2.2×10^6/g of macroconidia. The striking difference in conidial numbers appears important, since several workers (1, 3, 5) have found that a high incidence of infection requires very high populations of spores. The increase in disease development within dry areas may be related to an increase in the saprophytic and parasitic activities of the fungus on the dry litter following irrigation but not on the continually moist litter.

Temporary drought stress probably exerts an additional, but undetermined role on the host plant. This effect was indicated by the following experiment. When root-pruned Merion bluegrass plants were dipped into a suspension of 3.0×10^6 macroconidia/ml and transplanted into sterile soil, little or no infection of the crown occurred unless the plants were subjected to a temporary drought stress. Since mechanical wounding of the roots, very high concentrations of inoculum, and the temporary absence of biological competition did not result in infection in the absence of temporary drought stress. The role of drought stress in triggering the saprophytic and parasitic activities of *F. roseum* is being investigated.

REFERENCES

1. BEAN, G. A. 1966. Fusarium blight of turfgrasses. Golf Superintendent 34:32–34.
2. ——. 1966. Observation of Fusarium blight of turfgrasses. Plant Dis. Rep. 50:942–945.
3. ——. 1969. The role of moisture and crop debris in the development of Fusarium blight of Kentucky bluegrass. Phytopathology 59:479–481.
4. COUCH, H. B., and E. R. BEDFORD. 1966. Fusarium blight of turfgrasses. Phytopathology 56:781–786.
5. CUTRIGHT, N. J., and M. B. HARRISON. 1970. Some environmental factors affecting Fusarium blight of Merion Kentucky bluegrass. Plant Dis. Rep. 54:1018–1020.

38

Drought stress: an important factor stimulating the development of *Helminthosporium sativum* on Kentucky bluegrass[1]

P.F. COLBAUGH & R.M. ENDO

Saprophytic and parasitic activities of *Helminthosporium sativum*, which causes leaf-spot and root rot of Kentucky bluegrass (*Poa pratensis* L.), were greatest following periods of temporary drought stress. Increases in the number and severity of infections and of conidial production on litter were observed in dry areas of turf following irrigation but not in areas receiving adequate water. Field measurements and laboratory studies on temperature, relative humidity, and aeration within the litter of moist and drought-stressed areas indicated that the dry litter did not support a physical environment that favored the growth of bluegrass isolates of *H. sativum*.

Moist bluegrass litter completely inhibited conidial germination and mycelial growth of *H. sativum*, but dry litter immediately after remoistening did not. The inhibitory property was restored to remoistened litter about 7 hours following remoistening. Laboratory studies on the nature of the inhibition indicated that a volatile inhibitor was present on moist litter but not on dry litter. The chemical identity of the inhibitor was not determined.

The release of protein and carbohydrate into water was shown to be 300% greater from remoistened litter than from continuously moist litter. The increased release of nutrients from dried litter after remoistening, the absence of an inhibitor on dry litter at the time of remoistening, and the reduction of microbial numbers and activities during desiccation of litter are believed to be important factors associated with the drying-wetting cycles which trigger the saprophytic and parasitic activities of the fungus. Additional index words: *Helminthosporium sativum*, Irrigation, Kentucky bluegrass, Soil moisture stress.

Although the environment within a community of turfgrass plants seems ideal for the development of fungal diseases, most facultative fungal pathogens of turf cause disease infrequently and are generally active for only short periods. A possible explanation is that the competitive and antagonistic activities of the microflora on turfgrass litter are responsible for their suppression (4). The facultative fungal parasite *Helminthosporium sativum* P. K. & B. was selected for an investigation of the possible importance of biological antagonism because it has been well established that this fungus is readily in-

---

[1] Contribution from Department of Plant Pathology, University of California, Riverside.

hibited by soil microorganisms (8). In addition, we have noted that the *Helminthosporium* leaf spot disease in the field was most common and severe in the dry rather than the moist areas of bluegrass. This relationship was explored since Cook and Papendick (3) had demonstrated that *Fusarium roseum* f. sp. *cerealis* 'Culmorum' was more destructive in dry soils than in moist soils because the activity of competing microorganisms was greatly reduced and that chlamydospores of the pathogen germinated and initiated disease at low soil moisture levels.

MATERIALS AND METHODS

The distribution and incidence of the *H. sativum* leafspot disease was determined during the summer within a continuously moist and a drought-affected area of a 5-year-old bluegrass (var. 'Sydsport') field plot. Counts of leaf sheath and leaf blade lesions were made within a 30.5-cm area at distances of 0, 0.3, 0.6, 1.2, 2.4, and 3.0 m from the drought-stressed areas. Conidial production on litter taken from moist and from drought-stressed areas was determined by recovering conidia of *H. sativum* from the litter samples by a modification of Ledingham and Chinn's mineral oil flotation technique (5). Ten grams (dry wt) of freshly collected litter from each area were placed in Erlenmeyer flasks containing 300 ml of distilled water and shaken vigorously for 3 min to separate conidia from the debris. The wash water was filtered through four layers of cheesecloth and centrifuged to sediment the suspended conidia and debris. The supernatant liquid was discarded and 10 ml of mineral oil were mixed thoroughly with the pellet. Before allowing the oil and water phases to separate, 30 ml of distilled water were mixed with the mineral oil suspension. After a 1-hour separation period, the water phase which contained debris from the pellet was discarded. Twenty 0.1 ml aliquots of the mineral oil fraction were placed on microslides and the number of conidia typical of *H. sativum* was counted. The total volume of the mineral oil fraction was used for determination of the numbers of conidia per gram (dry wt) of tissue analyzed.

Conidial germination studies

Conidia of *H. sativum* used in germination studies on litter were produced on autoclaved barley (*Hordeum vulgare* L.) seed. Conidia were collected from air-dried seed and mixed with sterilized talc before dusting them onto the litter with an insufflator. Conidial germination was determined following incubation of the infested litter in 9.0-cm diameter petri dishes held at 26 C for 24 hours. Germination was assessed after staining germ tubes with aqueous phenolic rose bengal and viewing them with a microscope equipped with an epi-eluminator.

Nutrient release studies

Studies on the release of nutrients from air-dried and from moist bluegrass litter were performed following placement of each of the samples into deionized water. Ten grams (dry wt) of partially decomposed, moist or air-dried bluegrass litter were placed in 1-liter graduated cylinders containing 500 ml of deionized water. Ten-milliliter samples of the leach water in each cylinder were withdrawn immediately after placing the tissue in water and at 30-min intervals during a 5-hour period. A uniform distribution of nutrients in solution during sampling was insured by slowly inverting the cylinders containing the suspended litter before removing samples with a pipet. Each sample of leach water was passed through a 0.45-μ millipore filter to remove bacteria and frozen prior to analytical determinations of nutrient content. Collections of the leach water at each time interval were subjected to chemical determination for their content of total carbohydrate and protein. Total carbohydrate in the samples was determined by the anthrone procedure (1) and total protein was determined by the Lowry method (6).

RESULTS AND DISCUSSION

Field studies of Helminthosporium leaf spot during a 2-year period demonstrated that the greatest disease activity on bluegrass was manifested from June to September. The increased activity during the summer agrees with studies of this disease in New York (7), Minnesota (2), and Nebraska (9). The highest incidence of leaf blade and leaf sheath lesions occurred within intermittently drought-stressed areas of bluegrass, whereas the incidence of disease in areas receiving adequate water was low. The number of conidia of *H. sativum* recovered from the dry litter collected from drought-stressed areas was 30 times greater than the number recovered from equivalent weights of litter taken from continuously moist areas.

The increased incidence of lesions and the increased sporulation could have been caused by either a more favorable physical or microbiological environment for fungal growth within the drought-stressed areas than within the continuously moist areas. Field measurements of temperature, relative humidity, and gaseous atmospheres were made within the litter of moist and dry areas of bluegrass. The average temperatures in dry areas during the day were 45 C and 35 C in the moist areas. Relative humidity measurements of the litter taken with an electric hygrometer demonstrated that humidities were reduced rapidly to low levels (50%), even after a morning irrigation, while humidity within moist areas remained high (89%). Analysis of the gaseous atmosphere within the litter by gas chromatography showed that the concentration of CO_2 was increased only slightly within the moist litter as compared to atmospheric concentrations found within litter of drought-affected areas. Laboratory studies on the effects of these same factors on the fungus indicated that the physical environment of moist litter was more favorable for fungal development than dry litter.

H. sativum has been recognized by numerous workers to be a very weak competitor in the presence of other microorganisms (8). Supportive evidence for the involvement of microbiological activity in suppressing the ability of the fungus to grow on continuously moist litter was demonstrated by conidial germination studies (Fig. 1). Conidia which were placed on moist litter did not germinate, even though adequate moisture was present, but when washed from the surface of moist litter, they germinated readily. The

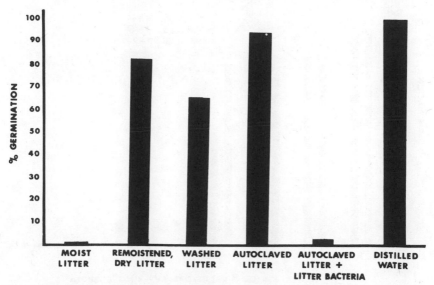

Fig. 1—Germinability of conidia of *Helminthosporium sativum* clone, T431, on Kentucky bluegrass litter subjected to various treatments before applying conidia.

inhibitory effects of moist litter could be reduced to varying degrees by washing, sterilizing, or air-drying the litter. The inhibitory property was restored if microorganisms from moist litter were added to the sterilized litter. Immediately after remoistening dried litter, germination of *Helminthosporium* conidia was very high, but as the period following remoistening was increased, the litter exhibited progressively greater inhibition of conidial germination until complete restoration of inhibition occurred about 7 hours following remoistening (Fig. 2).

The nature of the inhibition observed on moist litter is currently under investigation. Conidial germination was inhibited by a volatile factor produced by microorganisms found on moist litter. The demonstration of the presence of a volatile inhibitor(s) on moist litter was shown by separating conidia of *H. sativum* on glass microslides by a 20-mesh wire screen placed on samples of moist litter or autoclaved moist litter in the bottom of separate petri dishes. Following incubation of the test conidia at 27 C for 12 hours, the germination of conidia placed over the autoclaved litter was 95% while only 4% of the conidia held over nonsterile moist litter germinated.

Germination of *H. sativum* conidia was also inhibited by the effluent gas from five glass columns (3 × 30 cm) containing sterilized litter which was recolonized by each of five different litter-inhabiting bacteria. Passage of effluent gas from each of the infested columns for 24 hours over water agar (Difco), which was dusted with conidia, resulted in complete inhibition of germination. The effluent gas from similar glass columns containing only autoclaved litter gave no inhibition of conidial germination on agar. The identity of the volatile inhibitor has not been determined, but it was shown not to be high concentrations of CO_2 and/or a deficiency of O_2.

After air-dried litter is remoistened, large quantities of sugars and pro-

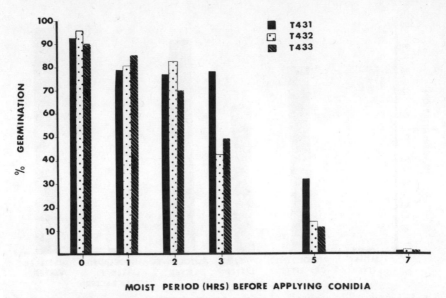

Fig. 2—Germination of condida of three clones of *Helminthosporium sativum* on re-moistened bluegrass litter when the moist period before applying conidia was varied from 0 to 7 hours.

teins are released. Total carbohydrates and proteins which were released into water during a 5-hour period from both dry and continually moist litter is shown in Fig. 3. Both the level and rate of release from dried litter was 300%

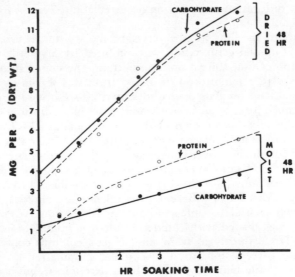

Fig. 3—Release in water of carbohydrates and of proteins from moist or air-dried blue-grass litter.

greater than that from continually moist litter. Since abundant nutrients are present when the dried litter is remoistened, there is probably sufficient food to nourish not only the varied microflora of the litter but the parasite *H. sativum* as well.

Since attempts by plant pathologists to develop an artificial inoculation procedure in the field for this disease have failed, the present findings were used to devise a successful inoculation technique. Fresh Kentucky bluegrass clippings were air dried, and dusted with conidia. The infested clippings were applied to a 4-year-old Kentucky bluegrass sod in which the litter in one-half of the plot was allowed to dry and the litter in the remaining half of the plot was kept moist. Both plots were then irrigated and kept moist for 48 hours. Severe disease developed in the plot in which the litter was allowed to dry, but only a trace amount of leaf infection developed in the plot where the litter was kept moist. These results were twice verified in the greenhouse with field-grown sod held in three soil temperature tanks maintained at 21, 27, and 32 C. Infection and disease development were greatest on drought-stressed plants held at 21 and 27 C while less disease occurred on drought-stressed plants held at 32 C. The lowest incidence and severity of disease were observed on plants maintained in a moist condition at each of the temperatures used.

CONCLUSIONS

On the basis of these studies, temporary periods of drought stress are believed responsible for initiating the sapropytic activity of *H. sativum* on litter and the initiation of disease in the field. The following factors appear to control these phenomenon. When bluegrass litter is dried, an inhibitory property which normally keeps the fungus in a state of fungistasis disappears while bacterial populations and activities are reduced. When dry bluegrass litter is remoistened, an abundant release of carbohydrates and proteins occurs that favors rapid germination, growth, and infection by *H. sativum*. When the inhibitory property is reestablished, saprophytic growth of the fungus is inhibited. Thus, we believe that numerous cycles of temporary drought stress favor the saprophytic and parasitic development of the fungus and the initiation of disease.

ACKNOWLEDGMENT

We wish to express our gratitude to Dr. V. B. Youngner for his advice and assistance during the course of these studies.

REFERENCES

1. BARTNICKI-GARCIA, S., and W. J. NICKERSON. 1962. Isolation, composition and structure of cell walls of filamentous and yeast-like forms of *Mucor rouxii*. Biochim. Biophys. Acta 58:102–119.
2. BEAN, G. A., and R. D. WILCOXSON. 1964. *Helminthosporium* leaf spot of bluegrass. Phytopathology 54:1065–1070.
3. COOK, R. J., and R. I. PAPENDICK. 1970. Soil water potential as a factor in the

ecology of *Fusarium roseum* f. sp. *cerealis* "Culmorum". Plant Soil 32:131–145.

4. ENDO, R. M. 1972. The turfgrass community as an environment for the development of facultative fungal parasites. *In* V. B. Youngner (ed.) The biology and utilization of grasses. Academic Press, New York. 426 p.

5. LEDINGHAM, R. J., and S. H. F. CHINN. 1955. A flotation method for obtaining spores of *Helminthosporium sativum* from soil. Can. J. Bot. 33:298–303.

6. LOWRY, O. H., N. J. ROSENBROUGH, A. L. FARR, and R. J. RANDALL. 1951. Protein measurement with the folin phenol reagent. J. Biol. Chem. 193:265–275.

7. MOWER, G. R. 1961. Histological studies of suscept-pathogen relationships of *Helminthosporium sativum* P. K. & B., *Helminthosporium* Drechs, and *Curvalaria lunata* (Wakk.) Boed. on leaves of Merion and Commercial Kentucky bluegrass (*Poa pratensis* L.) Ph.D. thesis, Cornell University. 155 p.

8. SIMMONDS, P. M. 1947. The influence of antibiosis on the pathogenicity of *Helminthosporium sativum*. Sci. Agr. 27:625–632.

9. WEIHING, J. L., S. G. JENSON, and R. I. HAMILTON. 1957. *Helminthosporium sativum*, a destructive pathogen of bluegrass. Phytopathology 47:744–746.

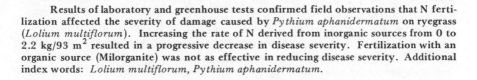

39

Influence of nitrogen fertilization on severity of pythium blight of ryegrass[1]

T.R. FREEMAN

Results of laboratory and greenhouse tests confirmed field observations that N fertilization affected the severity of damage caused by *Pythium aphanidermatum* on ryegrass (*Lolium multiflorum*). Increasing the rate of N derived from inorganic sources from 0 to 2.2 kg/93 m^2 resulted in a progressive decrease in disease severity. Fertilization with an organic source (Milorganite) was not as effective in reducing disease severity. Additional index words: *Lolium multiflorum, Pythium aphanidermatum*.

In the southern United States it is common practice to overseed dormant, warm-season grasses with a cool-season grass during the winter months. This practice is especially useful on golf courses in resort areas in order to maintain desirable playing conditions. Although some changes in the grass species used are occurring, annual ryegrass (*Lolium multiflorum* Lam) is still the predominant grass used for overseeding. Diseases present an acute problem in the cultivation of these temporary grasses and each year many plantings are destroyed by disease outbreaks. The most damaging disease is pythium blight incited primarily by *Pythium aphanidermatum* (Edson) Fitzpatrick.

Damage caused by pythium blight is evident as a reduced stand or aerial blighting after emergence (2). In this latter case, the white mycelium of the fungus often grows profusely over the grass plants; hence, this phase of the disease is referred to as cottony blight (4). Pythium blight is most prevalent during periods of warm temperature and high humidity. Under such conditions destruction and sometimes complete loss of grass plantings occur in a matter of hours (1). Field observation over a number of years indicated that factors other than environmental may be affecting disease occurrence and severity.

Moore et al. (3) reported that several factors including nutrition, pH, and soil moisture affected *Pythium ultimum* Trow damage on bentgrass (*Agrostis tenuis* Sibth). Field observations suggested a possible relationship

[1] Contribution from Department of Plant Pathology, University of Florida, Gainesville, FL 32601.

between N fertilization and incidence and severity of disease. On the sandy soils encountered in Florida, soluble N is readily leached and must be applied frequently to maintain the grass. To help overcome this leaching, many use slow release organic sources of N. With the widespread use of the organics, it became increasingly apparent that pythium blight was more severe on ryegrass fertilized with either these sources or low levels of inorganic sources than it was on grass that received adequate levels of readily available N. To determine if this was a true difference, the effects of rates and sources of N on disease development were evaluated under controlled conditions. The purpose of this presentation is to report results of these laboratory and greenhouse tests and to postulate on their significance in governing the occurrence and control of pythium blight.

MATERIALS AND METHODS

Initial exploratory experiments were carried out in the greenhouse using a 1:1 fine sand-peat mixture (fumigated) in 10-cm clay pots. Annual ryegrass was planted and, 1 week after emergence, fertilized with various levels of NH_4NO_3 to give rates of N varying from 0 (CK) to 2.25 kg/93 m^2. One week after fertilization plants were uniformly inoculated with a 1.2-cm plug cut from a 3-day culture of *P. aphanidermatum*. Disease severity was measured at 48 and 72 hour intervals by measuring the diameter of the affected area. Initial experiments were at ambient temperatures in the greenhouse. Later experiments were conducted in environmental chambers at 25 and 30 C. In these later tests, grass was grown on moist filter paper in deep Petri dishes in environmental chambers. This grass was fertilized with various rates and sources of N. Disease severity was evaluated in the same manner as used in the initial studies. In prolonged experiments lasting longer than 7 to 10 days, additional nutrients were provided by watering the plants with Hoagland's solution. In all tests, treatments were replicated three times.

RESULTS

In the initial exploratory experiments, supplying N at the rates 0, 0.45, 0.90, 1.35, and 2.25 kg/93 m^2 resulted in a progressive decrease in area damaged. At the higher rate, disease damage was 40% less than at the 0 rate. However, evidence of N toxicity was noted at the 2.25 kg rate and this rate was abandoned for the next series of tests in which temperature was a variable. Results of this latter test are presented in Table 1. These results clearly show that increasing the rate of N resulted in a progressive decrease in disease severity at both temperatures. The preceding results were confirmed using plants grown under more controlled conditions in liquid culture. In these experiments, in addition to NH_4NO_3, the materials $NaNO_3$, NH_3SO_4, and Milorganite (sewage sludge; Milwaukee Sewage Commission, Milwaukee, Wis.) were also used as sources of N. No significant differences were noted between disease severity on plants fertilized with NH_4NO_3 and $NaNO_3$. Disease severity on Milorganite treatments was about equal in severity to that of the check. NH_4SO_4 was toxic to the grass under the conditions of this test and

Table 1—Diameter (cm) of diseased area of ryegrass growing under various levels of N fertilization (derived from NH_4NO_3) 48 and 96 hours after inoculation with *Pythium aphanidermatum*.

Rate of N/93 m^2	48 hours		96 hours	
	25 C	30 C	25 C	30 C*
0 kg	4.3	6.5	10.0	10.0
0.45 kg	3.3	5.8	8.1	10.0
0.90 kg	2.3	4.5	6.8	10.0
1.35 kg	1.8	2.8	5.6	10.0

*Despite similar area affected, condition of grass indicated a progressive decrease in disease severity as N was increased.

disease severity could not be accurately determined. A comparison of disease severity on grass growing under a 1.35 kg/93 m^2 rate of N derived from Milorganite, NH_4NO_3, and $NaNO_3$ and a water check is shown in Fig. 1.

DISCUSSION

Results of these tests clearly indicate that, under certain conditions, N fertilization definitely affects the severity of pythium blight on annual ryegrass. Thus, they tend to confirm field observations made over a number of years. However, it should be pointed out that the results reported herein have not been verified by large-scale field experiments. Nevertheless, they indicate that field tests are warranted and they also form a firm basis for such tests. Certainly it would be to the advantage of the golf course superintendent if disease severity could be reduced by manipulation of his fertility program. Such a manipulation can easily be accomplished on sandy soils, such as those encountered in Florida, where leaching of soluble nutrients is prevalent and grass is grown under conditions approaching hydroponics.

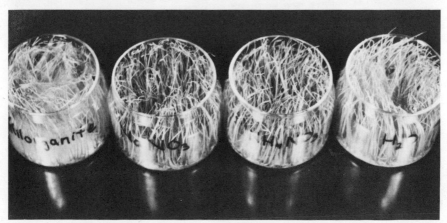

Fig. 1—Comparison of Pythium blight on ryegrass fertilized with 1.35 kg of N/93 m^2 derived from Milorganite, $NaNO_3$, NH_4NO_3, and H_2O check (left to right).

REFERENCES

1. FREEMAN, T. E. 1960. Effects of temperature on cottony blight of ryegrass. Phytopathology 50:570. (abstr.)
2. ———. 1969. Diseases of southern turfgrasses. Florida Agr. Exp. Sta. Bull. 713A. (Technical)
3. MOORE, L. D., H. B. COUCH, and J. R. BLOOM. 1963. Influence of environment on diseases of turfgrasses. III. Effect of nutrition, pH, soil temperature, air temperature and soil moisture on Pythium blight of Highland bentgrass. Phytopathology 53: 53–57.
4. WELLS, H. D., and B. P. ROBINSON. 1954. Cottony blight of ryegrass caused by *Pythium aphanidermatum.* Phytopathology 44:509--510. (abstr.)

40

Comparison of light-frequent, heavy-infrequent, and alternating applications of fungicides to control Fusarium Patch [1]

C. J. GOULD & R. L. GOSS

Both frequent-light and infrequent-heavy applications of benzimidazole fungicides protected *Agrostis* turf from attack by *Fusarium nivale*. Turf quality, however, was usually improved either by mixing a dithiocarbamate fungicide with the benzimidazole or by alternately applying the two types of fungicides. An alternating program should also be helpful in reducing chances for development of benzimidazole-resistant strains. Additional index words: **Agrostis, Benzimidazole, Dithiocarbamate, Fungicides,** *Fusarium nivale*, **Fusarium Patch.**

The Pacific Northwest climate is unusually favorable for development of Fusarium Patch (Pink Snow Mold) caused by *F. nivale* (Fr.) Ces. Frequent use of fungicides in spring and fall has been necessary to control the fungus on putting greens. Mercurials, used for many years, are no longer recommended. Fore [the coordination product of zinc ion and manganese ethylenebisdithiocarbamate] and Tersan LSR [maneb (manganese ethylenebisdithiocarbamate) + zinc salt] are effective when applied regularly at 10- or 14-day intervals. This requires much labor and schedules cannot always be followed. For these reasons, the search for more persistent fungicides has continued with major emphasis since 1967 on the benzimidazole fungicides.

Benzimidazoles ⟨e.g., Tersan 1991 [benomyl or methyl 1-(butylcarbamoyl)-2-benzimidazole-carbamate], Mallinckrodt's MF-509 [dimethyl 4,4′-o-phenylenebis (3-thioallophanate)], and Cleary's 3336 [Diethyl 4,4′-o-phenylenebis (3-thioallophanate)]⟩ have given excellent control of *F. nivale* and are now recommended. During this research, it was noted that, on some plots treated in May or June, control often persisted until October or November without additional applications. The 1971/72 experiments, therefore, were designed to measure the length of time that single applications of benzimidazoles and other fungicides could protect turf against *Fusarium* (1).

[1] Scientific Paper No. 4090 from the Departments of Plant Pathology and Agronomy, College of Agriculture Research Center, Washington State University, Project 1394.

Table 1—Effect of fungicides on disease, color, and quality of Highland bentgrass turf treated once or repeatedly in 1971/72.

Fungicide	Treatments*	Proprietary product in 38 l. water/ 93 m²	No. spots/m² of *F. nivale* Oct 15, 1971	Feb 11, 1972	Color† Dec 17, 1971	Apr 3, 1972	Jun 21, 1972	Quality† Jun 21, 1972
		—g—						
Untreated			43.7	21.9	6.8	8.2	7.4	7.0
Fore	R	227	41.8	0.0	9.2	9.4	8.4	7.6
Fore	S	454	2.0	22.5	6.2	8.2	7.4	7.4
Fore	S	907	5.4	14.4	5.4	8.6	8.0	7.6
Tersan 1991	R	57	0.0	1.2	8.4	8.4	8.0	7.6
Tersan 1991	S	57	0.0	12.5	7.6	8.6	7.2	6.4
Tersan 1991	S	113	0.3	4.3	7.6	8.2	6.4	6.2
Tersan 1991	S	227	0.0	3.2	7.8	8.4	7.0	6.6
Tersan 1991	S	454	0.0	0.9	8.2	8.0	7.0	6.4
T.1991/Fore	Alt	57/227	0.2	0.0	9.2	8.9	8.2	7.6
MF-509	R	57	2.6	1.4	8.6	9.6	9.0	7.8
MF-509	S	170	0.0	8.5	7.6	8.2	6.8	6.4
Daconil 2787	R	170	50.4	.0.2	5.6	6.8	6.6	6.2
Daconil 2787	S	340	10.7	28.7	5.0	6.6	7.4	6.6
Dyrene	S	454	29.1	19.5	4.2	8.6	7.4	6.6

*Single (S) applications made on Sep 23, repeated (R) applications begun Sep 23 and repeated 12 times at approximately 3-week intervals; alternating (Alt) treatments of 57 g/92 m² Tersan 1991 applied on Sep 23, 227 g Fore applied 3 weeks later, etc.　　†Color and quality rated from 1 to 10 with 10 being best.

MATERIALS AND METHODS USED IN 1971/72 EXPERIMENTS

Fungicides were applied at the rates shown in Table 1 either once on September 23, 1971 or twelve times at 3-week intervals from September 23 to May 30, 1972. Three-week intervals were used because, on this schedule, differences in the effectiveness of various materials in controlling the fungus were more apparent. Occasionally, the 3-week interval had to be altered slightly because of weather. In one treatment, applications of Tersan 1991 were alternated with Fore.

Fungicides were applied to *Agrostis tenuis* Sibth. cv 'Highland' bentgrass in five replications of 2.3 m² each. The grass was mowed at 6.4 mm height. Diameters of the *F. nivale* areas were relatively constant (2.5 to 5.0 cm) so spots were counted and numbers used to evaluate control. The color and quality of turf in each plot were rated periodically on a scale of 1 to 10 with 10 indicating the best.

RESULTS AND DISCUSSION OF THE 1971/72 EXPERIMENTS

The first outbreak of *F. nivale* occurred soon after applications began on September 23. Data collected on October 15 (Table 1) represent effects of this first treatment. All benzimidazole treatments and Fore at above normal rates gave reasonable or excellent control. Normal rates of Fore,

Dyrene [2,4-dichloro-6-(o-chloroanilino)-s-triazine], and Daconil 2787 (chlorothalonil or tetrachloroisophthalonitrile) were ineffective, and high rates of the latter two were only partially effective.

Another less severe attack of *F. nivale* occurred in February after snow had remained on the plots for several days. All fungicides previously applied at 3-week intervals controlled the disease during this outbreak. Control with the single September application of Tersan 1991 at 454 g was as good as that achieved from repeated applications and even single applications at 113 g and 227 g provided fair control. The single 170 g application of MF-509 gave some control, but one treatment of Tersan 1991 at 57 g was inadequate as were the single applications of the other fungicides.

Fungicidal effects on quality of turf are as important as their effects on pathogenic fungi. Although the single applications of Tersan 1991 and MF-509 were promising for providing prolonged control of *Fusarium,* turf quality was inferior to that of turf repeatedly treated with the same fungicides. Also, the quality of turf treated repeatedly with Tersan 1991 was consistently below that of plots on which Fore was applied regularly or alternated with Tersan 1991. Fore was alternated with Tersan 1991 to control organisms unaffected by Tersan 1991; to supply sulfur which western Washington turf needs; to control algae; and hopefully, to retard the possible development of strains to *F. nivale* resistant to Tersan 1991.

Turf improvement following the alternating program with Fore and Tersan 1991 at usual rates in 1971/72 led to expanded experiments in 1972/73 with different rates and schedules of benzimidazoles alternating with Fore.

MATERIALS AND METHODS IN THE 1972/73 EXPERIMENTS

Techniques used in the 1972/73 experiments were similar to those used in the 1971/72 tests unless otherwise stated. All but one material were applied as sprays. Treatment rates and schedules are shown in Table 2. In several treatments the benzimidazoles were applied initially at high rates, and subsequently at lower rates. The results shown in Table 2 are representative of two other concurrent tests.

RESULTS AND DISCUSSION OF THE 1972/73 EXPERIMENTS

Development of *F. nivale* was insufficient to provide data on disease control, but results were obtained of treatment effects on color, density, and overall turf quality.

The best turf usually was produced when Fore (a dithiocarbamate) was used regularly, or when a dithiocarbamate was mixed with a benzimidazole such as in Bromosan [diethyl 4,4'-o-phenylenebis (3-thioallophanate) + thiram] and MF-565 [dimethyl 4,4'-o-phenylenebis (3-thioallophanate) + maneb], or when a dithiocarbamate was used in an alternating program with a benzimidazole. An alternating program of 3 or 6 weeks appeared to be superior to one of 12 weeks. The maximum rate for the initial application of a benzimidazole (50% active) on an alternating schedule apparently should

Table 2—Effect of 1972/73 fungicidal treatments on color and density of turfgrass.

Main fungicide type	Proprietary product in 38 l. water/93 m² (g)	Alternating fungicides*	Scheduled interval in weeks	Sep 11	Oct 2	Oct 23	Nov 3	Dec 21	Jan 16	Feb 6	Feb 28	Mar 22	Apr 10	May 1	May 21	Color Jan 19	Color Apr 3	Color May 21	Density Jan 19	Density Apr 3	Density May 21
Untreated	—	—	—													7.2	6.0	7.6	7.4	6.2	8.2
Tersan 1991	57	—	3	+	+	+	+	+	+	+	+	+	+	+	+	6.8	5.4	7.2	6.0	4.4	8.2
Tersan 1991	57	F	3	+	F	+	F	+	F	+	F	+	F	+	F	7.0	8.4	10	7.2	7.4	10
Tersan 1991	227–57‡	F	6	227		F		57		F		57		F		7.2	8.2	9.6	7.2	7.2	9.8
Tersan 1991	227	F	12	+				F				+				6.4	7.6	8.4	6.4	6.8	9.0
Tersan 1991	396	F	12	+				F				+				7.6	7.8	8.2	6.4	6.4	9.4
Tersan 1991	567	F	12	+				F				+				6.4	8.6	8.8	6.6	6.2	9.0
Bay Dam 18654	57	—	3	+	+	+	+	+	+	+	+	+	+	+	+	7.0	5.2	7.4	6.4	6.0	8.6
Bay Dam 18654	227–57‡	F	6	227		F		57		F		57		F		7.0	8.2	9.0	6.6	7.2	9.8
Bay Dam 18654	396	F	12	+				F				+				6.8	8.2	8.2	7.2	7.0	9.4
Fungo§	57	—	3	+	+	+	+	+	+	+	+	+	+	+	+	7.4	7.9	8.2	7.6	7.4	9.4
Fungo	227–57‡	F	6	227		F		57		F		57		F		7.6	8.8	9.4	8.0	8.6	9.8
Fungo	396	F	12	+				F				+				7.0	9.4	8.8	7.6	8.4	9.8
Cleary 3336§	57	—	3	+	+	+	+	+	+	+	+	+	+	+	+	7.4	7.2	8.0	7.8	7.2	9.0
Cleary 3336	227–57‡	F	6	227		F		57		F		57		F		7.4	9.0	9.4	7.6	8.0	9.8
Cleary 3336	396	F	12	+				F				+				7.0	8.2	8.8	7.2	6.8	9.6
Bromosan	113	—	3	+	+	+	+	+	+	+	+	+	+	+	+	8.0	8.6	9.0	8.2	8.4	9.8
MF-565	142	—	3	+	+	+	+	+	+	+	+	+	+	+	+	7.4	9.0	8.8	8.8	8.4	9.8
MF-571 (dry)§	1928	—	3	+	+	+	+	+	+	+	+	+	+	+	+	8.0	7.2	8.0	7.4	6.8	9.6
Fore	227	—	3	+	+	+	+	+	+	+	+	+	+	+	+	7.8	9.2	10	8.0	8.2	10

*†Indicates rate listed for major fungicide in second column; F refers to Fore at 227 g/93 m².   †Color and density rates from 1 to 10 with 10 being best.   ‡First application was at 227 g and subsequent applications were at 57 g.   §Cleary 3336—diethyl 4,4'-o-phenylenebis (3-thioallophanate), Fungo—dimethyl 4,4'-o-phenylenebis (3-thioallophanate), MF-571—dimethyl 4,4'-o-phenylenebis (3-thioallophanate)—granular.

not be over 113 to 170 g of product. The new thiophanate compounds produced turf equal to and often better than that treated with Tersan 1991.

Turf treated repeatedly with either Tersan 1991 or BAY DAM 18654 〈Methyl [1-[[(5-cyanopentyl) amino] carbonyl]-1 H-benzimidazol 2-yl] carbamate〉 was lighter-colored than that left untreated. The color was much better on plots where Fore was alternated with these benzimidazoles. Injury from repeated use of Tersan 1991 was more severe than previously observed, perhaps because the turf contained considerable *Poa annua* L. mixed with Highland bent. Two other experimental areas which contained higher percentages of bent were less adversely affected by Tersan 1991.

SUMMARY

Results from these and other experiments indicate that: (i) most benzimidazole turf fungicides effectively control *F. nivale*, although they differ in their phytotoxicity; (ii) some, and perhaps all such fungicides, have a residual action that will permit greater latitude in timing applications; (iii) occasional heavier than normal applications provide prolonged control, but at the expense of turf quality; and (iv) the latter condition may be overcome by the application of dithiocarbamate fungicide separately or in combination. Such procedures could: (i) provide turf managers with greater flexibility in their operating schedules; (ii) reduce costs by saving on labor and perhaps on materials; and (iii) provide improved disease control because of the greater latitude in timing of treatments.

REFERENCES

1. GOULD, C. J., R. L. GOSS, and V. L. MILLER. 1972. Prolonged control of *Fusarium nivale* on bentgrass turf by single applications of benomyl. Phytopathology 62:761. (abstr.)

41

Fungicide tolerance — a rapidly emerging problem in turfgrass disease control[1]

H. COLE, JR., C. G. WARREN, P. L. SANDERS

Isolates of *Sclerotinia homoeocarpa* from benomyl control failure locations were compared with isolates from nonproblem turfgrass areas in terms of culture plate morphology and greenhouse disease symptom development. Fungicide tolerance was evaluated for 54 isolates in fungicide-amended acid potato dextrose sugar (PDA). Growth inhibition was determined for benomyl, Thiabendazole, thioallophanate-ethyl and methyl, and Bay Dam 18654. Isolates from control failure locations grown on fungicide-amended PDA were over 100 times as tolerant to benomyl as isolates from other areas. Tolerance to benomyl was associated with tolerance to other benzimidazole configuration fungicides.

Selected tolerant and nontolerant isolates were used as inoculum in greenhouse fungicide experiments on turfgrass. The results indicated that isolates from control failure locations were comparable in all respects except tolerance to nontolerant isolates of *S. homoeocarpa*. Disease symptoms on creeping bentgrass (*Agrostis palustris* Huds. cv 'Penncross') following inoculation with benomyl-tolerant isolates were well within the range of symptoms expressed following inoculation with benomyl-sensitive isolates.

In greenhouse fungicide experiments with creeping bentgrass benomyl or Bay Dam 18654 provided no control of tolerant isolates. With the tolerant isolate S-50, benomyl spraying resulted in more severe disease symptoms than the unsprayed check plants. Actidione and Dyrene were equally effective in controlling both tolerant and nontolerant isolates. Additional index words: *Agrostis palustris*.

Sclerotinia homoeocarpa F. T. Bennett (dollar spot) is a severe pathogen of irrigated temperate zone turfgrasses. For many years cadmium and mercury compounds have been the mainstay fungicides for its control. Recently the fungitoxic, systemically translocated benzimidazole compounds, primarily benomyl (Tersan 1991), were found to be effective against *S. homoeocarpa* and are rapidly replacing the older materials for Sclerotinia dollar spot control. In addition to benomyl, other related configurations, including thiabendazole and the thioallophanates, are also receiving wide usage for control of this pathogen. The mode of action of the benzimidazole configuration against fungal cells is thought to be quite specific, involving DNA synthesis (2). Recently, instances of complete dollar spot control failures involving benzimidazole use have been noted.

In light of this situation, *in vitro* studies were initiated to compare fungal isolates from the problem areas and to assess the level of Benzimidazole tolerance exhibited. Culture plate *in vitro* tolerance and possible tolerance relationships between benomyl and other benzimidazole fungicides were investigated through greenhouse turfgrass fungicide experiments. Benzimidazoles also were tested in the greenhouse in combination with broad spectrum protectant fungicides.

MATERIALS AND METHODS

Pathogen collection and identification

Samples of affected turfgrass were collected from areas where benomyl control failures had been reported and from areas where there were no control problems. Affected tissue was washed in dilute sodium hypochlorite solution (Chlorox 1:10 dilution) for 2 min, washed in sterile distilled water, and portions of the affected leaves were placed on acid potato dextrose agar (PDA) in petri dishes (Difco potato dextrose agar, pH 5.6 with 1 ml of 95% lactic acid added to each one after autoclaving).

Isolates thus obtained were compared to known isolates with respect to morphology. Cultures were maintained on PDA in tubes. The isolates also were grown on sterile autoclaved rye grain (*Secale cereale* L.). This inoculum was transferred to 8-week-old seedling stands of *Agrostis palustris* Huds. cv 'Penncross' growing in pots in the greenhouse. After inoculation, the bentgrass was incubated for 7 days in a saturated atmosphere. Experimental design on the greenhouse bench was a randomized block plan. Fifty-four isolates including nontolerant types from the Pennsylvania State University *S. homoeocarpa* collection were evaluated. Disease symptoms and overall virulence were compared among isolates. Data were recorded in terms of infection center diameters, blighting severity, and amount of aerial mycelium produced.

In vitro fungicide tolerance

Laboratory petri dish experiments were conducted with 54 isolates. The data reported in this paper are from 10 selected isolates: 5 suspected benomyl-tolerant isolates (isolates S-46, S-47, S-49, S-50, and S-51) and 5 benomyl-sensitive isolates (isolates S-7, S-8, S-9, S-24, and S-25).

Under natural conditions, the pathogen spreads from leaf to leaf within infection centers by mycelial proliferation, hence, inverted 5-mm dia. plugs containing mycelium and the agar beneath were transferred to the center of fungicide-amended PDA plates. All plugs were taken from the advancing peripheries of fungal colonies in petri dishes. Commercial fungicide formulations were used to amend the PDA plates. The chemicals were suspended in sterile, distilled water and added in the appropriate quantities to the partially cooled, sterile medium. All concentrations were calculated on a weight per volume active ingredient basis. The supplemented medium was then poured into sterile, plastic petri plates, allowed to cool, and used immediately.

Dosages tested were 0, 1, 10, 100, and 1,000 μg fungicide-active ingredient per milliliter of agar. Fungicides tested were 2-[4-thiazolyl] benzimidazole, (thiabendazole); methyl 1-[butylcarbamoyl]-2-benzimidazolecarbamate, (benomyl); methyl 1-[5 cyanopentyl] amino carbonyl-1H-benzimidazole, (Bay Dam 18654); dimethyl 4,4′-o-phenylenebis [3-thioallophanate], (thioallophanate-methyl); and diethyl 4,4′-o-phenylenebis [3-thioallophanate], (thioallophanate-ethyl). Each chemical treatment was replicated 3 times. All cultures were incubated in the dark in a controlled temperature cabinet at 24 ± 1 C. Colony diameters were recorded at regular intervals. The diameter measurements were converted to radial growth in millimeters per 24 hours.

Greenhouse fungicide experiments

Two isolates were selected which exhibited similar virulence and symptom patterns in greenhouse pathogenicity tests, but differed in benomyl tolerance *in vitro*. Isolate S-50 tolerated benomyl dosages over 100 times in excess of that tolerated by S-9 in agar plant growth experiments. Inoculum was prepared by growing the two isolates on autoclaved rye grain. The host grass species was Penncross creeping bentgrass, grown in 10-cm plastic pots. Grass age at the time of experimentation was 8 weeks, based on seedling emergence. Fungicide dosages were calculated and applied to the pots on an area basis, converted from the standard 93 centare dosages commonly used in turfgrass reesarch. Dosages are reported in terms of g/93 centare equivalencies. Fungicides and dosages tested were as follows: benomyl, 28.2 and 56.4 g, 50% wettable powder (WP) formulation; Bay Dam 18654, 28.2 and 56.4 g, 50% WP; Dyrene (2,4-dichloro-6-(o-chloranilino)-s-triazine), 112.8 and 225.6 g, 50% WP; and Actidione (3-[2-(3,5-Dimethyl-2-oxycyclohexyl)-2-hydroxyethl] glutarimide), 56.4 and 112.8 g, 2% WP. The fungicides were applied as an aqueous spray to the pots, at a dilution rate of 12 liters/93 centares. After the pots were sprayed with fungicides and allowed to dry, each pot of grass was inoculated by placing a few kernels of rye grain inoculum on the foliage in the center. The pots were then placed beneath individual plastic covers and incubated for 3 days under partial shade in a greenhouse. Temperature beneath the cover was 24 to 28 C. Experimental design for pot position on the greenhouse bench was a randomized block plan with 3 replications. Each pot was considered a replicate.

Disease severity was evaluated 7 days after inoculation on the basis of infection center diameter. A 0 to 5 rating scale was employed: 0 = no disease, 1 = infection center < 2 cm in diameter, 2 = 2.1 to 4 cm, 3 = 4.1 to 6 cm, 4 = 6.1 to 8 cm, 5 = 8.1 to 10 cm or essentially complete foliage surface.

RESULTS

Pathogen collection and identification

The isolates from the control failure locations (designated benzimidazole-tolerant) were similar to the nontolerant isolates in terms of overall appearance in culture, as well as microscopic details of morphology. When inoculated on Penncross bentgrass, typical Sclerotinia dollar spot symptoms

Table 1—Symptom severity on 8-week-old Penncross bentgrass in the greenhouse following inoculation with various isolates of *S. homoeocarpa*.

Type of isolate	Number of isolates tested	Infection center					
		Diameter*		Severity+		Aerial mycelium‡	
		Mean	Range	Mean	Range	Mean	Range
Nontolerant	43	48§	20–90	2.9	1–5	3.0	1–5
Benzimidazole tolerant	11	59	35–75	2.9	2–4	3.2	2–4

* Diameter of infection centers in mm.   + Severity rating based 0 to 5 scale: 0 = no lesions and no blighting; 1 = trace of foliar lesions and no blighting; 2 = scattered foliar lesions and blighting; 3 = lesions overall some blighting; 4 = overall blighting; 5 = complete death of all foliage.   ‡ Mycelium rating based on 0 to 5 scale: 0 = no visible mycelium; 1 = trace of mycelium threads on foliage; 2 = scattered mycelial threads; 3 = mycelium on most areas of infection center; 4 = mycelium overall; 5 = infection center completely covered with mycelium to extent foliage beneath is not visible.
§ Data presented represents mean of means. Each isolate value averaged represented mean of 5 replications. Hence, diameter value for nontolerant isolates was the mean of 215 infection centers, i.e., 43 isolates X 5 reps.

developed, consisting of bleached straw-colored lesions with reddish-brown margins. These appeared on cut tips of grass leaves and further down towards the crown area. None of the isolates, either tolerant or nontolerant, produced conidia or any other spore form. After several weeks in PDA culture, both sensitive and tolerant isolates produced flake-like pseudosclerotia.

Pathogenicity and virulence results were similar for both benomyl tolerant and nontolerant isolates on 8-week-old Penncross. The tolerant isolates were well within the range exhibited by nontolerant isolates for infection center diameters, severity of foliar blighting, and aerial mycelium production on the diseased foliage (Table 1).

In vitro fungicide tolerance

All isolates from benomyl control failure sites grew well on PDA agar containing 100 µg/ml benomyl. Isolates from areas where no control problems have been reported were uniformly sensitive to benomyl, with complete growth inhibition at 1 µg/ml of agar. Isolates which were tolerant to benomyl were also tolerant to thiabendazole, Bay Dam 18654, thioallophanate-methyl, and thioallophanate-ethyl. The thioallophanates have been shown to undergo biotransformation to alkyl 2-benzimidazolecarbamate in plants (5); hence, in this paper, they will be considered benzimidazole fungicides (Table 2).

In addition to tolerance expression by certain isolates to benzimidazole fungicides, stimulation of mycelial growth was observed at low levels of these fungicides. Stimulation varied from very slight effects to rather striking growth increases. Not all tolerant isolates exhibited stimulation effects to low dosages.

Greenhouse fungicide experiments

Infection center development and disease severity for nontolerant isolate S-9 and tolerant isolate S-50 were similar, with mean severity ratings of

Table 2—Mycelial growth of *S. homoeocarpa* on PDA agar amended with various benzimidazole fungicides.

Fungicide	Formulation, % Al	Dosage, μg/ml agar	Radial growth, mm/day			
			S-9	S-24	S-50	S-62
Benomyl	50% WP	0	15.1	16.4	14.0	8.5
		1	0.0	0.0	14.0	7.5
		10	0.0	0.0	13.4	6.2
		100	0.0	0.0	8.8	4.5
		1000	0.0	0.0	0.0	0.0
Thiabendazole	43% fl	0	15.7	16.1	15.8	11.3
		1	0.0	2.5	14.0	10.8
		10	0.0	0.0	13.8	7.8
		100	0.0	0.0	3.6	0.0
		1000	0.0	0.0	3.6	0.0
Bay Dam 18654	50% WP	0	13.3	13.8	12.2	9.6
		1	0.0	0.0	11.9	9.1
		10	0.0	0.0	11.5	8.4
		100	0.0	0.0	8.4	4.1
		1000	0.0	0.0	3.2	0.0
Thioallophanate methyl	50% WP	0	13.3	13.8	12.4	7.7
		1	0.0	0.0	12.0	7.4
		10	0.0	0.0	10.6	6.8
		100	0.0	0.0	9.9	6.3
		1000	0.0	0.0	6.5	5.2
Thioallophanate ethyl	50% WP	0	14.4	16.8	13.3	9.5
		1	0.0	0.0	12.5	9.1
		10	0.0	0.0	11.2	7.4
		100	0.0	0.0	11.5	6.9
		1000	0.0	0.0	9.2	5.5

4.3 and 4.0, respectively, for the unsprayed check pots. Sensitive isolate S-9 was controlled completely with benomyl and Bay Dam 18654, both singly and in combination with Actidione or Dyrene. Actidione and Dyrene alone resulted in partial disease control. With tolerant isolate S-50, benomyl and Bay Dam 18654 resulted in no suppression of disease severity. Infection centers in benomyl sprayed pots were significantly more severe than in the unsprayed pots. Both the 18.2 and 56.4 g/93 centare dosages received mean ratings of 5.0, i.e., complete death of all foliage. A similar trend was noted with Bay Dam 18654. The Actidione and Dyrene, either alone or in combination with the benzimidazoles, resulted in partial suppression of disease severity. Both Actidione and Dyrene provided equivalent disease control of S-9 and S-50 when applied alone.

DISCUSSION

The data obtained in the present experiments indicate that the benzimidazole-tolerant isolates of *S. homoeocarpa* are morphologically similar to the nontolerant isolates. Several field reports from turf managers (personal communications) have postulated that the Sclerotinia dollar spot infection centers occurring in benzimidazole control failure locations exhibited larger amounts of aerial mycelium than those in nontolerant areas. Our greenhouse data, however, would place the tolerant isolates well within range demonstrated by nontolerant isolates for all criteria measured. Based on fungal morphology and disease symptoms, benzimidazole-tolerant isolates cannot be separated, and hence should be considered as part of the *S. homoeocarpa* classification. Field reports of greater mycelial proliferation may be related to a severity phenomenon rather than indicating a morphological or cultural variant. All our data would tend to support the severity hypothesis.

Laboratory tolerance to benomyl was clearly correlated with tolerance to other benzimidazole configurations, including thiabendazole, Bay Dam 18654 carbamate, thioallophanate-ethyl, and thioallophanate-methyl.

The real significance in an epidemiological sense of tolerance by *S. homoeocarpa* and other pathogens (1, 3, 4) to the benzimidazole fungicides will not be determined until combinations of propagules of tolerant and sensitive isolates are introduced in known numbers into field plot situations, where survival potential under various fungicide regimens can be measured. Such work with *S. homoeocarpa* is presently underway. In shifting from broad spectrum protectant eradicants such as mercury to narrow spectrum systemics such as the benzimidazoles, the tolerance phenomenon can be expected to be a progressively greater problem.

REFERENCES

1. BOLLEN, G. J., and G. SCHOLTEN. 1971. Acquired resistance to benomyl and some other systemic fungicides in a strain of *Botrytis cinerea* in cyclamen. Neth. J. Plant Pathol. 77:83–90.
2. CLEMONS, G. P., and H. D. SISLER. 1970. Localization of the site of action of a fungitoxic benomyl derivative. Pest. Chem. Phys. 1:32–43.
3. GEORGOPOULOS, S. G., and C. DOVAS. 1973. A serious outbreak of strains of *Cercospora beticola* resistant to benzimidazole fungicides in Northern Greece. Plant Dis. Rep. 57:321–324.
4. SCHROEDER, W. T., and R. PROVVIDENTI. 1969. Resistance to benomyl in powdery mildew of cucurbits. Plant Dis. Rep. 53:271–275.
5. SOEDA, Y., K. SHOGO, and T. NOGUCHI. 1972. Identification of alkyl 2-benzimidazolecarbamates as a major metabolite of thiophanates fungicide in/on the bean plant. Agr. Biol. Chem. 36:817–823.

42

Distribution, host range, and control of St. Augustine Decline[1]

R. W. TOLER

St. Augustine Decline was first observed in 1966 by lawn service operators in South Texas. The disease spread to 56 counties in the state of Texas by 1972, and has been observed in Louisiana and Mexico. In 1968 the disease agent was transmitted to St. Augustinegrass (*Stenotaphrum secundatum* Walt. Kuntz) and [*Setaria italica* (L.) Beauv.] millet. The symptoms developed earlier on millets (7 to 14 days) than on St. Augustinegrass (21 to 30 days). Transmission and *in vitro* studies determined the disease was caused by a strain of Panicum mosaic virus. Host range includes Proso (*Panicum miliaceum* L.), Pearl (*Pennisetum glaucum* (L.) R. Br.), and Foxtail (*Setaria italica* (L.) Beauv.) millets, as well as crabgrass (*Digitaria sangiunalis* (L.) Scop) and St. Augustinegrass. The symptoms on Proso were severe mosaic and necrosis, on Pearl millets terminal necrosis, and on Foxtail a uniform mottling. Symptoms on crabgrass were mottling and reddening, and on St. Augustinegrass mosaic, yellowing and necrosis. Inoculation techniques were developed to screen for sources of resistance in 1968. Of the genetic materials observed, Florida accession FA 110 had the highest level of resistance to the virus causing St. Augustine Decline. Additional index words: St. Augustinegrass, St. Augustine Decline, Alternate Hosts, Susceptibility, Floratam, Panicum mosaic virus SAD strain.

Lawn and turfgrass production is a major enterprise in Texas. It is estimated that 41% of the home lawns in Texas are in bermudas (*Cynodon* sp.), 56% in St. Augustinegrass (*Stenotaphrum secundatum* Walt. Kuntze), and 3% in other grasses. In the Gulf Coast area of the State 96% of the lawns are St. Augustinegrass (4).

Two virus diseases of St. Augustinegrass have been reported. Todd (10) reported the natural occurrence of sugarcane mosaic virus (SCMV) on St. Augustinegrass at Canal Point, Florida, in 1964. Abbott and Tippet (1) also reported St. Augustinegrass inoculated with four strains of SCMV A, B, D, and H by an airbrush became infected. Saladini and Zettler in 1972 found that strain E was the sugarcane mosaic virus strain infecting St. Augustinegrass in South Florida (8, 9). In 1966 Dale (2) reported the infection of St. Augustinegrass seedlings inoculated with maize dwarf mosaic virus (MDMV).

A new disease of St. Augustinegrass was observed in the Lower Rio Grande Valley in 1966. Symptoms of the disease were chlorosis and mottling

---

[1]Contribution from Department of Plant Sciences, Texas A&M University, College Station, Texas.

of the leaf blades. Mosaic or mottling became progressively more severe until a general chlorosis existed. As a result of shortened internodes, stolen growth was retarded. The disease was named St. Augustine Decline (SAD) (6). By March of 1969 SAD had been found in 13 counties, and in 1972 it was identified in 56 counties in the state. St. Augustine Decline was first observed in Louisiana and Mexico in 1971 (3).

Transmission studies revealed the causal agent was mechanically transmissible (11). Symptoms in St. Augustinegrass occur in 30 to 60 days after mechanical inoculation. Attempts to transmit the virus through soil, soil transmission and insect transmission with leafhoppers and chinch bugs were not successful.

Host range studies revealed the causal virus failed to infect oats, *Avena sativa* L. 'Alamo'; bermudagrass, *Cynodon dactylon* (L.) Pers. 'Common'; centipedegrass, *Eremochloa ophiuroides* (Munro) Hack.; barley, *Hordeum vulgare* (L.) 'Blackhulless CI66'; rice, *Oryza sativa* L. 'Nato'; canarygrass, *Phalaris arundinacea* L.; sugarcane, *Saccharum officinarum* L.; grain sorghum, *Sorghum vulgare* Pers. 'AKS614'; Johnsongrass, *Sorghum halepense* (L.) Pers; wheat, *Triticum aestivum* L. 'Commanche'; corn, *Zea mays* L. 'Boone County White'; lambsquarters, *Chenopodium album* L.; tomato, *Lycopersicon esculentum* Mill. 'Homestead'; tobacco, *Nicotiana tabacum* L. 'Samsun NN'; and bean, *Phaseolus vulgaris* L., 'Bountiful.'

Susceptible hosts included St. Augustinegrass, *Stenotaphrum secundatum*; crabgrass, *Digitaria sanguinalis* (L.) Scop; and several millet species. The susceptible millet species included *Panicum miliaceum* L., *P. havardii* Vasey, *P. maximum* Jacq., *P. antidotale* Retz., *Setaria italica* (L.) Beauv., *S. sphacelata* (Schum.) Stapf and C. E. Hubb and *Pennisetum glaucum* (L.) R. Br. Millet species found to be resistant were *Panicum virgatum* L., *P. amarulum* Hitchc. and Chase, and *P. stapfianum* Nash. Four cultivars of *P. miliaceum* were tested and the two were susceptible ('White Proso' and 'RB170603'). Three of seven cultivars of *Pennisetum glaucum* were also susceptible ('Starr', 'Tift 23-B', and 'Gahi 2').

St. Augustine Decline causal agent was purified by filtration, ultracentrifugation, and sucrose density gradient. The incitant was observed to be a polyhedral virus with a mean diameter of 24 mm. Sedimentation constant was 102S and ultraviolet absorption ratio 280:260 was 0.76 (5). Other physical properties included a dilution end point of 10^{-5} for the purified virus, thermal inactivation point of 56 C, and longevity of 15 days in infected tissue at 25 C. The virus was serologically related to Panicum mosaic virus (PMV) and has been named St. Augustine Decline (SAD) strain of Panicum mosaic virus (PMV-SAD) (5).

Control of SAD was sought through the mechanism of host resistance. A method for screening breeding material in the greenhouse for resistance was developed. The technique consisted of carborundum wipe inoculation with infective juice and 0.01 M phosphate buffer pH 7.5 at 1:1 weight to volume ratio. Proso millet was used as an assay host and as the susceptible indicator along with common St. Augustine. Breeding material was read for symptom development 30 and 60 days after inoculation. After 60 days, inoculated plants were assayed on proso millet and common St. Augustine to detect plants with immunity, those in which the virus failed to multiply; and symptomless carriers, those in which the virus multiplied but failed to show symptoms (7). Initially 91 accessions were screened with 33 showing some level of resistance. Of these resistant materials, nine were selected for field testing. The field test consisted of planting the resistant selections in plots containing infected grass at five locations (San Antonio, Corpus Christi, Houston, Fort Worth, and Bryan, Texas). The Florida selection FA 110 appeared to be resistant to infection with SAD at all locations. Foundation material of the cultivar was multiplied by the Florida Agricultural Experiment Station and jointly released in 1972 with the Texas Agricultural Experiment Station to certified growers in both states. The cultivar name is 'Floratam'.

REFERENCES

1. ABBOTT, E. V., and R. L. TIPPET. 1964. Additional hosts of sugarcane mosaic virus. Plant Dis. Rep. 48:443-445.
2. DALE, J. L. 1966. Infection of St. Augustinegrass with virus causing maize dwarf mosaic. Plant Dis. Rep. 50:441-442.
3. HOLCOMBE, G. E., K. S. DERRICK, R. B. CARVER, and R. W. TOLER. 1972. St. Augustine Decline found in Louisiana. Plant Dis. Rep. 56:69-70.
4. HOLT, Ethan C., W. Wayne ALLEN, and Marvin H. FERGUSON. 1964. Turf grass maintenance costs in Texas. Texas Agr. Exp. Sta. Bull. 1027:5-19.
5. LEE, T. A., Jr., and R. W. TOLER. 1973. Purification and characterization of the virus causing St. Augustine Decline. (Abst.) Phytopathology 63:444.
6. MC COY, Norman L., Robert W. TOLER, and Jose AMADOR. 1969. St. Augustine Decline (SAD)—A virus disease of St. Augustinegrass. Plant Disease Rep. 53: 955-958.
7. ———, ———, and R. H. LEISY. 1971. Selecting propagules of St. Augustinegrass for possible sources of resistance to the virus causing St. Augustine Decline. Proc. 3rd Ann. Texas Conf. on Insect, Plant Disease, Weed and Brush Control. 3:65-71.
8. SALADINI, J. L., and F. W. ZETTLER. 1972a. Survey for viral diseases of St. Augustinegrass in Florida. Plant Dis. Rep. 56:822-823.
9. ———, and ———. 1972b. Characterization of strain E of sugarcane mosaic virus infecting St. Augustinegrass. Plant Dis. Rep. 56:885-889.
10. TODD, Edwin H. 1964. Sugarcane mosaic on St. Augustinegrass in Florida. Plant Dis. Rep. 48:442.
11. TOLER, R. W., N. L. MC COY, and J. AMADOR. 1969. A new mosaic disease of St. Augustinegrass. (Abst.) Phytopathology 59:118.

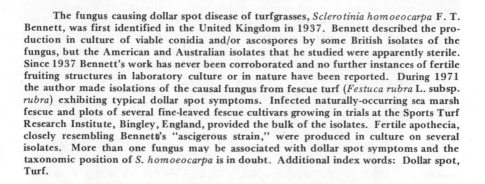

43

Apothecial production of
Sclerotinia homoeocarpa
F.T. Bennett[1]

N. JACKSON

The fungus causing dollar spot disease of turfgrasses, *Sclerotinia homoeocarpa* F. T. Bennett, was first identified in the United Kingdom in 1937. Bennett described the production in culture of viable conidia and/or ascospores by some British isolates of the fungus, but the American and Australian isolates that he studied were apparently sterile. Since 1937 Bennett's work has never been corroborated and no further instances of fertile fruiting structures in laboratory culture or in nature have been reported. During 1971 the author made isolations of the causal fungus from fescue turf (*Festuca rubra* L. subsp. *rubra*) exhibiting typical dollar spot symptoms. Infected naturally-occurring sea marsh fescue and plots of several fine-leaved fescue cultivars growing in trials at the Sports Turf Research Institute, Bingley, England, provided the bulk of the isolates. Fertile apothecia, closely resembling Bennett's "ascigerous strain," were produced in culture on several isolates. More than one fungus may be associated with dollar spot symptoms and the taxonomic position of *S. homoeocarpa* is in doubt. Additional index words: Dollar spot, Turf.

Dollar spot, caused by the fungus *Sclerotinia homoeocarpa* F. T. Bennett, is a common disease of turfgrasses throughout the world. The disease symptoms were first described by Monteith and Dahl in 1932 (5). F. T. Bennett, working in England, was responsible for isolating and naming the causal organism in 1937 (1). Bennett described the production in laboratory culture of viable conidia and/or ascospores by some British isolates of the fungus, but the American and Australian isolates that he studied apparently were sterile. He designated three distinct "strains" of the fungus based on the kinds of spores produced, namely: a "perfect" British strain, producing both ascospores and conidia; an "ascigerous" British strain, producing both ascospores and microconidia; "nonsporiferous" British, American, and Australian strains.

The ascigerous stage reported by Bennett consisted of cup or disc-shaped ascocarps characteristic of certain Discomycetes. Ascocarps arose from an extensive stroma which develops when the fungus is grown on sterile grains or grain agar. Bennett considered the stroma to consist in part of microsclerotia and placed the fungus in the genus *Sclerotinia*. Because the

---

[1]Contribution no. 1506 of the Rhode Island Agricultural Experiment Station.

"perfect" strain produced conidia in cupulate conidiophores similar in form to ascophores, he adopted the binomial *Sclerotinia homoeocarpa*.

Since 1937, Bennett's work has never been corroborated and no further instances of fertile fruiting structures in laboratory culture or in nature have been reported. In 1970, Fenstermacher, working with American isolates of the fungus, reported abortive apothecial production on several occasions, the apothecia remaining sterile in each instance (4).

MATERIALS AND METHODS

While on sabbatical leave at the Sports Turf Research Institute in Britain in 1971, the author made mycelial isolations of the causal fungus from fescue turf (*Festuca rubra L. subsp. rubra*) exhibiting typical dollar spot symptoms. Infected naturally-occurring sea marsh fescue and infected plots of various fine-leaved fescue cultivars growing in trials at the Institute's experiment ground provided the bulk of the isolates. A number of these isolates were cultured on oat agar or on sterile grains, and produced fertile apothecia 3 months or more after seeding the media with mycelial fragments. Bottles containing the cultures were subject to the fluctuating temperatures and light intensity of a northeast-facing laboratory window over the period October 1971 to March 1972, at which time fertile apothecia were apparent in abundance (Fig. 1 and 2).

RESULTS AND DISCUSSION

This procedure followed closely that described by Bennett and the apothecia so produced closely resembled his "ascigerous strain." Average ascus size, 162.9 × 12.5 μ, and spore size, 20.7 × 8.3 μ (freshly discharged spores), were somewhat smaller than the values quoted by Bennett, more closely approximating his "perfect" strain. However, conidia were not recorded in any of the fruiting cultures.

Ascospores were generally unicellular within the ascus, but infrequently spores had a medium septum. Germination in water was rapid, most spores developing a single septum during this period (Fig. 3). Occasionally, spores discharged onto the interior surface of the bottles germinated to form microconidia (Fig. 3, inset). Microconidia normally occurred on areas of collapsed mycelium or on the stromal surface, clustered in minute cream-colored pustules. The spherical, hyaline spores, approximately 2 μ in diameter, arise from short sterigmata (Fig. 4). The function of the microspores is not known; they do not germinate in water and apparently are not necessary in sexual reproduction since a single ascospore culture will produce fertile apothecia.

During the period October 1971 to June 1972, the fescue turf areas from which the mycelial isolates of the dollar spot fungus were collected were examined critically for the natural occurrence of fruiting bodies of *S. homoeocarpa*. Apothecia of three fungi very similar to, but not identical with the described dollar spot fungus, were found. Pathogencity tests have not been completed, but in England it seems likely that more than one fungus

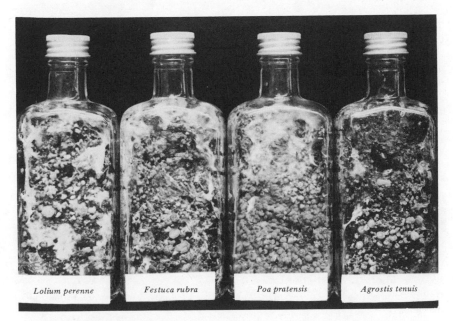

Lolium perenne   Festuca rubra   Poa pratensis   Agrostis tenuis

Fig. 1—Apothecial production by *S. homoeocarpa* on sterilized seed of four grasses.

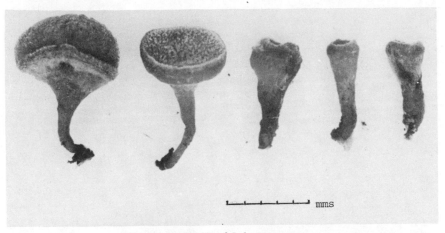

mms

Fig. 2—Apothecia of *S. homoeocarpa.*

may produce dollar spot symptoms, especially if the turf is of sea marsh origin.

In 1945, Whetzel established the family Sclerotiniaceae for the stromatic, inoperculate Discomycetes. He restricted the genus *Sclerotinia* to species in which the apothecium arises from a tuberoid sclerotium and excluded *S. homoeocarpa* from this genus (6). Whetzel considered the dollar

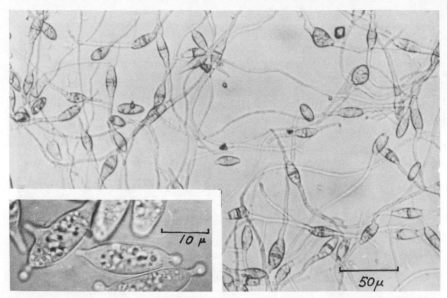

Fig. 3—Germinating ascospores of *S. homoeocarpa*. Inset: microspore formation on ascospores.

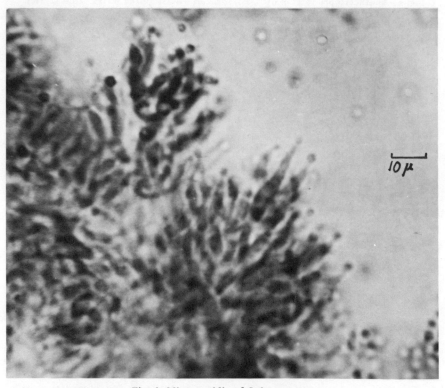

Fig. 4—Microconidia of *S. homoeocarpa*.

spot fungus (referred to as *S. heterocarpa*) to be a species of *Rutstroemia*, synonymous with a previously described fungus *Ciboria armeriae* v. Höhnel (7).

It seems likely that Whetzel did not have an opportunity to examine the Bennett material, but the fragmentry specimens available to the author and the fruiting bodies described in this paper would place the fungus in the genus *Rutstroemia*. Difficulties arise, however, in that the genus *Rutstroemia*, as designated by White in 1941, (8) has recently been deemed taxonomically unacceptable by Dumont and Korf (3). Dumont suggested that at least three distinct genera could be distinguished in *Rutstroemia* sensu White based on characters of apothecial structure (2). Until this situation is resolved the proper taxonomic placement of *S. homoeocarpa* remains in doubt.

REFERENCES

1. BENNETT, F. T. 1937. Dollar spot disease of turf and its causal organism, Sclerotinia homoeocarpa N. Sp. Ann. Appl. Biol. 24:236–257.
2. DUMONT, K. P. 1971. Sclerotiniaceae II. Lambertella. Mem. New York Bot. Gard. 22(1):1–178.
3. ———, and R. P. KORF. 1971. Sclerotiniaceae I. Generic nomenclature. Mycologia 63:157–168.
4. FENSTERMACHER, J. M. 1970. Variation within *Sclerotinia homoeocarpa* F. T. Bennett. M.S. Thesis. Dept. Plant Pathology-Entomology, Univ. of Rhode Island, Kingston.
5. MONTEITH, J., and A. S. DAHL. 1932. Turf diseases and their control. Bull. U. S. Golf Ass. 12:85–187.
6. WHETZEL, H. H. 1945. A synopsis of the genera and species of the Sclerotiniaceae, a family of stromatic, inoperculate Discomycetes. Mycologia 37:648–714.
7. ———. 1946. The cypericolous and juncicolous species of Sclerotinia. Farlowia 2: 385–437.
8. WHITE, W. L. 1941. A monograph of the genus Rutstroemia (Discomycetes). Lloydia 4:153–240.

ABSTRACTS

Abstracts of all papers not published herein but presented at the Conference are included below to round off this Section. These abstracts, unlike the printed papers, have not been refereed.

SECTION 5 ABSTRACT–RELATIONSHIP BETWEEN NUTRITION AND PLANT GENOTYPE IN THE DEVELOPMENT OF *HELMINTHOSPORIUM* LEAF SPOT ON CULTIVARS OF KENTUCKY BLUEGRASS

Thirteen cultivars of Kentucky bluegrass (*Poa pratensis* L.) were grown at three levels of nitrogen nutrition, respectively. Expanded shale (Weblite) was used as the plant support medium. Nitrogen levels were established by using a standard Hoagland's solution (1.0N) and Hoagland's solutions were modified to contain either 0.1 X N or 3.0 X N. The plants were inoculated with an aqueous spore suspension of *Helminthosporium sorokinianum* Sacc. ex. Sorokin 11 weeks from the time of seeding. In general, the highest degree of disease resistance occurred in the plant groups grown at the 0.1 X N nutritional regime. When the disease ratings for the three nutritional regimes were averaged for each cultivar, their comparative resistance ranked as follows: 'Anheuser' > 'Belturf' > 'Geary' > 'Pennstar' = 'Windsor' = 'BA 6124' > 'Park' = 'Kenblue' = 'Cougar' = 'Fylking' = 'Merion' > 'Newport' = 'Delta'. It was also found, however, that the potential for nutritionally-induced alteration of susceptibility to *H. sorokinianum* varied among cultivars. Anheuser, for example, was highly resistant to the pathogen under all three nutritional regimes. The cultivar Delta was highly susceptible at all nutritional levels. Park, on the other hand, was highly resistant to *H. sorokinianum* when grown at 0.1 X N and highly susceptible under 3.0 X N nutrition. These studies indicate that while the resistance of Kentucky bluegrasses to *H. sorokinianum* is generally increased under low nitrogen nutrition, the total range of susceptibility of a given cultivar is not fully known until it has been evaluated under a broad spectrum of nutritional regimes. —H. B. Couch and L. D. Moore, Virginia Polytechnic Institute and State University.

SECTION 5 ABSTRACT—RESIDUAL CONTROL OF SCLEROTINIA DOLLAR SPOT WITH SYSTEMIC FUNGICIDES

Systemic fungicides offer great potential for residual control of dollar spot (*Sclerotinia homoeocarpa*), which should help reduce the number of costly spray applications which have to be made. This study was initiated to determine if spray intervals longer than the 2 weeks currently recommended on the fungicide labels could be used. Fungicides used were: benomyl 50% wettable powder (WP) (Tersan 1991) (methyl-1-butylcarbamoly]-2-benzimidazolecarbamate), Triarimol 25% WP (a-2,4-Dichlorophenyl]-a-phenyl-5-pyrimidinemethanol), Thiophanate-methyl 70% WP (Topsin M) (1,2-bis[3-methoxy-carbonyl-2-thioureido]-benzene, thiphanate-methyl 50% WP (Fungo) 1,2-bis[3-methoxycarbonyl-2-thioureido]-benzene, and Daconil 2787 Tetrachloroisophthalonitrile. Benomyl, thiophanate-methyl (50% WP) and triaimol were applied at 28 and 56 g rates/m^2; thiophanate methyl (70% WP) at 14 and 28 g rates and Tetrachloroisophthalonitrile at the 113 g/m^2 rate. The first applications were made on June 23. The systemic fungicides all held the dollar spot in check for 6 weeks (August 4) at which time a few spots began to appear. The Tetrachloroisophthalonitrile and the untreated control did not hold the dollar spot in check. A second spray was made on August 18 after the disease had been allowed to increase for an additional 2 weeks. This second spray was still holding on Sept. 28, 5 weeks later. This demonstrates that the spray intervals can be extended up to 5 weeks with the systemic fungicides where *Sclerotinia* dollar spot is the primary disease problem.—J. M. Vargas, Jr., Michigan State University.

SECTION 5 ABSTRACT—NEW SYSTEMIC FUNGICIDES FOR TURF AND ORNAMENTALS

The introduction of systemic fungicides for turf and ornamentals has made possible changes in management procedures for these crops. Sustained disease control for a limited spectrum of pathogens is possible by substantial dosages which are incorporated or drenched into the root zone. Uptake of the chemical by the plant from this reservoir provides control for *Sclerotinia* spp., *Rhizoctonia* spp., *Fusarium* spp., *Thielaviopsis* spp., and *Botrytis* spp. In many instances disease control is better and frequent retreatment associated with protective fungicides is not needed. Deficiencies in these compounds leave substantial room for improvement in their chemistry and formulation.—W. A. Small, Mallinckrodt Chemical Works.

DISCUSSION

W. A. MEYER—How do you account for the high number of spores present in dry thatch before wetting?

P. F. COLBAUGH—After remoistening dry thatch there is an absence of an inhibitory property and this coupled with increased release of nutrients stimulates microbial activity. In addition, the population of microorganisms is reduced upon drying so the environment for saprophytic activity is increased as well as providing a substrate for parasitism which is favored after remoistening. In terms of sporulation, the fungus is able to establish itself on fresh clippings to a very high degree after remoistening. We have found that a large number of spores are born on these fresh clippings if they are allowed to desiccate and then are remoistened. Of course, this can serve as a secondary disease agent. In other words, these are intermittently desiccated areas. They aren't dry all the time because there are living plants associated with them, but they are dried and remoistened, dried and remoistened. This continued activity in spurts provides conditions for increased fungus activity.

J. M. VARGAS—In Michigan we have found nematodes to be important in the development of Fusarium blight and in some cases this is the only pathogen present. What observations have been made concerning this in California? Have any surveys been made which would correlate nematodes with Fusarium blight? Have data been obtained that would relate nematodes with turfgrass diseases in general in California?

R. M. ENDO —We really don't have any concrete data, but certainly *Fusarium rosium* is a parasite which might be influenced in this way. Therefore, anything that would weaken the turf would facilitate a higher incidence of infection, colonization, and more severe disease. In other words, anything that would injure the root system should result in enhanced disease. Nematodes feeding on roots might well weaken the turf enough to increase disease incidence.

J. M. VARGAS—I don't know about the East Coast of the United States, but at least in the northern Midwest the same root rot and crown rot stage that is observed in California is very important. We very seldom find foliar blight from *Fusarium* in the northern Midwest.

H. W. INDYK—Among the turfgrasses are there other species besides Kentucky bluegrass that are susceptible to Fusarium blight?

R. M. ENDO —Yes, recently we have found it on golf greens, but I really don't know how severe it is on bentgrass greens, because we have had so few samples. Since it is severe in other areas of the United States, I believe that we are going to find increased susceptibility of grasses in California.

H. W. INDYK—Among the turfgrasses studied in New Jersey, Kentucky bluegrass is highly susceptible to *Fusarium roseum*. On the basis of experience with bluegrass lawns repeatedly infected each year for 5 or more years with Fusarium blight, overseedings with bluegrasses were totally unsuccessful. Lawns overseeded with Manhattan ryegrass showed no indication of infection. Thus, it appears that Manhattan ryegrass has at least some resistance to Fusarium blight.

H. WEITZ—Why does the term Fusarium blight continue to be used in southern California when in fact the disease is not a blight but a crown and stem rot?

R. M. ENDO —I think you have this same problem when you give a common name to any disease. This is influenced largely by the environment and the susceptibility of a variety. Thus, whenever a common name is given to a disease the same problem is recognized. There really is no satisfactory answer; common names mean different things to different people.

C. W. GOLDBERG—Have any shifts in stability of turf resistance been observed in Virginia with the use of the new systemics, since they are growth-regulating compounds?

H. B. COUCH—We haven't looked at any shifts in stability with these growth-regulating compounds. Our main interest has been in nutrition. We have indications that turfgrass in Virginia, Kentucky, and North Carolina has increased disease susceptibility following use of systemics. These observations have been made concerning blights of bentgrasses. Thus, there are probably some very pronounced shifts taking place with the systemics that require further research effort. I think that this is likely to be one of the more important areas for future research.

P. M. HALISKY—I question the desirability of using the term "contact" fungicide for a nonsystemic material. A preferable term might be "protectant" fungicide. If a systemic fungicide is sprayed, rather than drenched, it would be considered contact. Of course, systemics are also protectants from within as well as from without. Even so, I believe that "protectant" versus "systemic" would be preferable to "contact" versus "systemic."

J. M. VARGAS—Maybe we need a new term, but I don't think that it is "protectant." Protectant is often used to imply something entirely different; i.e., protectant fungicide versus erradicant fungicide. This would mean that all systemic fungicides are protectants. I would prefer seeing nonsystemics called "surface" fungicides.

R. E. ENGEL—Does the old concept that high nitrogen increases damping-off of seedling turf conflict with newer concepts that low nitrogen increases *Pythium* on ryegrass seedlings?

T. E. FREEMAN—Seedling blight caused by *Pythium* has usually been considered to be more severe with increasing nitrogen fertilization. Many people consider this to be the case with other pythium diseases although research in this area is not conclusive. It was not the case with pythium blight on ryegrass.

W. A. MEYER—Could it be possible that high nitrogen reduction of pythium blight holds for only the one ryegrass cultivar tested?

T. E. FREEMAN—We only tested common ryegrass and thus data on other cultivar response are not available. It's quite possible that only common ryegrass reacts this way.

Weeds and insects

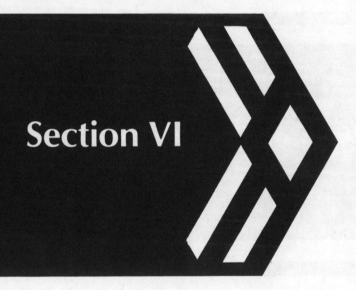

Section VI

44

Herbicide influence on rate of establishment of warm-season turfgrasses

B.J. JOHNSON

The establishment of warm-season turfgrasses is often hindered by weed competition because adequate chemical control practices have not been developed. Experiments were conducted on 'Tifway' bermudagrass (*Cynodon dactylon* (L.) Pers.), centipedegrass (*Eremochloa ophiuroides* (Munro) Hack.), and St. Augustinegrass (*Stenotaphrum secundatum* (Walt.) Kuntze) to determine the effects of various herbicide treatments during establishment. Dimethyl tetrachloroterephthalate (DCPA) applied immediately after sprigging Tifway bermudagrass resulted in satisfactory weed control, but sequential treatments of DCPA and monosodium methanearsonate (MSMA) + 2,4-dichlorophenoxyacetic acid (2,4-D) resulted in excellent weed control with a higher percent turf ground cover at the end of the growing season. Single treatments of 2-chloro-4,6-bis-(ethylamino)-*s*-triazine (simazine) and 2-chloro-4-(ethylamino)-6-(isopropylamino)-*s*-triazine (atrazine) at 1.12 kg/ha applied immediately following sprigging of centipedegrass and St. Augustinegrass controlled grassy weeds satisfactorily and resulted in an increased rate of turf ground cover compared to the untreated plots. Two applications of 3,5-dichloro-N-(1,1-dimethyl-2-propynyl)benzamide (pronamide) applied to centipedegrass at sprigging and at 3 weeks after sprigging controlled weeds sufficiently for optimum turf ground cover at the end of the first growing season. Additional index words: Turf, Lawn, Turf ground cover, Weed control, Atrazine, Simazine, Pronamide, DCPA, MSMA, 2,4-D.

The successful establishment of warm-season grasses for lawns depends largely on the weeds present during the first growing season. Newly planted turf is often poorly established and unattractive in appearance after the first year because of weeds.

Numerous studies have been conducted on the phytotoxicity and weed control effectiveness of herbicides on established warm-season turfgrasses. Fewer studies have been conducted with herbicides during the establishment of centipedegrass (*Eremochloa ophiuroides* (Munro) Hack.) and St. Augustinegrass (*Stenotaphrum secundatum* (Walt.) Kuntze). Lewis and Gilbert (5) reported that 1-(2-methylcyclohexyl)-3-phenylurea (siduron) could not be safely applied to centipedegrass at seeding. Johnson (4) found severe phytotoxicity to newly sprigged centipedegrass and St. Augustinegrass from postemergence treatments of monosodium methanearsonate (MSMA) under greenhouse and field conditions. Varying degrees of phytotoxicity to bermudagrasses (*Cynodon dactylon* (L.) Pers.) as a result of herbicide application at the time of sprigging have been reported. Duble and Holt (1) found no discoloration or injury to newly sprigged 'Tifgreen' bermudagrass treated with dimethyl tetrachloroterephthalate (DCPA), but a reduced rate of spread of Tifgreen when treated with O,O-diisopropyl phosphorodithioate S-ester with N-(2-mercaptoethyl)-benzenesulfonamide (bensulide). Fullerton et al. (3) reported no influence on ground cover by Tifgreen from DCPA treatments when applied to plots sprigged in June, but significantly less ground cover occurred when sprigged in July or August. In an earlier study, Fullerton et al. (2) found that DCPA retarded the establishment of Tifgreen, 'Elliot,' and 'Sunturf' bermudagrass when applied at the time of sprigging compared with establishment in untreated check plots. Lewis and Gilbert (5) found that siduron was phytotoxic to Tifgreen when applied immediately following sprigging. Additional information is needed on the performance of herbicides applied immediately following sprigging of turfgrass varieties. Therefore, experiments were initiated to determine the effect of herbicide treatments on the establishment of 'Tifway' bermudagrass, centipedegrass, and St. Augustinegrass, and to determine the frequency of treatments necessary to obtain optimum weed control during the turf establishment period.

MATERIALS AND METHODS

General information

Tifway bermudagrass, centipedegrass, and St. Augustinegrasses were sprigged in separate experiments at Experiment, Georgia, in May 1971 and 1972. The sprigging rates for Tifway bermudagrass were 0.5, 1.0, and 2.0 m²/are. However, since sprigging rates did not influence the rate of Tifway spread at the end of the first growing season, the results reported were an average from all rates. Centipedegrass and St. Augustinegrass were sprigged at 1.5 m²/are rate. The soil type was either a Cecil sandy loam or Cecil sandy clay loam. A fertilizer treatment of 560 kg/ha of 10-4.4-8.3 (N-P-K) was applied prior to planting. Additional nitrogen was applied at a rate of 48 kg/ha on monthly intervals during the establishment period.

Irrigation water was applied twice a day for the first week following sprigging, then once a day for the second and third week, and as needed to maintain favorable growing conditions during the remainder of the season.

The percent turf ground cover and weed control ratings were visually estimated at various intervals from 7 to 24 weeks during the first year after sprigging. The weed control ratings were based on a scale from 0 to 100 with 0 representing no control and 100 representing complete control. The weed population consisted of a uniform stand of large crabgrass (*Digitaria sanguinalis* L. Scop.) and goosegrass (*Eleusine indica* L. Gaertn.).

All treatments were arranged in a randomized complete block design with four replications. All data were analyzed statistically and treatment means were compared using Duncan's Multiple Range Test. The data discussed are an average of 1971 and 1972 treatments unless otherwise stated.

Experiment 1

Tifway bermudagrass sod was shredded and stolons were planted. Herbicide treatments were applied as follows: (i) no herbicide, (ii) DCPA at 11.2 kg/ha at sprigging, (iii) DCPA at 11.2 kg/ha at sprigging plus five postemergence treatments of MSMA + 2,4-dichlorophenoxyacetic acid (2,4-D) at 2.24 + 0.28 kg/ha, (iv) DCPA at 11.2 kg/ha at sprigging plus nine postemergence treatments of MSMA + 2,4-D at 2.24 + 0.28 kg/ha, (v) five postemergence treatments of MSMA + 2,4-D at 2.24 + 0.28 kg/ha spaced to maintain satisfactory weed control, and (vi) nine postemergence treatments of MSMA + 2,4-D at 2.24 + 0.28 kg/ha spaced to maintain complete weed control. The first postemergence treatments were applied 3 and 5 weeks after sprigging in 1971 and 1972, respectively, and the final treatment was made 15 and 17 weeks after sprigging, respectively. The time interval between postemergence treatments of MSMA + 2,4-D was generally 1 to 3 weeks in plots that received 5 treatments and 1 to 2 weeks in plots that received 9 treatments.

Experiment 2

Centipedegrass and St. Augustinegrass were sprigged in separate tests but treated with the same herbicides and rates. The treatments consisted of single and repeated applications of 2-chloro-4-(ethylamino)-6-(isopropylamino)-s-triazine (atrazine) and 2-chloro-4,6-bis(ethylamino)-s-traizine (simazine). Single treatments of each herbicide at 0, 1.12, 2.24, and 3.36 kg/ha were applied to plots immediately after sprigging. Repeated treatments of each herbicide were applied for a total of 6.72 kg/ha in two, three, or six applications. Plots receiving two applications were treated at sprigging and again at 16 weeks after sprigging. Plots receiving three applications were treated at sprigging and again at 8 and 16 weeks. The plots that received six applications were treated at sprigging and at 3 to 4 week intervals thereafter for five additional applications.

Experiment 3

Pronamide (3,5-dichloro-N-(1,1-dimethyl-2-propynyl)benzamide) was applied to centipedegrass immediately following sprigging and at various time intervals during establishment in 1971 and 1972. The treatments for both years were (i) untreated check, (ii) 0.84 kg/ha applied in each of one and two applications, and (iii) 0.84 kg/ha applied immediately following sprigging and 1.68 kg/ha applied 3 weeks after sprigging. In 1972 additional treatments were (i) 0.56 kg/ha applied in each of three and four applications, (ii) 0.84 kg/ha applied in each of three and four applications, (iii) 1.68 kg/ha applied in each of one, two, three, and four applications, and (iv) 3.36 kg/ha applied immediately following sprigging. Pronamide was applied at sprigging, and 3, 6, and 10 weeks after sprigging for the first, second, third, and fourth treatments, respectively.

Table 1—Effects of herbicide treatments on the control of weeds and percent ground cover of Tifway bermudagrass. (Average 1971 and 1972).

Treatments†			Turf ground cover				Weed control
Herbicide	Rate	Application no.	7 weeks	11 weeks	18 weeks	24 weeks	
	kg/ha				%		
Untreated check	—	—	22b*	29bc	33e	36d	0d
DCPA	11.2	1	11c	26c	56d	68c	87c
DCPA + MSMA + 2,4-D	11.2 2.24 + 0.28	1 5	14c	31b	74c	86b	95b
DCPA + MSMA + 2,4-D	11.2 2.24 + 0.28	1 9	13c	32b	72c	86b	99a
MSMA + 2,4-D	2.24 + 0.28	5	32a	54a	83b	91ab	89c
MDMA + 2,4-D	2.24 + 0.28	9	33a	59a	89a	96a	99a

* Values with a common letter within columns are not significantly different at the 5% level according to Duncan's Multiple Range Test.   † The first MSMA + 2,4-D treatment was applied 3 to 5 weeks after sprigging and the last treatment was applied 15 to 17 weeks after sprigging.

RESULTS AND DISCUSSION

Turf ground cover

The percent ground cover of Tifway bermudagrass was significantly higher at 7 weeks following sprigging in plots treated only with postemergence treatments of MSMA + 2,4-D than in other plots (Table 1). MSMA + 2,4-D did not cause any phytotoxicity when applied as early as 3 weeks following sprigging. DCPA retarded the early growth of Tifway and the ground cover was greater in untreated plots than in treated plots at 7 weeks. However, the ground cover of DCPA treated plots was similar to untreated plots at 11 weeks and higher than untreated plots at 18 and 24 weeks. The low ground cover (36%) of turf in untreated plots at 24 weeks was due to weeds that emerged soon after sprigging and continued to compete with the turfgrass throughout the growing season. The turf ground cover in single DCPA treated plots at 24 weeks after sprigging was 68%. When sequential treatments of MSMA + 2,4-D were applied following DCPA for postemergence weed control, regardless of number of applications, the ground cover of Tifway was 86%. Nine postemergence applications of MSMA + 2,4-D alone resulted in the highest degree of ground cover at the end of the first growing season (96%).

Atrazine applied as a single treatment to centipedegrass at 1.12 kg/ha resulted in the highest (50%) turf ground cover at the end of the growing season (Table 2). There was no significant difference in turf ground cover of centipedegrass plots treated with single applications of either atrazine or simazine at 1.12 or 2.24 kg/ha rates. The turf ground cover was higher in these plots than in untreated plots where only 19% ground cover was obtained.

The ground cover of St. Augustinegrass was the highest at the end of the growing season in plots receiving single applications of atrazine, regardless of

Table 2—Effects of atrazine and simazine treatments on season weed control and percent ground cover of centipedegrass and St. Augustinegrass. Ratings made 21 to 24 weeks after sprigging. (Average 1971 and 1972).

Treatments				Turf ground cover	
Herbicide	Total rate	Application no.	Weed control	Centipede	St. Augustine
	kg/ha		———————%———————		
Atrazine	6.72	6	90bcd*	23def	36bcd
	6.72	3	91abc	27cdef	29cde
	6.72	2	90bcd	27cdef	46abc
	3.36	1	78e	30bcde	50ab
	2.24	1	76c	39abc	56a
	1.12	1	57f	50a	58a
Simazine	6.72	6	99a	36bcd	11e
	6.72	3	97ab	32bcde	20de
	6.72	2	89bcd	15f	18de
	3.36	1	87cd	23def	22de
	2.24	1	83cde	42ab	42abc
	1.12	1	81de	42ab	54ab
Untreated check	—	—	0g	19ef	38bcd

* Values with a common letter within columns are not significantly different at the 5% level according to Duncan's Multiple Range Test.

rate, and in simazine plots treated at 1.12 and 2.24 kg/ha rates. Ground cover by St. Augustinegrass was significantly greater in atrazine-treated plots at 1.12 and 2.24 kg/ha (58 and 56%) than in untreated plots (38%), but turf cover on plots treated with the same rates of simazine (54 and 42%) did not significantly differ from the check. The percent ground cover of St. Augustinegrass was never as good from repeated treatments of atrazine or simazine at 1.12 and 2.24 kg/ha as it was from single treatments at the same rate. On the other hand, there was no difference in centipedegrass ground cover from similar treatments with simazine or with single or repeated atrazine treatments at 2.24 kg/ha (Table 2). The centipedegrass ground cover was higher in the single-treated plots (1.12 kg/ha) than in plots treated repeatedly with the same rate. St. Augustinegrass was more susceptible to injury from repeated treatments of either herbicide than was centipede.

Pronamide applied in two applications resulted in higher ground cover of centipedegrass (59 to 66%) at the end of the growing season in 1971 than did untreated (6%) or single-treated (47%) plots (Table 3). In 1972, single pronamide treatments of either 0.84 or 1.68 kg/ha resulted in ground cover of centipedegrass comparable to plots that received multiple pronamide treatments.

Weed control

The weeds were satisfactorily controlled (87%) in Tifway bermudagrass from a single treatment of DCPA applied immediately following sprigging

Table 3—Effects of pronamide treatments on the control of weeds and rate of centipede-grass establishment at 24 weeks after sprigging.

Treatments		Weed control		Turf ground cover	
Rate	Time applied	1971	1972	1971	1972
kg/ha	weeks		%		
Untreated	—	0b*	0g	6c	9e
0.84	0	52a	30f	47b	42abcd
0.84 + 0.84	0 3	56a	70cd	59ab	54abc
0.84 + 1.68	0 3	59a	87ab	66a	55abc
1.68	0	—	49e	—	46abcd
1.68 + 1.68	0 3	—	82abcd	—	41bcd
0.84 + 0.84 + 0.84 + 0.84	0 3 6 10	—	83abc	—	51abc
1.68 + 1.68 + 1.68 + 1.68	0 3 6 10	—	97a	—	25de
0.84 + 0.84 + 0.84	0 3 6	—	91a	—	67a
1.68 + 1.68 + 1.68	0 3 6	—	88ab	—	55abc
0.56 + 0.56 + 0.56	0 3 6	—	69cd	—	55abc
0.56 + 0.56 + 0.56 + 0.56	6 3 6 10	—	74bcd	—	65ab
3.36	0	—	66d	—	34cd

* Values with a common letter within columns are not significantly different at the 5% level according to Duncan's Multiple Range Test.

(Table 1). Excellent control (95 to 99%) of weeds was obtained in plots treated with DCPA at sprigging and followed with sequential postemergence treatments of MSMA + 2,4-D. When only postemergence treatments were used, five applications of MSMA + 2,4-D controlled 89% of the weeds compared with 99% control in plots treated with 9 MSMA + 2,4-D applications.

The control of weeds with atrazine and simazine during the establishment of centipedegrass and St. Augustinegrass varied with the number of treatments (Table 2). Simazine applied as a single treatment at 1.12 kg/ha controlled 81% of the weeds at the end of the growing season. The weed control rating for a similar treatment of atrazine was only 57%. There was no difference in weeds controlled in plots treated with either atrazine at 2.24

kg/ha or simazine at 1.12 kg/ha. However, at least 90% of the weeds were controlled with repeated atrazine treatments (total 6.72 kg/ha applied in two, three, or six applications). Similar results were obtained from repeated simazine treatments (89 to 99%). These results show that single applications of simazine at 1.12 kg/ha and atrazine at 2.24 kg/ha satisfactorily controlled the weeds (76 to 81%) throughout the first growing season following the sprigging of centipedegrass and St. Augustinegrass, and that higher rates or repeated applications are unnecessary.

Pronamide applied in either 1 or 2 applications to centipedegrass at the time of sprigging or at sprigging and again at 3 weeks resulted in poor weed control (52 to 59%) in 1971 (Table 3). In 1972 the weed control was greater in plots treated with repeated pronamide applications. The control was 87% in plots treated with 0.84 kg/ha at sprigging followed with 1.68 kg/ha applied to the same plots 3 weeks later. The control of weeds in plots that received two applications of pronamide in 1972 was as good as in plots treated with three or four applications.

These studies indicate that herbicides can safely be applied to warm-season grasses immediately following sprigging without causing severe plant injury in the central Georgia area. DCPA retarded the growth of Tifway bermudagrass early in the season. However, the turfgrass recovered with subsequent ground cover of 68% in DCPA treated plots as compared with 36% in untreated plots at the end of the growing season.

Treatments of MSMA + 2,4-D were not phytotoxic to Tifway even when applied up to nine times during the first growing season.

Single treatments with either atrazine or simazine, at 1.12 kg/ha, generally resulted in the highest ground cover of centipedegrass and St. Augustinegrass. The control of weeds was not as good from 1.12 kg/ha of either atrazine or simazine as with higher rates. However, the weed control was sufficient to give maximum turf ground cover of both grasses at the end of the growing season.

The control of weeds was significantly higher from repeated applications of pronamide than from single treatments.

REFERENCES

1. DUBLE, R. L., and E. C. HOLT. 1965. Preemergence herbicides as they influence bermudagrass establishment. Golf Course Rep. 33(3):50–52.
2. FULLERTON, T. M., A. M. DAVIS, and R. E. FRANS. 1967. The effect of selected preemergence herbicides and fertilizer levels on the establishment of several turfgrasses. Proc. S. Weed Conf. 20:69–74.
3. ——, C. L. MURDOCK, A. E. SPOONER, and R. E. FRANS. 1970. Effects of DCPA on winter injury of recently established bermudagrass. Weed Sci. 18:711–714.
4. JOHNSON, B. J. 1972. Tolerance of turfgrasses to postemergence treatments of MSMA. Georgia Agr. Res. 14(2):7–8.
5. LEWIS, W. M., and W. B. GILBERT. 1966. The effect of siduron on crabgrass and goosegrass control and the establishment of five warm-season and three cool-season turfgrasses. Proc. S. Weed Conf. 19:150–154.

45

Influence of selected herbicides on rooting of turfgrass sod[1]

S.W. BINGHAM

Initially, a study was conducted in which the soil surface was treated with herbicides prior to laying sod. In later studies, sod was placed on freshly prepared soil, and then herbicides were applied over the top, as is desirable for crabgrass (*Digitaria sanguinalis* L. Scop.) control. Sod strips (0.093 m^2) were laid on 1.25-cm mesh hardware cloth stretched over a frame. Turfgrass strips, under good management practices and irrigation, were allowed 28 days for root development through the hardware cloth into the soil. Root development was indicated by using a tripod and winch to measure the force required to pull the sod strips from the soil. The strips were removed by pulling on the four corners of the frame in a vertical direction.

Bensulide [*O,O*-diisopropyl phosphorodithioate *S*-ester with *N*-(2-mercaptoethyl) benzenesulfonamide] and benefin (*N*-butyl-*N*-ethyl-α,α,α-trifluoro-2,6-dinitro-*p*-toluidine) gave similar responses on the rooting of turfgrasses. The order of turfgrasses, from least to most inhibited, was 'Kentucky 31' fescue (*Festuca arundinacea* Schreb.), 'Merion' Kentucky bluegrass (*Poa pratensis* L.), and bermudagrass (*Cynodon dactylon* L. $\times$ *C. transvaalensis* Davy. 'Tifgreen'). At rates normally used for crabgrass control, bluegrass rooting strength was reduced more than 50%.

DCPA (dimethyl tetrachloroterephthalate) and siduron [1-(2-methylcyclohexyl)-3-phenylurea] produced little effect on tall fescue and Kentucky bluegrass. Siduron caused complete inhibition of rooting in Tifgreen bermudagrass. Normal rates of DCPA reduced rooting about 30% in the bermudagrass. Additional index words: Preemergence herbicides, Crabgrass control. Kentucky bluegrass, Bermudagrass.

Herbicides used for preemergence control of crabgrass (*Digitaria sanguinalis* L. Scop.) and annual bluegrass (*Poa annua* L.) have gained popularity because they do not cause discoloration of turfgrasses as is commonly observed with chemicals during postemergence control (4). Surface applications of crabgrass herbicides prevented rooting of bermudagrass (*Cynodon dactylon* L. Pers.) from stolon nodes (1). Placement of DCPA (dimethyl tetrachloroterephthalate) was an important factor in root inhibition. Gaskin (6) found fewer rhizomes and tillers were present on bluegrass after treatment with preemergence crabgrass herbicides. Established root systems were not appreciably altered by these herbicides (1). However, Callahan (5) observed more injury during the summer from both disease and wilting of

---

[1]Contribution no. 264, Dept. of Plant Pathology and Physiology, Virginia Polytechnic Institute and State University, Blacksburg, Va.

turfgrasses following application of preemergence herbicides than on untreated turfgrass.

Residues of preemergence herbicides remain in the soil for various lengths of time as is necessary through the period of crabgrass germination (3, 7). No noticeable injury to turfgrass shoots was detected after several years of annual treatments along with good maintenance programs which included protection against diseases (4, 7).

Bluegrass sod developed new roots from the shoots to tack the sod to the soil below (8). Regrowth of old roots was not appreciably involved. Some preemergence crabgrass herbicides are effective inhibitors of new root initiation and growth into the soil (1, 2).

In many situations, it becomes necessary to resod a golf green or turfgrass area as severe disease or heavy traffic damage leads to turfgrass loss. Sod farming for the establishment of new turf areas is also becoming quite popular. This research was initiated to determine the influence of preemergence crabgrass herbicides on the rooting of turfgrasses from sod into the soil.

METHODS AND MATERIALS

Growth and treatment of sod

Sod was obtained from established stands of 'Merion' Kentucky bluegrass (*Poa pratensis* L.), 'Kentucky 31' fescue (*Festuca arundinacea* Schreb.), and 'Tifgreen' bermudagrass (*Cynodon dactylon* L. X *C. transvaalensis* Davy. 'Tifgreen'). These grasses were maintained as lawn turf on a loam soil with normal fertilization for good growth and color. Bluegrass and fescue were clipped 5 to 7 cm, often enough to prevent growth beyond 8 to 10 cm. Bermudagrass was maintained at 1-cm cutting height. Growth was generally good and the bermudagrass received supplemental irrigation until sod was placed. All sod was cut at 2.5-cm thickness.

In all studies, the soil to receive the sod was prepared by plowing, disking, tiller raking, and smoothing with hand rakes. In the first experiment, the soil surface was treated with the herbicides prior to laying the sod. In the second and third studies, the sod was placed and the herbicide treatments were applied over the top of the sod. Bensulide [O,O-diisopropyl phosphorodithiate S-ester with N-(2-mercaptoethyl)benzenesulfonamide], DCPA, benefin(N-butyl-N-ethyl-a,a,a-trifluoro-2,6-dinitro-p-toluidine) and siduron [1-(2-methylcyclohexyl)-3-phenylurea] were used at ½, 1, and 2 times normal rates for crabgrass control. Dicamba (3,6-dichloro-o-anisic acid) was used at higher rates than normal for broadleaf weed control.

Frames with 1.25-cm hardware cloth bottoms were prepared to contain 0.093 m^2 of sod. The sod strips were fitted into the frames on the hardware cloth. The frames were then placed on the freshly tilled soil with good contact between sod and soil through the hardware cloth. Soil was also pulled up around the frames to prevent the sod from drying around the edges.

Duplicate sod strips were used with a split plot design with herbicide rates as main plots and grass species as subplots in four replications. Irrigation water was applied as needed to promote good sod root development.

Measurement of root and shoot development

Frames containing the sod strips were clamped in a slightly larger frame made of angle-iron. Plastic-covered cables attached to each corner and through a pulley arrangement with a winch gradually pulled the sod strips from the soil. A scale was mounted in one cable to obtain the force required to lift the sod from the soil. The total force required was recorded from a calibration chart. These measurements were made after 28 days for root growth and development into the soil below the hardware cloth and represented the degree of root development.

Visual injury ratings on shoot growth were also obtained in these studies. Ratings were based on a scale of 0 = no injury; 1,2,3 = some discoloration; 4,5,6 = some loss of turfgrass density and definite discoloration; 7,8,9 = severe loss of turfgrass shoots and discoloration; and 10 = dead turfgrasses.

RESULTS AND DISCUSSION

Bensulide and benefin applied to freshly tilled soil, prior to placing bluegrass sod on the treated soil, caused severe effects on the rooting of sod into the soil (Table 1). Bensulide and benefin prevented the penetration of roots through the treatment zone. DCPA, siduron, and dicamba caused little inhibition of root development under this condition.

Table 1—Influence of herbicides on rooting of Kentucky bluegrass sod during 28 days as measured by the force required to pull the sod vertically from the soil.

Chemical	kg/ha	Kg to pull 0.093 m² sod vertically from soil			Visual injury rating§
		Exp I†	Exp II‡	Exp III‡	Exp I
Bensulide	7	15 de*	42 bcd	42 abc	2 a
	14	15 de	25 efg	32 de	3 a
	28	8 e	20 fg	25 f	7 b
DCPA	6	41 a	53 a	49 a	2 a
	11	37 ab	56 a	45 ab	2 a
	22	45 a	42 bcd	40 bcd	4 a
Benefin	2	20 cd	42 bcd	33 def	3 a
	3	11 de	27 efg	36 cde	3 a
	7	11 de	18 g	26 f	4 a
Siduron	6	29 bc	40 cd	26 f	3 a
	11	40 a	51 ab	32 def	2 a
	22	37 ab	29 ef	28 ef	3 a
Dicamba	1	41 a	47 abc	42 abc	2 a
	2	40 a	42 bcd	42 abc	2 a
	4	36 ab	35 de	26 f	3 a
Check	—	39 a	56 a	45 ab	2 a

* In the same column figures followed by the same letter are not significantly different (5% level).
† Soil was prepared, herbicide applied, and sod placed on the treated area.   ‡ Sod was placed on prepared soil and herbicide applied over top of the sod in experiments II and III.   § Visual injury was based on 0 = no injury and 10 = dead turfgrass with varying symptoms represented by figures in between.

The application of herbicides over freshly laid sod was less inhibitory in the case of bensulide and benefin than the above type treatment. DCPA and siduron showed inhibitory effects, especially at high treatment levels. Madison (8) reported that sod initiated new roots from the nodes after cutting and placing bluegrass sod. DCPA and siduron are inhibitory to root initiation and less pronounced effects are prevalent on root growth from older roots. Bensulide and benefin inhibited root growth under both methods of application, but root initiation was inhibited less than roots growing into the thin layer of chemical under the sod.

Irrigation was maintained to allow sod with roots only to 2.5-cm depth to live. This was more frequent than necessary for sod with normal root systems. The force required to pull the sod from the soil was a good measure of inhibitory response on the roots and was better than visual injury ratings of the shoot in this respect (Table 1).

Kentucky 31 fescue rooted well into the soil from 2.5-cm thick sod and required a greater force to vertically pull 0.093 m² from the soil than in the case of bluegrass (Tables 1 and 2). The reaction of both species to the herbicides was similar, but Kentucky 31 fescue was less sensitive to the herbicides. Benefin and bensulide caused more pronounced effects on sod establishment than the other herbicides. Some waiting period appears necessary between benefin and bensulide treatment and moving of sod.

Bermudagrass was affected more severely by preemergence herbicides than the other species tested (Table 3). Siduron caused the greatest response

Table 2—Influence of herbicides on rooting of Kentucky 31 fescue sod during 28 days as measured by the force required to pull the sod vertically from the soil.

Chemical	kg/ha	Kg to pull 0.093 m² sod vertically from soil		Visual injury ratings§
		Exp I†	Exp II‡	Exp I
Bensulide	7	76 bcd*	44 cde	1
	14	75 bcd	51 bcd	1
	28	13 g	36 de	3
DCPA	6	92 a	56 abc	1
	11	80 abc	65 ab	1
	22	88 ab	53 bc	1
Benefin	2	66 de	53 bc	1
	3	54 ef	36 de	1
	7	46 f	33 e	3
Siduron	6	68 cd	55 abc	2
	11	80 abc	53 bc	1
	22	66 de	49 bcde	2
Dicamba	1	80 abc	49 bcde	0
	2	79 abcd	56 abc	1
	4	84 ab	36 de	2
Check	—	85 ab	71 a	1

* In the same column figures followed by a common letter are not significantly different (5% level).
† Soil was prepared, herbicide applied, and sod placed on the treated area.   ‡ Sod was placed on prepared soil and herbicide applied over top of the sod.   § Visual injury ratings were based on 0 = no injury and 10 = dead turfgrass with varying symptoms represented by figures in between.

Table 3—Influence of herbicides on rooting Tifgreen bermudagrass sod during 28 days as measured by the force required to pull the sod vertically from the soil.

Chemical	kg/ha	Kg to pull 0.093 m^2 sod vertically from the soil	
		Exp II†	Exp III
Bensulide	7	25 cd*	54 ab
	14	15 cde	35 cd
	28	11 de	20 de
DCPA	6	47 b	50 bc
	11	44 b	60 ab
	22	27 c	49 bc
Benefin	2	29 c	50 bc
	3	27 c	53 b
	7	16 cde	10 ef
Siduron	6	11 de	30 d
	11	11 de	10 ef
	22	5 e	6 ef
Dicamba	1	73 a	53 b
	2	29 c	22 de
	4	11 de	3 f
Check	—	73 a	71 a

* In the same column figures followed by the same letter are not significantly different (5% level).
† Sod was placed on prepared soil and herbicide applied over top of the sod in both experiments.

and reduced root development from stolon nodes to nil. DCPA, which resulted in little or no injury to bluegrass or Kentucky 31 fescue, caused appreciable reduction in rooting of bermudagrass from sod. Previous research has demonstrated that new roots from stolon nodes are necessary in sod establishment in new locations (1, 2).

Some waiting period is essential between time of treatment of bluegrass and bermudagrass with preemergence crabgrass herbicides and the effective movement of sod to a new location. The length of the waiting period must be greater for bensulide and benefin on bluegrass than for DCPA and siduron. This period may be extended further for Tifgreen bermudagrass with all herbicides, but siduron was too injurious for practical use on this turfgrass. Further research is needed to evaluate root responses following annual and semiannual treatments for control of crabgrass and annual bluegrass.

REFERENCES

1. BINGHAM, S. W. 1967. Influence of herbicides on root development of bermudagrass. Weeds 15:363–365.
2. ———. 1968. Effect of DCPA on anatomy and cytology of roots. Weed Sci. 16: 449–452.
3. ———, and R. E. SCHMIDT. 1967. Residue of bensulide in turfgrass soil following annual treatments for crabgrass control. Agron. J. 59:327–329.
4. ———, and ———. 1964. Crabgrass control in turf. Proc. S. Weed Conf. 17:113–122.
5. CALLAHAN, L. M. 1972. Phytotoxicity of herbicides to a penncross bentgrass green. Weed Sci. 20:387–391.

6. GASKIN, T. A. 1964. Effect of preemergence crabgrass herbicides on rhizome development in Kentucky bluegrass. Agron. J. 56:340–342.
7. JUSKA, F. V., A. A. HANSON, and A. W. HOVIN. 1970. Phytotoxicity of preemergence herbicides. U. S. Golf Ass. Green Sec. Rec. 8:2–5.
8. MADISON, J. H. 1970. Rooting from sod by *Poa pratensis* L. and *Agrostis tenuis* Sibth. Crop Sci. 10:718–719.

46

Annual bluegrass control aided by soil analysis for arsenic

R.P. FREEBORG & W.H. DANIEL

The objective of this study was to develop a procedure to test soil for available arsenic to supplement the use of *Poa annua* L. (annual bluegrass) as a bioassay plant in determining toxic levels of arsenic required for its control. This soil test procedure is similar to that routinely used in the extraction of available phosphorus. Arsenic and phosphorus are extracted with Bray P-1 ($0.03N$ NH_4F; $0.025N$ HCl) from 1.5 g of soil. Soils are also analyzed for percentage of sand and silt. An estimate is made of existing annual bluegrass population on the site. These data are then used in the determination of arsenic concentrations required to obtain a desired percentage control. Additional index words: Arsenic toxicity, Calcium arsenate, Soil test, Atomic absorption, Bioassay, *Poa annua* L.

Professional turf managers have found annual bluegrass, *Poa annua* L., to have major drawbacks. Its tolerance to heat, drought, and low temperature is poor. Where these conditions exist, it is not likely to survive and is considered a weed grass. Where survival is dependable however, it is maintained as a permanent turf.

Good organic matter content, good drainage, and adequate irrigation encourage good performance and survival of annual bluegrass. The privately operated Oakland Hills Country Club at Detroit, Michigan, has excellent annual bluegrass on one 18-hole golf course. The soil is sandy and well drained. An abundant earthworm population helps keep thatch accumulation to a minimum.

In sharp contrast, the Country Club of Indianapolis has predominantly silt loam soils which are poorly drained. For years there has been annual bluegrass infestation in the fall, survival in the winter, and thinning, often to the extent of complete loss in the summer. In mid-1950 arsenic was applied to stop yearly invasion. Since then treated fairways have become predominantly perennial bluegrass. The accumulation in the upper root zone of available arsenic ions has resulted in long-term selective annual bluegrass control with adequate survival of perennial grasses (3).

As early as 1929, arsenic was observed to control annual bluegrass. The Pennsylvania State University Field Day report, 1940, showed partial control with sodium arscnite on bentgrass putting greens. Since 1951, Daniel has observed control first with lead arsenate and then calcium arsenate (2).

Lead arsenate with its very low solubility persisted for long periods, but required higher rates to obtain control. Although calcium arsenate was more variable in response than lead arsenate, the former was less expensive, less was required for control, and it did not contaminate the environment with lead. Therefore, calcium arsenate has become the most widely used chemical for control today.

Granular arsenic formulations are predominantly used. These are usually carried on vermiculite. They flow freely and can be used in either gravity flow or broadcast spreaders. There are other preemergent controls available. None, however, can offer the gradual elimination of annual bluegrass achieved when arsenic is used. Also, arsenic permits germination of seeded perennial grasses while inhibiting germination and growth of annual bluegrass, especially when arsenic levels are below 19.5 g of active ingredient (ai) per square meter.

Current recommendations require split applications to obtain gradual control (6). Applications, which begin in late summer before fall germination of annual bluegrass, should consist of 5 to 15 g of ai/m², with 48% tricalcium arsenate (Chip-Cal) as a source of arsenic. After rain or irrigation apply another 5 to 15 g of ai/m². If a major part of the turf is perennial bluegrass or a desirable grass, make a third application at the above rate about 2 weeks later.

When annual bluegrass is the predominant species, two applications before fall germination should be adequate. The following spring, after frost is out of the ground, apply another 5 to 15 g of ai/m². Apply well ahead of the germination date for smooth crabgrass [*Digitaria ischaemum* (Schreb.)] and crabgrass [*Digitaria sanguinalis* (L.) Scop.]. This should also eliminate chickweed (*Stellaria media*, Cyrill.), prevent crabgrass, and weaken existing annual bluegrass.

In late summer of the following year, apply another 5 to 15 g of ai/m² to assure continued toxicity. Final target rates are from 40 to 70 g of ai/m². Throughout the program, overseed repeatedly at light rates with selected perennial grasses as needed.

Existing annual bluegrass plants serve to indicate toxicity levels. If plants are chlorotic and stunted, toxicity is adequate. If toxic levels have not been obtained, continue treatments in spring and late summer until toxicity is observed. Then reduce applications to 3 to 5 g of ai/m² for yearly maintenance.

Until recently the only practical method available to determine the level of arsenic toxicity was to watch for the existing annual bluegrass to become chlorotic and stunted, usually in spring and fall. Now the use of annual bluegrass as a bioassay plant can be supplemented with information derived from a soil test for available arsenic which was developed at Purdue University (5). The data from this soil test can be used to determine existing levels of arsenic as well as what levels are required to control annual bluegrass.

The procedures involved are in part similar to those used routinely in the analysis for available phosphorus. Available arsenic is extracted with Bray P-1 extractant ($0.03N$ NH_4F; $0.025N$ HCl). Atomic absorption spectrophotometry is used to measure arsenic.

Determination of arsenic concentrations required for control is based on data obtained from soils where arsenic had been used previously to control annual bluegrass. Samples were collected from 26 golf courses in the Midwest. These were taken from the 0 to 5 cm depth, where most applied arsenic is retained (5). Soil was air-dried, crushed, and passed through a 20-mesh screen. Then a 1.5-g sample was weighed and analyzed for microgram amounts of arsenic and phosphorus, and percentage of free iron oxides. The percentage of sand, silt, and clay, percentage of organic matter, and pH were also determined. Statistical analysis showed that microgram of arsenic and percentage of silt and sand were most important in the determination of annual bluegrass control. Phosphorus was also included in the final analysis to predict toxic levels of arsenic because of its reported interactions with arsenic (1, 4).

These data were used to generate a table that would permit prediction of arsenic concentrations required to obtain a desired percentage of control. Table 1 shows predictions for microgram amounts of arsenic per 1.5 g of soil required to obtain an estimated percent annual bluegrass control. This prediction table is made up of most combinations of levels of *Poa annua* control, concentrations of phosphorus, and percentages of silt and sand.

Thus, a soil is analyzed for microgram amounts of arsenic and phosphorus, percent of silt and sand, and an estimate is made of the existing annual bluegrass population. These data are then compared with those in the table to predict arsenic concentrations required to obtain desired control. This information will then indicate whether additional arsenic is needed, whether existing concentrations are adequate, or whether they are approaching levels that could be toxic to desired turfgrasses.

There are now two criteria to aid in determination of concentrations of available arsenic in the soil and level of toxicity; the field bioassay with annual bluegrass as an indicator, and a soil test to measure available arsenic. However, there is no way to prescribe exactly how much arsenic is needed for establishment of toxic levels on any individual turf area. Conditions such

Table 1—Prediction of arsenic concentrations required for control of *Poa annua*.

Arsenic	*Poa annua* control	Phosphorus	Silt	Sand
µg	%	µg	%	%
1	20	40	10	5
to	40	60	20	10
165	60	80	30	15
	80	100	40	20
	100	120	50	25
		140	60	30
		160	70	35
		180		40
				45
				50
				55
				60
				65
				70
				75
				80
				85

as temperature or soil moisture affect the susceptibility of annual bluegrass to arsenic and can always vary.

In renovation, often a 2- to 3-year program is required before adequate control can be obtained. Bare, thin areas, where *Poa annua* fails, must be filled in through the development of desirable turf. The process is often difficult, requiring patience and perseverance. The importance of developing additional interpretational aids is obvious. Information now available through soil tests for arsenic is but another step towards satisfactory pre-emergent *Poa annua* control.

REFERENCES

1. BEARD, J. B. 1973. Turfgrass science and culture. Prentice-Hall, Inc., Englewood Cliffs, N. J.
2. DANIEL, W. H. 1955. *Poa annua* control with arsenic materials. Golf Course Rep. 23(1):5-8.
3. ———. 1970. Annual grass weed control. p. 393-396. *In* Proc. First Int. Turfgrass Res. Conf. Sports Turf Res. Inst., Bingley, Yorkshire, England.
4. FERGUSON, M. H. 1959. *Poa annua* control. U.S. Golf Ass. J. 12(5):25-28.
5. FREEBORG, R. P. 1971. Arsenic concentrations required for *Poa annua* control as determined by soil tests. Ph.D. Thesis, Purdue University, West Lafayette, Indiana. 137 p.
6. KERR, C. F. 1969. Program for gradual removal of *Poa annua*. Golf Superintendent 37(4):28-29.

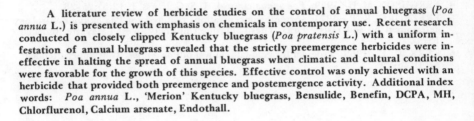

47

Annual bluegrass control with herbicides in cool-season turfgrasses

A.J. TURGEON

A literature review of herbicide studies on the control of annual bluegrass (*Poa annua* L.) is presented with emphasis on chemicals in contemporary use. Recent research conducted on closely clipped Kentucky bluegrass (*Poa pratensis* L.) with a uniform infestation of annual bluegrass revealed that the strictly preemergence herbicides were ineffective in halting the spread of annual bluegrass when climatic and cultural conditions were favorable for the growth of this species. Effective control was only achieved with an herbicide that provided both preemergence and postemergence activity. Additional index words: *Poa annua* L., 'Merion' Kentucky bluegrass, Bensulide, Benefin, DCPA, MH, Chlorflurenol, Calcium arsenate, Endothall.

Attempts at controlling annual bluegrass (*Poa annua* L.) with chemicals date back to the 1930's when lead arsenate, an insecticide, was found to discourage its occurrence in turf (23). Since then, numerous herbicides have been reported as promising for annual bluegrass control. The chemistry of these herbicides is highly variable, ranging from simple inorganic chemicals to complex aromatic compounds. The objective of this paper is to explore the inventory of existing herbicides in terms of their reported activity and apparent potential for controlling annual bluegrass.

Herbicides are categorized as preplant, preemergence, or postemergence depending upon the timing of their applications with respect to the weed and the crop. A specific herbicide is not necessarily limited to one category. For example, calcium arsenate may be applied to an annual bluegrass-infested turf as a postemergence treatment to reduce the severity of infestation. The residual activity of this herbicide may also preclude the development of new annual bluegrass from seed (preemergence) while allowing some germination of overseeded turfgrasses (preplant). Most herbicides, however, are primarily preemergence or postemergence in their activity.

PREEMERGENCE HERBICIDES

A preemergence herbicide functions by maintaining a chemical barrier to the development of weeds from seed germination. Successful use of preemergence herbicides for annual bluegrass control is dependent upon: effective residual activity during the seed germination period; little or no injury to the desirable turfgrasses within the plant community; and at least a partial death or "turnover" of the existing annual bluegrass population. An additional factor peculiar to a turfgrass community is the necessity for rapid development of desirable turfgrasses in voids caused by the death of existing weeds. Where annual bluegrass exists in patches measuring approximately 10 cm or less, its death allows adjacent turfgrass plants to fill in the voids when environmental conditions are favorable. Where substantially larger voids exist, however, reestablishment of desirable turfgrass cover is slow and replanting operations are sometimes practiced to accelerate the development of a satisfactory turf. Successful establishment of new turf from overseeding is limited by the persistance of previously applied herbicides.

Many preemergence herbicides have shown potential for preventing annual bluegrass infestations from introduced seed; however, some are so injurious to desirable turfgrasses that their use for this purpose is not practical (5). The extent of injury is not always predictable and may vary with turfgrass variety and from year to year (15, 17). A serious concern with successive annual applications of preemergence herbicides is the higher incidence of diseases in some treated turf (3). Nevertheless, preemergence herbicides are used extensively by turfgrass managers in their attempts to control the spread of annual bluegrass. The additional benefit of crabgrass (*Digitaria sanguinalis* L. Scop.) control, as well as the prevention of other annual grasses, further explains the widespread acceptance of preemergence herbicides.

Currently, the most popular preemergence herbicides for annual bluegrass control are: O,O-diisopropyl phosphorodithioate S-ester with N-(2-mercaptoethyl) benzene sulfonamide, (bensulide); dimethyl tetrachloroterephthalate, (DCPA); and N-butyl-N-ethyl-a,a,a-trifluoro-2,6-dinitro-p-toluidine, (benefin). Bensulide is used primarily on bentgrass (*Agrostis* sp.) while DCPA and benefin are widely used on Kentucky bluegrass.

Bensulide

Bensulide was initially thought to be completely safe for use on bentgrass. Juska et al. (17) reported no injury on any of 12 bentgrasses tested. Neidlinger (20) also reported no injury, and Perkins (21) described bensulide as a promising herbicide for the eradication of annual bluegrass with no injury occurring on 16 bentgrass varieties. In a 4-year study on 'Penncross' creeping bentgrass (*Agrostis palustris* Huds. 'Penncross') in Tennessee (3), bensulide appeared safe through the first 2 years of treatment at rates up to 22 kg/ha. However, severe loss of turf occurred during the summer of the third year. Injury resulted from an increased proneness to wilting, high temperature stress, and disease, even though a preventative fungicide treatment program was followed.

The actual control of annual bluegrass with bensulide has been quite variable. Juska and Hanson (16) observed approximately 56% control of annual bluegrass in greenhouse studies at 16.8 kg/ha. Goss (12) applied the same rate of bensulide to a mixed turf of annual bluegrass and colonial bentgrass (*Agrostis tenuis* Sibth.) and obtained 93% control. Engel et al. (9) found that control of annual bluegrass with 16.8 kg/ha of bensulide ranged from a trace to 82% 8 months after treatment, and 0 to 52% 16 months after treatment. Estimates of turfgrass quality ranged from 42 to 100% of the check. The basis for such variability is not completely understood. Bingham et al. (2) reported that the rate of bensulide required for annual bluegrass control in overseeded bermudagrass (*Cynodon dactylon* L.) was partially off-set by competing cool-season grasses. Hence, plant competition may also be important in determining the effectiveness of bensulide in bentgrass and other turfgrass communities. Studies by Bingham and Schmidt (1) revealed that more herbicide was required to injure milo roots in a bioassay of surface versus lower soil levels taken from bensulide-treated turf. This corresponded to higher levels of calcium, phosphorus, potassium, and organic matter in the surface soil. The persistance of bensulide in the soil varied with formulation; the emulsifiable concentrate was degraded more rapidly than the granular formulation. The authors also reported that detectable quantities of bensulide were found to depths of 12.75 cm in soil after four annual applications. In a study by Mazur et al. (19), no accumulation of bensulide occurred in soil after four annual applications and there was little or no downward movement of the herbicide. Differences in soil properties, herbicide formulation, and plant competition are in part responsible for the observed variable response of turf to bensulide.

DCPA

DCPA is widely used as a preemergence herbicide in turf for controlling crabgrass and other annual grasses. It has provided excellent control of annual bluegrass from seedings made into newly laid turf (11); however, essentially no control resulted when DCPA was applied to existing stands of annual bluegrass (7). The residual activity of DCPA in the soil appears to be limited to 2 or 3 months (12, 18) and, thus, it would require at least two applications per year to prevent annual bluegrass development from seed. DCPA has caused substantial injury to bentgrass putting-green turf, especially the cultivars Toronto (22) and Cohansey (14). Roberts and Brockshus (22) reported that applications of DCPA resulted in reductions in the quality and recuperative potential of bentgrasses, at rates of 11.2 and 16.8 kg/ha. Furthermore, turfgrass injury was greater at higher nitrogen fertility levels. Juska et al. (17) reported that stolons from treated greens failed to root well and the turf was less dense and ragged in appearance.

DCPA is generally considered safe to use on Kentucky bluegrass turf. Engel and Callahan (8) reported no significant inhibition of root or shoot growth of 'Merion' Kentucky bluegrass plugs that were planted in soil treated with 13.4 kg/ha of DCPA. However, Gaskin (10) measured significant reductions in tillering and rhizome growth in Merion Kentucky bluegrass treated at 11.2 kg/ha. Juska and Hanson (15) observed slight, but temporary, thinning of Kentucky bluegrass in July. Also, the susceptability of the turf to injury from cold weather and frost was greater in DCPA-treated turf. DCPA can apparently predispose turf to injury from environmental stresses.

Benefin

Benefin is another herbicide that is widely used for prevention of crabgrass in Kentucky bluegrass turf. In studies by Gibeault in Great Britain, it provided good preemergence control of annual bluegrass that was seeded into newly laid turf (11). However, its residual toxicity is of relatively short duration (18) and at least two applications per year would probably be necessary to prevent the development of new annual bluegrass plants from seed. The suitability of benefin for use on bentgrass turf is questionable. A 4-year study in Tennessee showed moderate to severe injury on Penncross creeping bentgrass from annual applications (3), and studies in Pennsylvania also showed serious bentgrass injury from benefin (21).

POSTEMERGENCE HERBICIDES

A postemergence herbicide provides a specific level of toxicity to existing stands of weeds. Selective kill of the entire weed population by postemergence herbicides may or may not be acceptable depending upon the nature and extent of the annual bluegrass infestation. Small voids created in the turf from the death of annual bluegrass may be quickly filled in by surrounding turfgrasses. Large bare areas, however, destroy the utility of the turf and may require replanting. Sometimes, seeding or other planting operations are performed prior to herbicide treatment in an attempt to establish some desirable turfgrass in sufficient uniformity throughout the turf to enhance the reestablishment of cover after chemical treatment.

Postemergence herbicides that are used for annual bluegrass control include: calcium and lead arsenates; 7-oxabicyclo[2.2.1]heptane-2,3-dicarboxylic acid, (endothall); 2,3-dihydro-2,6-pyridazinedione (MH); and a mixture of MH and methyl hydroxyfluorene-9-carboxylates (chlorflurenol) available commercially as Po-San (Mallinckrodt Chemical Works, St. Louis, Mo.).

Arsenates

Calcium and lead arsenates are frequently listed as preemergence herbicides; however, their principal activity is in controlling existing stands of annual bluegrass with the accumulation of an adequate level of arsenate in the soil (6). The specific arsenate concentration necessary for selective toxicity to annual bluegrass varies with such factors as: soil texture, drainage, pH, and the phosphorus-arsenate balance in the soil (4). Clay and organic colloids in the soil can tie up arsenate rendering it unavailable to plants. The selectivity of arsenate is reportedly reduced in persistently wet soils; hence, poor drainage should be corrected before initiating an arsenate program. Arsenate forms insoluble iron and aluminum compounds at low soil pHs while solubility is comparably reduced at high pHs due to an excess of calcium carbonate in the soil. Phosphorus tends to counteract the toxicity of arsenate, probably due to a competition for uptake of these similar anions by plants. Hence, turfgrass injury from excessive arsenate treatments can be mitigated by a timely application of soluble phosphorous. Juska et al. (17) reported that calcium arsenate severely injured some bentgrass varieties, especially 'Old Orchard', while lead arsenate was quite safe when both were applied at 244 kg/ha for 5 consecutive years. Engel et al. (9) reported that the quality of bentgrass fairway turf was reduced to 50% of normal when calcium arsenate was applied at 488 kg/ha. Also, late summer applications were more injurious than those made in April. Some Kentucky bluegrass developed in calcium arsenate-treated plots, indicating greater safety of this herbicide to Kentucky bluegrass than to bentgrass. The authors suggested that no more than 244 kg/ha of calcium arsenate be applied at any one time and that applications should be made during cool weather periods. Juska and Hanson (15) reported slight thinning of Kentucky bluegrass in July from calcium arsenate at 829 kg/ha; however, the susceptability of several turf-grasses to injury from cold weather and frost was greater following both calcium arsenate and lead arsenate treatments. In Illinois, Turgeon et al. (24) found that two annual applications of calcium arsenate at 488 kg/ha had apparently caused thatch development in Kentucky bluegrass. This was cor-related with a complete absence of earthworms in the upper 8-cm of soil. The arsenates are unique herbicides in that they can be used to reduce the existing stand of annual bluegrass, and also prevent the development of new annual bluegrass from seed. They are also highly unpredictable and may cause rapid and severe turfgrass deterioration unless used with considerable care.

Endothall

Another postemergence herbicide of considerable contemporary interest is endothall. Engel and Aldrich (7) reported substantial reductions in the annual bluegrass content of colonial bentgrass fairways following several ap-plications of endothall in spring of 0.56 kg/ha. Cockerham and Whitworth (5) reported selective injury to annual bluegrass in bermudagrass turf at 4.48 and 6.72 kg/ha, but recovery was rapid necessitating repeated treatments. Turgeon et al. (25) reported substantial reductions of annual bluegrass in Kentucky bluegrass following a single application in September at 2.24 and 4.48 kg/ha. The best control was obtained with three applications at 2-week intervals with 1.12 kg/ha. In all cases, the turf was temporarily browned, with Kentucky bluegrass recovering selectively after 3 to 4 weeks. Granular formulations of endothall provided superior selectivity over foliar sprays in greenhouse studies; however, field results were variable. Several mor-phologically-differing biotypes of annual bluegrass responded differently to endothall treatments; a root treatment with 50 ppm endothall was adequate to kill an upright-growing biotype while twice that concentration only stunted a prostrate-growing biotype. The selectivity of endothall in turf was at-tributed to differences in absorption and action of the herbicide in root ap-plications, while morphological differences among grass species, spray re-tention, and action contributed to selectivity following foliar applications (26).

MH, Chlorflurenol

Engel and Aldrich (7) evaluated repeated applications of MH at 1.12 or 2.24 kg/ha for suppressing annual bluegrass in colonial bentgrass fairways. Although substantial seedhead suppression resulted, bentgrass injury was so severe that this approach to annual bluegrass control was abandoned. More recently, Goss and Zook (13) studied the effects of MH plus chlorflurenol (Po-San) on annual bluegrass-infested turfs in Washington. They reported substantial inhibition of seedhead formation with some temporary discoloration of Merion Kentucky bluegrass and bentgrass. Other effects included: reduction of the mowing requirement; control of some broadleaf weeds; density reduction of annual bluegrass stands with some increase in the density of perennial turfgrasses; and reduction of viability in seed from annual bluegrass plants. Young seedlings of annual bluegrass were also reported killed by fall applications. The authors recommended overseeding with desirable turfgrasses in conjunction with fall applications of MH and chlorflurenol.

FIELD EVALUATION OF HERBICIDES

A Merion Kentucky bluegrass site was selected with a uniform infestation of annual bluegrass averaging approximately 40%. Various preemergence and postemergence herbicides were applied: April 27, 1972, September 3, 1972, and April 17, 1973 to replicated plots measuring 1.5 m × 1.8 m. The turf was mowed 3 times per week to a height of 1.9 cm and irrigation was supplied in sufficient quantity to prevent wilt. The plots were fertilized with 10-6-4 monthly to supply 3 kg of N/are per year. Data was taken as percent annual bluegrass at three observations dates: July 23, 1972; January 25, 1973, and June 11, 1973.

The annual bluegrass percentage of plots treated with bensulide, benefin, DCPA, and MH + chlorflurenol increased sharply during the experimental period (Table 1). Climatic conditions through 1972 and early 1973 in central Illinois were characterized by mild temperatures and abundant rainfall. No

Table 1—Percent annual bluegrass in closely-clipped Kentucky bluegrass at three observation dates as affected by various herbicides applied three times.

Treatment	Formulation*	Rate, kg/ha	Percent annual bluegrass		
			Jul 23, 1972	Jan 25, 1973	Jun 11, 1973
Bensulide	G	16.8	61	75	88
Benefin	G	3.4	48	80	96
Calcium arsenate	G	292.3	18	18	17
DCPA	WP	16.8	60	87	98
Endothall	G	4.5	13	62	82
Endothall	S	4.5	12	25	37
MH +	S	1.1	34	75	96
Chlorflurenol	EC	0.6	—	—	—
Check	—	—	52	85	98

* G = granular, WP = wettable powder, S = salt concentrate, EC = emulsifiable concentrate.

loss of annual bluegrass in the check plots was observed at any time during this period. The sharp increase of annual bluegrass in the check plots indicated very favorable growing conditions for this species. Assuming that the preemergence herbicides did prevent new annual bluegrass plants from developing from seed, the competitive ability of the existing plants was sufficient to allow it to almost completely take over the Kentucky bluegrass. These results indicate that a preemergence herbicide program for annual bluegrass control is inadequate unless the existing plants die from environmental stress or are subdued in some way. Calcium arsenate reduced the stand of annual bluegrass and held it at approximately 18% through the observation period. Initially, endothall also reduced the annual bluegrass population but the lack of any long-term residual activity of this herbicide allowed annual bluegrass to quickly repopulate the plant community after each treatment. The combination of MH and chlorflurenol was ineffective in preventing nearly complete take over of the turf by annual bluegrass. Apparently, under such ideal climatic conditions and close mowing, the spread of annual bluegrass can only be controlled by herbicides which provide both postemergence and preemergence activity while not injuring Kentucky bluegrass seriously.

REFERENCES

1. BINGHAM, S. W., and R. E. SCHMIDT. 1967. Residue of bensulide in turfgrass soil following annual treatments for crabgrass control. Agron. J. 59:327-329.
2. ———, ———, and C. K. CURRY. 1969. Annual bluegrass control in overseeded bermudagrass putting green turf. Agron. J. 61:908-911.
3. CALLAHAN, L. M. 1972. Phytotoxicity of herbicides to a Penncross bentgrass green. Weed Sci. 20:387-391.
4. CARROW, R. N., and P. E. RIEKE. 1970. Arsenic and phosphorus tests from selected golf courses. (Unpublished progress report.)
5. COCKERHAM, S. T., and J. W. WHITWORTH. 1967. Factors affecting *Poa annua* L. control. Weeds 15:98-101.
6. DANIEL, W. H. 1955. *Poa annua* control with arsenic materials. Golf Course Rep. 23(1):5-9.
7. ENGEL, R. E., and R. J. ALDRICH. 1960. Reduction of annual bluegrass, *Poa annua*, in bentgrass turf by the use of chemicals. Weeds 8:26-28.
8. ———, and L. M. CALLAHAN. 1967. Merion Kentucky bluegrass response to soil residue of preemergence herbicides. Weeds 15:128-130.
9. ———, A. MORRISON, and R. D. ILNICKI. 1968. Preemergence chemical effects on annual bluegrass. Golf Superintendent 36(2):20-21, 39.
10. GASKIN, T. A. 1964. Effect of preemergence crabgrass herbicides on rhizome development in Kentucky bluegrass. Agron. J. 56:340-342.
11. GIBEAULT, V. A. 1967. Investigations on the control of annual meadowgrass. J. Sports Turf Res. Inst. 42:17-40.
12. GOSS, R. L. 1964. Preemergence control of annual bluegrass (*Poa annua* L.) Agron. J. 56:479-481.
13. ———, and F. ZOOK. 1971. New approach for *Poa annua* control. Golf Superintendent 39(1):46-48.
14. GRIFFIN, H. M. 1969. Management basis for bent greens in southern areas. U. S. Golf Ass. Green Section Record 7(1):10-13.
15. JUSKA, F. V., and A. A. HANSON. 1964. Effect of preemergence crabgrass herbicides on seedling emergence of turfgrass species. Weeds 12:97-101.
16. ———, and ———. 1967. Factors affecting *Poa annua* L. control. Weeds 15:98-101.

17. ———, ———, and A. W. HOVIN. 1970. Phytotoxicity of preemergence herbicides. U. S. Golf Ass. Green Section Record 8:2-5.

18. KAUFMAN, D. D. 1972. Persistance and degradation of commonly used turf herbicides in our environment. Proc. Scotts Turfgrass Res. Conf. 3:93-130.

19. MAZUR, A. R., J. A. JAGSCHITZ, and C. R. SKOGLEY. 1969. Bioassay for bensulide, DCPA, and siduron in turfgrass. Weed Sci. 17:31-34.

20. NEIDLINGER, T. J. 1965. *Poa annua* L.: Susceptibility to several herbicides and temperature requirements for germination. M.S. Thesis. Corvallis, Oregon State University. 97 p.

21. PERKINS, A. T. 1968. Effective turfgrass weed control. U. S. Golf Ass. Green Section Record 6(1):11-15.

22. ROBERTS, E. C., and D. R. BROCKSHUS. 1966. Kind and extent of injury to greens from preemergence herbicides. Golf Superintendent 34:13, 16, 18, 36.

23. SPRAGUE, H. B., and G. W. BURTON. 1937. Annual bluegrass (*Poa annua* L.) and its requirements for growth. New Jersey Agr. Exp. Sta. Bull. 630, 24 p.

24. TURGEON, A. J., T. D. HUGHES, and J. D. BUTLER. 1971. Thatch accumulation in bluegrass after applying preemergence herbicides two years. Twelfth Illinois Turfgrass Conf. Proc. p. 19-29.

25. ———, W. F. MEGGITT, and D. PENNER. 1972. Role of endothall in the control of annual bluegrass in turf. Weed Sci. 20:562-565.

26. ———, D. PENNER, and W. F. MEGGITT. 1972. Selectivity of endothall in turf. Weed Sci. 20:557-561.

48

Tillering response of Kentucky bluegrass and annual bluegrass to TIBA[1]

B.A. RIEGER & J. L. EGGENS

Application of suitable growth regulators may help to extend the vegetative phase of annual bluegrass (*Poa annua* L.) and at the same time reduce its seed production without damaging the other more valuable components of the turf. The response of Kentucky bluegrass (*Poa pratensis* L.) and annual bluegrass to the auxin transport inhibitor, 2,3,5-triiodobenzoic acid (Regim—8, TIBA) in greenhouse monocultures was investigated.

The chemical was applied to both speices in 10, 100, and 1,000 ppm active ingredient (ai) concentration once at three dates. Plants sprayed between 5 and 8 weeks after seeding with the highest concentration produced significantly more tillers in both Kentucky bluegrass and annual bluegrass. In annual bluegrass there was also a significant decrease in leaf width and in CO_2 released, while no significant differences were found in the dry weight of any of the eight, weekly clippings.

The highest concentration of solution sprayed at the latest date seemed to be most effective in reducing the leaf width and increasing CO_2 production as well as causing other visible phenological changes such as foliage color and density, upright versus procumbent growth type, and decrease of seed stalk number. Additional index words: Regim—8, Growth regulator, *Poa annua* L., *Poa pratensis* L.

Annual bluegrass (*Poa annua* L.) is found as a very troublesome weed throughout North America. In the cool regions of North America the turf is usually irrigated regularly and annual bluegrass can be found all year round (5). In the cooler, humid regions, such as most of Ontario, golf courses have a fairly high perpetual population of annual bluegrass.

The more recent preemergence herbicides can prevent germination of annual bluegrass. However, despite their predicted effectiveness as indicated by a number of brand advertisements, undesireable side effects limit their usefulness. In the southeast United States, where bermudagrasses [*Cynodon dactylon* (L.) Pers.] are the primary perennial turfgrasses, a relatively new herbicide on the market, Pronamide[2], may give a complete control (7); how-

[1]Contribution of Dept. of Horticultural Science, University of Guelph, Guelph, Ontario, Canada. This project was supported by the Ontario Ministry of Agriculture and Food, Toronto, Ontario, Canada.

[2]International Union of Chemistry name. Manufactured by Rohm & Haas, Philadelphia, Pa. 19105 and marketed under the trade name Kerb.

ever, in the cooler humid regions of Ontario, where Kentucky bluegrass (*Poa pratensis* L.) is the main fairway grass, this has not yet been proven.

One of the approaches to annual bluegrass control offered in Ontario is the "Common Sense Maintenance" program to develop and maintain strong, healthy turf as the primary annual bluegrass combatant. This can't be regarded as a solution of broad applicability, because it is uncertain at best, and must be based upon individual skills and circumstances (6). Thus, many golf course superintendents in Ontario choose, rather, to develop a management program, whereby they can "live with the annual bluegrass" (8).

During the last days of June, July and August in Ontario, when temperatures rise above 27C, annual bluegrass usually becomes dormant and subsequently dies out, leaving unsightly hard-to-play areas for golfers. Certain management practices, most often syringing (frequent light sprinkler irrigation), are used during the periods of excessively high temperatures to overcome the problem by mitigating temperature extremes in the microclimate.

Syringing may be economically feasible on putting greens because they represent a comparatively small area, but it can hardly be justified on fairways. On the other hand, ever increasing use of specific growth regulating chemicals in field and horticultural plant production suggests that externally applied growth regulating substances may bring improvement to the effectiveness of this kind of management program for putting greens and fairways.

Some chemical growth regulators, in addition to herbicides, have been tested widely on horticultural crops as special cultural agents to reduce plant height, influence flowering, promote uniform maturity, accelerate lateral shoot growth and induce male sterility. In an ever increasing number of crops, successful experimental applications of the growth regulator chemicals have prompted the use of these substances on an industrial scale. Applications of these substances have become accepted as general practice both in horticultural and field crop production as an aid in mechanical field harvesting, increasing yields (5), chemical pruning (3), and improving the quality of produce.

The inhibition of bud development of *Vicia faba* L. by the auxin produced in the apical shoot has been known through the work of Thimann and Skoog (12). Leopold (9) showed that the inhibition of tillering in two species of grasses, barley (*Hordeum* sp.) and teosinte (*Euchlaena mexicana*), similar to the control of branching in dicots could also be governed by the auxin. There is still relatively little information known regarding the effect of auxin transport inhibitors in turfgrasses.

In the gramineae family it is a well-known phenomenon that a number of "true winter-type" overwintering species and cultivars without going through a certain, close to 0 C chilling effect fail to develop reproductive organs and remain in the vegetative stage for a long time (4).

Tillering, which is the development of axillary buds of grass plants into branch shoots or tillers, has been an object for studying the effect of environmental factors, photoperiod (11), temperature (2), nutritional status, moisture, soil conditions, competition of other plants and other environmental effects as related to cultural practices, or ecology of the grasses involved (1).

The two experiments described here were conducted with the most common Ontario fairway grasses, Kentucky bluegrass and its worst weed grass, annual bluegrass. A dimethylamine salt of 2,3,5-triiodobenzoic acid, (TIBA) $I_3C_6H_2COOH$, one of the auxin transport inhibiting growth regulators, recommended and used in large scale crop production of wheat (*Triticum aestivum* L.) and soybeans [*Glycine max* (L.) Merr.] was evaluated.

The objective of using this auxin transport inhibitor was to first study the tolerance and reaction of Kentucky bluegrass to TIBA, and then learn about the responses of annual bluegrass to this chemical. We have assumed that it may be possible to find suitable growth regulators and methods which will enable us to extend the vegetative phases of annual bluegrass by postponing or eliminating its summer dormancy, thus helping the grass to survive as a component of good-quality golf fairways.

EXPERIMENTAL PROCEDURE

Two greenhouse experiments were conducted in 1972 using a foliar spray of Regim—8[3], a 14.2% solution brand preparation (equivalent to 13.1%, 2,3,5-triiodobenzoic acid concentration).

The greenhouse was maintained at 20 C during the night; the day temperature was somewhat higher as it was effected by sunshine and outdoor temperatures. Each culture received 50 cc 20–20–20 fertilizer solution (30 g/7 liters) every 2 weeks from the third week after seeding until terminating the experiments. The cutting height was 3.2 cm.

Sterilized sandy loam topsoil was used. Each of 8 replications consisted of 12 plots in "Garden Paks"[4] fiber trays seeded (17.5 cm × 10.5 cm × 6 cm) in three rows 3.5 cm apart.

At each spraying date three TIBA spray solutions of 10, 100, and 1000 ppm ai concentration, respectively, and one control (water) spray were applied.

Experiment I

The first experiment seeded with Kentucky bluegrass 'Baron,' Feb. 26, 1972, was designed to study the TIBA tolerance of the cultivar. The plots were thinned to 20 plants per tray by March 30; the sprays were applied by a high pressure 250 cc volume hand sprayer, giving a fine leaf coverage, on April 3, April 10, and April 17 marked as the 6th, 7th, and 8th weeks in the record notes, tables, and figures. The plots were clipped weekly beginning April 20. Tiller counts were taken April 14, May 2, May 17, and at the date of termination, June 20. These were marked in the record as the 8th, 10th, 11th, and 17th weeks after seeding. Descriptive observational remarks were noted about the visible changes in the plot or plants wherever applicable.

---

[3]Manufactured by the Chemagro Corp., Kansas City, MO 64120.
[4]Manufactured by Ranco Container Products Ltd., Burlington, Ontario, Canada.

Experiment II

The second experiment, seeded August 25, 1972 with annual bluegrass, was thinned between September 5 and 24. Spraying dates were Sept. 25, Oct. 2, and Oct. 10, marked as the 5th, 6th, and 7th weeks after seeding. The number of tillers per plot were recorded and the grass was clipped at weekly intervals from Sept. 25 to Nov. 24, and the dry weights recorded. Visual estimates of color, blade and flowerhead density, and number of panicles were recorded. At the termination date, Feb. 20, 1973, the root development of each plot of the first four replications was visually rated. These visual estimates and ratings, although interesting, are not presented here. The plants in each plot were individually examined and grouped into classes according to the number of visible flowerheads or seedheads as possible representatives of the propagative development of studying their frequency distribution.

We attempted to measure the respiration rate of some plants, on the assumption that it may be related to differences in the tiller number, visual estimates of blade color, and density of the most effective treatments as compared to those found in the controls. For this purpose on Nov. 23, the top 24 mm-long sections were cut off from 20 blades picked at random from each plot of the control and of the treatments of highest concentrated sprays in the first four replications. The blades were put in 85 mm-long 25 mm-dia glass vials, sealed with 1.35-mil plastic sheet cover, and left to respire for 3 hours at 20 C. Blanks were included in each replication for reference. Then atmosphere samples were drawn from the vials by a 2-cc hypodermic syringe and CO_2 was measured by thermal conductivity using a Beckman GC-5 gas chromatograph (10).

The total area of the same 20 leaf blades was measured using a suction planimeter calibrated by a 25 mm $\times$ 40 mm piece of paper (10 cm^2) cut up to 20 slices of 25-mm length.

RESULTS AND DISCUSSION

Kentucky bluegrass

To establish the most effective spray concentration and stage of growth for application, the TIBA sprays were applied at 10, 100, and 1,000 ppm concentration when plants were 6, 7, and 8 weeks old. No noticeable adverse effects from the TIBA were observed on Kentucky bluegrass plants. Morphological changes could be observed approximately 8 days after spraying. These changes consisted of more upright, but somewhat restricted growth, slightly narrower leaf blades which were a greyish-green color. The changes were more marked in plants receiving higher concentrations and were also visible for a longer period with increasing concentrations and later dates of spraying.

The visible morphological changes might have been regarded as evidence of physiological processes which resulted in significant increase in tiller numbers for the highest concentration (1,000 ppm) sprays. Sprays applied

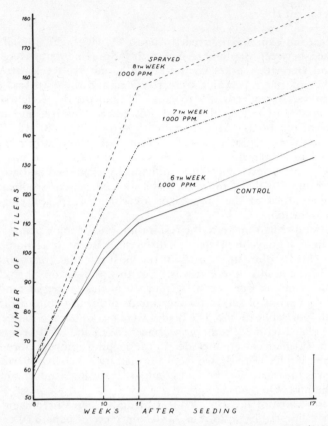

Fig. 1—Cumulative tiller counts per 20 Kentucky bluegrass plants. LSD (0.05) indicated by vertical bars. There was no significant difference in the 8th week.

at later dates also resulted in progressively greater increase of tiller number (Fig. 1). Lower concentrations did not significantly increase the tiller number, although similar patterns of morphological changes and trends of increase in tiller number in plants sprayed with higher concentration solutions could also be noticed, especially for a short period following foliar spraying.

Annual bluegrass

Morphological changes

Morphological changes occurred similar to those in the Kentucky bluegrass, but earlier and in a more pronounced form. The leaf blades appeared slightly twisted 2 days after treatment in plants receiving the 1,000 ppm concentration spray. This was followed by retarded upright growth of the leaf blades in 1 week. In 2 weeks these plants appeared to be definitely finer textured and darker colored and were easily distinguishable from the control plants. This change was especially marked in the plants sprayed at the latest date when they were in their 7th week and seedstalk development on some of them was imminent. The younger the plants were at the time of treatment, the less noticeable were the changes, and the faster the growth regulatory effect of TIBA worn off.

Tillering

The highest concentration sprays applied 6 to 7 weeks after emergence significantly and progressively increased tiller production starting approximately 2 weeks after spraying. Spraying the plants 2 weeks earlier also initiated an increase of tillering; however, in this early stage of development the inhibiting of auxin transport seemed to drastically reduce the physiological processes necessary for further tiller formation.

Lower concentration and earlier spraying did not bring about consistently significant increases in the number of tillers produced as compared to that of the control (Table 1).

Root and seedhead development

Figure 2 shows the frequency distribution of seedhead-bearing plants. The relatively small number (80) of plants analyzed and the fact that these

Table 1—Average cumulative tiller number per 20 *Poa annua* L. plants.†

| | | | No. of tillers | | | | |
| | Treatment | | Days after planting | | | | |
Spray	Time	ppm	31	46	59	73	87
Water	5th week	0	74.5	102.9	151.5	178.2	194.6
TIBA	5th week	10	71.8	96.0	149.1	180.6	191.8
	5th week	100	74.3	104.4	142.9	164.9	180.8
	5th week	1000	73.4	126.3*	168.4*	179.9	184.3
Water	6th week	0	72.0	99.9	146.6	182.5	189.5
TIBA	6th week	10	70.9	102.6	144.9	170.9	189.1
	6th week	100	73.9	100.6	133.4	158.0	171.0
	6th week	1000	72.6	106.4*	191.5*	222.0*	232.1*
Water	7th week	0	72.0	97.9	146.9	173.9	185.6
TIBA	7th week	10	76.1	105.5	142.9	165.1	174.4
	7th week	100	71.9	96.5	159.0*	176.0	192.4
	7th week	1000	73.4	98.6	205.4*	267.1**	293.1**
Average control			73.1	100.2	148.2	178.4	189.9

*,** Significantly higher than control at 0.05 and .01 levels, respectively.   † Every second date of counting.

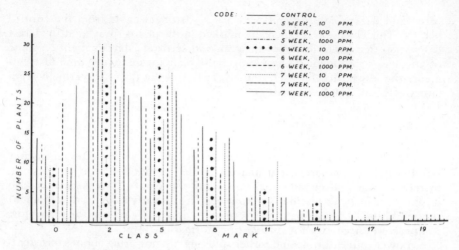

Fig. 2—**Seedhead frequency on 80 annual bluegrass plants. Class 0: plants bearing no seedheads, classes 2-17: plants with classmark ± 1 seedheads, class 19: plants with 19 or more seedheads.**

plants were grown during the decreasing daylight winter season in a greenhouse do not encourage the authors to accept the figures at face value. Still, one cannot overlook the fact that in the 0 class those plants with the highest frequency received the latest spray of the 1,000 ppm concentration TIBA. This in turn was followed by plants from the plot sprayed with the same concentration TIBA just a week earlier.

Dry matter production

Despite the fact that significantly more CO_2 evolution was monitored in the atmosphere of respiring leaf blades from control plants than in those receiving the 1,000 ppm concentration sprays (Table 2), it was not demonstrated statistically that there were significant differences in the dry matter

Table 2—**TIBA effect on the width of the leaf blade and respiration in** *Poa annua* **L.**

Treatment spray			Leaf blade CO_2 ppm	
Chemical	Time	Area, cm^2	In vial	Release per cm^2
Water check	5th week	13.0 a*	1678 a*	97.9 a*
TIBA 1,000 ppm	5th week	11.0 b	1471 bc	86.6 bc
TIBA 1,000 ppm	6th week	10.5 bc	1436 c	80.5 c
TIBA 1,000 ppm	7th week	10.3 c	1535 b	92.5 ab
Blank vial			503 d	

* Values not followed by the same letter are significantly different at the 0.05 level.

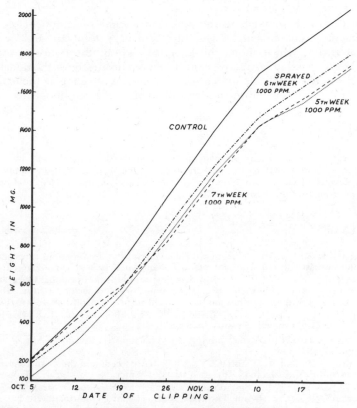

Fig. 3—Cumulative dry weight of annual bluegrass clippings per 20 plants.

(weight) production of the weekly clippings. Neither were there significant differences in the dry matter weight of the total plant weighed at the date of termination, Feb. 14, 1973. The trend, however, that the TIBA increased the dry matter production might still be valid based on Fig. 3, although this inference might not be strong enough to bring about differences justifiable by statistical analysis. On the other hand, the higher respiration rate might also be the simple consequence of the broader blades (larger leaf area) (Table 2) probably containing a larger number of cells respiring and producing more dry matter in the control plants.

CONCLUSION

The aim of the foregoing investigation was to explore the possibilities of force-manipulating the development of annual bluegrass, a short-season monocotyledonous plant, by an external auxin transport inhibitor, in order to keep it longer in the vegetative stage of development similar to that change occurring in "true winter-type" wheats if not exposed to adequate chilling effect. The very modest success with this "true spring-type" wild grass in increasing the tillering and at the same time decreasing seedhead formation by using Regim—8 sprayed on the grass at the time of imminent seedstalk development is encouraging. The turf is a very dynamic and complex ecological entity, which should be kept throughout the entire season in a pleasing, ready-to-play, attractive condition even if infested with annual blue-grass. This may complicate and make the solution of changing the bane and managing for proper use all the more challenging, but not impossible.

ACKNOWLEDGMENT

The authors wish to express their appreciation to Mr. B. Barabas, University of Guelph, for his help in making the fine drawings for the figures. Help in supplying the chemical Regim—8 and information on its use is also acknowledged to Chemagro Corporation, Kansas City, Missouri 64120.

REFERENCES

1. BEARD, J. B. 1970. The plant characteristics, dissemination, environmental adaptation and cultural requirements of *Poa annua* L. Rasen, Turf, Gazon 1:33–35.
2. BOGART, J. E. 1972. Factors influencing competition of annual bluegrass (*Poa annua* L.) within established turfgrass communities and seeding stands. Michigan State Univ. M.S. thesis. *In* Poa annua still hold surprises. Golfdom 46(10):1–75.
3. CATHEY, H. M., G. L. STEFFENS, N. W. STUART, and R. H. ZIMMERMAN. 1966. Chemical pruning of plants. Science 153:1382–1383.
4. CHOUARD, P. 1960. Vernalization and its relations to dormancy. Ann. Rev. Plant Physiol. 77:191–238.
5. ENGEL, R. E., and R. D. ILNICKY. 1969. Turf weeds and their control. *In* A. A. Hanson and F. V. Juska (ed.) Turfgrass science. Amer. Soc. of Agron., Madison, Wis.
6. HART, Jack E. 1970. Common sense approach to *Poa annua* control. Proc. Royal Canadian Golf Ass. 21st Ann. Turfgrass Conf. Toronto, Ontario. p. 20–21.
7. HORN, G. C., G. S. SMITH, Mike T. AYER, B. E. REHBERG, Randy BRIGGS, and Leonard REID. 1972. Farewell to *Poa annua*. Golf Supt. 40(8):11–16.
8. HYND, William. 1970. I have been living with *Poa annua*. Proc. Royal Canadian Golf Ass. 21st Ann. Turfgrass Conf. Toronto, Ontario. p. 22–27.
9. LEOPOLD, A. C. 1949. The control of tillering in grasses by auxin. Amer. J. Bot. 36:437–440.
10. LOUGHEED, E. C., E. W. FRANKLIN, and R. B. SMITH. 1969. Ethylene analyses by automatic gas chromatography. Can. J. Plant Sci. 49:386–391.
11. MOSER, L. E., S. R. ANDERSON, and R. W. MILLER. 1968. Rhizome and tiller development of Kentucky bluegrass (*Poa protensis* L.) as influenced by photoperiod, cold treatment, and variety. Agron. J. 60:632–635.
12. THIMANN, K. V., and F. SKOOG. 1932. Studies on the growth hormone in plants III. Proc. Nat. Acad. Sci. 19:714–716.

49

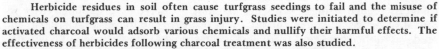

Use of activated charcoal to nullify the harmful effects of chemicals in turfgrass[1]

J.A. JAGSCHITZ

Herbicide residues in soil often cause turfgrass seedings to fail and the misuse of chemicals on turfgrass can result in grass injury. Studies were initiated to determine if activated charcoal would adsorb various chemicals and nullify their harmful effects. The effectiveness of herbicides following charcoal treatment was also studied.

Activated charcoal improved stands when seedbeds contained 2,4-D, A-820, bandane, benefin, bensulide, DCPA, dicamba, MBR-8251, mecoprop, nitralin, picloram, oxadiazon, silvex, simazine, and terbutol. Twelve other chemicals either did not inhibit seedings or were not deactivated by charcoal.

Charcoal alleviated damage to established turfgrass from 2,4-D, 2,4,5-T, bromoxynil, dicamba, endothall, linuron, silvex, and simazine. Injury from nine other chemicals was not reduced by charcoal.

The herbicidal activity of bensulide was not reduced where charcoal was used in seedbeds the year before. The activity of bensulide, and possibly DCPA and siduron, was reduced where charcoal was used on turfgrass 5 months earlier. No reduction was noted where charcoal was used 17 months earlier. Higher rates of charcoal caused greater reductions; higher herbicide rates counteracted these reductions. Additional index words: Residues, Herbicides, Seedling survival, Grass injury, Adsorption.

Turfgrass seedings often fail to grow normally in soil containing herbicide or chemical residues (2, 4, 5). The misuse or accidental use of chemicals on established turfgrass often results in injury to the grass. Experimental work with such crops as cabbage (*Brassica oleracea* var. *capetata*), beets (*Beta vulgaris* L.), and strawberries (*Fragaria* sp.) has shown that activated charcoal reduces the harmful effects of herbicide residues (1, 6).[2]

Field tests were initiated from 1967 to 1973 to determine if activated charcoal could adsorb and nullify the harmful effects of various chemicals and herbicides used on turf.[3] Effects of activated charcoal on the future performance of herbicides was also studied.

---

[1] Contribution No. 1518, Rhode Island Agr. Exp. Sta., Kingston, RI 02881.

[2] References to charcoal, chemicals, and plant response are listed in a bulletin entitled "GRO-SAFE activated charcoal" prepared by ICI America Inc., Atlas Chemicals Division, Wilmington, Delaware.

[3] See appendix at the end of this chapter for a list of herbicide and chemical names.

MATERIALS AND METHODS

Various herbicides and chemicals were applied to the soil surface of prepared seedbeds and/or to established stands of grass. The grasses used in the various tests were Kentucky bluegrass (*Poa pratensis* L.), red fescue (*Festuca rubra* L.), colonial bentgrass (*Agrostis tenuis* Sibth.), creeping bentgrass (*Agrostis palustris* Huds.), velvet bentgrass (*Agrostis canina* L.), and 'Manhattan' ryegrass (*Lolium perenne* L.). Plots were replicated in complete or split block designs. The activated charcoal was applied using a conventional hand sprayer with from 2,338 to 7,015 liter/ha of water as a carrier. The source of charcoal in early tests was AQUA-NUCHAR (West Virginia Pulp and Paper Co.) while in recent tests GRO-SAFE was used (ICI America Inc., Atlas Chemicals Division).

In the seedbed studies turfgrass seedings were made at various intervals after chemical application. In soil seedings, the top 2.5-cm layer was loosened and activated charcoal was applied. After the charcoal dried, it was mixed with the loose soil by pulling a rake across the plots four times alternating at right angles. All plots were raked in this manner. The area was then seeded and raked two times. In turfgrass areas the grass was chemically killed and turfgrass seeded using a grooving machine. Charcoal was applied after removal of debris and then the area was seeded. The loose soil, charcoal, and seed was rubbed back and forth across the grooves with the back of a wooden rake. Turfgrass stands were visually estimated at various intervals after seeding. This served to indicate the extent of residual toxicity from chemicals.

Where charcoal was applied to established grasses in an attempt to alleviate chemical damage, it was sprayed at various times after chemical treatment. Visual estimates of turfgrass color were made using a 0 to 100% scale to indicate grass injury. The zero represented completely brown turf and the 100 represented completely green turf. Visual estimates of turfgrass stand were sometimes used when grass injury was permanent.

Herbicides were applied to areas where charcoal had been used in the seedbeds or on established grass to determine if the charcoal would affect herbicide activity. Seedbed areas from earlier tests were overseeded with crabgrass [*Digitaria ischaemum* (Schreb.) Muhl.] in the winter. The following spring half of each plot was treated with a preemergence crabgrass herbicide. In the established grass test, charcoal was applied in November and preemergence crabgrass herbicides were applied in April. Estimates of crabgrass cover or crabgrass plant counts were made in each plot. These measurements were used to indicate changes in herbicidal activity.

The data from these tests were analyzed at the 5% level and means were separated using Duncan's multiple range test (3).

RESULTS AND DISCUSSION

Chemicals in seedbeds

The effect of adding activated charcoal in turfgrass seedbeds containing herbicides and chemicals is shown in Tables 1 through 6. Improved grass stands resulted from charcoal use when the soil contained bandane, benefin,

Table 1—Turfgrass stand 11 weeks after seeding a Kentucky bluegrass, red fescue, and colonial bentgrass mixture in soil treated 7 weeks earlier (June 1967) with herbicides.

Herbicide	Rate, kg/ha	Charcoal, kg/ha	
		0	224
		——— Stand, % ———	
Nitralin	1.7	28 e*	97 a
Terbutol	11.2	55 d	92 ab
Bensulide	11.2	60 d	96 a
DCPA	11.2	73 c	96 a
Bandane	39.2	83 b	95 a
Siduron	13.4	94 a	97 a
None	---	94 a	95 a

* Means followed by the same letter are not significantly different at the 5% level.

Table 2—Turfgrass stand 12 weeks after seeding a Kentucky bluegrass and red fescue mixture in soil treated 4 weeks earlier (June 1972) with herbicides.

Herbicide	Rate, kg/ha	Charcoal, kg/ha	
		0	336
		——— Stand, % ———	
Terbutol	11.2	15 f*	75 abc
Benefin	2.2	18 cf	90 a
DCPA	11.2	42 de	83 ab
Oxadiazon	3.4	50 cd	89 a
Bensulide	11.2	60 bcd	77 abc
A-820	4.5	69 abc	87 ab
Bentazon	4.5	86 ab	82 ab
Siduron	13.4	87 ab	83 ab
None	---	91 a	87 ab

* Means followed by the same letter are not significantly different at the 5% level.

Table 3—Turfgrass stand 6 weeks after seeding a Kentucky bluegrass, red fescue, and colonial bentgrass mixtures in soil treated 6 days earlier (August 1967) with herbicides.

Herbicide	Rate, kg/ha	Charcoal, kg/ha	
		0	224
		——— Stand, % ———	
Mecoprop	3.4	3 e*	57 bc
Silvex	1.1	20 de	74 ab
Dicamba	.6	40 cd	85 a
2,4-D	1.7	46 c	86 a
Picloram	.3	47 c	69 ab
None	---	82 a	80 a

* Means followed by the same letter are not significantly different at the 5% level.

bensulide, DCPA, nitralin, oxadiazon, and terbutol. These herbicides are used in turfgrass areas for preemergent crabgrass control. Grass stands in soil with A-820 were not significantly improved by charcoal; however, unpub-

Table 4—Turfgrass stand 9 weeks after seeding a Kentucky bluegrass and red fescue mixture in soil treated 15 days earlier (July 1968) with a mixture of herbicides.

Herbicide	Charcoal, kg/ha	
	0	224
	Stand, %	
Mixture†	48 c*	94 ab
None	97 a	---

* Means followed by the same letter are not significantly different at the 5% level.
† Herbicide mixture contained per hectare: 2,4-D 1.1 kg, dicamba 0.28 kg, silvex 0.6 kg, mecoprop 1.1 kg, and picloram 0.07 kg.

Table 5—Turfgrass stand 9 weeks after seeding a Kentucky bluegrass and red fescue mixture in soil treated 3 days earlier (September 1972) with chemicals.

Chemical	Rate, kg/ha	Charcoal, kg/ha	
		0	336
		Stand, %	
Amitrole + Simazine	3.4 + 10.0	0 h*	4 h
MBR-8251	4.5	6 h	27 g
S-21634	4.5	32 fg	33 fg
Cacodylic acid	44.8	33 fg	35 fg
Paraquat	1.1	35 fg	36 fg
DSMA	4.5	37 ef	33 fg
None	---	35 fg	35 fg
Sodium arsenite†	---	40 def	45 bcde

* Means followed by the same letter are not significantly different at the 5% level.
† 122 liters/ha of a 44% solution.

Table 6—Turfgrass stand 9 weeks after seeding a Manhattan ryegrass and red fescue mixture in soil treated 2 days earlier (October 1972) with chemicals.

Chemical	Rate	Charcoal, kg/ha	
		0	560
		Stand, %	
Diesel fuel	4,950 liter/ha	0 b*	0 b
Hydraulic oil	4,950 liter/ha	0 b	0 b
Simazine	3.4 kg/ha	0 b	19 a
Gasoline	4,950 liter/ha	14 ab	30 a
Dalapon	9.5 kg/ha	26 a	30 a
None	---	26 a	27 a

* Means followed by the same letter are not significantly different at the 5% level.

lished recent tests have shown significance. Charcoal was not needed for siduron as siduron did not inhibit grass establishment.

Charcoal improved grass stands in soils containing herbicides used for the control of broad-leaved weeds. These were 2,4-D, dicamba, mecoprop,

Table 7—Velvet bentgrass stand 4 months after grooving and overseeding a putting green treated 5 weeks earlier (May 1968) with herbicides.

Herbicide†	Rate, kg/ha	Charcoal, kg/ha	
		0	336
		Stand, %	
DCPA	11.2	0 c*	65 b
Bensulide	16.8	23 c	94 a
Bandane	39.2	58 b	94 a
Tricalcium arsenate	215.0	65 b	79 ab
Siduron	13.4	83 ab	98 a

* Means followed by the same letter are not significantly different at the 5% level.
† Treated also in May 1965.

Table 8—Kentucky bluegrass stand 8 weeks after grooving and overseeding a lawn area treated 7 weeks earlier (July 1971) with herbicides.

Herbicide	Rate, kg/ha	Charcoal, kg/ha	
		0	224
		Stand, %	
Bensulide	14.0	9 e*	23 abc
DCPA	11.2	13 de	30 a
None	---	30 a	31 a†

*Means followed by the same letter are not significantly different at the 5% level.
† Charcoal rate was increased to 336 kg.

and silvex. Other chemicals which inhibited seedings and were deactivated by charcoal were MBR-8251, picloram, and simazine.

Some chemicals which inhibited seedings were not deactivated by charcoal. These were diesel fuel, hydraulic oil, and the combination of amitrole + simazine. With evidence that simazine is adsorbed (Table 6), failure to deactivate the combination might result from failure to adsorb the amitrole or from the higher simazine rate.

Chemicals which did not inhibit seedings and did not require charcoal were cacodylic acid, bentazon, dalapon, DSMA, gasoline, paraquat, S-21634, and sodium arsenite. However, results might be influenced by such variables as irrigation amount and frequency, time between treatment and seeding, soil mixing depth, and chemical and charcoal rates.

Results from seedings made in established turfgrass (putting green and lawn) are presented in Tables 7 and 8. Improved turfgrass stands were obtained when charcoal was used in areas previously treated with bandane, bensulide, and DCPA. Although stands were improved by using charcoal with siduron and tricalcium arsenate the results were not significant. The data suggest charcoal may not adsorb arsenate.

Chemicals on grass

The effect of applying activated charcoal to a creeping bentgrass putting green after it received an application of 2,4-D + 2,4,5-T (brush killer) is shown in Tables 9 and 10. Improved grass color, indicating less grass injury, was noted where charcoal was used. Less damage was caused when charcoal was applied within 3 hours after treatment although improved grass color was evident from charcoal use up to 14 days later. To alleviate damage from chemicals the best time to apply the charcoal would be as soon after chemical application as possible.

Results from the use of charcoal to alleviate damage from chemicals

Table 9—Creeping bentgrass color in a putting green treated 7 weeks earlier (September 1968) with 2,4-D + 2,4,5-T at 3.0 + 1.5 kg/ha.

	Charcoal, kg/ha	
Charcoal after treatment	0	224
	Green, %	
1 day	28 d*	68 b
3 hours	28 d	73 ab
½ hour	35 c	78 a
Untreated grass	75 a	---

* Means followed by the same letter are not significantly different at the 5% level.

Table 10—Creeping bentgrass color in a putting green treated 9 weeks earlier (September 1968) with 2,4-D + 2,4,5-T at 3.0 + 1.5 kg/ha.

	Charcoal, kg/ha	
Charcoal after treatment	0	224
	Green, %	
8 days	25 c*	55 b
14 days	28 c	50 b
Untreated grass	75 a	---

* Means followed by the same letter are not significantly different at the 5% level.

Table 11—Turfgrass stand in a Kentucky bluegrass, red fescue, and colonial bentgrass lawn treated 7 months earlier (October 1972) with chemicals.

Chemical	Rate	Charcoal after treatment†		
		None	3 hours	1 day
		Stand, %		
Paraquat	1.1 kg/ha	2 h*	2 h	2 h
Dalapon	9.5 kg/ha	3 h	3 h	5 h
Cacodylic acid	44.8 kg/ha	25 g	18 g	28 g
Diesel fuel	2,853 liters/ha	40 f	53 de	48 ef
Gasoline	2,853 liters/ha	43 ef	55 de	45 def
Hydraulic oil	2,853 liters/ha	55 de	60 d	60 d
Simazine	3.4 kg/ha	20 g	94 abc	95 ab
None	---	90 abc	95 ab	97 ab

* Means followed by the same letter are not significantly different at the 5% level.
† 560 kg/ha.

applied to lawn grasses are shown in Tables 11, 12, and 13. Charcoal did not reduce grass injury caused by amitrole + simazine, bromacil, cacodylic acid, dalapon, diesel fuel, gasoline, hydraulic oil, MH, or paraquat. These chemicals are either not readily adsorbed by charcoal or they entered the plant system before charcoal could make physical contact. Inorganic substances are usually not adsorbed by activated charcoal.

Little permanent grass damage resulted from 2,4-D, bromoxynil, endo-

Table 12—Turfgrass color and stand in a Kentucky bluegrass, red fescue, and colonial bentgrass lawn treated (October 1972) with herbicides.

Herbicide	Rate, kg/ha	Charcoal†	Time after herbicide	
			3 weeks	7 months
			% green	% stand
2,4-D	4.5	None	67 c*	83 bc
2,4-D	4.5	3 hours	100 a	94 abc
2,4-D	4.5	1 day	95 ab	89 abc
2,4-D + silvex	3.4 + 3.4	None	55 c	81 c
2,4-D + silvex	3.4 + 3.4	3 hours	90 ab	90 abc
2,4-D + silvex	3.4 + 3.4	1 day	89 ab	91 abc
None	--	None	90 ab	90 abc
None	--	3 hours	100 a	95 ab
None	--	1 day	100 a	97 ab

* Means within columns followed by same letter are not significantly different at 5% level.
† Applied after herbicide treatment at 560 kg/ha.

Table 13—Turfgrass color and stand in a Kentucky bluegrass, red fescue, and colonial bentgrass lawn treated (June 1973) with chemicals.

Chemical	Rate, kg/ha	Charcoal†	Time after chemical	
			9 days	6 weeks
			% green	% stand
Amitrole + simazine	3.4 + 10.1	None	15 gh*	0 f
		4 hours	50 e	0 f
Bromacil	11.2	None	3 i	0 f
		4 hours	28 f	9 ef
Linuron	3.4	None	20 fg	18 e
		4 hours	100 a	88 ab
MH	11.2	None	88 b	55 d
		4 hours	100 a	50 d
Bromoxynil	5.6	None	60 de	87 abc
		4 hours	98 ab	88 ab
Endothal	3.4	None	63 cd	89 ab
		4 hours	90 ab	96 a
2,4-D + silvex	4.5 + 2.2	None	73 c	73 c
		4 hours	95 ab	80 bc
2,4-D + dicamba	4.5 + 2.2	None	73 c	79 bc
		4 hours	95 ab	85 abc
None	---	None	100 a	90 ab
		4 hours	100 a	96 a

* Means within columns followed by the same letter are not significantly different at the 5% level.
† Applied after chemical treatment at 560 kg/ha.

Table 14—Crabgrass stand 11 weeks after seeding in soil treated 8 weeks earlier (May 1967) with bensulide.

	Charcoal, kg/ha	
Bensulide, kg/ha	0	224
	Stand, %	
0	88 a*	---
16.8	0 b	88 a

* Means followed by the same letter are not significantly different at the 5% level.

Table 15—Effect of bensulide on crabgrass control in turfgrass areas treated the previous year with activated charcoal in seedbeds.

1967		1968 Bensulide, kg/ha	
Bensulide	Charcoal	0	11.2
kg/ha		Control, %	
0	0	0 d*	93 a
0	336	7 d	78 b
11.2	0	34 c	97 a
11.2	336	7 d	93 a

* Means followed by the same letter are not significantly different at the 5% level.

Table 16—Effect of bensulide on crabgrass in turfgrass areas treated the previous year with activated charcoal in seedbeds.

1971		1972 Bensulide, kg/ha	
Bensulide	Charcoal	0	10.1
kg/ha		$\#/m^2$	
0	0	140 abc*	0 f
0	336	86 cd	0 f
16.2	0	22 def	0 f
16.2	560	97 bcd	0 f

* Means followed by the same letter are not significantly different at the 5% level.

Table 17—Crabgrass control from bensulide applied to turfgrass areas treated the previous year with activated charcoal in seedbeds

1972		1973 Bensulide, kg/ha	
Bensulide	Charcoal	0	12.3
kg/ha		Control, %	
0	0	0 c*	98 a
0	336	0 c	99 a
11.2	0	0 c	98 a
11.2	336	16 bc	93 a

* Means followed by the same letter are not significantly different at the 5% level.

thall, 2,4-D + dicamba, and 2,4-D + silvex; however the use of charcoal did reduce grass discoloration.

Simazine and linuron caused permanent grass injury but charcoal nullified this effect. The success of charcoal with these two chemicals may result from the location of the chemical on the surface of the grass. There it is adsorbed by the charcoal before it is washed into the root zone. These chemicals enter the plant system primarily through the roots, not the foliage. If a chemical enters the plant more readily through the foliage, then washing it off the plant and applying the charcoal to the soil surface could improve the chance of success with charcoal. To be successful, the charcoal must contact the chemical so the chemical can be adsorbed. How the chemical will enter the plant must also be considered.

Future herbicide performance

Data in Table 14 show that the control of crabgrass was nullified by the use of charcoal in soil treated 8 weeks earlier with the preemergence crabgrass-control herbicide bensulide. This suggests that such herbicides may not work in the areas previously treated with charcoal.

The results from using bensulide in turfgrass areas where charcoal was used in the seedbed the previous year are shown in Tables 15, 16, and 17. The herbicidal activity of bensulide was reduced in only one of the three tests and by only 15%. It appears that one can expect preemergence crabgrass herbicides to perform satisfactorily in the season after the use of charcoal in seedbeds.

The control of crabgrass from preemergent herbicides used in lawn areas treated earlier with a surface application of charcoal is presented in Tables 18, 19, and 20. The effectiveness of bensulide at the standard rate (11.2 kg/ha) was reduced when used 5 months after charcoal was applied at 224 and 448 kg/ha. At a lower charcoal rate (112 kg/ha), the reduction was not significant for bensulide or for DCPA, siduron, nitralin, bandane, and tricalcium arsenate, which was only tested at the lower rate. The adsorptive effect of charcoal when applied to the grass surface is potentially greater than when mixed with soil in seedbeds.

Table 18—Crabgrass control from herbicides applied to a Kentucky bluegrass and red fescue lawn treated 5 months earlier (November 1967) with activated charcoal.

Herbicide	Rate, kg/ha	Charcoal, kg/ha	
		0	112
		Control, %	
Bensulide	11.2	93 abcde*	78 de
DCPA	11.2	98 abc	80 bcde
Siduron	13.4	89 abcde	77 e
Nitralin	1.7	84 abcde	83 abcde
Bandane	39.2	85 abcde	88 abcde
Tricalcium arsenate	234.1	77 de	78 de

* Means followed by the same letter are not significantly different at the 5% level.

Table 19—Crabgrass control from bensulide applied to a Kentucky bluegrass and red fescue lawn treated 5 months earlier (November 1967) with activated charcoal.

Bensulide, kg/ha	Charcoal, kg/ha			
	0	112	224	448
	Control, %			
11.2	93 abcde*	78 de	40 f	31 f
22.4	99 a	93 abcde	80 cde	36 f
44.8	100 a	99 ab	98 abc	89 abcde

* Means followed by the same letter are not significantly different at the 5% level.

Table 20—Percent crabgrass control from herbicides applied to a Kentucky bluegrass and red fescue lawn treated 17 months earlier (November 1967) with activated charcoal.

Herbicide	Rate, kg/ha	Charcoal, kg/ha		
		0	224	448
		Control, %		
Bensulide	11.2	82 bc*	78 c	74 c
DCPA	11.2	97 a	95 a	95 a
Siduron	13.4	98 a	99 a	93 ab

* Means followed by the same letter are not significantly different at the 5% level.

Crabgrass control was not reduced from bensulide, DCPA, and siduron treatments made 17 months after charcoal application. Possibly most of the adsorptive sites on the charcoal particle were occupied. It was also noted that higher rates of charcoal caused greater reductions in bensulide effectiveness, while increased herbicide rates counteracted the retarding effect of charcoal.

One interesting observation of these studies was that grass treated with charcoal in the fall started to grow earlier or grew faster in early spring. There was a 90% increase in grass clipping weights in early April from areas treated with 448 kg/ha of charcoal. This temporary flush of growth may have been due to early soil warming from heat absorbed by the black charcoal or to the absorption of harmful substances in the soil.

ACKNOWLEDGMENTS

The author expresses his appreciation to the various companies for supplying herbicides and to ICI America, Inc. for activated charcoal (GRO-SAFE) and for partial financial support from both ICI America, Inc. and Stauffer Chemical Company.

APPENDIX

Common name	Chemical name
A-820	N-sec-butyl-4-tert-butyl-2,6-dinitroaniline
amitrole	3-amino-s-triazole
bandane	polychlorodicyclopentadiene isomers
benefin	N-butyl-N-ethyl-a,a,a-trifluoro-2,6-dinitro-p-toluidine
bensulide	O,O-diisopropyl phosphorodithioate S-ester with N-(2-mercaptoethyl)benzenesulfonamide
bentazon	3-isopropyl-1H-2,1,3-benzothiadiazin-(4)3H-one 2,2-dioxide
bromacil	5-bromo-3-sec-butyl-6-methyluracil
bromoxynil	3,5-dibromo-4-hydroxybenzonitrile
cacodylic acid	hydroxydimethylarsine oxide
dalapon	2,2-dichloropropionic acid
DCPA	dimethyl tetrachloroterephthalate
dicamba	3,6-dichloro-o-anisic acid
diesel fuel	- - - -
DSMA	disodium methanearsonate
endothal	7-oxabicyclo[2,2,1]heptane-2,3-dicarboxylic acid
gasoline	- - - -
hydraulic oil	- - - -
linuron	3-(3,4-dichlorophenyl)-1-methoxy-1-methylurea
MBR-8251	1,1,1-trifluoro-4'-(phenylsulfonyl)methanesulfono-o-toluidide
mecoprop	2-[(4-chloro-o-tolyl)oxy]propionic acid
MH	1,2-dihydro-3,6-pyridazinedione
nitralin	4-(methylsulfomyl)-2,6-dinitro-N,N-dipropylaniline
oxadiazon	2-tert-butyl-4-(2,4-dichloro-5-isopropoxyphenyl)-Δ^2-1,3,4-oxadiazoline-5-one
paraquat	1,1'-dimethyl-4,4'-bipyridinium ion
picloram	4-amino-3,5,6-trichloropicolinic acid
S-21634	1-methyl-4-phenylpyridinium chloride
siduron	1-(2-methylcyclohexyl)-3-phenylurea
silvex	2-(2,4,5-trichlorophenoxy)propionic acid
simazine	2-chloro-4,6-bis(ethylamino)-s-triazine
sodium arsenite	same
terbutol	2,6-di-tert-butyl-p-tolyl methylcarbamate
tricalcium arsenate	same
2,4-D	(2,4-dichlorophenoxy)acetic acid
2,4,5-T	(2,4,5-trichlorophenoxy)acetic acid

REFERENCES

1. AHRENS, J. F. 1965. Detoxification of Simazine- and atrazine-treated soil with activated carbon. Proc. Northeast. Weed Control Conf. 19:364–365.
2. DUICH, J. M., B. R. FLEMING, A. E. DUDECK, and G. J. SHOOP. 1962. The effect of certain pre-emergence chemicals on grass germination and seedling grasses. Proc. Northeast. Weed Control Conf. 16:479–483.
3. DUNCAN, D. B. 1955. Multiple range and multiple F tests. Biometrics 11:1–42.
4. JAGSCHITZ, J. A., and C. R. SKOGLEY. 1965. Pre-emergence and broadleaf herbicide effects on turfgrass establishment. Proc. Northeast. Weed Control Conf. 19:580–586.
5. ———, and ———. 1966. Turfgrass response to seedbed and seedling applications of preemergence and broadleaf herbicides. Proc. Northeast. Weed Control Conf. 20:554–560.
6. SCHUBERT, O. E. 1967. Can activated charcoal protect crops from herbicide injury. Crops Soils 19:10–11.

50

Effects of certain preemergence herbicides on *Diochondra* spp.

H.H. WILLIAMS

The response of *Dichondra* spp. to various application rates of five herbicides for the control of three weeds was investigated in a field study. In an effort to document probable causes of failure when herbicides are used, especially by the home gardener, the test sites selected were home lawns where environmental factors are usually quite variable. Due to wide variance in data accrued between replications, the results obtained were considered to be insufficiently definitive. Some quantitative and qualitative, measurements were developed delineating the comparative performance of these five herbicides as to effectiveness and toxicity at several application rates. Additional index words: Weed control, Ground cover, Lawns, Herban, Devrinol, Casoron, Telvar, Dymid.

Dichondra spp. is of limited value for lawns throughout the world (13). However, in southern California it is regarded as a desirable option to lawn grasses. Currently, the most limiting factor restricting its wider acceptance appears to be satisfactory weed control techniques.

Herbicides specific for dichondra have not received much attention. Thus, it is expedient that available herbicides be screened for the control of weeds in dichondra.

This study focuses on three weeds of diversified physiology and growth habit that frequently infest dichondra lawns. Attention is given to factors, including light quality and quantity, nutrient balance and levels, physical characteristics of the soil, and management practices such as irrigation and mowing, which have been observed to be interacting influences on herbicide activity. Extremes within these parameters are often significant among sites where dichondra is grown, especially in home lawns (15, 16).

Thus, more information is needed to develop specific recommendations for use of home lawn chemicals. Such information would be invaluable in determining why products have failed to perform up to expectations. Such data would find use in developing and screening new products and would facilitate their registration.

It is the intent of this study to generate such information.

MATERIALS AND METHODS

In July 1969, field studies were initiated to determine the comparative responses of three weed species, yellow oxalis (*Oxalis corniculatus* L.), marsh pennywort (*Hydrocotyle sibthorpioides* Lem.), and annual bluegrass (*Poa annua* L.) infesting a home lawn of dichondra to several concentrations of the following commercially available preemergence herbicides:

1) Herban (norea) 76% ai wettable powder (WP) 1-5-(3a,4,5,6,7,7a-hexahydro-4,7-methanoindanyl-3,3-dimethylurea (Hercules) (7, 8, 9)
2) Devrinol 50 ai WP (napropamide) 50% 2-(alpha-naphthoxy-N,N-diethylpropionamide (Stauffer) (12)
3) Casoron (dichlobenil) 50% ai WP & 4% granule, 2,6-dichlorobenzonitrile (Thompson-Hayward) (3, 10)
4) Telvar (monuron) 80% ai WP, 3-(p-chlorophenyl)-1,1-dimethylurea (DuPont) (1, 4, 7, 11)
5) Dymid (diphenamid) 80% ai WP, N,N-dimethyl-2,2-diphenylacetamide (Elanco) (5, 6, 7, 11).

These products were supplied through the courtesy of the respective manufacturers. Complete application data are given in Table 1.

One hundred plots, each 1.86 m², were laid out in randomized replications for 20 different treatments (2). Additionally, check plots were also established. Eighty of these plots were located on a home lawn in San Marion and included four replications of each treatment. Twenty plots were located in Monterey Park about 16 km (10 miles) away. (Data from this test site were generally not included in the tabulation of results.)

Table 1—Herbicides were applied on the following dates: July 3-4, 1969, July 9, 1969*, October 31, 1969, and February 8, 1970.

Herbicide, Trade name	Rate, kg of ai/ha
Herban	1.121
	2.242
	4.484
	8.968*
	13.452*
Devrinol	11.21
	22.42
	44.84
Casoron W-50	1.121
	2.242
	4.484
Casoron G-4	1.121
	2.242
	4.484
Telvar	0.56
	1.121
	2.242
Dymid	11.21
	22.42
	44.84

Note: First application: July 3-4, 1969, July 9, 1969*; Second application: October 31, 1969; Third application: February 8, 1970.

Wide diversity among environmental features of the sites selected was typical of conditions as they occur on many home lawns.

For each treatment, sufficient water was added to the herbicide to make a 600 ml suspension for each 9.29 m². One hundred twenty milliliters of this suspension was sprayed on each 1.86 m² plot with a Hayes Hose Sprayer (Hayes Spray Gun Co., Pasadena, Calif.)[1], providing four randomized replications per treatment at one site. The entire test site was then irrigated with from 1 to 2.5 cm of water, utilizing the existing sprinkler system. Up to three successive applications of each treatment were made between July 4, 1969 and February 8, 1970.

Initial population counts of the dichondra and all weed species present were taken by visual estimate of percentage stand within each plot. Evaluation of comparative responses to the activity of the herbicides was then based on a similar appraisal of increases or decreases in population with adjustments being made for density of stand and extent of distribution throughout the plot. A scale of 0 to 10 was used to indicate absence to full coverage, respectively.

Dichondra damage was rated on a scale of 0 to 10, with 0 indicating no damage and 10 representing complete obliteration. Periodic evaluation determined any subsequent loss or gain in density of stand. Results are presented as averages of the four replications at each observation time.

RESULTS AND DISCUSSION

Because of wide diversity in results between replications, data were not considered to be sufficiently definitive to warrant statistical analysis. Therefore, the conclusions reported here tend to be general.

The responses observed varied according to the specific herbicide, its application rate, its formulation, i.e., wettable powder (WP) versus granular, and the weed species involved, and the season of application. Wide variation in data among replications was noted and attributed to variation inherent in relevant site characteristics. See Tables 2 to 5 for specific data.

As can be noted in Table 6, Telvar and Dymid, when used at rates commonly included in fertilizer-pesticide combinations, produced poor control of annual bluegrass and oxalis. Telvar was less effective in the control of annual bluegrass than of oxalis at the highest rate (2.242 kg/ha) tolerable to the dichondra. Dymid was ineffective in oxalis control but reduced stands of annual bluegrass at the highest rate with no apparent toxicity to dichondra.

Devrinol showed promise as a control of pennywort and annual bluegrass but was ineffective on oxalis. However, rates higher than manufacturer recommendations appeared to be necessary (12). With Devrinol generally no toxicity was apparent except for a distinct yellowing and stunting of dichondra at the Monterey Park site that persisted for several weeks. This re-

---

[1]Mention of a trademark or proprietary product does not constitute an endorsement of the product and does not imply its approval to the exclusion of other products that may be suitable.

Table 2—Oxalis control over three successive periods and overall rating following three successive chemical treatments. Scale: 0 represents no control; 10 represents complete control. Minus quantities represent an increase in growth.

Chemical	Rate, kg of ai/ha	Time period*			
		1	2	3	Overall
Herban	1.121	2.5	1.75	0.75	3.25
	2.242	4.0	−0.5	−0.25	2.25
	4.484	3.25	0.25	0.25	3.5
	8.968	3.6	1.6	−1.3	4.0
	13.452	---	---	---	---
Devrinol	11.21	0.75	0.0	−1.0	−0.5
	22.42	3.0	0.25	0.25	3.0
	44.84	3.5	−3.25	1.5	2.5
Casoron	1.121	3.75	2.0	−5.0	3.25
(WP)	2.242	3.75	1.25	−3.0	2.0
	4.484	2.75	1.0	−1.25	2.75
Casoron	1.121	2.75	2.0	−0.75	3.0
(Granule)	2.242	---	---	---	---
	4.484	2.3	2.3	0.0	4.66
Telvar	0.56	2.75	0.75	−0.25	2.75
	1.121	2.5	1.25	0.0	3.75
	2.242	---	---	---	4.66
Dymid	11.21	3.0	0.0	−1.0	2.0
	22.42	−1.5	0.5	−0.75	−1.75
	44.84	0.75	−0.5	−0.25	0.25
Control	---	---	---	---	---

* 1 = July 9 to October 29, 1969; 2 = October 29, 1969 to January 27, 1970; 3 = January 27 to April 18, 1970. Overall = July 9, 1969 to April 18, 1970.

Table 3—Pennywort control over three successive periods and overall rating following three successive chemical treatments. Scale: 0 represents no control; 10 represents complete control. Minus quantities represent an increase in growth.

Chemical	Rate, kg of ai/ha	Time period*			
		1	2	3	Overall
Herban	1.121	0.5	0.0	4.25	4.75
	2.242	4.0	−0.5	−0.25	2.25
	4.484	2.75	0.75	1.0	4.5
Devrinol	11.21	0.0	1.75	1.0	3.75
	22.42	2.75	3.0	0.25	6.0
	44.84	3.3	3.0	0.66	7.0
Casoron	1.121	−0.25	3.75	1.25	1.0
(WP)	2.242	−0.5	−1.5	6.0	4.0
	4.484	1.25	0.25	3.75	3.75
Casoron (G)	1.121	4.0	1.0	0.0	5.0
Control	---	---	---	---	---

* 1 = July 9 to October 29, 1969; 2 = October 29, 1969 to January 27, 1970; 3 = January 27 to April 18, 1970. Overall = July 9, 1969 to April 18, 1970.

Table 4—Annual bluegrass control over three successive periods and overall rating following three successive chemical treatments. Scale: 0 represents no control; 10 represents complete control. Minus quantities represent an increase in growth.

Chemical	Rate, kg of ai/ha	Time period*			
		1	2	3	Overall
Herban	1.121	−0.5	−1.75	2.5	2.5
	2.242	1.75	0.0	1.25	3.0
	4.484	2.3	0.0	0.0	2.3
	8.968	4.0	−4.0	0.5	−0.5
	13.452	---	---	---	1.5
Devrinol	11.21	5.25	2.75	−0.5	7.5
	22.42	6.5	0.5	2.5	7.5
	44.84	4.25	1.75	0.0	6.0
Casoron	1.121	4.25	2.0	−0.25	7.0
(WP)	2.242	4.5	−3.5	0.0	2.0
	4.484	4.25	−2.5	−0.75	1.0
Casoron	1.121	3.25	1.5	−0.5	5.0
(Granule)	2.242	2.0	---	---	2.0
	4.484	1.5	−3.5	0.3	−1.75
Telvar	0.56	1.75	1.5	−0.75	2.75
	1.121	−2.5	0.25	1.25	1.25
	2.242	2.3	5.3	−3.6	3.0
Dymid	11.21	2.5	−1.75	1.0	1.75
	22.42	−0.5	−0.25	3.25	2.5
	44.84	3.6	3.3	0.66	4.75
Control	---	−1.0	−4.0	−3.0	−4.5

* 1 = July 9 to October 29, 1969; 2 = October 29, 1969 to January 27, 1970; 3 = January 27 to April 18, 1970. Overall = July 9, 1969 to April 18, 1970.

Table 5—Stand of dichondra and apparent herbicidal toxicity over three successive periods following two successive chemical treatments. Scale: (A) 0 represents no dichondra; 10 represents full distribution over the plot (not necessarily weed free). (B) 0 represents no apparent toxicity; 10 represents complete obliteration.

Chemical	Rate, kg of ai/ha	Percent of *Dichondra* (A) and toxicity rating (B)	Time periods*			
			0	1	2	3
Herban	1.121	A	9.1	8.5	10.0	10.0
		B		1.25	0.0	0.0
	2.242	A	9.25	8.75	10.0	10.0
		B		1.0	0.0	0.0
	4.484	A	9.1	9.4	10.0	10.0
		B		0.75	0.0	0.0
	8.968	A	7.5	6.0	---	---
		B		3.75	--- †	---
	13.452	A	8.5	4.5	---	---
		B		4.25	--- †	---
Devrinol	11.21	A	7.5	8.5	10.0	10.0
		B		0.0	0.0	0.0
	22.42	A	9.0	8.5	10.0	10.0
		B		1.25	0.0	0.25

(continued on next page)

Chemical	Rate		0	1	2	3
	44.84	A	9.25	7.3	9.1	10.0
		B		1.0	0.0	0.6
Casoron (WP)	1.121	A	8.75	7.75	10.0	8.25
		B		1.75	0.0	2.25
	2.242	A	8.75	7.1	10.0†	10.0
		B		3.5	0.0	0.25
	4.484	A	8.5	8.1	10.0	---
		B		5.5	0.0†	---
Casoron (Granule)	1.121	A	8.5	8.1	10.0	---
		B		1.75	0.0	---
	2.242	A	8.5	7.5	4.0	---
		B		3.75	0.0†	9.25
	4.484	A	8.0	3.0	---	---
		B		7.0	--- †	---
Telvar	0.56	A	9.5	9.5	10.0	10.0
		B		0.0	0.0	0.0
	1.121	A	8.1	8.75	9.6	---
		B		0.75	0.0	1.3
	2.242	A	7.75	6.75	---	---
		B		2.0	1.3†	---
Dymid	11.21	A	9.1	9.0	10.0	10.0
		B		0.0	0.0	0.0
	22.42	A	7.75	8.2	10.0	---
		B		0.0	0.0	---
	44.84	A	7.5	7.5	---	---
		B		1.25	---	1.75
Control	---	A	6.6	7.0	7.0	---
		B		0.0	0.0	---

* Time periods: 0 = Initial
1 = July 9 to August 16, 1969
2 = August 16 to October 29, 1969
3 = October 29, 1969 to January 27, 1970
First application: July 3–4, 1969
Second application: October 31 to November 1, 1969

† Exceptions: Number of replications

Number of replications	Chemical	Rate, kg of ai/ha
3	Casoron W-50	2.242
4	Casoron W-50	4.484
2	Casoron G-4	2.242
4	Cosoron G-4	4.484
1	Telvar	2.242
4	Herban	8.968
4	Herban	13.452

sponse, considered aesthetically acceptable, was observed only at the high rate of treatment (44.84 kg/ha).

Herban gave moderate control of pennywort, oxalis, and annual bluegrass in descending order at rates 4.484 kg/ha or less and with low toxicity. Higher rates were prohibitively toxic.

Casoron gave significant control of annual bluegrass at the 1.121 kg/ha rate as a wettable powder and was decreasingly less effective on oxalis and pennywort. The same rate as Casoron granule caused a marked reduction in

Table 6—Summary: Comparative response of three weed species to treatments of five herbicides at various concentration levels and application times and the response of dichondra and apparent toxicity. 0 represents no reduction in stand; 10 represents complete obliteration.

| Chemical | Rate of ai/ha | Response | | | | Toxicity* |
		Oxalis	Pennywort	*Poa annua*	*Dichondra**	
Herban	1.121	3.25	4.75	2.5	0.6	1.25
	2.242	2.25	2.25	3.0	0.5	1.0
	4.484	3.5	4.5	2.3	−0.3†	0.75
	8.968	4.0	---	−0.5	1.5	3.75
	13.452	---	---	1.5	4.0	4.15
Devrinol	11.21	−0.5	3.75	7.5	1.0	0.0
	22.42	3.0	6.0	7.5	0.5	1.25
	44.84	2.5	7.0	6.0	1.95	1.0
Casoron (WP)	1.121	3.25	1.0	7.0	1.0	1.75
	2.242	2.0	4.0	2.0	1.65	3.5
	4.484	2.75	3.75	1.0	0.4	5.5
Casoron (Granule)	1.121	3.0	5.0	5.0	0.4	1.75
	2.242	---	---	2.0	1.0	3.75
	4.484	4.66	---	1.75	5.0	7.0
Telvar	0.56	2.75	---	2.75	0.0	0.0
	1.121	3.75	---	1.25	0.65	0.75
	2.242	4.66	---	3.0	1.0	2.0
Dymid	11.21	2.0	---	1.75	0.1	0.0
	22.42	−1.75	---	2.5	0.45	0.0
	44.84	0.25	---	4.75	0.0	1.25

* Date of August 16, 1969.   † Minus quantity represents an increase in stand.

the stand of pennywort. Higher rates of both formulations were intolerably toxic. Granular applications of Casoron produced greater injury than wettable powder at comparable rates.

Much additional research appears to be necessary to correlate site variability and effective application rates before valid recommendations can be made for extensive use of these herbicides by home gardeners.

ACKNOWLEDGMENT

The author gratefully acknowledges the assistance of Mr. Thomas Jacobs, student in Turfgrass Science at Los Angeles Trade-Technical College, in the initial phases of this study. Dr. and Mrs. Robert E. Lovett of San Marino and Mr. and Mrs. Lee H. Wakeman graciously tolerated the use and abuse of their respective front lawns for these experiments.

REFERENCES

1. BINGHAM, S. W. 1972. The nature of biochemical mechanism of herbicide selectivity. p. 27–47. *In* R. E. Schmidt et al. (ed.) Proc. Scotts Turfgrass Res. Conf., Vol. 3. O. M. Scott and Sons Co., Marysville, Ohio
2. DAY, B. E., et al. 1959. Weed control workbook. Univ. Calif. Davis, Davis, Calif.
3. DOWNING, C., et al. 1970. Studies on the initial effect and residual characteristics of several preemergent herbicides in relation to overseeding and *Poa annua* control. Calif. Turfgrass Culture 18(3):17–18.

4. E. I. DUPONT DE NEMOURS AND COMPANY. 1963. Telvar: Monuron weed killer. Tech. data GC-18614. Wilmington, DE 19899.

5. ELANCO PRODUCTS COMPANY. 1965a. Dymid for selective weed control in dichondra. Product information bull. Indianapolis, IN 46206.

6. ————. 1965b. Technical report on Dymid, a selective preemergence herbicide. Rep. No. G5-1. Indianapolis, IN 46206.

7. ELMORE, C. L. 1966. Spotted spurge control in turf. Field trial report. Agr. Ext. Serv. Univ. Calif., Davis, Calif.

8. HERCULES POWDER COMPANY. 1964. Hercules 7531: Experimental selective preemergence herbicide. Tech. data Ad-1. Wilmington, DE 19899.

9. ————. Plant tolerance to Herban. Wilmington, DE 19899.

10. PHILIPS-DUPHAR, N. V. 1970. 2,6-dichlorobenzonitrile. *In* Herbicide handbook. Weed Sci. Soc. Amer. Monograph 3:139–145.

11. PRESTON WEED CONTROL COMPANY. 1964–65. Weed control manual. Whittier, CA 90602.

12. STAUFFER CHEMICAL COMPANY. 1972. Devrinol. Technical information release. Agr. Res. Center. Mountain View, CA 94040.

13. THARP, B. C., and Marshal C. JOHNSTON. 1961. Recharacterization of dichondra (Convolvulaceae) and a revision of the North American species. Brittonia 13:346–360.

14. WILLIAMS, H. H. 1964. Physiology and morphology of dichondra as related to cultural practices. *In* All about dichondra. LASCA LVS. 14(3):54–63. Los Angeles State and County Arboretum. Arcadia, CA 91006.

15. YOUNGNER, V. B. 1972. Ecological forces affecting weeds and their control. p. 1–25. *In* R. E. Schmidt et al. (ed.) Scotts Turfgrass Res. Conf. Proc. O. M. Scott & Sons Co., Marysville, OH 43040.

16. ————, and F. J. NUDGE. 1968. Chemical control of annual bluegrass as related to vertical mowing. Calif. Turfgrass Culture 18(3):17–18.

17. ————, and S. E. SPAULDING. 1964. Dichondra in California. *In* All about dichondra. Los Angeles State and County Arboretum LVS. 14(3):51–53. Los Angeles State and County Arboretum. Arcadia, CA 91006.

51

Frit fly damage to turfgrass

S.-O. DAHLSSON

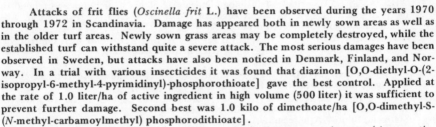
Attacks of frit flies (*Oscinella frit* L.) have been observed during the years 1970 through 1972 in Scandinavia. Damage has appeared both in newly sown areas as well as in the older turf areas. Newly sown grass areas may be completely destroyed, while the established turf can withstand quite a severe attack. The most serious damages have been observed in Sweden, but attacks have also been noticed in Denmark, Finland, and Norway. In a trial with various insecticides it was found that diazinon [O,O-diethyl-O-(2-isopropyl-6-methyl-4-pyrimidinyl)-phosphorothioate] gave the best control. Applied at the rate of 1.0 liter/ha of active ingredient in high volume (500 liter) it was sufficient to prevent further damage. Second best was 1.0 kilo of dimethoate/ha [O,O-dimethyl-S-(*N*-methyl-carbamoylmethyl) phosphorodithioate].

In Scandinavia the frit fly is well known for its damage to spring oats (*Avena sativa* L.). Recent attacks in turf areas were unexpected. Since attacks outside Scandinavia have been reported to result in widespread damage and because of the great economic importance of the possible damage to turf, it is recommended that the public be made aware of the frit fly and its larva. Additional index words: Insects, Diazinon, Dimethoate, Fenitrothion, Methyoxychlor, Insecticides, *Oscinella frit* L.

BIOLOGY OF THE FRIT FLY

The frit fly (*Oscinella frit* L.) belongs to the family Chloropidae. The fly is 1 to 2 mm long and black. At first the larva is 1 mm long and white. It grows to 3 mm and becomes yellow-whitish (Johansson, 1960; Andersson, 1967).

The eggs are laid partly on the ground and partly on the plants (Jones, 1969). In turfgrass it is likely that the eggs are laid on the leaf blade or in the sheaths. When the larva is hatched it moves down in the sheath and feeds on the main shoot. The result is death of the main shoot.

Under normal Scandinavian conditions there are three generations of the fly per season (Thygesen, 1971). The insect passes the winter in the larva stage and as soon as the temperature is high enough, over 12 C (Andersson, 1967), the life cycle continues. The first two generations come about late May and late June, and the third generation normally appears in late August or in the beginning of September. The greatest number of flies appears in the third generation, but this development depends very much on the weather.

PREVIOUS ATTACKS

In recent literature, the frit fly is described by Johansson (1960), Andersson (1967), Skirde (1967), Jones (1969), Thygesen (1971), Franz (1971), Dahlsson (1971, 1972).

Although knowledge of frit fly attacks was known to occur in other countries, the attacks in Scandinavian turf areas were unexpected. In 1970 the damage was of great economic importance.

CONTROL TRIAL 1971 THROUGH 1972

An experiment was initiated to evaluate four insecticides for the control of frit flies. The following herbicides were applied to turfgrass:
1) Control
2) Diazinon (0.05 liter/100 m^2 Basudin, 20%, 200 g/liter)
3) Fenitrothion [O,O-dimethyl O-(4-nitro-m-tolyl) phosphorothioate] (0.02 liter/100 m^2 Folithion E, 560 g/liter)
4) Dimethoate (0.025 liter/100 m^2 Dimetoat NA 40, 430 g/liter)
5) Methoxychlor [1,1,1-trichloro-2,2-bis(p-methoxyphenyl)ethane] (0.05 liter/100 m^2 BT Metoxyklor, 375 g/kg)
High volume = 500 liter/ha

To make sure of an attack, *Festuca rubra* L. var. *rubra* 'Reptans' was sown in three replications at three different times. Thereby, it was possible to offer acceptable plant material to the larva during a longer period of the year. Very few attacks were noted from the first and second generations of the fly. The third generation resulted in a heavy attack in older turf as well as in the younger grass, and afforded an opportunity to determine the best insecticides. For detailed information the reader is referred to earlier papers by Dahlsson (1971, 1972).

RESULTS

It is clear that no preventive spraying is possible. That means the spraying has to be done when the fly or the larva is present. When risks of attacks are high, it is necessary to watch the area intensively in order to spray at the proper time.

The insecticide diazinon gave the best control. Since the insecticide must come into contact with the larvae or the insect, a second spraying is recommended. The interval between the two sprayings should be 10 to 14 days. Second best control was obtained from dimethoate.

In the experiment conducted in 1972 the insect attacks were not as intensive. Consequently, there were smaller differences among the different insecticides, although the results reconfirmed the findings from 1971.

DISCUSSION

Seemingly a large population of frit flies were built up during 1971 and 1972. As a result there were good reasons to expect serious attacks in the Spring of 1973. But for some unknown reason such attacks did not occur in 1973. Only a few single flies were found, and no damage of importance was reported.

There have been attempts to explain the attacks of the frit fly and the rapid multiplication of the population. One suggestion was that larger areas for seed production gave the flies better possibilities to survive. It is also claimed that an increased use of fungicides against *Fusarium* killed the natural enemies of the frit fly such as fungi and bacteria. The results of this experiment do not suggest any explanation for the rapid multiplication of the frit fly population. The main purpose of this investigation was to find a practical way of controlling the flies. The results provide us with information on insecticides for best control if there is another invasion of the fly.

REFERENCES

1. ANDERSSON, Hugo. 1967. Inventering av förekomst av fritflugor (Diptera, Cloropidae) i stråsäd 1961–63. Statens Växtskyddsanstalts Medd. 14:115, 1–27.
2. DAHLSSON, Sven-Ove. 1971. Fritflugan—skadegörare i gräsmattor. Weibulls Gräs-tips. Dec. 1971:3–9. (English summary, p. 8).
3. ———. 1972. Mer om fritflugan. Weibulls Gräs-tips. Dec. 1972:28–29. (English Summary, p. 29).
4. FRANZ, W. 1971. Ein neuer Rasenschädling. Gesunde Pflanzen Heft 7, Juli 1971.
5. JOHANSSON, Erik. 1960. Skadegörande flugarter i stråsäd och vallgräs och möjligheterna för deras bekämpning. Statens Växtskyddsanstalts Medd. 11:78, 459–471.
6. JONES, M. G. 1969. Oviposition of frit fly (*Oscinella frit* L.) on oat seedlings and subsequent larval development. J. Appl. Ecol. 6:411–424.
7. SKIRDE, W. 1967. Oscinis frit—ein Rasenschädling. Rasen und Rasengräser H. 1.45–47.
8. THYGESEN, Th. 1971. Pas på fritfluen ved anlaeg af plaener. Gartner Tidende Nr 33, 1971, 453.

52

Biology and control of the ground pearl in relation to turfgrass infestation[1]

C.A. KOUSKOLEKAS & R.L. SELF

The ground pearl *Margarodes meridionalis* Morr., (Homoptera: Coccoidea: Margarodidae), is a subterranean scale insect that infests the roots of lawn grasses and is of major concern to homeowners.

Research on biology and control of ground pearls throughout the United States has led generally to inconclusive results. Investigations on this pest were conducted in Alabama in from 1968 through 1971. Some aspects of its biology were clarified but, in general, its life history remains incompletely understood. The number of ground pearls varies considerably even within small infested areas and this is a handicap to several lines of research.

The quantitative relationship between number of ground pearls present and damage to grass is unknown. The direct damage to lawns frequently is masked by several factors. Proper lawn care, primarily through irrigation and fertilization, helps the grass overcome the damage but the beneficial effect may be only temporary.

Available information indicates that no insecticide has been consistently effective. In Alabama, applications of Thimet + Zinophos, Dasanit, and Dyfonate at 13.5 kg/ha reduced the populations more than other insecticides tested. The relative susceptibility of the developmental stages to insecticides is unknown; therefore, timing of insecticidal applications for maximum effectiveness has not been established. There are promising approaches to chemical control and these are worthy of investigation. Additional index words: Scale Insect, Insecticides, Turfgrasses.

Ground pearls are scale insects (Homoptera: Coccoidea: Margarodidae) with subterranean habits. They often infest the roots of lawn grasses in the southeastern United States. These insects are called ground pearls because of the pearl-like appearance of cysts which enclose the immature stages. The insects feed with sucking mouthparts that extend through the wall of the cyst and are inserted into the grass root. There are several species of subterranean margarodid scales in North America. The species present in Alabama, *Margarodes meridionalis* Morr., is of increasing concern to homeowners because of widespread and extensive damage to lawns. Problems also are encountered in grass farms. In other states, it is also a pest of golf courses.

[1]Contribution from Auburn University Agricultural Experiment Station, Auburn, AL 36830.

Little is known about biology and control of this insect. In recent years, due to the importance of the problem, investigations have been initiated at several institutions. Usually the projects were either abandoned or results were never published, probably because of time-consuming procedures involved or inconclusive findings. As a result, there is currently a lack of information on important aspects, such as survey methods, sampling techniques, procedures for processing the soil samples to recover the pearls, laboratory rearing techniques, and quantitative relationships of population levels to damage.

LIFE HABIT AND BIOLOGY STUDIES

Studies conducted at the Auburn University Agricultural Experiment Station provided the following information on biology of this pest. Cysts of various sizes are found in the soil throughout the year. Most cysts are 0.5 to 2.0 mm in diameter. Encysted stages survive for long periods under drought conditions or without food supply. There is probably one generation a year. There are indications, however, that some individuals require 2 years for completion of the life cycle. Females reach maturity and emerge from the cysts in late May. The wingless female moves in the soil for a short time, then settles down and secretes waxy filaments that cover the body completely. Eggs (100/female) are deposited parthenogenetically within this cottony matrix. Oviposition begins in June and continues into July. Egg hatching extends into August. After hatching, the young (crawlers) start feeding on grass roots, and cover themselves through formation of a cyst. Males are considered rare. However, several males were obtained during our investigations.

All favorite lawn grasses, namely centipedegrass *Eremochloa ophiuroides* (Munro) Hack., hybrid bermudagrasses *Cynodon* spp., zoysia *Zoysia matrella* (L.) Merr., and St. Augustinegrass *Stenotaphrum secundatum* (Walt.) Kuntze, were found infested. Damage to lawns is manifested as irregular areas where the grass is unthrifty or dying. However, the quantitative relationship between number of cysts and damage to grass is unknown. In addition, the detrimental effect to the grass is masked frequently by the interplay of several biological and physical factors, such as fungi, nematodes, irrigation, and fertilization. To further complicate the picture, the number of ground pearls varies considerably from place to place even within a small infested area. Cysts may abound within a ring of infested grass whereas a few centimeters away the count may be zero. It appears that the number of cysts present is more consistent at the interphase between damaged and healthy grass. This variability of the populations is a serious handicap to satisfactory sampling.

EXPERIMENTS ON CHEMICAL CONTROL

Chemical control tests were conducted at three locations. Several tests based on small plots 0.3 to 1.0 m^2 led to inconsistent results, suggesting that plot size is a limiting factor. Personal communications with other researchers revealed that inconclusive findings also were the rule in other states.

Promising results were obtained in a replicated experiment in 1969–70 when 25 m^2 plots were used. Six insecticides, most in granular formulation were tested for effectiveness on a heavily infested centipedegrass lawn at 13.5 kg of active ingredient/ha. This experiment was initiated on the assumption that the crawlers were the most vulnerable stage of this pest. Accordingly, the lawn was treated in July 1969 when crawlers were beginning to hatch. The following spring the grass was properly fertilized and received abundant water. Posttreatment sampling was done in May 1970 prior to emergence of the new generation females. Samples consisted of soil cores 5 cm in diameter and 8 cm deep taken with a bulb planter. Four samples were collected per replicate. To recover the cysts, the following procedure was used: the grass blades were sheared off, each soil core was broken by hand, and the soil was placed in a liter jar 3/4-filled with water; the jar was shaken for 1 min, allowed to stand for 1 min, and the water was decanted through sieves to collect the floating cysts. The above procedure was repeated once; cysts were also collected from the surface of the precipitated soil. Relative effectiveness of treatments was based on the number of cysts recovered per sample. Only cysts 1 mm in diameter or larger were counted.

The results showed that Thimet [O,O-diethyl S-(ethylthio)-methyl phosphorodithioate] + Zinophos (O,O-diethyl O-2-pyrazinyl phosphorothioate), Dasanit [O,O-diethyl O-(p-(methylsulfinyl)-phenyl) phosphorothioate] and Dyfonate (O-ethyl S-phenyl ethylphosphorodithioate) (manufactured by American Cyanamid Co., Princeton, N. J., Chemagro Corp., Kansas City, Mo., and Stauffer Chemical Co., Mountain View, Ca., respectively.) reduced the populations more than other materials tested. Maximum reduction in the number of cysts was 80%. Additional observations indicated that proper fertilization and irrigation were helpful in improving the appearance of the grass which showed substantial recovery by July 1970. The following year, however, the lawn was grossly neglected and the grass appeared as damaged in Summer 1971 as it had in 1969 before treatment. The number of cysts had increased also to nearly pretreatment levels.

DISCUSSION

Although the beneficial effects in this test were short lived, the findings indicated that chemical control of ground pearls is feasible. Results further suggested that high level of control is necessary for long-term protection of lawns, that the hatching crawlers may not be the most vulnerable stage, and that good lawn care is important in reducing the damage.

At present, there is no single insecticidal treatment that guarantees long-range suppression of ground pearl populations. Moreover, the relative susceptibility of this pest's developmental stages to insecticides is unknown and consequently timing of applications for maximum effectiveness has not been established. Promising approaches to effective control include insecticidal treatments against the emerging females, applications of systemic insecticides in early spring against the developing stages, and, better yet, multiple applications during the year. Research along these lines undoubtedly will contribute valuable information toward solution of this difficult problem.

ABSTRACTS

Abstracts of all papers not published herein but presented at the Conference are included below to round off this Section. These abstracts, unlike the printed papers, have not been refereed.

SECTION 6 ABSTRACT—NEW TURF PROBLEM(S): RESISTANCE TO CHLORDANE IN THE JAPANESE BEETLE AND ATTENDANT THATCH

Continuous use of the insecticide chlordane for 10 or more years to control various species of grubs in turf on golf courses at two locations in Ohio led to the development of a strain of Japanese beetle, *Popillia japonica* Newman, resistant to chlordane and contributor to the accumulation of a deep layer of thatch.

The toxicity of soil, fortified with chlordane at 4.5 and 9.0 kg AI/ha, to third-instar larvae from these golf courses and from a previously untreated area at another location was determined in the laboratory. Mature beetles were also treated with dilutions of 0.0001%, 0.001%, 0.01%, 0.1%, and 1.0% of the following chemicals:

chlordane:	Octachloro-4,7-methanotetrahydroindane
aldrin:	Hexachlorohexahydro-endo,exo-dimethanonaphthalene
dieldrin:	Hexachloroepoxyoctahydro-endo,exo-dimethanonaphthalene
heptachlor:	Heptachlorotetrahydro-4,7-methanoindene
diazinon:	o,o-Diethyl-o-(2-isopropyl-4-methyl-6-primidinyl)phosphorothioate
carbaryl:	1-Naphthyl methylcarbamate

The chemicals were applied by the Potter Spray Tower method (C. Potter, Ann. Appl. Biol. 28(2):142–169, 1941).

The results of the larval tests showed high levels of resistance to chlordane. The adult test showed high levels of resistance to chlordane and cross-resistance to aldrin, dieldrin, and heptachlor. Diazinon and carbaryl were equitoxic to adults from both locations.

Replicated field tests at both locations on control of the resistant larvae showed that despite extensive irrigation immediately following applications of diazinon and other organophosphate insecticides, unacceptable control was obtained. These compounds provided excellent control when little or no thatch was present. Chemical analysis of the thatch and soil showed that adsorption into the thatch was a primary reason for the poor control achieved when considerable thatch was present.—H. D. Niemczyk, Ohio Agricultural Research and Development Center.

DISCUSSION

R. L. DUBLE—How long does the inhibition of root pegging persist after the application of DCPA?

S. W. BINGHAM—In some cases DCPA can reduce rooting from stolons for an entire growing season. In most instances inhibition of bermudagrass pegging into the soil is on the order of 1 to 2 months. In these instances the ground could be 70 to 80% covered with stolons and vegetation, but one could pass his hand under the stolons and pick the entire cover up or roll it back.

R. P. FREEBORG—What effect does TIBA have on rhizome counts of *Poa pratensis*?

B. A. RIEGER—We attempted to find differences in rhizome production, but in the short period of our experiments no differences could be observed.

R. E. ENGEL—Have available arsenic levels been monitored from month to month on any of the areas where *Poa annua* restriction is being studied?

R. P. FREEBORG—No, analysis was made only after thinning of plots was observed.

W. H. DANIEL—Those plots that had prior arsenic treatments in the spring had touch-up treatments later and for the first time *Poa annua* response was observed. Treatments with liquid phosphorus fertilizer applied in light applications caused plants to grow normally again. Use of liquid phosphorus fertilizers is considered an important corrective treatment under these conditions. Other chemicals are being used now for the control of *Poa annua*. These offer a greater degree of finesse in management, if the applicators of these growth regulators are well informed. I would suggest that at least within the technical service a counteractant product be available for corrective treatments if and when necessary.

G. C. NUTTER—What are recommended fertilization and clipping practices for bermudagrass establishment on plots where weed control tests are conducted?

B. J. JOHNSON—Fertility level should be maintained at an optimum growing level. The grass should maintain an active growth rate. Clipping heights of about 3.5 cm for Tifway bermudagrass and 5.0 cm for centipedegrass and St. Augustinegrass have proven satisfactory.

D. V. WADDINGTON—When activated charcoal is used to nullify the harmful effects of chemicals on turfgrass, how much water is used to apply the charcoal, does the amount of water vary depending on whether charcoal was applied to soil or grass, and does watering-in improve effectiveness of charcoal applied to grass?

J. A. JAGSCHITZ—We used from 2,338 to 7,015 liters/ha of water. This amount of water was used for convenience in application. We didn't want to have any sprayer problems and we wanted uniform application to the soil or grass surface. We sprayed right onto the soil surface and only mixed it into the top 2.5 cm. As far as getting it onto the turf is concerned, we timed our application so that it would be very close to the time the chemical was applied. Since no rain fell between chemical and charcoal applications, we tried to use as little water as possible in applying the charcoal. The objective was to place the charcoal on the grass where the chemical was. Now with a material like Simazine where we had good results, the chemical must have been on the grass blades since this material goes to the roots with time. If it had rained following Simazine application and the chemical had moved to the soil and then into the plant, results would have been different. Timing of application is very important. Where the chemical is absorbed by the root and on or in the root zone, then the charcoal must be applied with sufficient water to reach this area. Most spray equipment can handle 0.45 kg of charcoal/3.8 liters of water without any problems.

C. M. SWITZER—Is there any interaction between charcoal activity and soil type? I assume that there would be differences in charcoal effectiveness in reducing harmful effects of chemicals depending on soil properties.

J. A. JAGSCHITZ —Our experiments were conducted on a silt loam soil. I would expect somewhat different results under other soil conditions because soil minerals and organic matter could differ. Organic molecules would compete with the chemical for adsorption sites on the charcoal. However, a handful of charcoal has an adsorptive area comparable with that of a football field and probably there are sufficient sites for both natural soil materials as well as herbicide residues when charcoal is used at rates of 560 kg/ha.

D. L. KLINGMAN—Are the phenoxy herbicides effective on broadleaf weeds when 24 hours intervene between herbicide treatment and application of charcoal?

J. A. JAGSCHITZ —In our experiments we were not evaluating effectiveness of weed control. Your basic question was, would the charcoal absorb the herbicide? I believe that the herbicide would be effective since during the 24-hour period the phenoxy herbicides enter the plant system and initiate control. In other field herbicide weed control tests we have had good results where heavy rains washed the materials off of leaf surfaces where entry is usually necessary for good control. From a practical point of view, if too much herbicide has been applied to the turf, the first concern would be to prevent turfgrass injury, degree of weed control would be secondary. In this instance the charcoal should be applied as quickly as possible. Also, we feel that a herbicide once in contact with the charcoal is still available to do its job. But, it is unavailable in the sense that it is not mobile as it was before. Thus, herbicides in contact with charcoal will go through degradation just as they would under other conditions.

W. A. SMALL—We have had experience with charcoal in St. Louis, Missouri, on high clay soil. In these experiments we have duplicated the same sort of results obtained in Rhode Island using rates of from 224 to 336 kg/ha of charcoal. We used about the same amount of water as a carrier as was used in the Rhode Island studies. We found that in using charcoal on turf, washing it from the leaves improves the appearance of the turf. This can be accomplished without losing effectiveness of the treatment when removal from foliage is timed immediately prior to drying.

J. A. JAGSCHITZ —I don't believe that in all situations the charcoal should be immediately washed off the grass. This may have worked well with bensulide on high clay soils in Missouri. If the herbicide residue is in the soil beneath the grass, then it should be watered-in so that the grass will not look black and the charcoal will get to the site where the residue problem is. If the chemical is applied by mistake to the surface of the blades and it will not cause problems until it is washed off and into the root zone where it enters the plant (Simazine for example), then I would want the charcoal to be on the blades so the residue will be adsorbed more readily. More work in regard to the interaction of charcoal treatments, watering, and various herbicides is needed.

Turfgrass culture

Section VII

53

Alternative method of greens management[1]

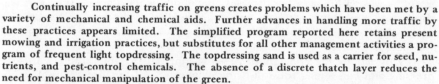

J. H. MADISON, J. L. PAUL, W. B. DAVIS

Continually increasing traffic on greens creates problems which have been met by a variety of mechanical and chemical aids. Further advances in handling more traffic by these practices appears limited. The simplified program reported here retains present mowing and irrigation practices, but substitutes for all other management activities a program of frequent light topdressing. The topdressing sand is used as a carrier for seed, nutrients, and pest-control chemicals. The absence of a discrete thatch layer reduces the need for mechanical manipulation of the green.

This report discusses topdressing composition, frequency of application, rate of buildup, and problems of mixing and handling. The effects of such a program are considered on playability, on thatch development, pests, and labor requirements.

The program is being evaluated over several years to define any long-term problems. On the basis of the first 16 months of continuing test, results indicate that the simplified program based on topdressing presents an economical alternative to traditional management programs. Additional index words: *Agrostis,* Turfgrass, Topdressing.

Greens management has become more complicated and uses more labor and a larger part of an increasing budget than ever before. Causes include increased traffic and higher aesthetic standards. Some golf courses in California now receive traffic of more than 100,000 players each year.

Increased fertilizer and water have been used to stimulate more growth for the self-healing repair of greens. However, increased moisture and succulence have led to more soil compaction and pest problems. Compaction has been relieved by hole punching operations which prepare a seed bed for weeds such as *Poa annua* L.

A green maintenance program during the growing season may include the following: daily mowing; daily irrigation plus 0 to 2 times a day syringing, depending on weather; fertilization at 2- to 4-week intervals; spraying with iron sulfate solution at 2- to 4-week intervals; monthly to annual use of arsenates for *Poa annua* control; verticutting from 3 to 10 or more times a year; coring at 3- to 16-week intervals; topdressing 2 to 4 times a year; overseeding in season; and applying insecticides at 3- to 6-week intervals, fungi-

[1]Contribution of the Department of Environmental Horticulture, College of Agricultural and Environmental Sciences, University of California, Davis, CA 95616.

cides at 3-day to 3-week intervals, and herbicides two or three times a year. To carry out these operations may require a capital investment in equipment on the order of $10,000 at 1973 prices. With traffic continuing to increase, it seems to us that if such a program fails to grow a desirable green turf, there is little more we can do to stimulate the grass.

An alternative approach to maintenance appears necessary, and it is such an alternate program that is reported here.

In 1958 some tests were run with compost made by the Dano process. A load of compost was dumped adjacent to a test plot of bentgrass. The evening sea breezes at Davis, California, daily blew some of the light, dry fraction of compost across one corner of one test plot. The elevation of the grade was increased up to 10 cm in 2 years by the wind-drifted compost. The grass in this naturally topdressed area was outstanding in quality except in a period of high temperatures during the second summer when it suffered "scald" injury.

Subsequent experiments with topdressing in 1960 showed the following. When topdressing contained peat, fir bark, or redwood sawdust, the higher the organic content of the topdressing, the less the turf quality and the more prone it was to hot weather diseases. Secondly, when a greens-type turf was topdressed monthly with sand only, turf quality at the end of 2 years was equal to that of any plot even though the topdressed area was neither sprayed for pests nor cored.

This led to the concept of a management program centered on topdressing and containing the following elements. All fertilizers would be applied in the topdressing; all pesticides would be applied in the topdressing; coring, thatching and vertical mowing would be replaced by topdressing; turfgrass seed in the topdressing would provide continual competition with weed seeds.

Among benefits anticipated were: operations reduced to mowing, irrigating (including syringing), and topdressing; elimination of soil and thatch layers which arise from semiannual topdressing; no new thatch formed, as stolons would be continually buried; maintenance of existing good infiltration rates by continuous creation of a fresh surface uncontaminated by fines, blown or carried in; reduction of weeds by burial of seeds, by eliminating mechanical operations that disturb the surface to form a seed bed, and by continuous addition of turf seeds to compete with weed seeds; reduced disease problems through burial of clippings to reduce potential for inoculum growth; reduction of grain; reduced labor demands; reduction of machine inventory.

Work on the project has gone into the third growing season. Not all details have been worked out; however, we feel that the program has been sufficiently defined so that the method can be presented, and that the interested superintendent can begin to make cautious trials, or the commercial houses can begin development of a salable mixed topdressing material.

MATERIALS AND PROCEDURES

The experimental area is 18 m^2 surrounded by 1 to 2 m of border. The area had been used in a previous soils study and contained three soil mixes replicated six times in plots individually 3 X 6 m. Treatments cross the area in strips 1-m wide so that each treatment crosses six plots including two replications of the three soils. The turf is *Agrostis stolonifera* L. 'Pencross.'

Soils are 30-cm deep and consist of: 1) windblown beach sand 90% in the fine-medium sand range (sand no. 2 in Davis et al., 1970); 2) a river sand of 90+% of medium, coarse, and very coarse sand (no. 5 in Davis et al., 1970); 3) a blend mixed off-site of shredded Canadian sphagnum peat, sand no. 5 as in Davis et al., 1970, and the native Yolo silt loam in proportions recommended by a laboratory making recommendations for putting green mixes. During the 1971 growing season the grass was grown uniformly with only mowing, irrigation, fertilization, and such pest control measures as appeared critically needed. A thatch of 15-mm thickness developed during this time.

Treatments were begun in May 1972 with three replications of five treatments used. Variables were limited to topdressing frequency. In 1973 a fixed topdressing interval of 21 days was used and variables were the omission or inclusion of various pesticides in the topdressing.

In 1972 various treatments were followed: 1) topdressing 40 times a year with 90 liters/are, applications weekly during the growing season; 2) topdressing 20 times a year with 180 liter/are, applications fortnightly in season; 3) topdressing 13 times a year with 270 liter/are; 4) and 5) checks in which common golf course practice was followed with topdressing 4 times or 2 times per year following coring. When need was critical an insecticide was applied separately to control caterpillars. Fertilizer was applied in the topdressing except for checks where it was applied monthly.

In 1973 check treatment followed common practice with coring and topdressing quarterly and periodic use of fertilizers and pesticides. All experimental treatments used 15 topdressings per year at 21-day intervals during the growing season. Treatments consisted of 90 liter/are of topdressing 1) with no pesticide, 2) with preventative fungicide, 3) with insecticide, or 4) with both insecticide and fungicide.

During the cold season from mid-November to mid-February, intervals were longer and based on apparent nitrogen need. As there was no cold weather stolon growth of consequence, sand was omitted from the winter topdressing and the remaining mixture was applied with a fertilizer spreader. The program adds a calculated 13.5 mm/year of sand.

The topdressing contained wettable powders added at recommended rates. Different materials were used singly on different dates. For each are the topdressing contained:

Seed	100 g
K_2SO_4	150–175 g
Gypsum (dolomite for acid soils)	70–100 g
Iron chelate	20–25 g
Zinc chelate	10–15 g
Milorganite	2,200 g
NH_4NO_3	500 g
$(NH_4)_2SO_4$	210 g
Sand (32% coarse, 60.5% med., 4.3% fine)	90 liters
Insecticides	
Diazinon O,O-Diethyl-O-(2-isopropyl-4-methyl-6-pyrimidinyl)phosphorothioate Geigy Chemical Co.	

| Sevin N-methyl-1-naphthyl-carbamate | 570 g |
| Union Carbide Chemical Co. | |

Fungicides

Captan N(trichloromethyl)thio-4-cyclohexene-1,2-dicarboximide	85 g
Cheveron Chemical Co.	
Daconil-2787 Tetrachloroisophthalonitrile	56 g
Diamond Alkali Co.	
Dexon P-dimethylaminobenzenediazo sodium sulfonate	110 g
Chemagro Co.	
Thiram Tetramethylthiuramdisulfide	85 g
E. I. DuPont de Nemours & Co.	

Fertilizer was based on the sources of N, mixed in proportions determined optimum by research at Rhode Island (1). This mix was used to remove fertilizer as a possible source of contention in the experimental results. Minerals other than nitrogen were applied as assurance rather than on the basis of demonstrated need, hence an acceptable range is indicated. The lower value was used. Phosphorous was contained in the Milorganite.

RESULTS AND DISCUSSION

The program's suitability for growing turf and the ability of the program to produce a good putting or bowling surface should be evaluated. At present the program appears to do both well. Greens may grow somewhat faster and be more resilient than with standard maintenance.

Topdressing interval

Interval appears critical to the success of the program. There is a minimum amount of sand that can be evenly applied by a topdressing machine. If the interval is short and topdressing frequent, too much sand is applied and there is insufficient cushion. With lack of cushion, pitched shots kill the grass where the ball strikes and recovery is slow. When the interval is too long the green runs out of nitrogen and loses color. For our program, a 21-day interval sustained both good nutrition and an adequate cushion. By use of a slow release nitrogen source, the interval could be lengthened. In the check using quarterly topdressing, the interval is too long and alternate layers of sand and thatch occur as on most greens in the United States.

Thatch

A significant benefit of the topdressing program is an absence of problems related to thatch. The reported practice keeps stolons separated and covered. They are kept moist and susceptible to decay and no distinguishable layer develops. The original 15 mm of thatch has been buried. In August 1973, after 16 months of topdressing, the layer is still present but is open and permeable due to decay.

Sand

Sands used at present for topdressing tend to be too coarse and are a source of irritation to the player and to the course mechanic who sharpens mowers. For this topdressing program the sand must be fine enough to drop out of sight, and, after watering in, the players should be unaware that topdressing has taken place. The sand used should all pass a 1.0-mm screen. Ideally, more than 80% should be in the USDA size grade fine to medium sand (0.1 to 0.5 mm). Such sands are finer than those commonly sold but are available as waste sands, fill sands, blend sands, etc. Ninety-six percent of the sand used fell between 0.1 and 1.0 mm, while 32% in the coarse fraction was coarser than desired but represented a sand readily available to Northern California golf courses.

Change in grade

Use of frequent topdressing is often questioned because of a fear of excessive changes in grade. Examination of established golf greens shows that the grade naturally increases and greens are often inches to over a foot higher than when built. Because the change is gradual, most persons are unaware of it, though layers of thatch and sand from years of accumulation are visible each time a cup is cut. Our limited data indicate the present program is raising the grade about 20 mm/year. Some of this is from stolons which will decay, so the change should be less than 150 mm in a decade. With higher nitrogen levels and more stolon growth this could be increased. We do not foresee problems.

Weed control

Weeds have not been a problem. *Poa annua* infested the mixed soil in the beginning but has virtually disappeared from the area. There has been no invasion of weeds though other plots in the area have been invaded by species of *Cotula, Gnaphalium, Erodium, Matricaria,* and others. Herbicides are not used as they are not necessary and invariably weaken the grass.

Insect control

Only Diazinon and Sevin have been tested. Diazinon was selected because it is somewhat systemic in its action, Sevin because it is an alternative chemical much used on golf courses. Caterpillars have posed an insect problem, but these have been readily controlled by those treatments containing insecticide in the topdressing. Because of an absence of thatch, caterpillars cannot burrow as deeply as usual. This results in increased damage from birds which hunt them. Insecticide appears to be a necessary component of the topdressing during the warm months. Further insecticide tests are planned, including the feasibility of bait in the topdressing.

Disease control

There has been little disease on the turf. Before beginning topdressing *Fusarium* patch appeared in the winter on partly shaded areas [*F. nivale* (Fr.) Snyder and Hansen]. Since beginning the topdressing program, only one spot has been seen. There has not been time to make reliable judgements, however.

Because of different soil textures, the border of the plots which is a silt loam remains overly wet. When summer temperatures exceed 38 C for several days *Pythium* often appears in these border areas and it is necessary to control it [*P. aphanidermatum* (Edson) Fitzpatrick]. It does not spread to the experimental areas. The application of dry fungicides in the topdressing during summer heat has caused injury as they tend to result in a temporary leaf scorch. Fungicides need to be screened for suitability for dry application, even though the need for them seems lessened.

Infiltration rate

Initially the mean infiltration rates of the three soils were 117 cm/hour, 60 cm/hour, and 1.5 cm/hour, respectively, for the coarse-medium and medium-fine sands, and the soil mix. With use, these all decreased and have now been limited by the texture of the topdressing sand, to a maximum of 18 to 35 cm/hour. Infiltration of the laboratory specification mix remains low at 0.1 to 0.8 cm/hour and the sand topdressing has not improved soil conductivity where the buried layer is limiting.

Depth of rooting

Initially all plots rooted to the bottom interface at 30 cm. Cores cut 30-cm deep and 5-cm in diameter have been used to observe rooting. Rooting is seasonably variable and is greater following soil warm-up in the spring. The turf growing in soil mix roots seasonally from 5- to 20-cm deep. The coarser Robertson sand shows the densest roots with seasonal depth variation from 10 to 20 cm. Rooting is dense but shallow in the Dillon sand, with depths from 6 to 12 cm. When topdressing was applied weekly, rooting was reduced.

Dry spots

Hydrophobic spots appear at times. This phenomenon is associated with sands. A study of this problem is presented elsewhere (3).

Mixing

We used a concrete mixer. Separation of materials was prevented by having the sand suitably damp. Damp sand will not spread with a fertilizer spreader though it is readily handled by a topdressing spreader. When biocides are added to the topdressing, they are added last and the operator must be protected from dust and fumes. Skill in mixing and handling is acquired with practice, though early runs are apt to create problems. Where several courses near each other follow this program, joint production of topdressing will no doubt prove practical.

Application

Evenness of application varies with the moisture content of the sand. All applications should be immediately irrigated to wash the sand out of sight and wash in the soluble fertilizer salts. When sand is too damp and a wavy application results, brooming may be required ahead of irrigation. We emphasize again that the player should not see sand on the green following topdressing.

SUMMARY

Preliminary work on a new greens management system is reported. In this system the only operation beyond mowing and irrigation is the application of topdressing based on sands less than 1.0 mm and fine to medium sand (0.1 to 0.5 mm) to which are added fertilizer minerals, turf seeds, and when needed, insecticides and fungicides.

Advantages that may accrue include no thatch, no spraying, no vertical mowing, no aeration, burial of disease inoculum, burial of weed seeds, maintenance of high infiltration rates if initially high, and reduced maintenance costs.

Disadvantages include finding suitable sands, operator care required when mixing in hazardous pesticides because of higher dust hazard, and the need for accuracy and timing so the turf retains adequate mat but is without discrete layers of sand and thatch.

ACKNOWLEDGMENT

The authors are pleased to acknowledge the help of the U.S. Golf Association. Mssrs. A. M. Radko and W. H. Bengeyfield of the USGA have listened sympathetically to the ideas during their development, and have provided research funds through the USGA to assist in making an investigation possible.

REFERENCES

1. BELL, R. S., and J. A. DE FRANCE. 1944. Influences of fertilizers on the accumulation of roots from closely clipped bent grasses and on the quality of turf. Soil Sci. 58: 17–24.
2. DAVIS, W. B., J. L. PAUL, J. H. MADISON, and L. Y. GEORGE. 1970. A guide to establishing sands and amendments used for high trafficked turfgrass. Univ. Calif., Agr. Extension Pub. AXT-n113. 93 p.
3. HENRY, M. 1973. Nonwettable sands; a problem of putting green soils. Univ. Calif., M.S. Thesis, 72 p.

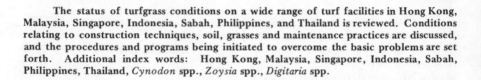

54

Turfgrass developments in Southeast Asia

I. GREENFIELD

The status of turfgrass conditions on a wide range of turf facilities in Hong Kong, Malaysia, Singapore, Indonesia, Sabah, Philippines, and Thailand is reviewed. Conditions relating to construction techniques, soil, grasses and maintenance practices are discussed, and the procedures and programs being initiated to overcome the basic problems are set forth. Additional index words: Hong Kong, Malaysia, Singapore, Indonesia, Sabah, Philippines, Thailand, *Cynodon* spp., *Zoysia* spp., *Digitaria* spp.

Turfgrass developments during the last 2 years in Hong Kong, Malaysia, Singapore, Indonesia, Sabah (North Borneo), Philippines, and Thailand have been significant. A wide range of turfgrass surfaces including golf greens, tees and fairways, bowling greens, football pitches, cricket grounds, race courses, and sports stadia have been maintained at below optimum standards because of a lack of understanding of the basic biological requirements of grasses and their relationship with soils. This in turn reflects a lack of knowledge of modern construction and maintenance techniques.

HONG KONG

In Hong Kong golf green surfaces are composed either of 'Tifgreen' bermudagrass (*Cynodon dactylon* (L.) Pers.), Korean grass (*Zoysia tenuifolia*), or sometimes a mixture of the two. The greens, which are constructed of solid laterite which is completely structureless and impervious to water, have no tile or any other drainage system. Root growth and general turf vigor are poor under the cool, damp conditions which often exist in Hong Kong during February and March. *Helminthosporium curvularia* and *Piricularia* leaf spotting diseases together with *Rhizoctonia solani* regularly decimate large areas of the greens. Growth under these conditions is particularly poor because of physical impedance to root development as well as to the effects of water ponding and sour thatch conditions. Irrigation requirements often are not fully understood. Badly designed and improperly spaced pop-up sprinkler heads often do more harm than good, especially when allied to an improperly drained and contoured surface. Shading by trees together with branch and leaf droppings cause indifferent thin and diseased turf growth.

In one instance, prior to building a new golf course, samples of the local soil were sent to the U.S. Golf Association for the appropriate physical tests. A specification based on a number of false premises, due to the failure of the club to provide all the relevant data, was executed with poor results. Drainage and base layers, mixing, and the construction of the various strata were handled indifferently, resulting in a combination of areas of overdrainage and impeded drainage. The fact that tile drainage was not provided in the base of the green in a climate where some 37 cm of rain may fall in 1 day is one measure of the lack of existing knowledge. Similarly, no attention was given to the basic excavation or the contouring of the green bases. The result combined a sharply dipping front apron with the leading edge of the water table which regularly discharged along the fore part of the green with resultant damage to grass growth. All these points seem elementary but they in fact do constitute a serious liability in this part of the world. The climate and difficult soils magnify many of these problems which are especially important under the local conditions.

Although irrigation has been provided for greens either by manual or automatic systems, tees usually are not included and, as a result, during dry periods they receive excessive wear as do the fairways through the winter period between October and March. During the rest of the year approximately 200 cm of rain may fall. Under these circumstances growth of grass on fairways is particularly good. Tees recover to a certain extent and greens develop better until July when the effects of the continuous heavy rain on the structureless, ill-drained surface, in conjunction with poor root development and mat build-up, cause death of the grass from suffocation and disease.

Similar conditions are to be found on football fields where, because of heavy wear, lack of management, and incorrect construction, the turf is literally worn bare. The indigenous grasses, *Cynodon dactylon* L. Pers. (bermudagrass), *Zoysia matrella* (manilagrass), *Chrysopogon aciculatus* (lovegrass), *Eremochloa ophiuroides* (centipedegrass), *Axonopus compressus* (tropical carpetgrass), *Paspalum conjugatum* (buffalograss), together with other species grow to form a coarse sward, which is well adapted to the climate but incapable of withstanding mechanical damage. Generally, these areas are mowed at a low height of cut and are never rested nor do they receive treatment apart from one dressing at the end of the season (May) when the heavy rains start. The same is true of cricket fields, race courses, and sports stadia where, due to lack of knowledge, incorrect materials are applied frequently, fertilizing is inadequate, and there is a lack of understanding of turf management techniques. For example, the Sports Stadium in Hong Kong is also used frequently for various parades and military tatoos, it is hardly surprising that there are serious subsurface drainage problems as well as completely impeded surface drainage conditions.

MALAYSIA AND SINGAPORE

In Malaysia and Singapore there is a distinct similarity between the turfgrass surfaces as these two countries have a comparable climate. For example, golf fairways are composed mainly of *Axonopus compressus,* known locally as cowgrass, buffalograss, manilagrass, and lovegrass. Tees are composed mainly of cowgrass and the greens consist of "Serangoon" grass which is a mixture of a number of *Digitaria* species, particularly *Digitaria didactyla* and *Digitaria longifolia.* These *Digitaria* species are characterized by a very soft woolly type of foliage which grows in whorls thus producing a very nappy surface. Unless correct management in terms of mowing, vertical cutting, mat control, and topdressing are properly and thoroughly carried out a very inaccurate and uneven putting surface is produced.

Because of continuous damp conditions the disease problem for most of the year is serious. During some seasons rain falls practically every day in Singapore although long spells of up to 6 weeks without rain also occur. Disease organisms including *Rhizoctonia, Pythium, Piricularia, Helminthosporium, Fusarium,* and *Curvularia* spp. are continuously present, and management must be directed toward improving physical conditions and the application of chemical controls if a useable surface is to be maintained. In these areas also there has been little understanding of drainage techniques or proper methods of construction. The various stadia and football fields are heavily used but generally tend to be in better shape than in Hong Kong due to a more equable climate without the large variations in temperature, better soils, and the relatively continuous rainfall.

THAILAND

In Thailand, at the Royal Bangkok Sports Club which numbers a golf course, race course, sports fields, cricket ground, tennis courts, and swimming pool amongst its facilities, turfgrass problems are intense. The whole area is very low and is subject to flooding, the natural soil is a glei, and the only way it can be even partially protected is by construction of a large ditch around the whole periphery of the club. Even so, flooding does occur during certain periods of the year. Manilagrass is used for green and tee surfaces, tennis courts, and the cricket square. Other areas are a mixture of the indigenous grasses including the following species: *Cynodon dactylon, Axonopus compressus, Eremochloa ophiuroides, Paspalum conjugatum,* and *Paspalum dilatatum,* and *Brachiaria, Zoysia* and *Digitaria* spp. A large number of new golf courses have recently been constructed in Thailand and Tifgreen bermudagrass has been used successfully on these. It performs well under local conditions, although management techniques on greens, fairways, and tees aren't as thorough as they could be. Modern concepts concerning turfgrass management are being developed in this area.

PHILIPPINES

In the Philippines some golf greens are planted to Taiwan grass (*Zoysia tenuifolia*) grown almost exclusively on black sand. The low nutrient regime (fertilizing is very infrequent and drainage is especially good) suits this particular grass which, if overfed, tends to produce an uneven and thick mat that requires continuous raking, vertical cutting, and other similar techniques.

On other courses Tifgreen is used and although it is generally somewhat impoverished, it does reasonably well under the local conditions. In this area much is being done to upgrade and update the various items of machinery and the materials used for course maintenance.

SABAH (NORTH BORNEO)

In Sabah (North Borneo) there are a number of golf course developments which when completed will relieve the pressure on the local 9-hole course at Kota Kinabalu. This course is constructed on a tidal plateau and at least once a day it is flooded as the tide comes in. The greens here are planted to *Zoysia matrella*.

INDONESIA

In Indonesia, golf greens are largely composed of *Digitaria* species. Management practices lack sophistication, as shown by this example. An attempt at greens improvement and reconstruction consisted of digging holes, lining them with concrete, replacing the soil, and planting grass. The result was 18 marshes.

SUMMARY

All of these problems fall into the following categories: incorrect construction methods, lack of understanding of turfgrass maintenance methods and grass/soil relationships, and particularly difficult soils which may be either lateritic, degraded granites, or alluvial materials. These soils possess an indifferent structure and generally tend to be infertile. Because of drainage problems, anaerobic conditions have developed and a very low pH (often 3.5 to 4.0) exists. Severe mineral deficiencies frequently occur, i.e., phosphate fixation together with deficiencies of iron and magnesium, in lateritic soils. Heavy rainfall causes structural deterioration and this combined with the lack of both surface and subsurface drainage in many cases further aggravates the problem. Because of compaction, water tends to run off the surface or to stand in pools. No attempt has been made to aerate or to improve the soil texture so as to improve moisture penetration. Therefore, root growth seldom exceeds 2.5 cm. High temperatures allied with the wet regime also reduce organic matter which generally is in very short supply.

Little work has been done on the use of the best local grasses for particular purposes. Indigenous grasses, which may or may not possess the most suitable characteristics, have been used; however, there is a lack of understanding as to how to produce a satisfactory surface using these species. In some cases Tifgreen has been introduced as well as other improved grasses and selections, but due to a lack of understanding of more intensive management regimes these often have failed.

Machinery, which often consists only of mowers that are dull and improperly set, is limited. Aeration and topdressing equipment, fertilizer spreaders, and irrigation systems often are nonexistent. Where they have been provided (or purchased) they have been considered of little value because of incorrect working, breakage of parts, and maladjustment. Often the surface of the ground is so hard that penetration cannot be made by hollow or slitting tines and this opeartion can only be carried out after surface saturation by heavy rain.

The need to employ a large proportion of the population often results in a golf course complex with, for example, three 18-hole courses, employing 70 to 80 people. Also, there is a political complication in that jobs must be found; this means the labor bill is often excessively high. This, to a certain extent, has reduced the rate of mechanization. This slow rate has generally been due to the lack of understanding or unavailability of the equipment, but this situation is now being remedied.

The question of economics has not been considered and no worthwhile records or budgets were produced in most cases. Annual budgets generally have been worked out by inexperienced committee members. This situation has taken place in the area since around the turn of the century. It is only in the last 2 years that steps have been taken to remedy this situation.

MANAGEMENT APPROACH AND METHODS

The objective of development programs generally has been to introduce a basic understanding of turf culture with respect to cost and maintenance as well as construction methods, soil treatments, and the introduction of the appropriate grass species and cultivars. This has been achieved by means of discussions with individual clubs, local ministries of agriculture, and the organization of symposia and practical demonstrations, as well as regular inspections and reports to monitor the effects of management development. Results have been assessed and discussed, together with the implications, with the various organizations concerned. In certain cases individual training of course managers and their senior staff has been carried out. The importance of correct management techniques and construction methods, especially with regard to drainage and the amelioration of soils, and various methods of construction to suit the climate have been demonstrated.

Amelioration of the soil has been considered to be of particular importance, anticompaction and aeration treatments being given priority, as well as generally increasing the pH level to a more suitable 5.0 to 5.5. Also, the introduction of tile and other drainage systems, the application of balanced fertilizers at proper times, the addition of organic matter, and the use of improved grasses have been given special attention. With respect to the latter, most species which grow under these conditions can be reproduced only by vegetative means.

Mowing machinery must be accurately adjusted and kept sharp. Starting a golf tournament at 7 a.m. gives a distinct advantage to the early player as compared with the player who starts about 1 p.m. There can be a large difference in the smoothness of the surface and the resultant effects in terms of holdability and putting accuracy are well known.

Providing subsurface and surface drainage using both downward penetration into the soil profile as well as contouring to promote run-off of excess water has been given special attention. When providing drainage, erosion control measures which emphasize topographical considerations and natural vegetation are essential.

GRASS

Trials using selections of local indigenous grasses together with various Tifton varieties have enabled much information to be obtained about the growth characteristics, requirements, and performance of the candidate grasses. Turf protection is taking place through the use of cultural measures to alleviate disease problems, allied with the application of fungicides such as Benlate, Manzeb, Captan, PCNB, and Thiram, are being introduced on a larger scale. Ants, termites (*Termes flavipes*), cutworms, army worms (*Pseudaleta unipuncta*), earthworms, and mole crickets present a pest control problem, and use is being made of insecticides such as Chlordane, Lindane, Sevin, Malathion, and other organophosphorus insecticides. Weed control is not as much a problem because of the large labor force organized for hand weeding. While broad-leafed weeds can be controlled by a number of herbicides, the incursion of indigenous bermudagrass, for example, in the Serangoon greens of Malaysia and Singapore is a serious problem which can only be approached by complete removal of stems, stolons, and roots. It is very difficult to remove all traces and the slightest portion of a stem or root left behind means a new colony.

The introduction of machinery and its use in optimum maintenance programs for the conditions and climate is another important aspect of turfgrass development in the area. Also of importance is the close examination of labor requirements and turfgrass economics in general, along with the introduction of appropriate recording and budgeting systems.

Personnel in the various departments of agriculture and universities are being encouraged to take an active part in these developments and a number of experimental programs are underway in Hong Kong and Malaysia. The general growth rate in the area is probably three to four times that encountered in temperate countries and once the optimum soil and management conditions are provided rate of growth is no problem. Correct maintenance treatments, together with the optimum nutritional programs, can be carried out on a more intensive basis than in temperate countries.

The only long-term answer to these problems is to provide scientifically constructed greens, tees and fairways, football, cricket, and tennis facilities which can be maintained with understanding and the application of modern techniques.

ACKNOWLEDGMENTS

The author wishes to express his appreciation to the following for their assistance: Dr. W. H. Bengeyfield, Western Director, U. S. Golf Association Green Section; V. A. Gibeault, Environmental Horticulturist, University of California; Dr. G. W. Burton, USDA, Tifton, Georgia; Dr. V. B. Youngner, Professor of Agronomy, University of California; and Dr. T. E. Freeman, Professor of Plant Pathology, University of Florida.

FURTHER READING

GREENFIELD, I. 1972. Turf culture. Leonard Hill Ltd., London.

HANSON, A. A., and F. V. JUSKA (ed.). 1969. Turfgrass science. Agronomy monograph 14. Amer. Soc. of Agron., Madison, Wis.

ROYAL HONG KONG GOLF CLUB. 1971. Proceedings of the symposium on sports turf in Hong Kong. Royal Hong Kong Golf Club, Hong Kong.

SINGAPORE GOLF ASSOCIATION. 1973. Proceedings of the seminar on sports turf maintenance. Singapore Golf Ass., Singapore.

55

Thatch decomposition in bermudagrass turf [1]

R.L. DUBLE & R.W. WEAVER

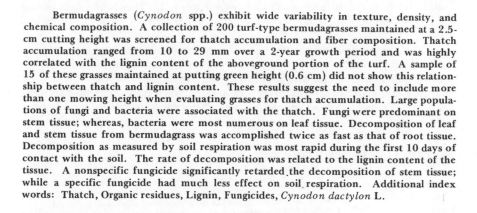

Bermudagrasses (*Cynodon* spp.) exhibit wide variability in texture, density, and chemical composition. A collection of 200 turf-type bermudagrasses maintained at a 2.5-cm cutting height was screened for thatch accumulation and fiber composition. Thatch accumulation ranged from 10 to 29 mm over a 2-year growth period and was highly correlated with the lignin content of the aboveground portion of the turf. A sample of 15 of these grasses maintained at putting green height (0.6 cm) did not show this relationship between thatch and lignin content. These results suggest the need to include more than one mowing height when evaluating grasses for thatch accumulation. Large populations of fungi and bacteria were associated with the thatch. Fungi were predominant on stem tissue; whereas, bacteria were most numerous on leaf tissue. Decomposition of leaf and stem tissue from bermudagrass was accomplished twice as fast as that of root tissue. Decomposition as measured by soil respiration was most rapid during the first 10 days of contact with the soil. The rate of decomposition was related to the lignin content of the tissue. A nonspecific fungicide significantly retarded the decomposition of stem tissue; while a specific fungicide had much less effect on soil respiration. Additional index words: Thatch, Organic residues, Lignin, Fungicides, *Cynodon dactylon* L.

Thatch may be defined as the accumulation of living and dead grass leaves, stems, and organic debris between the soil surface and the green vegetation in a turf (6). Thatch accumulation is a direct result of management practices that produce abundant vegetative growth (8). High rates of N fertilization, infrequent mowing, and irrigation are contributing factors to thatch accumulation (1). Many improved turfgrass cultivars such as 'Tifgreen' bermudagrass (*Cynodon dactylon* L.) have a vigorous shoot growth rate that encourages thatch accumulation (1).

Decomposition of thatch involves the assimilation of tissue carbohydrates and is dependent on soil microbes. Thus, the rate of decomposition depends largely upon the soil microenvironment, the type and number of organisms present, and the chemical composition of the thatch (7). High decomposition rates are associated with favorable moisture and temperature conditions and dense microbial populations (10). The C/N ratio of the or-

---

[1] Contribution from the Texas Agricultural Experiment Station, Texas A&M University, College Station, Texas.

ganic material has only limited value to characterize its suitability for microbial decomposition (10). The lignin content of the carbohydrate fraction is an important factor in the decomposition of thatch (4, 8). Other carbohydrate fractions are readily decomposable, but lignin is highly resistant to microbial degradation and reduces the accessibility of other carbohydrates to microbial attack (2). The lignin/cellulose ratio of the organic material has been shown to be associated with the rate of decomposition of thatch by soil microbes (5) and of forage by rumen microbes (9).

Microbial activity is a function of the populations of fungi, bacteria, protozoa, and other soil organisms and their interrelationships. The application of fungicides to the soil ecosystem generally triggers a sequence of replacements within microbial populations, resulting in the preservation of metabolic activity (3). Domsch demonstrated that soil bacteria play a significant role in the decomposition of organic residues, particularly in remoistened air-dry soil (3). He also demonstrated that the decomposition of cellulose and cutin is inhibited by some fungicides. In general, nonspecific fungicides exert a temporary inhibition of soil respiration; while specific fungicides have no influence on soil respiration (3). Thus, the effect of soil fungicides on thatch decomposition must be determined on an individual basis.

The purpose of this paper is to show that decomposition of thatch in bermudagrass turf is a function of plant genotype, soil microenvironment, and management. Field and laboratory experiments were conducted to investigate the effects of bermudagrass varieties, soils, fungicides, and clipping management on thatch accumulation and microbial decomposition in bermudagrass turf.

MATERIALS AND METHODS

Thatch measurements

Thatch is defined herein as the depth of organic material between the soil and the green vegetative cover. Measurements were made using a ruler on 5-cm dia. plugs removed from the turf. Measurements were made on three to five plugs taken at random from each plot. A nursery with 200 bermudagrass varieties or introductions was sampled periodically for thatch accumulation. These grasses were mowed at a 2.5-cm cutting height, fertilized at a rate of 0.5 kg of N/100 m^2 per month, and watered at the severe wilting stage. Fifteen selections from this nursery were sprigged into replicated plots and maintained at putting green height (0.6 cm). These plots were fertilized at a rate of 0.75 kg/100 m^2 per month and watered daily during the growing season. After the grasses were established, the plots were measured at monthly intervals for thatch accumulation.

Lignin and cellulose determinations

Each time thatch measurements were taken, samples consisting of the thatch and vegetative cover were collected for chemical analysis. This procedure was followed to avoid the complications involved in separating the thatch from the sod profile. The samples were dried at 70 C and ground to pass a 1-mm screen. Lignin and cellulose was determined according to the procedures of Van Soest and Marcus (9).

Microbial activity

Plate counts of microbial populations were made on eight soil types after 6-weeks incubation with leaf, stem, and root tissue from bermudagrass. A check in which plant material was excluded was also run on each soil. Respiration measurements were taken at 5-day intervals during the 42-day incubation period. A continuous flow of air was passed through the incubation chambers and then through a $0.5N$ NaOH solution. The alkali solution was replaced every 5 days with a fresh solution and was titrated with acid to determine the amount of CO_2 respired. Nitrate concentrations in the soil were determined with a nitrate electrode at the conclusion of the experiment.

A separate respiration experiment was conducted with a single soil type to measure the effect of two fungicides, p-(Dimethylamino) benzenediazo sodium sulfonate (Dexon made by Chemagro Corp.) and tetramethylthiuram disulfide (Thiram made by DuPont) on microbial activity. The fungicides were applied at 150 and 300 ppm to the soil in which leaf, stem, and root tissue was incubated for 27 days at 27 C.

RESULTS AND DISCUSSION

Thatch measurements

The 200 bermudagrass selections maintained at a 2.5-cm cutting height accumulated from 10 to 29 mm of thatch over a 2-year growth period. In general, the finer-textured selections (*C. transvaalensis*) accumulated the greatest thatch at the 2.5-cm mowing height. In these bermudagrasses the thatch was composed primarily of a mass of stems entwined between partially decomposed leaf tissue. Although growth rate was not measured, stolon (tiller) production was apparently related to thatch accumulation in bermugrass mowed at a 2.5-cm height.

Fifteen of these 200 bermudagrasses were established in replicated plots on a putting green and mowed at a 0.6-cm height. During a 5-month growing season thatch accumulation ranged from 3.5 to 11.5 mm. At this mowing height the finer-textured (*C. transvaalensis*) selections produced the least thatch and the dwarf selections ('Pee Dee' and 'Tifdwarf', selections from *C. dactylon* + *C. transvaalensis* hybrids) produced the greatest amount of thatch. The upright-growth habit of the finer-textured selections allowed the mower to remove much of the tiller production; whereas, the decumbent growth habit of the dwarf selections allowed the stolons (tillers) to accumulate. The mower removed only leaf tissue from the dwarf selections; but, leaf and stem tissue was removed from the other selections. This difference was illustrated by the scalping in the finer-textured plots compared to the dwarf plots. When the 15 grasses were classified into two groups based on growth habit, the upright group all had below 7.0 mm of thatch and averaged 5.8 mm and the decumbent group were all above 10.0 mm and averaged 11.2 mm of thatch. There were six decumbent types and nine upright types in this study.

Lignin and cellulose determinations

Bermudagrass turfs maintained at a 2.5-cm cutting height exhibited a range of 6 to 16% lignin after 2-years growth. The cellulose content of the same plant material (thatch and green vegetative cover) ranged from 16 to 27%. Grass clippings from the same plots contained 3.4 to 6.4% lignin and and 18 to 27% cellulose. Thus, lignin accumulated in the thatch as decomposition progressed. When the turf from a single plot was separated into living tissue, partially decayed tissue, and decayed tissue (that not recognizable as either leaf or stem tissue), the lignin content was 6.5, 11.3, and 19.5%, respectively. In this study there was a close correlation between thatch accumulation and the lignin content or the lignin/cellulose ratio, 0.79 and 0.83, respectively. However, this relationship was not expressed where the grasses were mowed at putting green height (0.6 cm). When mowed at this shorter height for a 5-month period, those grasses that accumulated the most thatch, the dwarf types, had the lowest lignin content and the lowest lignin/cellulose ratio. If the data for the October sampling date (Table 1) is examined, a negative correlation is apparent between thatch accumulation and the lignin content or the lignin/cellulose ratio. This apparent contradiction to the relationship established for the 2.5-cm mowing height may be explained by examination of the existing turf in the closely mowed plots. The dwarf- or decumbent-type grasses which produced the most thatch retained most of

Table 1—Thatch accumulation and fiber content of bermudagrass selections mowed at a 0.6-cm height 3 days/week.

Bermudagrass selection	Growth habit	May		Jul		Aug		Oct		Oct
		L*	C†	L	C	L	C	L	C	Thatch
		% dry weight								mm
Tifdwarf	Decumbent	4.1	21.7	5.9	18.7	8.3	16.8	7.5	16.8	11.9
Tifgreen	Decumbent	4.0	21.0	6.5	19.1	9.0	17.3	8.5	17.5	11.2
Champion's	Decumbent	3.8	20.2	7.0	20.5	7.1	18.7	8.1	17.2	10.3
Texturf 1 F	Decumbent	3.4	20.6	5.6	22.3	8.5	18.2	7.0	18.5	11.3
TAMU	Decumbent	4.3	21.5	5.6	17.5	7.3	18.1	8.0	16.9	11.5
Pee Dee	Decumbent	3.9	22.3	6.7	20.0	7.7	17.5	7.9	18.1	11.0
286584	Upright	3.4	21.2	7.3	22.7	13.7	18.6	8.5	18.0	3.5
289917	Upright	3.9	22.9	7.5	21.0	10.3	22.3	10.5	19.6	5.5
289918	Upright	3.8	21.6	8.5	22.7	11.5	20.4	9.7	18.9	5.6
289926	Upright	4.3	21.3	8.3	23.7	12.0	23.0	11.0	20.6	7.0
290892	Upright	4.0	19.8	7.5	20.3	8.4	19.6	10.9	21.3	6.2
291581	Upright	4.5	21.6	7.3	20.8	10.0	20.3	8.2	19.7	6.0
291691	Upright	4.2	20.8	7.7	20.9	10.5	20.7	8.0	19.1	6.2
291961	Upright	4.0	23.1	9.2	22.6	10.1	21.2	12.3	21.3	5.9
Tifway	Upright	3.9	20.7	7.9	21.5	8.3	19.9	9.3	18.7	6.3

* L = lignin. † C = cellulose.

their leaf tissue at the 0.6-cm mowing height; whereas, the upright-type grasses were scalped at the close mowing height. Thus, the chemical analyses which were conducted on the aboveground portion reflected the stemminess of the scalped plots. This relationship establishes the need to examine grasses at more than one mowing height when thatch accumulation or carbohydrate content are variables under investigation.

Microbial activity

The variability of microorganisms in soils was demonstrated by the populations observed in the eight soils studied (Table 2). However, the populations of fungi and bacteria are readily adjusted to the energy source available in the soil. Fungi populations showed the greatest increase on the fibrous stem tissue and bacteria increased the greatest on leaf tissue which contains the highest fraction of soluble carbohydrates. The populations of microfauna (protozoa, nematodes, etc.) were not measured and may be of equal importance to the decomposition of grass residues.

Respiration measurements made throughout the incubation period indicated considerable differences between soils with regard to microbial activity (Table 3). Although respiration was measured for 42 days, the greatest

Table 2—Microorganism populations in soils after 6 weeks incubation with leaf, stem, and root tissue from bermudagrass.

Soil source	Fungi, 10^3/g soil				Bacteria, 10^6/g soil			
	Check	Leaves	Stems	Roots	Check	Leaves	Stems	Roots
Temple (clay)	59	101	123	25	37	23	35	11
Lubbock (loam)	48	60	115	9	6	60	9	20
El Paso (loam)	35	49	62	38	10	53	36	22
Beaumont (clay)	74	273	410	382	5	16	10	19
Overton (sand)	30	158	154	113	2	23	18	24
Wesloco (loam)	53	61	115	55	14	59	39	34
Stephenville (sand)	43	148	104	69	5	78	28	27
Beeville (loam)	6	72	644	69	3	63	32	10
Average	43	115	216	95	10	49	26	21

Table 3—Carbon evolution and nitrate concentrations in soils as influenced by bermudagrass residues.

Soil source	C evolved, mg				NO_3-N, ppm			
	Check	Leaves	Stems	Roots	Check	Leaves	Stems	Roots
Temple (clay)	3.9	18.8	15.0	7.9	24	41	3	17
Lubbock (loam)	3.6	11.9	13.8	4.6	20	18	0	16
El Paso (loam)	4.5	19.9	16.5	10.2	76	74	53	80
Beaumont (clay)	2.5	17.0	12.6	8.8	0	4	0	5
Overton (sand)	5.3	18.8	18.0	10.3	57	81	38	73
Weslaco (loam)	2.8	13.5	15.7	8.8	42	53	18	34
Stephenville (sand)	2.5	18.9	23.0	9.4	25	58	20	36
Beeville (loam)	1.1	11.0	12.3	4.3	0	0	0	0
Average	3.3	16.4	15.9	8.0	30.5	41.2	16.5	32.6

* 0.08 g of plant residues were added to 10 g of soil.

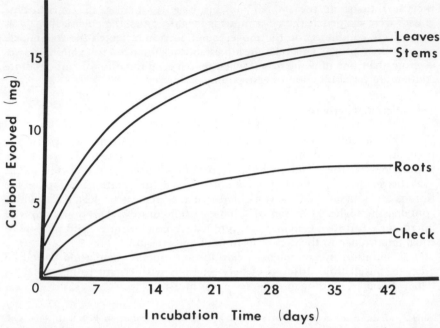

Fig. 1—Decomposition rates of leaf, stem, and root tissue averaged over eight soil types.

activity occurred during the first 5 days. In some soils very little activity was observed without added substrate (carbon sources) in the form of leaf, stem, or root tissue. On the other hand, the high organic soil from Beaumont demonstrated high activity without added substrate. In all eight soils the leaf and stem tissue was decomposed much more readily than root tissue (Fig. 1). In all soils at least 35% of the leaf tissue and less than 15% of the root tissue was decomposed. Stems were broken down almost as rapidly as the leaves. Chemical analysis of the leaf, stem, and root tissue for lignin showed 2.5, 6.3, and 11.7%, respectively. The slow rate of decomposition and relatively low population of microorganisms associated with the root tissue may be related to the high lignin content of the tissue.

Nitrate concentrations found in the soils after the 42-day incubation with the various plant fractions indicated that stem tissue required supplemental nitrogen for decomposition, but that leaf tissue contributed nitrogen to the soil upon decomposition (Table 3). In some soils (Beaumont and Beeville) available nitrogen may have limited the decomposition of plant residues.

The two fungicides applied to the leaf, stem, and root tissue generally reduced the decomposition of the tissue (Table 4). Since the fungi were most active on stem tissue, the fungicides would be expected to affect their decomposition more than that of the other tissues. Thiram reacted as expected, but Dexon slightly increased the decomposition of stem tissue. This response may be explained by the specificity of Dexon for *Pythium*. The saprophytic fungi were apparently not affected or perhaps stimulated by the application

Table 4—Decomposition of bermudagrass tissue as influenced by two fungicides.

Treatment*	Total C evolved	Added C respired
	mg	%
Stems	21.4	32
Stems + Thiram X	5.3	8
Stems + Thiram 2X	2.5	4
Stems + Dexon X	23.8	35
Stems + Dexon 2X	24.7	37
Leaves	22.8	34
Leaves + Thiram X	10.8	16
Leaves + Thiram 2X	11.2	17
Leaves + Dexon X	14.6	22
Leaves + Dexon 2X	17.1	25
Roots	13.3	20
Roots + Thiram X	12.7	19
Roots + Thiram 2X	10.2	15
Roots + Dexon X	11.2	17
Roots + Dexon 2X	13.2	20

* Fungicides were added at rate (X) of 150 ppm to 15 g of soil.

of Dexon to the soil. The decomposition of leaf tissue was not affected by Thiram as much as that of stem tissue. As indicated by the plate counts, the bacteria may have been responsible for much of the decomposition of leaf tissue.

ACKNOWLEDGMENT

The authors express appreciation to the O. J. Noer Research Foundation, Inc. for financial support of this investigation.

REFERENCES

1. BEARD, James B. 1973. Turfgrass: science and culture. Prentice-Hall, Inc. Englewood Cliffs, N. J. 658 p.
2. BONNER, J., and J. E. VARNER. 1965. Plant biochemistry. Academic Press. New York. 1054 p.
3. DOMSCH, K. H. 1964. Soil fungicides. Ann. Rev. Phytopath. 2:293-320.
4. ———, and W. GAMS. 1969. Variability and potential of a soil fungus population to decompose pectin, xylan, and carboxymethylcellulose. Soil Biol. Biochem. 1: 29-36.
5. DUBLE, R. L., and R. W. WEAVER. 1972. Thatch accumulation in relation to the lignin/cellulose ratio in bermudagrass. Agron. Abst. p. 62.
6. HOLT, E. C. 1969. Turfgrasses under warm, humid conditions. In A. A. Hanson and F. V. Juska (ed.) Turfgrass Science. Agronomy 15:SB-528. Amer. Soc. Agron., Madison, Wis. 715 p.
7. HUTCHINGS, I. J., and T. L. MARTIN. 1934. Influence of the carbon-nitrogen ratios of organic matter on rate of decomposition in the soil. Agron. J. 26:333-341.
8. LEDEBOER, F. B., and C. R. SKOGLEY. 1967. Investigations into the nature of thatch and methods for its decomposition. Agron. J. 59:320-323.
9. VAN SOEST, P. J., and W. C. MARCUS. 1964. A method for the determination of cell wall constituents of forages using detergents and the relationship between this fraction and voluntary intake and digestibility. J. Dairy Sci. 47:704-705.
10. WITKAMP, Martin. 1963. Microbial populations of leaf litter in relation to environment conditions and decomposition. Ecology 44:370-376.

56

Responses of several densely seeded turfgrasses to variable close cutting in the greenhouse[1]

F.B. LEDEBOER

Six cool-season turfgrass cultivars, 'Pennfine' and 'Manhattan' perennial ryegrass (*Lolium perenne* L.), Italian ryegrass (*Lolium multiflorum* L.), 'Pennlawn' creeping red fescue (*Festuca rubra* L.), 'Jamestown' chewings fescue (*Festuca rubra* var. *commutata* Gaud.), and 'Seaside' creeping bentgrass (*Agrostis palustris* Huds.) were evaluated under two cutting heights (0.6 and 0.9 cm) and three preplant fertilizer treatments (0-14-14, 14-0-44, and check). The experiment was conducted in an unheated greenhouse with all vents open to simulate overseeded bermudagreen conditions. Turf density, quality, and color were related to cultivar and cutting height. These parameters were reduced by 0.6 cm cutting. Ryegrasses produced inferior turf to fescues and bentgrass. Plant count, extra tiller production, and plant mortality per unit area were responsible for overall turf quality. Only fescues, but Jamestown in particular, had low plant mortality and sufficiently high tiller production to maintain high turf quality under both cutting levels. Seaside bentgrass attained good density but remained in the soft seedling stage throughout the study. Seed bed application of 14-0-44 increased vigor and color of grasses over 0-14-14 and check treatments but increased seedling mortality. Other parameters were affected little and obscured by subsequent uniform nitrogen treatments. Additional index words: Winter overseeding, Quality comparison, Low cutting.

On golf courses throughout the southern United States low-growing and fine-textured hybrid bermudagrasses (*Cynodon dactylon* X *C. transvaalensis*) are predominantly used for greens. With the exception of limited locations in southern Florida and along the Gulf coast where frost occurs only infrequently, these greens are overseeded each fall with heavy rates of cool-season turfgrass species (4). Under these conditions they are utilized as winter annuals to provide a green playing surface during the cool season (6). Bermudagrasses in these regions are dormant and without green surface tissues from the first killing frost until well into spring.

To provide a playable surface quickly, extremely heavy seeding rates of 10 to 50 million seeds/are of rapidly germinating grass species are used from late September to November after the bermudagrass turf has been thinned by verticutting (1, 3, 4). Seeds are brushed into the remaining turf and then covered lightly with sandy loam.

---

[1] Research conducted at the South Carolina Agricultural Experiment Station, Clemson University, South Carolina.

Under the close cutting requirements of 0.6 cm or less for putting greens, naturally tall growing species are often thinned severely before a satisfactory winter stand is achieved (F. B. Ledeboer, personal observation in field studies conducted at Clemson University, Clemson, South Carolina). In years past Italian ryegrass (*Lolium multiflorum* L.) was used predominantly but frequently was unsatisfactory because it did not tolerate early close mowing (2).

The purpose of these investigations was to determine the growth characteristics and performance of several cool-season grass species and cultivars in response to simulated putting green conditions and to ascertain what morphological factors are contributing to good turf quality under the imposed treatments.

MATERIALS AND METHODS

During Winter 1970–71 an overseeding experiment was conducted at Clemson University, Clemson, South Carolina, in an unheated, clear-glass greenhouse. Side and top vents were left open throughout the 12-week test period in December through February to approximate actual open air conditions.

Cylindrical plugs, 10 cm in diameter and 15 cm deep, of closely cut (0.6 cm) Tifgreen bermudagrass sod (*Cynodon dactylon* X *C. transvaalensis*) were air-dried to kill the bermudagrass and prevent possible regrowth during the experiment. Plugs were fitted into suitable plastic containers which served as individual plots. A factorial design with three fertilizer treatments, two cutting heights, six grass cultivars, and four replications was developed. Differential seed bed fertilization consisted of 3.2 kg/are 0–14–14, 3.2 kg/are 14–0–44 (oxide basis) and unfertilized checks. Treatments were made prior to seeding and watered in thoroughly. Cutting heights of 0.6 and 0.9 cm were used. Grasses were cut at 2-day intervals using hand shears. The two heights were gauged by appropriate plastic collars fitted over the pot rim during cutting. All clippings were removed. Cutting commenced as soon as grass leaves reached about 1.5 cm.

Grass cultivars used are listed in Table 1. Seeding rates were adjusted to provide approximately 10 million seeds/are. Seeding and fertilization were accomplished by pushing a calibrated drop-type spreader on an elevated scaffold over a block of pots to be treated. Seeds were thoroughly brushed into the sod to establish good soil contact and were then topdressed with a 0.2

Table 1—Grass cultivars used in the experiment.

Variety	Type	Name
Manhattan	Perennial ryegrass	*Lolium perenne* L.
Pennfine	Perennial ryegrass	*Lolium perenne* L.
——	Italian ryegrass	*Lolium multiflorum* L.
Pennlawn	Creeping red fescue	*Festuca rubra* L.
Jamestown	Chewings fescue	*F. rubra* var. *commutata* Gaud.
Seaside	Creeping bentgrass	*Agrostis palustris* Huds.

cm layer of sandy loam. Watering was done by hand as needed. A uniform application of CaNO₃ at 3.5 kg/are was made 1 month after seeding and repeated 1 month later. Density, turf quality, and color data were obtained visually by two persons working individually. Plant counts, extra tillers, and plant mortality were determined from two 3.14 cm² cores taken at random from each pot at the end of the experiment.

RESULTS AND DISCUSSIONS

Germination data revealed no new information. Differential emergence of various cool-season species used for overseeding has been documented by Gill et al. (3) and by Schmidt and Blaser (6). Data were therefore omitted. Under greenhouse conditions germination occurred more rapidly but the difference between species used remained the same. Ryegrasses emerged within 4 days and were followed by red and chewings fescues and bentgrasses the following day. Seedling vigor data were also consistent with published information. Grasses used were rated as follows: Italian ryegrass > 'Manhattan' = 'Pennfine' > 'Jamestown' = 'Pennlawn' > 'Seaside.'

Under the imposed cutting schedule, early establishment and density were satisfactory only for Jamestown and Seaside (Table 2). Both grasses had significantly better density at 3 weeks under both cutting heights than all others. Italian ryegrass established very poorly, especially under low cut. During the experiment density of all grasses increased (density—12 weeks), but relative differences between tested varieties remained the same. Jamestown and Seaside maintained significantly denser turf than all others, while Italian ryegrass was most open at both cutting levels (Fig. 1).

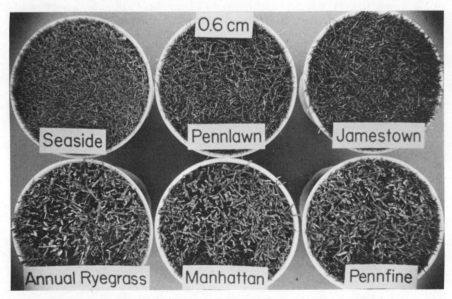

Fig. 1—Turf quality comparison of the six best cultivars at 0.6 cm cutting height 9 weeks after seeding.

Table 2—Summary of density, turf quality and color data in response to cutting height and seed bed fertilization.

Grass variety	Cutting height														
	% Density, 3 weeks			% Density, 12 weeks			Turf quality, 6 weeks			Turf quality, 12 weeks			Color, 3 weeks		
	0.6 cm	0.9 cm	Mean	0.6 cm	0.9 cm	Mean	0.6 cm	0.9 cm	Mean	0.6 cm	0.9 cm	Mean	0.6 cm	0.9 cm	Mean
Pennfine perennial ryegrass	48d*	62c	55.0	56e	77cd	65.7	5.2ef	6.7d	5.9	3.9fg	5.9e	4.9	6.4d	6.4d	6.4
Manhattan perennial ryegrass	41e	64c	50.3	58e	82c	70.0	5.4e	7.4cd	6.4	4.4f	6.5de	5.5	6.6cd	7.2c	6.9
Italian ryegrass	28f	46de	37.0	33f	58e	45.1	2.6g	4.8f	3.7	1.6b	3.0g	2.3	4.9f	5.9e	5.4
Pennlawn red fescue	49d	64c	56.6	76d	85c	80.0	6.3de	7.4cd	6.8	6.2de	7.3cd	6.7	7.3bc	7.9b	7.6
Jamestown chewings fescue	72b	87a	79.5	91ab	99a	95.1	9.0b	9.9a	9.5	8.7b	9.6a	9.3	8.6ab	9.1a	8.9
Seaside creeping bentgrass	74b	86a	80.0	90b	96ab	92.9	8.4bc	8.2bc	8.3	7.0cd	7.7c	7.4	·6.0de	6.7cd	6.3
Mean	52.0b	68.2a		67.4b	82.7a		6.1b	7.4a		5.3b	6.7a		6.6b	7.2a	
Fertilizer Rate/are															
0-14-14 3.2kg		58b			75b†			6.8a†			6.0a†			6.3c	
14-0-44 3.2kg		64a			75a			6.9a			6.1a			7.6a	
Check –		59b			74a			6.8a			5.8a			6.8b	

* Different letters following each set of data indicate significant differences at the 5% level. † Data obtained after an overall application of CaNO₃ at 3.5 kg/are.

Table 3—Summary of plant count, extra tiller production, and plant loss per unit area in response to cutting height and seed bed fertilization.

Grass variety	Cutting height														
	Plants/3.4cm²			Extra tillers/3.14cm²			% Extra tillers/3.14cm²			Dead plants/3.14cm²			% Dead plants/3.4cm²		
	0.6 cm	0.9 cm	Mean	0.6 cm	0.9 cm	Mean	0.6 cm	0.9 cm	Mean	0.6 cm	0.9 cm	Mean	0.6 cm	0.9 cm	Mean
Pennfine perennial ryegrass	13fg*	18defg	16	6.8d	4.2de	5.5	52.3d	23.4e	37.9	7.3bcd	4.6defg	6.0	35.9b	20.2cd	28.0
Manhattan perennial ryegrass	21def	25cde	23	1.7e	1.0e	1.4	8.1g	4.0h	6.0	8.2bc	4.0defg	6.1	28.1bc	13.8de	20.9
Italian Ryegrass	10g	16efg	13	1.2e	2.6de	1.9	12.0fg	16.3ef	14.1	13.8a	7.5bcd	10.7	58.0a	31.9bc	40.0
Pennlawn red fescue	16efg	23cde	20	21.0b	18.7b	19.8	131.2a	81.4c	106.3	6.3cde	2.3fgh	4.2	28.2bc	9.1ef	18.6
Jamestown chewings fescue	27cd	31c	28	30.2a	30.9a	30.7	111.8ab	99.8bc	105.8	1.5gh	.5kh	1.0	5.3f	1.6g	3.4
Seaside creeping bentgrass	58b	69a	64	12.7c	5.5de	9.1	21.9e	8.0g	15.0	11.1ab	5.8def	8.5	16.1d	7.8ef	11.9
Mean	24b	31a		21.1a	10.5a		56.3a	38.8b		8.0a	4.1b		28.6a	14.1b	
Fertilization Rate/are															
0-14-14 3.2kg		25b			12.5a						4.9b				
14-0-44 3.2kg		26b			10.7b						7.6a				
Check –		31a			11.0b						5.8b				

*Different letters following each set of data indicate significant differences at the 5% level.

Pilot studies conducted at Clemson under similar conditions have shown that low cutting (0.6 cm) under experimental conditions without traffic removed foliage too severely from ryegrasses. These grasses grow rapidly upright and cutting removes foliage before collars are formed on newly emerging leaves. Remaining leaf portions above the collar are apparently too short to maintain sufficient photosynthesis rates for plant survival. With Italian ryegrass the cut often occurs at or below the point of collar formation on the second, third, or later developing leaves. Ryegrass plants under severe foliage removal rarely produced primary tillers, consequently the stand density improved little with time.

Basal sheaths of turf-type perennial ryegrass (Manhattan and Pennfine), red and chewings fescues, and bentgrasses are shorter than in Italian ryegrass and appear to tolerate low cutting levels to the extent that seedlings will persist satisfactorily during the cool season.

Turf quality ratings (1 to 10 best) taken at 6 weeks and 12 weeks indicate that Jamestown at both cutting levels was significantly better than all other grasses (Table 2). Only Seaside at 0.6 cm and 0.9 cm was similar in performance to Jamestown at 0.6 cm at the 6-week time period. Pennlawn was intermediate, followed closely by both perennial ryegrasses. Italian ryegrass was unsatisfactory. All grasses declined in overall quality towards the end of the test period, but in the two fescues this deterioration was minimal. It was most severe in Italian ryegrass.

Visual color ratings taken after 3 weeks indicate overall, intensive green seedling grasses (1 to 10 best) (Table 3). Again, Jamestown at both cutting levels presented the best color and Italian ryegrass the poorest. Color ratings reflect the influence of yellowing and necrotic foliage on overall appearance. Very little yellowing occurred in highly rated plots. Cutting treatments were significant for density, quality, and color parameters. The 0.9 cm cut resulted in higher ratings in each case. While 0.9 cm may be slightly higher than the desirable cutting height in actual putting green conditions, measurements in the field have shown actual cutting heights to be close to 1.0 cm despite mower settings of 0.6 cm or less.

Fertilization, especially with P_2O_5 and K_2O, just prior to or at time of seeding is generally advocated for better overseeding establishment (5). In this study significant effects on density and quality were registered only with the nitrogen-potassium treatment in the 3-week density data (Table 1). Uniformly applied calcium nitrate thereafter obscured all differences. Early color ratings were depressed by 0-14-14 and increased by 14-0-44 treatments.

Table 3 shows analyses of data collected at the end of the 12-week test period. With the exception of Seaside bentgrass the plant count per 3.14 cm^2 plug did not vary greatly and tended to reflect seeding rates. Generally, the coarser the seeds or resulting individual plants were, the lower the plant count. Cutting height affected average plant count in that more plants persisted under the higher cuts.

Production of extra tillers under the low cutting levels appeared to be primarily responsible for overall turf quality. Number of extra tillers per unit area and the percent of extra tillers varied widely between the grasses. Cutting height did not affect tillering in number but influenced the percent of tillers. A higher percentage of tillers was produced under the low cut.

All ryegrasses produced only infrequent new tillers and therefore the stand remained very thin.

Pennfine produced more tillers at low cut than Manhattan or Italian ryegrass. Both red fescue cultivars had considerably larger numbers of tillers than the other grasses with Jamestown producing significantly more than Pennlawn. Under the low cut both cultivars had more than 1 extra tiller per plant. The number and percent of dead plants also varied significantly. On the average these figures were greater under low cut and with the coarser grasses. Most necrotic plants (13.8) and the greatest percentage (58.0%) were recorded for Italian ryegrass at 0.6 cm and the lowest for Jamestown at 0.9 cm cut (0.5 and 1.6%, respectively).

Responses to variable seed bed fertilization followed by overall treatments of $CaNO_3$ carried over into plant density, extra tillers, and number of dead plants per unit area. The plant count was higher in the unfertilized check. Extra tillers were highest with 0-14-14 and plant mortality was greatest with a base application of 14-0-44. Similar observations have been made on actual putting greens where early nitrogen applications—before the overseeded grasses had become fully established—resulted in severe thinning of the stand. Growth stimulation from nitrogen combined with very low mowing apparently produced unfavorable conditions for seedling survival.

Even though the turf-type perennial ryegrasses Pennfine and Manhattan produced a better overseeding cover than Italian ryegrass, seedling mortality and lack of tiller production caused the stand to remain fairly open. Results were comparable to actual field performance. Pennlawn red fescue presented a significant improvement over ryegrasses but in the overall evaluation this cultivar was still inferior to the performance of Jamestown chewings fescue. The major factor for its excellent turf quality appeared to be the ability of all seedlings to survive and produce a high number of new tillers under the low cutting regime. While dense and upright, Seaside bentgrass plants remained practically in the seedling stage throughout the test period. The turf remained soft and lacked the resilience necessary to withstand traffic.

The foliage canopy produced by the ryegrasses was suspended above the soil to the mowing level but there was little body below the foliage to provide a thick cover. By contrast, both fescue cultivars, especially Jamestown, produced an abundance of extravaginal tillers originating from the crown at oblique angles. This network of low growth provided an excellent dense turf cover of fine texture and good resilience.

REFERENCES

1. BEARD, J. B. 1973. Turfgrass science and culture. Prentice-Hall, Englewood Cliffs, N. J. p. 658.
2. ENLOW, C. R. 1928. Winter grass experiments at Gainesville, Florida. USGA Green Sect. Bull. 8(11):224-225.
3. GILL, W. J., W. R. THOMPSON, Jr., and C. Y. WARD. 1967. Species and methods for overseeding bermuda greens. Golf Supt. 35(9):10ff.
4. MADISON, J. H. 1971. Practical turfgrass management. Van Nostrand Reinhold Co., N. Y. p. 466.
5. MAPLES, P., Jr. 1973. Rx for overseeding bermuda greens. USGA Green Sect. Rec. 11(4):9-13.
6. SCHMIDT, R. E., and R. E. BLASER. 1961. Cool season grasses for winter turf on bermuda putting greens. USGA Green Sect. J. Turf Manage. 4(5):25-29.

57

Growth retardant effects on various grass tissues and organs[1]

V.B. YOUNGNER & F.J. NUDGE

Root growth, tillering, rhizome development, stolon branching, and reserve carbo-hydrates as affected by three growth retardants, (2 chloroethyl) trimethylammonium (CCC), α-cyclopropyl, α-4-methoxypropyl, α-5 pyrimidine methanol (ancymidol), and chloride 3-trifluromethyl-sulfonamido-p-acetotoluidide (fluoridimide), were studied in several experiments. CCC retarded root growth of bermudagrass (*Cynodon* spp.) slightly, but did not affect root growth of Kentucky bluegrass (*Poa pratensis* L.) until high rates were reached. Ancymidol inhibited root growth of Kentucky bluegrass only at high rates. Tillering of Kentucky bluegrass was stimulated by CCC and ancymidol but rhizome development was inhibited. Fluoridimide did not stimulate either tillering or rhizome development. Nodal branching of bermudagrass, St. Augustinegrass (*Stenotaphrum secundatum* Walt., Kuntze), and kikuyugrass (*Pennisetum clandestinum* Hachst.) was stimulated by CCC and ancymidol while internode elongation was restricted. Fluoridimide did not affect internode elongation or nodal branching of these species. Nonstructural carbohydrate percentages of bermudagrass were not affected by CCC. Additional index words: Root growth, Tillering, Rhizomes, Carbohydrate reserves, CCC, Ancymidol, Turfgrasses, Fluoridimide.

The use of chemical growth retardants on turfgrasses to reduce mowing and edging has great appeal. Although a number of chemicals effectively in-habit grass growth only maleic hydrazide; 6-hydroxy-3(2 H pyridazinone) (MH) and methyl 2 chloro-9-hydroxyflorine-9-carboxylic acid (fluorinol) are presently used on turf (4). Their use is confined to roadsides and similar areas not receiving close examination since turf quality is usually impaired (7).

Although several other growth retardants have not shown immediate phytotoxicity at rates inhibiting top growth, their effects on turf vigor after prolonged use are not known. Little is known about tillering, rhizome growth, stolon branching, and root growth as effected by these retardants even though directly related to long-term use. The physiology of growth re-tardants has been reviewed by Cathey (3) and by Sachs and Hackett (8). In reviewing the effects of (2 chloroethyl) trimethylammonium chloride (CCC) on cereals, Humphries (5) reported that most studies show a stimulation of

---

[1]Contribution from the Department of Plant Sciences, University of California, River-side, California 92502.

wheat (*Triticum aestivum* L.) root growth by this growth retardant. However, no similar responses have been reported for noncereal grasses.

Bokhari and Youngner (1, 2) showed that CCC stimulated tillering of wheat and a uniculm mutant of barley (*Hordeum vulgare* L.). Since dormant tiller primordia were observed in untreated uniculm barley, they suggested that CCC acts to stimulate the growth of existing primordia and perhaps to promote initiation of new primordia. Stem internode length was decreased by CCC but leaf length was unchanged. Heading was delayed or prevented by the higher CCC concentrations.

Juska and Hanson (6) reported that density of 'Merion' and common Kentucky bluegrass (*Poa pratensis* L.) turf in September was reduced by spring applications of CCC.

Several experiments were conducted at Riverside, California, to define certain specific effects of three growth retardants on turfgrasses. The objective was to provide a basis for predicting their long term effects and practical value as partial substitutes for mowing.

MATERIALS AND METHODS

Plants for all studies were grown in the greenhouse either in nutrient solution cultures previously described (9) or in 12.8-cm clay pots of a peat, sand, and soil potting mixture. Treatments were replicated four times in solution culture studies and five times in pot studies. Plants were propagated vegetatively as single tillers or as single node stolon cuttings from a selected clone of each species or variety. Fertility in soil cultures was maintained by watering at weekly intervals with a dilute complete nutrient solution.

Three growth retardants, CCC, a-cyclopropyl, a-4-methoxypropyl, a-5 pyrimidine methanol (ancymidol), and 3-trifluromethyl-sulfonamido-p-acetotoluidide (fluoridimide), were selected for grass growth retardation and low phytotoxicity on the basis of preliminary studies. One or more of these chemicals were used in each experiment. Application rates determined by preliminary experiments ranged from an effective but nonphytotoxic low rate to a high rate that produced moderate to severe injury for each material. All applications in pot cultures were made as soil drenches avoiding direct contact with the foliage. In solution cultures the retardant was applied in the nutrient solution. Specific rates and experimental methods will be indicated where necessary in the results section. Since a number of small experiments were conducted results will be discussed under headings of various growth responses rather than individual experiments.

RESULTS AND DISCUSSION

Root Growth

In a solution culture study where 'Santa Ana' bermudagrass (*Cynodon dactylon* L. X *Cynodon transvaalensis* Burtt-Davy) was given a single treatment of 500 ppm of CCC in Hoagland's nutrient culture solution, root growth was reduced by about 30% on clipped and 25% on unclipped plants in 8 weeks

Clipping	Mean dry wt (g) of Roots	
	CCC	Control
Weekly	0.35	0.49
Unclipped	1.13	1.49

However, root reduction by clipping within either the CCC treatment or the control was nearly 70%. These results indicate that if CCC treatments were substituted for a large part of the mowing requirement of Santa Ana bermuda a better root system might be maintained. Since top growth on the unclipped plants was reduced by 48% during the 8-week period mowing frequency would be significantly less with CCC applications.

Neither CCC nor ancymidol significantly reduced the root system of Kentucky bluegrass, 'Newport' until high rates were used (200 ml per pot of a 0.2M CCC solution and 200 ml per pot of a 50 mg/liter ancymidol solution). These rates were well above those necessary for inhibition of top growth and caused considerable leaf injury. Damage to the Kentucky bluegrass and bermudagrass turf root systems from these growth retardants thus does not appear likely if they are used at the lowest rates that will give effective inhibition of top growth. Root growth was reduced by fluoridimide at all rates which gave satisfactory top-growth inhibition (5.6 kg ai/ha and up).

Tillering and rhizome growth

Tillering of Newport Kentucky bluegrass was stimulated by moderate rates of CCC and moderate to high rates of ancymidol when the materials were applied as a soil drench (Table 1). Rhizome development was unaffected or inhibited at the same rates. Rhizomes that were produced on

Table 1—Effects of three growth retardants on tillering and rhizome development of Kentucky bluegrass 8 weeks after application as soil drenches.

	Mean no. rhizomes	Mean no. tillers
CCC		
0	7.8 a*	6.6 b
0.01 M	7.8 a	13.8 a
0.02 M	5.2 b	15.6 a
0.10 M	2.8 c	6.8 b
0.20 M	0.2 d	1.8 c
Ancymidol, mg/liter		
0	7.8 a	6.6 b
7.5	7.6 a	18.0 a
15.0	6.4 b	14.6 a
25.0	6.4 b	18.0 a
50.0	3.6 c	18.6 a
Fluoridimide, kg/ha		
0	7.8 a	6.6 a
5.6	1.0 b	8.6 a
11.2	0.8 bc	3.0 b
16.8	0.4 c	44.2 b
22.4	0.2 c	3.6 b

* Means in a given column followed by the same letter are not significantly different at the 5% level.

treated plants did not appear to be shorter than on untreated plants but accurate measurement was extremely difficult. Fluoridimide did not stimulate tillering and inhibited almost all rhizome development at the rates used in these studies.

Since tillering is the most important means of spread for the young Kentucky bluegrass plant, CCC and ancymidol would increase the rate of spread in a young turf. At later stages of growth when rhizome development becomes increasingly more important these same chemicals might reduce the density of a turf. Inhibition of rhizome initiation may be the reason that Juska and Hanson (6) observed reduced density following CCC applications since their studies were on 5-year-old Kentucky bluegrass turfs.

Stolon growth and branching

In a series of experiments, ancymidol and CCC inhibited elongation of stolon internodes of several pot-grown warm-season grasses while increasing initiation of nodal branches at rates shown in Table 1. At the two highest rates of ancymidol, St. Augustinegrass (*Stenotaphrum secundatum* Walt., Kuntze) internodes were only about 5 mm long, but short, otherwise normal appearing, leaves were produced at each node. All rates increased stolon branching by 25 to 30%. Internode shortening was not as extreme on bermudagrasses (*Cynodon* spp.), zoysiagrass (*Zoysia matrella* L., Merr.), and kikuyugrass (*Pennisetum clandestinum* Hachst), but the increase in stolon branching was approximately the same. Ancymidol produced a mass of greatly telescoped stems at the tips of kikuyugrass shoots which had been cut prior to application of the chemicals.

Nodal branching of stolons and culms on kikuyugrass and bermudagrass was greatest from CCC at rates of 0.01 and 0.02M. The higher rates of CCC caused severe injury. Fluoridimide produced little or no internode shortening or lateral branching on any of the stoloniferous warm-season grasses at rates from 5.6 to 22.4 kg/ha.

Nonstructural carbohydrates

Growth retardant effects on nonstructural carbohydrate percentages were studied only with CCC applied to Santa Ana bermudagrass at 500 ppm in solution culture. Carbohydrate percentages of roots and crowns were not significantly affected by CCC at this rate although top growth was reduced by nearly 50% by 8 weeks after application.

Portion	Clipped Weekly		Unclipped	
	CCC	Control	CCC	Control
		% carbohydrates		
Crowns	4.7	5.2	6.8	6.6
Roots	1.7	1.6	3.9	3.3

Clipping did reduce carbohydrate percentages within both treated and untreated groups.

These results suggest either that total leaf area of both CCC treated and untreated plants was essentially the same or that photosynthetic efficiency was increased by CCC while the leaf area was decreased. The latter is feasible since treated plants are more intensely green indicating a possible increase in chlorophyll concentration.

SUMMARY

These studies indicate that selected growth retardants may be safely used on many turfgrasses without serious danger of long-term deterioration. Root growth is not greatly inhibited and may be improved in time since mowing which does severely limit root development will be less frequent and severe.

Density may be improved or at least not impaired since tillering rate and nodal branching of stolons is stimulated by some growth retardants. However, their use on grasses that are largely dependent upon rhizome growth for spread and density may not be advisable as rhizome growth appears to be restricted. Photosynthetic efficiency of CCC treated bermudagrass does not appear to be affected.

Ancymidol and CCC might be viewed as general grass growth regulators as well as growth retardants since they stimulate development of previously initiated shoot primordia resulting in increased tillering and stolon branching. These chemicals might be used in a turf management program at various times during the year to achieve specific desired effects other than growth supression.

REFERENCES

1. BOKHARI, U. G., and V. B. YOUNGNER. 1971a. Effects of CCC on the growth of wheat plants and their untreated progeny. Agron. J. 63:809–811.
2. ———, and ———. 1971b. Effects of CCC on tillering and flowering of uniculm barley. Crop Sci. 11:711–713.
3. CATHEY, H. M. 1964. Pysiology of growth retarding chemicals. Ann. Rev. Plant Physiol. 15:217–302.
4. FOOTE, L. E., and B. F. HIMMELMAN. 1971. MH as a roadside grass retardant. Weed Sci. 19:86–90.
5. HUMPHRIES, E. C. 1968. CCC and cereals. Field Crop Abst. 21:91–99.
6. JUSKA, F. V., and A. A. HANSON. 1964. Effects of growth retardants on Kentucky bluegrass turf. Golf Course Rep. 32:60–64.
7. MADISON, J. H., J. M. JOHNSON, W. B. DAVIS, and R. M. SACHS. 1969. Chemical mowing of turfgrass. California Agr. 23:9–10.
8. SACHS, R. M., and W. P. HACKETT. 1972. Chemical inhibition of plant growth. Hortscience 7:440–447.
9. YOUNGNER, V. B., O. R. LUNT, and F. NUDGE. 1967. Salinity tolerance of seven varieties of creeping bentgrass, *Agrostis palustris* Huds. Agron. J. 59:335–336.

58

Effect of growth regulators on certain turfgrasses

C. BILLOT & A. HENTGEN

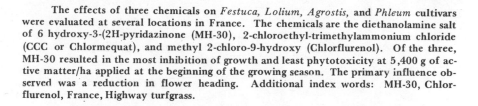

The effects of three chemicals on *Festuca, Lolium, Agrostis,* and *Phleum* cultivars were evaluated at several locations in France. The chemicals are the diethanolamine salt of 6 hydroxy-3-(2H-pyridazinone (MH-30), 2-chloroethyl-trimethylammonium chloride (CCC or Chlormequat), and methyl 2-chloro-9-hydroxy (Chlorflurenol). Of the three, MH-30 resulted in the most inhibition of growth and least phytotoxicity at 5,400 g of active matter/ha applied at the beginning of the growing season. The primary influence observed was a reduction in flower heading. Additional index words: MH-30, Chlorflurenol, France, Highway turfgrass.

Roadside embankments planted to grass require periodic mowing to reduce grass height and to prevent accumulation of dead material.

This study was undertaken to determine if the first mowing could be delayed and if the number of annual mowings could be reduced.

Three chemicals were selected for application: diethanolamine salt of 6 hydroxy-3-(2H) pyridazinone (MH-30), 2-chloroethyl-trimethylammonium chloride (CCC) (chlormequat), and methyl 2-chloro-9-hydroxy fluorene-9-carboxylate (Chlorflurenol). A review of the literature indicated that effectiveness of these chemicals depended largely on the time of application and the stage of growth at the time of application (2).

The economic value of using these chemicals, rates of application, and dates of application were investigated during 1970, 1971, and 1972 in trials set up in three different regions of France, i.e., Paris, Rhone Valley, and on the Atlantic coast. Particular attention was paid to defining effectiveness of the chemicals and the relationship between time of application and the stage of growth in different grasses.

Chemicals were applied to pure stands of *Festuca arundinacea* 'Manade'; *Festuca rubra nigrescens* 'Highlight' and *Festuca rubra multiflora* 'Bergere'; *Lolium perenne* 'Bocage'; *Agrostis tenuis* 'Holfior'; *Phleum bertolonii* 'Sport'; and *Poa pratensis* 'Prato.'

In 1970, CCC was applied at 3,000 g active matter and a mixture of MH-30 (335 g/liter) and 2,4-D (67 g/liter) was applied at 20 liter/ha. Applications were made at 1) beginning of growth in the spring; 2) 10 days after mowing of each variety; and 3) a combination of 1) and 2).

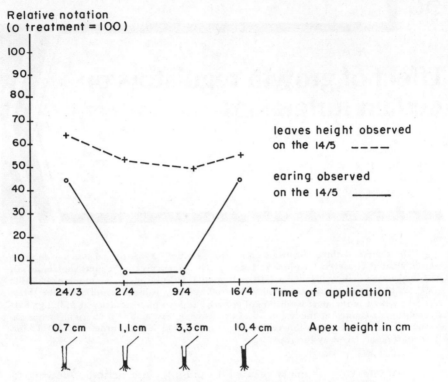

Fig. 1—MH-30 effect on *Festuca arundinacea* **(Manade) 1971.**

Only the MH-30 mixture applied in the spring reduced heading when compared to the control. Nevertheless, the results obtained in the different trials varied with each grass cultivar. The stage of growth at the time of treatment varied according to the region. The results showed that effectiveness was related directly to date of application and the earliness of cultivar, the latter depending on the site and on the climatic conditions of the year.

In 1971 the trial procedures were directed towards the utilization of maleic hydrazide. Chlorflurenol known for its effect on dicotyledonous plants and for its synergistic effect on grasses mentioned by Boeker (1) was selected for use in combination with MH-30.

The two treatments applied in 1971 were 1) MH-30 at 5,400 g active matter/ha and 2) MH-30 + chlorflurenol at 4,000 g active matter/ha (2,700 g + 1,300 g).

Chemical treatments included four different times of application. One application was completed at the beginning of shoot development, the other three treatments were subsequently applied at weekly intervals. Height measurements of apices above the tillering layer were collected before each application.

Both treatments, MH-30 alone and MH-30 + Chlorflurenol had similar effects, though some differences in efficiency were noticed in favor of the

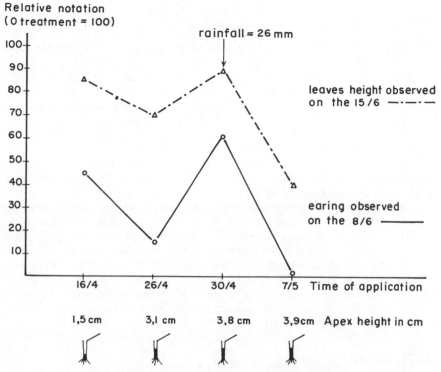

Fig. 2—MH-30 effect on *Agrostis tenuis* (Holfior) 1971.

MH-30 treatment applied at a later date. The fact that the results in all the other treatments were comparable can be explained either by the direct effect of Chlorflurenol on grasses or by the synergistic effect, since the dose of MH-30 in the mixture was less than twice that of the treatment with pure MH-30. In fact, the results of other trials with different doses of MH-30 set up elsewhere show clearly a decreased effectiveness for low rates (2,700 g active matter/ha) as compared to that of higher rates (5,700 active matter/ha).

The effectiveness of the treatments was more pronounced on the extent of heading, number of ears (flowers) per unit area, and, to a lesser degree, on the length of the leaves and stems. In some of the treatments no heading was observed.

Judging by the results it seems that there is a period of approximately 15 days, starting at the beginning of shoot growth, during which the treatments are most successful (Fig. 1 and 2).

There was evidence of a certain phytotoxic effect manifested by a yellow or red coloration of the leaves and a rolling of the lamina. From a general point of view, the effect of MH-30 alone was less toxic than that of the mixture MH-30 + Chlorflurenol which brought about a complete drying up of the leaves in all species with the exception of *Poa pratensis*.

CONCLUSION

The results of these trials show the advantage of maleic hydrazide alone as compared to that of the more phytotoxic mixture MH-30 + Chlorflurenol for growth control of selected turfgrasses. Its principal merit, when applied at the beginning of spring, is the prevention of heading (flowering). When the treatments are not followed by a rainy spell, it is possible to postpone the first cut of "utility" swards to a later date. This does not eliminate the necessity for later cuttings in order to keep the sward green. Its use for lawns is limited by the phytotoxic effect.

The efficiency of the treatment applied in spring seems to be in close relation with the physiological stage of the plants manifest by the height of the apex above the tillering layer.

Differences in maturity must be taken into account when setting the date for treatment. Treatment dates must be adapted either to the earliness of each species or to that of groups having the same growth patterns. Under these conditions, and if several species enter into the composition of the sward, one should determine the date of treatment according to the results of the botanical analysis made before the application in order to obtain an optimal efficiency. When the differences in earliness are too excessive, it would be logical to apply two treatments in order to ensure a satisfactory result.

REFERENCES

1. BOÉKER, P. 1970. Growth control. p. 464–468. *In* Proc. First Int. Turfgrass Res. Conf. Sports Turf Research Institute, Bingley, England.
2. WHITE, D. B. 1970. Chemical regulation of growth in turfgrass. p. 481–494. *In* Proc. First Int. Turfgrass Res. Conf. Sports Turf Research Institute, Bingley, England.

59

Influence of two new growth regulating chemicals on Baron Kentucky bluegrass[1]

W.G. BROWN & D.B. WHITE

A 'Baron' Kentucky bluegrass turf community showed 50% growth suppression 3 weeks after treatment with (Acetic acid di-)a-a'-imino-N-(phosphonomethyl)diammonium salt (MON 0175) and 3-trifluoromethyl sulfonamide-p-acetotoluidide (MBR 6033). MBR 6033 maintained influence for a period of 10 weeks. MON 0175 suppressed growth for a minimum of 12 weeks. Slight lightening of foliage color was observed during the 2-week period after treatment at the highest rate. Discoloration and/or normal color was replaced after the second week by a green darker than that of the control. Both chemicals reduced flower head development by 60 to 80%.

Growth regulators reduced root growth of sod transplanted 3 months after treatment. Turf treated with growth regulators and supplemental potassium produced twice the root growth of grass treated with growth regulators alone.

Development of hardiness apparently was not affected by growth regulator treatment. Additional index words: MON 0175, MBR 6033, Growth regulation, Bluegrass, Winter injury.

Research in growth suppression of turf with maleic hydrazide (MH), 2-chloroethyl trimethylammonium chloride (CCC) (chlormequat), succinamic acid dimethyl hydrazide (SADH), 2-chloroethyl phosphonic acid (ethephon), and 2,4-dichlorobenzyltributyl phosphonium chloride (phosphon) has shown these chemicals are not completely satisfactory because of variability of suppression, turf discoloration, and lack of persistence of growth retardation (3, 4, 5, 7, 8). Chlorflurenol (2-chloro-9-hydroxyfluorene-9-carboxylic acid) gave growth suppression that often appeared excellent, but seasonal variability of suppression and toxicity have limited use to rough turf situations where discoloration can be tolerated (1, 6). Chlorflurenol applied with maleic hydrazide (ratio 1:2) synergistically gave growth suppression as well as broadleaf weed control (1, 2).

Preliminary research at the University of Minnesota indicated two new chemicals with growth control properties. The objectives of the work reported here were as follows: 1) to ascertain seasonal variation in growth response and toxicity; 2) to investigate possible growth regulator interactions

[1]Paper No. 8374 Scientific Journal Series, Univ. Minn. Agr. Exp. Sta. Research supported in part by a grant from Monsanto Chemical Co., St. Louis, Mo.

with nitrogen (N) and potassium (K); 3) to assess the influence of nutrient by growth regulator interaction on cold hardiness.

PROCEDURES AND RESULTS

The chemicals used, MON 0175[2] and MBR 6033 (Sustar)[3], were applied to Kentucky bluegrass sod (*Poa pratensis* L. var. 'Baron'). Preliminary experiments at 5 kg/ha rates of Sustar and MON 0175 applied on April 27 and May 24, 1971 resulted in a 50% reduction in growth and seed head production for 4 weeks after treatment. Spring and summer applications of both chemicals at rates of up to 8 kg/ha resulted in slight leaf discoloration after 5 days.

The influence of nitrogen and potassium (1.2 kg and 0.6 kg/100m², respectively) on the response of growth retardants (2, 4, and 8 kg/ha) was evaluated by means of a split plot design. Applications of both fertilizer and growth retardant chemicals were made on August 1 and October 1, 1972. No interaction of nutrients with either chemical on blade growth was noted (Fig. 1 and 2). MON 0175 inhibited turf growth in excess of 50% for more than 7 weeks (Fig. 3). Growth suppression was less persistent with Sustar from summer application.

---

[2]Monsanto Chemical Co., St. Louis, Missouri. (Acetic acid di-) a,a'-imino-N-(phosphonomethyl) diammonium salt.
[3]Minnesota Mining and Manufacturing Co., St. Paul, Minnesota. (3-trifluromethyl sulfonamide-p-acetotoluidide).

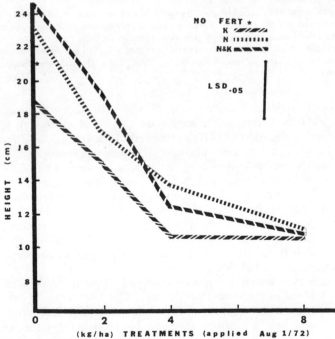

Fig. 1—Effect of MON 0175 concentrations on blade height of Baron Kentucky bluegrass in the presence of several nutritional regimes.

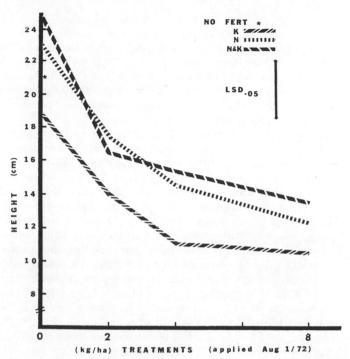

Fig. 2—Effect of Sustar concentrations on blade height of Baron Kentucky bluegrass in the presence of several nutritional regimes.

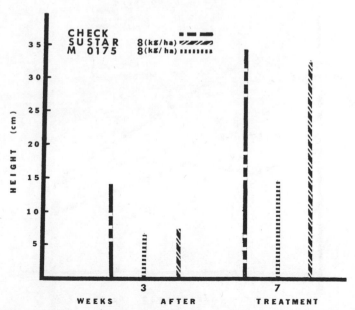

Fig. 3—Effect of MON 0175 and Sustar on blade height of Baron Kentucky bluegrass 3 and 7 weeks after treatment (applied August 1, 1972).

Root regrowth was estimated by removing plugs 6 weeks after treatment and trimming roots to 2.5-cm sod thickness. The sod plugs were planted on sand in 15.2 cm clear plastic pots. All pots were set at about a 30° angle on greenhouse benches so that newly formed roots would grow appressed to the clear plastic and could be counted. The number of visible roots formed along the side of the pots after 2 weeks was tabulated from three replicates of three pots for each factor.

Root regrowth was significantly affected by the potassium treatment (0.6 kg/100 m² applied August 1, 1972) resulting in a marked increase in root number over the unfertilized control (Fig. 4). MON 0175 at 2 kg/ha enhanced root growth in the presence of potassium. Root growth in the presence of nitrogen was not altered and when nitrogen was combined with potassium no root stimulation was observed. Root development was inhibited by MON 0175 above 4 kg/ha. Sustar treatments showed no interaction with nutrients. Root growth of Sustar-treated sod was severely inhibited (Fig. 5).

The root growth inhibition caused by Sustar persisted beyond the duration of blade growth suppression, indicating that Sustar treatment could possibly decrease drought tolerance and vigor under periods of stress.

Sustar and MON 0175 applied in the summer (August 1, 1972) caused almost no discoloration of turf even at the highest rates used (8 kg/ha). A dark green resulted from all rates of both chemicals with the 4 kg/ha rate cuasing the darkest coloration. Fall application on October 1, 1972 with MON 0175 caused severe injury. The treated plots, at all rates applied, showed a red-brown chemical burn within a week after treatment. Spring

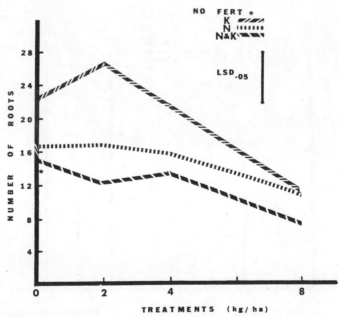

Fig. 4—Influence of nitrogen and potassium on the root growth of Baron Kentucky bluegrass 8 weeks after treatment with MON 0175.

(April, 1973) observations indicated almost complete kill of 'Baron' Kentucky bluegrass at the 8 kg/ha rate. A 25% kill was caused by the 2 kg/ha application. No injury was observed with Sustar despite the root growth suppression.

The influence of the retardants on freezing tolerance was studied to see if any effect on hardiness could be noted. Plugs of grass were removed at 2-week intervals subsequent to fall treatment. The grass was placed in a growth chamber and the temperature monitored by thermocouples placed in the crown area of several plugs. The temperature was lowered 2 C/hour and four plugs removed each hour. The plugs were allowed to grow for several days before kill ratings were taken. The killing temperature was designated as that temperature at which 50% of the plugs were killed (LT_{50}). No significant influence of chemicals (Fig. 6) or fertilizers (not shown) was observed on the ability of the Baron sod to withstand freezing temperatures.

CONCLUSIONS

MON 0175 and Sustar proved to effectively retard growth of Baron Kentucky bluegrass when applied in spring or summer. No interaction of nitrogen or potassium with either chemical on the growth of leaf blades was observed. The inhibition of growth was nearly constant irrespective of nutrients added. With the exception of the low rate of MON 0175, neither chemical interacted with fertilizer in root development. MON 0175 showed seasonal differences in toxicity which cannot be explained by a reduction in freezing tolerance. MON 0175 should not be used after September 1. Fall

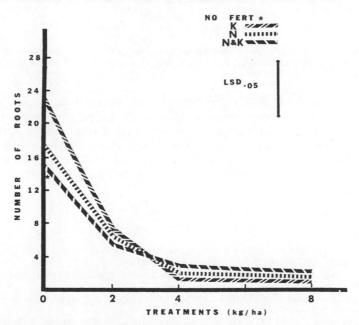

Fig. 5—Influence of nitrogen and potassium on the root growth of Baron Kentucky bluegrass 8 weeks after treatment with Sustar.

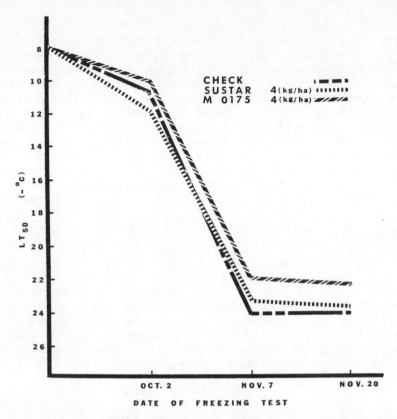

Fig. 6—Influence of MON 0175 and Sustar (4 kg/ha) on freezing tolerance of Baron Kentucky bluegrass treated August 1, 1972. Points represent 50% kill of sod plugs.

treatment with Sustar appears safe and the reduced root development does not seem to affect winterhardiness. A possible influence of reduced root development on drought tolerance deserves further research. Growth suppression obtained by spring and summer applications of Sustar and MON 0175 without disagreeable injury, with seed head inhibition, and with subsequent darker green coloration of the treated turf suggest their further use on a trial basis.

REFERENCES

1. BOEKER, P. 1970. Growth control. p. 464–468. *In* Proc. First Int. Turfgrass Res. Conf. Sports Turf Research Institute, Bingley, England.
2. BROWN, W. G., and C. M. SWITZER. 1970. Growth regulation in turf. Weed Abst. No. 63.
3. CABLER, J. F., and G. C. HORN. 1963. Chemical growth retardants for turfgrasses. Golf Course Rep. 31:1–35.
4. ESCRITT, J. R. 1954. Grass growth stunting with maleic hydrazide. J. Sports Turf Res. Inst. 29:269.
5. FOOTE, L. E., and B. F. HIMMELMAN. 1965. Maleic hydrazide as a growth re-

tardant. Final Rep. Investigation No. 616. Minnesota Highways Dept., U.S. Dep. Commerce and Minnesota Local Road Research Board.

6. MADISON, J. H., and J. M. JOHNSON, W. B. DAVIS, and R. M. SACHS. 1969. Testing fluorine compounds for chemical mowing of turfgrass. California Agr. Aug.

7. MC VEY, G. R. 1961. Fertilizer development and growth regulation. Twentieth short course on roadside development. The Ohio Dept. of Highways and Dept. of Landscape Architecture. Ohio State Univ. 83 p.

8. WHITE, D. B., D. HENG, T. B. BAILEY, and L. E. FOOTE. 1970. Chemical regulation of growth in turfgrass. p. 493–494. In Proc. First Int. Turfgrass Conf. Sports Turf Research Institute, Bingley, England.

60

Growth regulation of Kentucky bluegrasses with commercial and experimental growth regulators[1]

T.L. WATSCHKE

Posan [methyl 2-chloro-9-hydroxyfluorene-9-carboxylate; methyl 9-hydroxyfluorene-9-carboxylate; methyl 2,7-dichloro-9-hydroxyfluorene-9-carboxylate; diethanolamine salt of 6-hydroxy-3(2H)pyridazinone], Maintain CF-125 (same chemical formula as Posan, but different concentrations of constituents), and experimentals MBR 6033 (3'-trifluoromethylsulfonamido-p-acetotoluidide), C-19490 (undisclosed), and granular endothal [7-oxabicyclo(2.2.1)heptane-2,3 dicarboxylic acid] were evaluated for foliar growth inhibition on 'Merion', 'Pennstar', 'Delta', and 'K-109' Kentucky bluegrasses (*Poa pratensis*, L.). Growth was depressed a minimum of 4 weeks by all materials applied May 19, 1972. Posan and Maintain applied at 0.7 kg ai/ha had less discoloration and longevity than experimentals. Growth of all grasses was stimulated in excess of the control after the inhibitory effects subsided. Reapplication at half rates of Posan and Maintain in July to reduce the stimulatory effect caused discoloration comparable to the rate applied in May with only slight growth reduction. Delta and K-109 were injured significantly more than Pennstar and Merion by both rates of the experimental compounds. Application of growth regulators to intensively managed fine turf appeared to have limited value due to decreased aesthetic quality and post-retardation stimulation for some chemicals. Additional index words: Plant growth, Turfgrass, Chlorflurenol, Maleic hydrazide, Endothal.

Turfgrass managers are constantly seeking ways to decrease maintenance costs. Even though man-hours have been decreased by larger and more efficient equipment, mowing operations still require a major portion of maintenance time. The average homeowner also spends more time mowing his lawn than on any other maintenance practice.

The development of a turfgrass that would reach a desired height and then not grow without losing other desired attributes is not realistic. As an alternative, application of chemical growth regulators should be considered. Chemical retardation of growth for several weeks with a minimum loss of aesthetic quality would greatly reduce man-hours, money expended, and equipment wear (2, 11). Successful use of growth retardants occurred as early as 25 years ago to create attractive, compact plants (6, 13). Results with growth retardants on roadside grasses have been successful (4, 5). On

[1]Contribution from Department of Agronomy, The Pennsylvania State University, University Park, PA 16802. Journal Paper No. 4676, authorized for publication on April 12, 1974.

higher cut grass (> 10 cm) adequate retardation occurred with less injury than when applied to grass with a closer cut (4). Nitrogen applications reduced discoloration, but shortened the growth retardation period (R. E. Schmidt, unpublished information).

Maleic hydrazide has been used successfully in the fall during transition of bermudagrass putting greens to the overseeded species (1, 9). In general, growth retardants discolor or injure warm-season turfgrasses less than cool-season grasses and have no effect on germinating seeds (3).

Attempts to retard fine turfgrasses, grasses maintained at 5 cm or less, have not been successful (11, 12). Although growth retardation occurred, objectionable thinning accompanied the decrease in growth. Variety X material interactions also occurred (10, 11, 12). A post-retardation stimulation has consistently been recorded.

Turf retardation without a reduction in aesthetic quality is fast becoming a major area of industrial emphasis. Formulation and subsequent testing of new compounds is necessary to evaluate the potential for use on fine turf areas.

The purpose of this study was to evaluate three experimental compounds and two commercially available materials for retardation and injury effects on four Kentucky bluegrasses maintained under fine turfgrass conditions.

MATERIALS AND METHODS

Five growth regulators were applied to four Kentucky bluegrasses (*Poa pratensis* L.) at University Park, Pennsylvania. Three of the materials were experimental: C-19490 (formulation undisclosed), MBR 6033 (3'-trifloro-methylsulfonamido-*p*-acetotoluidide), and granular endothal [7-oxabicyclo (2.2.1)heptane-2,3 dicarboxylic acid]; the other two were commercially available: Posan [methyl 2-chloro-9-hydroxyfluorene-9-carboxylate; methyl 9-hydroxyfluorene-9-carboxylate; methyl 2,7-dichloro-9-hydroxyfluorene-9-carboxylate; diethanolamine salt of 6-hydroxy-3(2H)pyridazinone] (Mallinckrodt Chemical Works, St. Louis, Mo.), and Maintain CF 125 (same chemical formula as Posan, but different concentrations of constituents) (U. S. Borax). Formulations and application rates for these materials appear in Table 1.

'Pennstar,' 'Merion,' 'Delta,' and experimental 'K-109' Kentucky bluegrasses were randomized within three blocks. Blocks were split for treatment

Table 1—Formulations and rates of five growth regulator materials applied to four Kentucky bluegrasses in 1972.

Material	Formulation	Rate, kg ai/ha
Posan	Posan A, 1 EC + Posan B, 2 EC	1.68
Maintain	CF-125, 1 EC + Maintain 3, 3 EC	1.68
C-19490	4.2 EC	5.60, 8.40
MBR 6033	2 S	2.24, 4.48
Endothal	2.3 G	1.12, 2.24, 2.80, 3.36, 4.48

applications. On May 19, 1972, the spray materials were applied with a 0.9-m boom plot sprayer and the granular materials with a 0.9-m drop-type spreader on 0.9 × 1.8 m plots. Second applications of Posan and Maintain were made July 18 at half the initial rate. Adjacent to each treated plot was a check plot of equal size. Irrigation was applied when initial signs of wilt occurred and fertilizer (Milorganite 6-3-0) at 0.5 kg of N/100 m^2 was applied July 31.

Clippings from one pass of a battery powered reel-type mower (representing 0.68 m^2) were collected, weighed (fresh weight), and subtracted from the adjacent check plot weight. Depending on growing conditions, weights represented from 3 to 7 days growth. Following harvest, all plots were mowed at 2.5 cm. Turfgrass injury was recorded periodically throughout the season using a scale from 0 to 100. Ratings of 0 and 100 represented no discoloration to complete browning, respectively.

RESULTS AND DISCUSSION

Evaluation of growth inhibition was based on the difference in clipping weights between a treated and an adjacent untreated plot (Table 2). Fluctuation in weight difference from one sampling date to the next should not be interpreted to be solely due to an increase or decrease in inhibitory effect from the applied material because growth conditions varied prior to each harvest date.

For the first two dates (3 and 4 weeks after application), MBR 6033 at 4.48 kg/ha had the greatest inhibitory effect followed by the 2.24 kg/ha rate of MBR 6033 and the 8.40 kg/ha rate of C-19490. Inhibition from the low rate of MBR 6033 was negligible after these sampling dates. Yield differences of 5 g or less from zero were considered unimportant. Growth reduction from C-19490 at 8.40 kg/ha was higher than all others from June 30 to July 20. The 5.60 kg/ha rate of C-19490 began to inhibit growth to the same magnitude as the high rate of MBR 6033 beginning June 30. Initial resistance to dissolution by C-19490 and/or microbial or chemical decomposition of MBR 6033 during the high temperatures of July may have accounted for

Table 2—Effect of five growth regulators on Kentucky bluegrass growth in 1972.

| Treatment | | Difference in weight between treatment and check plots, g | | | | | | | | | | |
Material	Rate, kg/ha	Jun 8	Jun 15	Jun 26	Jun 30	Jul 6	Jul 13	Jul 20	Jul 27	Aug 3	Aug 8	Aug 24	Aug 30
Posan	1.68	17 cd*	0 cde	-7 c†	-6 d	-5 g	-4 e	-4 g	1 de	3 bc	1 b	-2 c	0 a
Maintain	1.68	9 cd	0 cde	2 b	4 c	0 cde	-1 cde	0 ef	3 cd	18 a	8 a	-1 bc	0 a
MBR 6033	2.24	45 ab	12 b	1 b	4 c	4 c	0 cde	0 ef	1 de	-2 c	8 a	2 abc	-3 a
MBR 6033	4.48	52 a	17 a	24 a	12 b	12 b	6 b	5 b	11 ab	16 a	10 a	5 a	5 a
C-19490	5.60	17 cd	5 c	15 a	13 b	9 b	7 b	4 bc	7 bc	8 abc	1 b	-2 c	1 a
C-19490	8.40	33 b	12 b	32 a	28 a	22 a	12 a	9 a	13 a	19 a	11 a	0 abc	-1 a
Endothal G	1.12	14 cd	2 cde	4 b	3 c	1 cd	3 bc	2 cde	6 cd	—	—	—	—
Endothal G	2.24	4 cd	-2 e	1 b	2 c	1 cd	1 cd	1 def	1 de	—	—	—	—
Endothal G	2.80	3 d	-1 e	1 b	-6 d	-2 def	0 cde	-1 f	-3 e	—	—	—	—
Endothal G	3.36	8 cd	-1 de	-2 bc	-1 cd	-4 ef	-3 de	-2 fg	3 cd	—	—	—	—
Endothal G	4.48	16 cd	3 cd	4 b	2 c	3 c	3 bc	3 cd	4 cd	11 ab	3 b	4 ab	1 a

* Means within columns with like letters do not differ according to Duncan's LSD Test (0.05).
† Minus sign indicates treatment outyielded check.

these differences. In Table 3, injury ratings are combined for all four blue-grasses. A rating of 10 or less should be considered tolerable. Injury was most severe in early June on the MBR 6033-treated plots. However, as time progressed plots treated with the high rate of C-19490 became the most severely injured.

Growth retardation from Posan and Maintain on June 8 was approximately one sixth and one eighth of that for MBR 6033 at 4.48 kg/ha. Application rates for the combinations of chlorflurenol and maleic hydrazide were kept low based on reports of turfgrass injury at higher rates from these compounds (4, 6, 7, 11). It was hypothesized that low rates, followed by a repeat application at half the initial rate would maximize retardation and minimize injury. Injury was kept within tolerable limits; however, the amount of retardation was not economically justifiable (Table 2 and 3). A post-inhibition stimulation occurred for Posan-treated turf.

Stimulation of growth on treated plots following inhibition was preceded by a color response. Treated plots were greener than the check. This phenomenon is not uncommon for injured turf that is recovering. Stimulation of growth probably resulted from utilization of carbohydrates accumulated during the period of reduced growth. Photosynthesis that occurred during growth suppression may have resulted in a storage of photosynthate which was readily available for growth once the retarding effect dissipated.

An August 8 check revealed that reapplication of Posan and Maintain at half rates on July 18 resulted in an increase in retardation without serious discoloration, particularly for Maintain. However, both Posan- and Maintain-treated plots outyielded the check on August 24. By August 30, no differences in retardation existed among the treatments and the difference in growth from the check was 5 g or less.

Granular endothal at 4.48 kg/ha was the only endothal treatment that consistently yielded less than the check and that difference was slight. As a result, weights for the lower rates of endothal were not taken after July 27 (Table 2). There was no evidence of appreciable injury to any of the varieties for any endothal rate (Table 3).

Table 3—Effect of five growth regulators on appearance of Kentucky bluegrass in 1972.

Treatment		Percent injury†					
Material	Rate, kg/ha	Jun 1	Jun 7	Jun 28	Jul 10	Jul 25	Aug 8
Posan	1.68	12 b*	7 b	0 c	0 c	6 c	0 c
Maintain	1.68	9 bc	6 bc	2 c	0 c	4 c	0 c
MBR 6033	2.24	21 a	18 a	13 b	3 c	5 c	2 c
MBR 6033	4.48	20 a	35 a	29 a	16 b	18 b	8 b
C-19490	5.60	10 bc	2 cd	15 b	6 c	3 c	3 c
C-19490	8.40	5 cd	6 bc	32 a	33 a	38 a	22 a
Endothal G	1.12	1 d	0 d	5 c	0 c	0 c	0 c
Endothal G	2.24	0 d	0 d	2 c	0 c	0 c	2 c
Endothal G	2.80	0 d	1 d	5 c	0 c	0 c	0 c
Endothal G	3.36	0 d	0 d	1 c	0 c	0 c	0 c
Endothal G	4.48	1 d	1 d	3 c	0 c	0 c	0 c

* Means within columns with like letters do not differ according to Duncan's LSD Test (0.05).
† For Posan and Maintain injury refers to discoloration, for others, ratings include thinning.

Inhibition of individual varieties differed when data for all treatments were pooled (Table 4). Differential response to retardants among different genera has been reported (7, 11). Even though many treatments (all granular endothal rates) caused only slight retardation in growth, differential varietal response was evident. Initially Merion had less retardation than Delta; however, by August 3 retardation of both Merion and Pennstar exceeded that of Delta. A delayed activity of C-19490, which retarded Merion and Pennstar more than any other treatment, undoubtedly caused the change. Although interactions were not significant, several trends existed with respect to grass response to the different treatments (Table 5).

Delta and K-109 had more injury in June than the more vigorous varieties Merion and Pennstar (Table 6). Susceptibility of Delta and K-109 to leaf spot (*Helminthosporium vagans*) undoubtedly compounded the injury from chemical treatment. Observations for injury were made by comparing an adjacent check with the treated plot to eliminate injury due to disease. When it is taken into account that all five granular endothal treatments caused little or no injury, the other materials were actually responsible for

Table 4—Growth retardation of four Kentucky bluegrasses treated with growth regulators in 1972.

Grass	Difference in weight between treatment and check plots, g					
	Jun 8	Jun 15	Jun 26	Jun 30	Jul 6	Jul 13
Merion	14 a*	4 a	6 a	5 a	3 a	3 a
Pennstar	18 ab	5 a	4 ab	3 a	4 a	3 a
Delta	25 b	4 a	7 ab	6 a	4 a	1 a
K-190	22 ab	4 a	10 b	6 a	4 a	2 a
	Jul 20	Jul 27	Aug 3	Aug 8	Aug 24	Aug 30
Merion	2 a	4 a	13 b	9 b	3 a	2 a
Pennstar	1 a	4 a	13 b	7 ab	1 a	0 a
Delta	1 a	4 a	6 a	2 a	−2 a†	−3 a
K-190	1 a	5 a	10 ab	6 ab	2 a	2 a

* Means within columns with like letters do not differ according to Duncan's LSD Test (0.05).
† Minus sign indicates treatments outyielded check plots for that date.

Table 5—Average retardation and injury to four Kentucky bluegrasses treated with five growth regulators in 1972.

Treatment		Retardation							
		Difference in weight between treatments and check, g				Percent injury			
Material	Rate, kg/ha	Merion	Pennstar	Delta	K-109	Merion	Pennstar	Delta	K-109
Posan	1.68	−1	−1	0	1	3	1	7	6
Maintain	1.68	2	3	2	5	1	0	7	5
MBR 6033	2.24	2	3	7	7	5	2	13	21
MBR 6033	4.48	13	12	14	14	9	4	33	38
C-19490	5.60	4	7	4	8	2	1	9	10
C-19490	8.40	14	15	12	14	9	10	33	41
Endothal G	4.48	4	5	2	5	0	0	2	2

Table 6—Injury to four Kentucky bluegrasses treated with growth regulators in 1972.

Grass	Percent injury†					
	Jun 1	Jun 7	Jun 28	Jul 10	Jul 25	Aug 8
Merion	5 a*	4 b	2 a	1 a	2 a	1 a
Pennstar	2 a	1 a	1 a	1 a	3 a	2 a
Delta	10 b	10 c	18 b	9 b	10 ab	3 ab
K-109	11 b	13 d	18 d	10 b	11 b	7 b

* Means within columns with like letters do not differ according to Duncan's LSD Test (0.05).
† Injurn is for both discoloration and thinning.

considerable injury to Delta and K-109 (Table 5). Injury to Delta and K-109 did not appreciably decline until August 8 (Table 6).

The value of the growth retardants used in this study on regularly mowed turf appears limited. Lowering of rates to eliminate injury reduced the length of time that materials were effective, making them uneconomical to use. Varieties differed in their response to retardants, with less injury to more vigorous types. Without question turfgrass growth can be retarded, and use of existing materials for minimum use and difficult to mow areas is feasible. However, continued evaluation of new compounds is necessary to assess the response of intensively maintained turfgrasses. Reduced phytotoxicity with increased retardation is a worthwhile goal.

REFERENCES

1. ALEXANDER, P. M., and J. G. WRIGHT. 1964. Transition aided by maleic hydrazide. Golf Course Rep. 32:36–40.
2. BEARD, J. B. 1973. Turfgrass science and culture. Prentice-Hall, Inc. Englewood Cliffs, N.J. p. 396–407.
3. CABLER, J. F., and G. C. HORN. 1963. Chemical growth retardants for turf-grasses. Golf Course Rep. 31(1):35–44.
4. DORE, A. T., and R. C. WAKEFIELD. 1972. Chemical growth control of a highway turf mixture. Northeast. Weed Sci. Soc. Proc. 26:224–231.
5. ——, ——, and J. A. JAGSCHITZ. 1970. Effect of growth retardants on Kentucky bluegrass and red fescue used for roadside turf. Northeast. Weed Sci. Soc. Proc. 25:123–130.
6. ENGEL, R. E., and G. H. AHLGREN. 1950. Some effects of maleic hydrazide on turfgrasses. Agron. J. 42:461–462.
7. ——, K. J. MC VEIGH, R. M. SCHMIDT, and R. W. DUELL. 1971. The effect of growth regulators on turfgrass species. Northeast. Weed Sci. Soc. Proc. 25:131–140.
8. ESCRITT, J. R. 1955. Maleic hydrazide as a grass growth regulator. J. Sports Turf Res. Inst. 9:76–84.
9. FOLKNER, J. S. 1956. Maleic hydrazide, an aid to summer-winter turf transition. Golf Course Rep. 24:5–7.
10. HART, S. W., and J. A. LA FRANCE. 1955. Effects of maleic hydrazide on the growth of turfgrasses. Golf Course Rep. 23(7):5–7.
11. JUSKA, F. V., and A. A. HANSON. 1964. Effects of growth retardants on Kentucky bluegrass turf. Golf Course Rep. 32:60–64.
12. RADKO, A. M. 1953. What about maleic hydrazide. USGA J. Turf Manage. 6:30–32.
13. U.S. Department of Agriculture. 1961. Dwarfing plants with chemicals. ARS–22–65, Washington, D. C.

61

Evaluation of cool-season turf species and planting techniques for overseeding bermudagrass golf greens[1]

C. Y. WARD, E.L. MC WHIRTER, W.R. THOMPSON, JR.

Bermudagrass (*Cynodon* spp.) greens are customarily overseeded during the fall season with cool-season grasses in order to enhance the appearance and putting quality during the period of dormancy exhibited by the hybrid bermudagrass. In addition, the cool-season grasses serve to reduce the attrition of the permanent sod during its dormancy period.

This paper presents the results of experimentation on seeding rates, dates of planting, and two cultural treatments (vertical mowing and soil topdressing) on the establishment, putting quality, and performance of numerous cultivars of cool-season grasses overseeded on bermudagrass golf greens. The most important cultivars include those of *Poa pratensis*, *Festuca rubra*, *Agrostis palustris*, *Agrostis tenuis*, *Lolium multiflorum*, and *Lolium perenne*.

Results of overseedings made at 2-week intervals over a 10-week portion of the fall season show the optimum seeding date for overseeding bermudagrass greens to be 15 to 20 days prior to the average date for the first killing frost. Overseedings made prior to the above-mentioned period received too much competition from the bermudagrass and were more susceptible to diseases, particularly *Pythium* spp. However, overseedings made later than the aforementioned period were slow to establish and were more subject to damage by freezing weather.

Cultural preparation of the bermudagrass turf just prior to overseeding was found to be a major factor in determining the uniformity and stand density of overseeded grass(es). Vertical mowing of the turf, three times just prior to overseeding, produced superior turf quality when compared to the other levels of vertical mowing (no mowing, one time, or two times) just prior to overseeding. "Soil" topdressing at the time of overseeding improved the speed of emergence, stand density, uniformity, and putting quality of the cool-season turf. Applying topdressing (1.9 hl/100 m^2) immediately before and after sowing of the seed allowed for faster germination with some improvement in turf quality over the method of applying topdressing only after seeding. Topdressing immediately before seeding was inferior to the above methods.

Perennial ryegrass consistently produced a better quality turf than any other overseeded grass when seeded in monostands. Red fescue and/or rough stalk bluegrass ranked second to perennial ryegrass, when overseeded on the bermudagrass, as monostands. Bentgrasses did not produce sufficient turf quality when seeded as monostands until 5 months after seeding. Kentucky bluegrass was inferior to all other species evaluated. It produced an unacceptable turf except when used in polystands. Additional index words: *Cynodon* spp., *Agrostis* spp., *Poa* spp., *Lolium* spp.

---

[1]Journal Article No. 2822. Mississippi Agricultural and Forestry Experiment Station.

Hybrid bermudagrasses (*Cynodon* spp.) are the most widely used turf-grasses for golf greens in the southern United States. Growth of these hybrid bermudagrasses stops at temperatures of 12 to 15C and they become completely dormant, turning brownish-gray, when frost occurs. It is a common practice to overseed bermudagrass golf greens in this region with cool-season grasses each fall season just prior to frost. An excessively high seeding rate is used so that the plants remain juvenile, and provide a dense, fine-textured turf for winter golf traffic. Overseeding is necessary to prevent wearing away of the dormant bermudagrass, to provide a pleasing color, and to insure a more visible target and a good putting surface for the golfer (5).

The overseeded cool-season grasses must persist under close, very frequent mowing for the time of seeding into the following spring when temperatures again favor the dominance of bermudagrass. The overseeded grasses may persist as much as 8 months along the northern limits of the "bermudagrass belt" to 3 months in southern limits of this belt (11).

Ideally, a turfgrass for overseeding greens should germinate and establish quickly, tolerate frequent close mowing, many frosts, and heavy traffic, then fade away with an unnoticed transition to bermudagrass in the spring.

The quality of turf obtained from overseeding golf greens is determined by species used, time of seeding, establishment practices, mowing height and frequency, watering, fertilization, and the level of thatch present in the greens (3, 4, 11).

Species Used for Overseeding Golf Greens

Prior to the development of the present turfgrass seed industry, annual ryegrass (*Lolium multiflorum* Lam.) was the only species widely used for overseeding bermudagrass golf greens. It is still widely used in monostands, but it is more often used in mixtures with finer textured grasses (7). Its popularity is due to low unit cost, local availability, rapid germination, fast seedling growth rate, and good wear resistance. Negatively, it is coarse in texture, lacks frost tolerance, is highly susceptible to *Pythium*, and often fades out too rapidly in the spring leaving a brown golf green (9). Because of these weaknesses of annual ryegrass and demands by golfers for a putting surface more nearly like bentgrass (*Agrostis* spp.), research was initiated during the late 1950's with overseeding finer textured cool-season grasses on bermudagrass golf green turf. A series of very extensive overseeding trials located on golf courses and at land grant universities throughout the South was conducted by Wilson and Latham (13). As a result of these trials, mixtures containing three or more species of cool-season grass for overseeding bermudagrass greens came into common usage. The mixture most often used is 15% bentgrass, 25% rough bluegrass (*Poa trivialis* L.), and 60% red fescue (*Festuca rubra* L.). Annual ryegrass is often added to this mixture for more wear resistance. Mixtures provide a broader genetic base against loss of stand due to diseases or severe cold weather, and give a more gradual transition in the spring. In the above mixture the red fescue and annual ryegrass provide rapid establishment, while the bentgrass persists much later in the spring season than the other species (5). The turf quality of a mixture has been shown to closely parallel that of monostands of the most aggressive species in the mixture (8). None of the slower establishing species are as effestive as annual ryegrass in competing with annual bluegrass (*Poa annua* L.) and other ubiquitous weeds present on golf greens (6). Research in Florida (7) showed little difference in the performance of monostands of 'Penncross' creeping bentgrass (*Agrostis palustris* Huds.), 'Pennlawn' red fescue, Kentucky bluegrass (*Poa pratensis* L.) common, or rough bluegrass. However, in Texas (6) rough bluegrass was found to be superior in early season to Kentucky bluegrass. Bentgrasses, though slow to establish, had a smoother transition than rough bluegrass. The latter fact was also noted in Virginia where rough bluegrass was among the first grasses to disappear in hot spring weather (10).

During the past decade many new cool-season turfgrass cultivars have been available for evaluation for overseeding golf greens. Among these, cultivars of perennial ryegrass (*Lolium perenne* L.) have received widespread acceptance. Perennial ryegrass has quick germination and establishment, is fine textured, very frost tolerant, and fades out more gradually than annual ryegrass, rough bluegrass, or the red fescues (5). Because of these desirable features and the textural advantage obtained with a single species, perennial ryegrass in monostands is replacing mixtures for overseeding golf greens. The high cost of seed and the high seeding rate required for this species deter its use on low budget golf courses.

Date of overseeding

Proper timing of overseeding bermudagrass golf greens in the fall can be critical. Overseedings made too early often fail because of excessive competition from the bermudagrass and high incidence of cottony blight [*Pythium aphanidermatum* (Edson) Fitzpatrick]. The date of overseeding golf greens will vary with geographical location. In Virginia, overseeding in early October was superior to overseeding in mid-September (11). Satisfactory winter turf was obtained in Florida when overseeding was delayed to late November (7). It is best to wait until night temperatures reach a low of 10 C which slows the aggressiveness of the bermudagrass (2).

The putting quality of the green is reduced during the establishment period. To restore it to an acceptable putting quality as soon as possible, conditions must be ideal for quick germination and seedling growth of the overseeded grass(es). Since bermudagrass is not dormant at the ideal time for overseeding, it must be retarded to reduce its competition. Vertical mowing in two or three directions followed by mowing 2 or 3 mm below the normal height of cut has been shown to reduce the growth rate of the bermudagrass and remove some of the thatch (2). The grooves made by the vertical mower should be very shallow and go in several directions so that the overseeded grass does not come up in rows. Repeated power spiking, six or more times, just prior to overseeding may enhance establishment of a more uniform stand (13). The application of a 2- to 6-mm layer of soil material prior to or immediately after seeding has been shown to improve the rate and uniformity of germination of the overseeded grasses more than any single practice (1).

The studies reported here were conducted on 'Tifgreen' and 'Tifdwarf' bermudagrass putting greens at Mississippi State Unviersity to evaluate the suitability of a wide array of cool-season turf cultivars as mono- and poly-stands for overseeding golf greens and to determine the optimum planting date, rate of seeding, time of soil topdressing, and intensity of vertical mowing on the establishment and quality of turf provided by overseeded cool-season grasses.

MATERIALS AND METHODS

Large blocks of 'Tifgreen' and 'Tifdwarf' bermudagrass (F1 hybrids of *C. dactylon* X *C. transvaalensis*) maintained as a golf putting green were used as the experimental area for these studies. The blocks were of sufficient size to allow species evaluations to be alternated to a different area each year. The soil was a Marietta very fine sandy loam with an inherent pH of 7.2. The entire experimental area was treated uniformly during the growing season, receiving two aerifications and four vertical mowings. Fertilization was 7.64 kg of N, 1.69 kg of P_2O_5, and 3.38 kg of $K_2O/100$ m^2 annually. The N was applied monthly at 0.84 kg/100 m^2 April to October and 0.44 kg/100 m^2 November to March. P and K were applied in two equal amounts in April and September based on soil tests. The experimental area was mowed at 4 to 6 mm daily in the warm season and three to five times weekly in the cool season. Plots were not mowed for about 10 days immediately after overseeding.

Procedure for species evaluations

Commercially available and experimental cultivars of cool-season turf grasses were overseeded in mid-October of 1961–1972. The bermudagrass turf was prepared for overseeding by vertical mowing in three directions with 1.27-cm spacing between blades set flush with a level surface. The area was then mowed at a height 2 mm below normal to remove about 50% of the existing green leaves. Seeds of each cultivar or mixture were preweighed and hand seeded using moist sand or sawdust as a carrier. For evaluation of cultivars as monostands, the seeding rates used were:

Cultivar	Rate, kg/100 m^2
annual ryegrass	21.2
bentgrasses	2.1
red fescues	10.6
bluegrasses	4.2
perennial ryegrass	17.0
timothy	4.2
meadow fescue	17.0

The seeds were worked down into the turf by brushing with a stiff bristle broom. Following seeding, the plots were topdressed with approximately 1.9 hl/100 m^2 of a sand-soil-peat mixture in a 7–2–1 ratio by volume, respectively. Following topdressing the plots were kept moist by sprinkler irrigations applied four times daily until germination was complete, after which plots received a minimum of 15 to 20 mm of water weekly. Plot size was 2.3 to 6.9 m² and except where specified, a randomized complete block design was used with three to five replications. Mowing was initiated at a height of 12 mm about 10 days after overseeding, then progressively lowered to 6 mm by the 20th day. The plots were sprayed periodically with fungicides to control diseases.

Plots were rated visually for putting turf quality at weekly or biweekly intervals from the time of establishment until transition the following spring. This parameter was judged to be a function of texture, color, density of stand, disease incidence, and uniformity. A scale of 1 to 10 was used, with 10 being the highest quality. Notations were also made on each cultivar for competitiveness against weeds, namely annual bluegrass, for frost damage, rate of emergence, fraying or shredding of leaf blades, and ease of mowing.

Seeding rate studies

During 1960–61, 1966–67, and 1971–72, overseeding experiments were conducted to determine the optimum seeding rates for monostands and mixtures of several cool-season turfgrasses on Tifgreen bermudagrass putting greens. The establishment procedures and method of ratings used were identical to those given in the section above. Seeding rates and cultivars used are listed in Table 5.

Date of seeding studies

The cultivars annual ryegrass, colonial bentgrass (*Agrostis tenuis* Sibth 'Highland'), and 'Pennlawn' red fescue were overseeded at 15-day intervals beginning September 1 and continuing through October 15. Later planting dates had proven to be unsatisfactory (W. R. Thompson, Jr., Mississippi Agricultural Experiment Station, unpublished data). The plots were rated for stand density at monthly intervals from November through the following May.

Soil topdressing studies

Preliminary studies (12) showed that the application of a 4-mm layer of soil topdressing immediately after overseeding significantly improved the stand density of annual ryegrass, red fescue, redtop, creeping bentgrass, and rough bluegrass (Table 1). In the study reported here, Tifgreen bermudagrass putting green turf with three distinct levels of thatch buildup was used. These differences in thatch accumulation were created by varying the frequency of core aerification. Each thatch level was replicated 12 times and served as whole plots. In mid-October of 1971 and 1972, one half of each 9.2 m² whole plot was overseeded to 'Medalist' perennial ryegrass at 17 kg/100 m² and the other half to a mixture consisting of 5.2 kg 'Dawson' red fescue, 2.1

Table 1—Emergence of overseeded cool-season species as influenced by soil topdressing applied as a uniform layer 5 to 6 mm thick consisting of sand, soil, and peat in 7–2–1 ratio, respectively.

Species or mixtures	Seeding rate	Number of seedlings 100 m²	
		Topdressed	No topdressing
	kg/100 m²	Thousands*	
Annual ryegrass	21.2	2183	2027
Pennlawn red fescue	10.6	3118	3742
Rough bluegrass	2.4	5457	4365
Redtop	2.5	4521	2650
Seaside bentgrass	2.5	4053	1871
Redtop and Seaside	1.25 & 1.25	3430	2650
Redtop and Highland	1.25 & 1.25	3118	2027
Means		3742 a†	2650 b

* Count made 30 days after seeding.   † Means followed by different letters are significantly different at the 0.05 level.

kg rough bluegrass, and 0.84 kg 'Penncross' creeping bentgrass per 100 m². Across the perennial ryegrass and the mixture, a 4- to 5-mm layer of soil top-dressing (7–1–2 sand–soil–peat mixture) was applied in a 0.91-m wide strip, in one of three ways: 1) immediately before seeding; 2) immediately after seeding; and 3) both immediately before and after seeding. A check plot which received no topdressing was included in each subplot. Cultural practices after seeding were the same as described for the species studies. The plots were rated weekly for density and uniformity of stand as a function of putting quality.

RESULTS

In Table 2, turf quality ratings by seasons are shown for monostands of commercially available turfgrass cultivars evaluated. Polystands will be discussed separately. The data are presented by seasons rather than monthly because a given cultivar normally performed in a comparable manner from week to week within a season. The seasons presented were chosen because they represent periods when overseeded grasses are most apt to exhibit an undesirable or a desirable characteristic. The fall season represented emergence and establishment; winter, the season of repeated recovery from frost and freeze damage; early spring, the season of maximum growth; and late spring the transition season which is a measure of resistance of disease and heat stress.

Perennial ryegrasses

Among the array of cultivars evaluated annually over the period 1966 to 1972, cultivars of perennial ryegrass consistently produced the most desirable turf putting quality. After rapid initial establishment the perennial ryegrasses maintained good putting quality until late spring transition when

Table 2—Putting turf quality by seasons of cool-season turfgrasses overseeded on *Cynodon* spp. for winter play (1966–1972).

Species or cultivar	Seeding rate	Early fall*		Dec 1–31		Jan–Feb		Mar 1–Apr 20		Apr 21–Jun 15	
		Excellence of turf quality (1–10; 10 = best)									
	kg/100 m²	L	H†	L	H	L	H	L	H	L	H
Lolium multiflorum											
Domestic	21.2	3.3	7.8	4.0	5.5	3.5	6.0	3.5	7.0	3.6	4.3
Pennington's	21.2	4.0	6.1	2.5	4.0	2.1	2.1	3.0	3.9	1.9	2.0
Magnolia	21.1	3.5	8.3	--	--	2.5	4.3	4.0	5.5	2.3	3.0
Lolium perenne											
Barenza	16.9	4.0	5.0	4.8	5.0	4.7	5.5	5.1	5.5	3.0	5.0
Combi ISI	16.9	3.3	3.9	5.0	5.3	3.0	4.6	5.5	5.7	2.5	6.6
Linn	16.9	3.3	5.0	5.3	7.0	--	--	5.0	9.0	3.0	4.0
Manhattan	16.9	3.8	7.3	4.5	5.8	4.6	7.0	6.1	7.4	3.1	7.3
Medalist 2	16.9	4.7	9.3	4.7	6.5	6.0	7.6	6.8	8.1	6.3	6.9
Medalist 4	16.9	3.8	5.1	4.8	5.3	3.4	5.29	6.0	6.5	3.7	7.6
NK-100	16.9	4.3	10.0	6.3	6.5	6.0	8.0	6.0	7.2	4.0	7.9
NK-200	16.9	3.9	5.0	6.0	6.5	5.5	6.0	6.2	7.0	4.0	7.0
Pelo	16.9	4.5	6.0	6.8	7.1	5.0	6.0	5.5	8.0	--	--
Pennfine	16.9	3.0	6.5	5.5	7.9	4.9	5.9	6.3	8.3	7.4	8.3
Valinge	16.9	4.3	5.1	6.5	6.5	--	--	6.0	8.8	--	--
Poa pratensis											
Adelphi	4.2	1.0		2.0		2.3		5.2		6.1	
Baron	4.2	1.2		3.0		2.8		5.3		6.5	
Canada	4.2	2.8		3.0		--		6.0		6.5	
Draylor	4.2	2.8		3.0		--		4.0		2.0	
Fylking	4.2	1.0	3.4	1.8	3.3	2.7	5.0	3.8	5.1	2.9	6.1
Newport	4.2	2.5		2.2		3.2		4.8		4.5	
Park	4.2	1.3	4.0	3.0	4.5	3.7	8.0	3.5	8.5	2.2	2.8
Pennstar	4.2	1.1		2.0		2.2		5.2		8.0	
Prato	4.2	1.0	5.8	2.5	6.0	4.0	6.5	2.8	7.8	4.0	7.8
Primo	4.2	1.3	1.7	2.5	3.5	2.0	3.3	5.6	5.8	5.0	6.8
Troy	4.2	1.8		3.8		--		4.3		5.0	
Merion	4.2	1.0	3.3	2.0	3.1	2.9	6.0	3.2	6.0	4.5	5.5
Windsor	4.2	3.5		3.0		3.8		4.3		3.2	
Miscellaneous Bluegrasses											
Poa trivialis	4.2	3.1	7.0	3.0	6.5	5.0	6.0	6.0	6.0	2.3	6.5
Poa ampla	10.6	4.0		5.0		3.0		6.0		2.0	
Festuca											
Dawson	10.6	5.0		6.2		7.0		8.2		6.5	
Golfrood	10.6	3.3	7.8	4.8	7.5	6.2	7.0	5.6	6.0	2.8	5.3
Highlight	10.6	2.9	7.0	4.8	7.4	4.1	6.9	5.0	5.5	3.3	6.6
Jamestown	10.6	3.2	8.3	4.0	8.0	4.3	6.2	5.6	6.2	3.5	6.9
Pennlawn	10.6	2.3	7.0	4.3	7.0	4.4	7.1	5.0	8.0	3.3	3.5
Rainer	10.6	3.3		6.0		6.5		9.0		5.6	
Ruby	10.6	3.8	7.0	5.8	7.0	4.2	8.0	3.0	7.8	1.5	2.3
Wintergreen	10.6	7.0		7.0		4.7		3.9		3.3	
Steinacher	10.6	2.5		4.0		--		6.8		--	
Agrostis											
Exeter	2.1	1.8	3.8	2.5	2.5	3.4	5.3	3.5	4.9	3.5	5.1
Holfior	2.1	2.0	4.0	3.0	4.1	3.0	3.5	4.0	5.3	4.5	6.2
Penncross	2.1	1.0	4.5	2.3	3.3	2.0	3.3	2.0	6.1	5.0	8.0
Seaside	2.1	1.0	4.3	2.0	3.0	2.3	6.0	4.6	7.0	5.0	7.8

* Period beginning 3 weeks after seeding and extending for 6 weeks.   † L = lowest rating recorded for season, H = highest.

all overseeded grasses declined in quality. The following desirable characteristics were noted for perennial ryegrass cultivars. These cultivars are highly resistant to *Pythium*, and are the most wear-resistant and most frost-tolerant of the cultivars tested. They are second only to annual ryegrass in speed of germination and establishment. The turf is dark green in color and possesses a medium to fine uniform texture. It easily withstands mowing at 5 mm and has a gradual transition in spring. Additionally, these cultivars are highly competitive with annual bluegrass and other weeds.

The perennial ryegrasses were 3 to 5 days slower in emergence and establishment than annual ryegrass, but much faster than all other species evaluated. The perennial ryegrass cultivars did have several undesirable characteristics.

Some varieties exhibited very fibrous leaves which tended to fray on the tip when mowed, especially in late spring. A large amount of seed was required for desired turf density, about 15 to 18 kg/100 m^2. When cut at 6 mm or higher, golf balls putted on perennial ryegrass had a tendency to zigzag more than on other grasses.

Among the perennial ryegrasses evaluated 'Pennfine' and 'Medalist 4' were superior to all others in that they exhibited the most uniform dark green color through the overseeded period. They also showed less shredding of the leaf blades when mowed, compared to other perennial ryegrass cultivars. 'Manhattan' perennial ryegrass was of comparable putting quality though it had a variable color in the spring season. 'Pelo' and 'NK-100' produced excellent turf quality from establishment until mid-March when leaf blades became very fibrous and shredding of the leaf blade tips occurred when mowed.

Annual ryegrass

Annual ryegrass emerged and established fastest of the grasses tested, followed by perennial ryegrass, meadow fescue, red fescue, rough bluegrass, creeping and colonial bentgrass, and Kentucky bluegrass. As may be seen in Table 2, annual ryegrass usually reached its peak quality in late fall then declined sharply in the winter due to its lack of frost tolerance. Its quality often improved again in the early spring, but the stand density was often reduced by *Pythium* blight. Annual ryegrass was usually the first species to fade out in the spring, often before the bermudagrass recovered sufficiently to produce a quality putting surface. The abrupt transition which often occurred with annual ryegrass is postulated to be partially due to its lack of heat tolerance, but primarily to its morphology. It is very coarse textured, having fewer basal leaves than most species tested and, therefore, close frequent mowing removes a higher percentage of its active leaf tissue which would greatly reduce the persistence of this species.

Among the varieties of annual ryegrass tested, none was superior to common commercial seed lots. This is not surprising since all varieties of annual ryegrass tested were developed for pastures rather than turfs.

Fine Fescues

Red and chewings [*Festuca rubra* var. *commutata* Gaud.] produced good putting turf quality, but were slower to germinate and establish than *Lolium* cultivars. They were finer textured than any other species evaluated and were second in frost tolerance to perennial ryegrass. Because of their fine texture and their upright growth habit they provide a highly desirable putting surface. During one experiment the Mississippi State University Golf Team was asked to rate monostands of four species for putting quality; red fescue was rated first by five of six players.

Among the new varieties, 'Dawson' and 'Jamestown' have exhibited outstanding and uniform color, putting quality, and a smoother transition in the spring season compared to the variety Pennlawn. The varieties, 'Golfrood,' 'Ruby,' and 'Wintergreen' have been equal or superior to Pennlawn in turf quality. The red fescues have been more diseased and erratic in transition than perennial ryegrass. They die out in spots 2 to 5 cm in diameter rather than as a gradual thinning.

'Highlight' chewings fescue is equal to Jamestown and Dawson red fescue in density, uniformity, fineness of texture and transition, but its yellowish-green color renders it less desirable in monostands or in mixtures with perennial ryegrass. Mixtures of red fescue with perennial ryegrass were excellent in turf quality and possessed very uniform dark color. These mixtures contained from 40 to 70% perennial ryegrass. A common mixture is a 50–50 blend seeded at 13 to 17 kg/100 m^2.

Bentgrass

The bentgrasses were found to germinate rapidly but due to their weak seedling vigor were very slow to establish. Up to 5 months were required for overseeded monostands of bentgrasses to develop an acceptable putting surface. Because the bentgrasses were slow to develop dense stands, they were often invaded by annual bluegrass and other weeds. As may be seen in Table 2, the bentgrasses reached their peak in mid- to late spring and at that time produced exceptional putting quality. Because they often persist into early summer they sometimes retarded the development of the bermudagrass sod. Also, they proved to be highly vulnerable to hot weather and will transition quickly if not irrigated daily in late spring.

Creeping bentgrass was superior to colonial bentgrass for overseeding. Among the creeping bentgrass cultivars, 'Seaside' was superior to Penncross in that it established more quickly and was slightly more aggressive toward annual bluegrass. Among cultivars of colonial bentgrass, 'Holfior' was superior to 'Exeter' in turf quality in early season. For practical use the bentgrasses are much too weak in seedling vigor to be used in monostands. They make a desirable contribution to mixtures during the spring and are of significant value to golf courses holding spring tournaments on overseeded greens.

Bluegrasses

As shown in Table 2, the Kentucky bluegrasses had unacceptable turf quality until early spring. They were the slowest of the cultivars tested to germinate and establish an acceptable stand density. 'Newport' exhibited the most seedling vigor among Kentucky bluegrass cultivars; whereas, 'Prato' had the best quality from late fall through transition. The Kentucky bluegrasses were totally unacceptable as monostands for overseeding bermudagrass golf greens. In addition to being the slowest species to reach an acceptable level of turf density, their growth habits were erratic. This, coupled with their medium to coarse texture, resulted in a bumpy putting surface.

Rough bluegrass was comparable to red fescue in speed of establishment. It produced an acceptable putting surface and exhibited good frost tolerance. Although too slow in establishment for pure stands, it performed well in mixtures. This species has a yellowish color which doesn't blend well with dark green grasses. As shown by Schmidt (11) it is subject to a sudden transition in the spring with high temperatures. In 1972–73 the variety 'Polis' was compared to a commercial seed lot. The two cultivars had identical putting quality ratings (1–10; 10 = best) in the fall, but Polis rated 6.4 in the spring, compared to 5.9 for the commercial lot. Most of the seed of rough bluegrass are produced in Europe and often contain weed seeds.

Big bluegrass (*Poa ampla*, L.) exhibited an excellent texture, but due to severe leaf tip shredding after about March 1 it rated unacceptable for overseeding. Big bluegrass established faster than any other bluegrass tested.

Miscellaneous cultivars

Two timothy (*P. pratense* L.) cultivars, 'N-95' and 'N4-124,' were evaluated in 1966–67. They produced acceptable turf quality, but transitioned in an erratic fashion.

Meadow fescue (*Festuca elatior* L.) cultivars were coarse in texture, susceptible to *Pythium*, and did not produce acceptable putting quality.

Dates and rates of seeding

Four commonly used cool-season turf grasses were each overseeded at two rates on Tifgreen bermudagrass putting green turf at four dates in 1960 as shown in Table 3. An unseeded check plot was included in each replication to measure damage to the bermudagrass caused by the cool-season cultivars. These dates were chosen because in the preliminary study overseedings made in November resulted in poor stands.

The effect on turf quality by the rates of seeding of each cool-season grass was small. With the exception of red fescue all seeding rates tested produced a satisfactory winter golf green turf. The seeding rates for red fescue used in this study were too low to produce a satisfactory turf. Schmidt (10)

Table 3—Influence of date of seeding on subsequent turf quality of cool-season turfgrasses overseeded on Tifgreen bermudagrass.

Species overseeded	Seeding rate	Turf quality for golf putting*							
		Date of overseeding							
		Sep 1		Sep 15		Oct 1		Oct 15	
	kg/100 m²	F†	S	F	S	F	S	F	S
Annual ryegrass	21.2	3	4	7	6	9	8	7	8
	42.4	4	4	6	6	7	6	6	8
Red fescue	1.70	1	2	2	2	2	3	4	4
	2.55	1	2	2	3	2	3	4	4
Highland bentgrass	1.70	1	2	1	2	3	5	5	4
	2.55	1	2	1	2	3	5	4	5
Redtop	2.55	1	2	2	5	2	5	4	6

* 10 = Excellent, 1 = Poor; a rating of 5 or higher is acceptable quality.   † F = fall; S = spring.

in Virginia and later work reported in this paper showed 8.5 to 12.7 kg/100 m² to be an ideal seeding rate for red fescue overseeded in monostands. Whether seeded at 21.2 or 42.4 kg, ryegrass produced satisfactory turf quality in fall and spring. The higher seeding rate resulted in weaker seedlings and also created a more favorable environment for disease. Redtop produced a satisfactory turf in the spring, but not in the fall. Highland bentgrass did not perform well as a monostand at any time in this study. The date of planting had a significant effect on subsequent turf qualtiy. The first seeding date was 67 days prior to the first killing frost. None of the cultivars performed satisfactorily on this date of seeding. The bermudagrass provided too much competition to the seedlings of the cool-season grasses on this date. Stand density was about 75% lower for overseedings made in early September compared to later seedings.

There was a species and seeding date interaction. Annual ryegrass performed best when seeded October 1, whereas redtop produced best results when seeded October 15. However, at no time did redtop produce outstanding turf quality. The following spring, all cultivars transitioned poorly, especially the annual ryegrass. From these data it was concluded that overseedings of cool-season grasses on bermudagrass greens at this location should be made 10 to 30 days prior to the first killing frost date.

In another seeding rate study 'NK-100' perennial ryegrass was overseeded at 5.3, 10.6, 21.2, and 42.4 kg/100 m². The overseeding was made October 12, 1967, on Tifgreen bermudagrass golf green turf. As shown in Table 4, the 21.2 kg seeding rate produced significantly higher turf quality than higher or lower seeding rates. The 5.3 kg/100 m² seeding rate did not produce an adequate stand density for good putting quality. This was also true for the 10.6 kg seeding rate, but this rate produced a putting quality comparable to that produced by the 52.6 kg seeding rate. Overseeding at 42.6 kg produced a very dense overcrowded turf, which resulted in the only Pythium outbreak in the entire experiment. Seeding at this rate also caused the grass to exhibit a less uniform color. These data were helpful in selecting

Table 4—Influence of seeding rate on turf quality of NK-100 perennial ryegrass over-seeded on Tifgreen bermudagrass (1967–68).

Seeding rate	Turf quality ratings*				Mean†
	Fall	Winter	Early spring	Late spring	
kg/100 m²					
5.3	4.0	5.1	5.4	3.5	4.5 c
10.6	5.8	6.8	5.9	4.2	6.2 b
21.2	9.5	8.2	6.8	7.5	8.0 a
42.4	7.8	6.5	7.2	4.2	6.4 b

* A rating scale of 1 to 10 was used, with 10 = best (5 is acceptable).   † Means followed by different letters are significantly different at the 0.05 level.

the recommended rate of 17 kg/100 m² used in present day overseeding for monostands of perennial ryegrasses.

In October 1971, 'Medalist' perennial ryegrass, 'Magnolia' annual ryegrass and common rough bluegrass were overseeded on Tifgreen bermudagrass golf green turf at the rates shown in Table 5. Perennial and annual ryegrass were overseeded alone, whereas each rate of rough bluegrass was overseeded with a constant rate of annual ryegrass, 12.7 kg/100 m².

Turf quality ratings were made at weekly intervals. The ratings made on four dates are shown in Table 5. They show that perennial ryegrass except for the 4.2-kg rate at the first rating date was equal or superior in turf quality to annual ryegrass and the mixture. By January the lowest seeding rate of perennial ryegrass had a more desirable putting turf quality than any seeding rate of annual ryegrass or the mixture. Increased seeding rates up to 17 kg improved the turf quality of perennial ryegrass at all ratings. Annual ryegrass putting quality was also improved by increased seeding rates but the

Table 5—Influence of seeding rate on quality of overseeded winter golf green turf. The base sod was Tifgreen bermudagrass managed as a putting green.

Species	Seeding rate	Turf quality rating*			
		Nov 4	Nov 18	Dec 9	Jan 4
	kg/100 m²				
Annual ryegrass	8.5	2.00 g†	3.00 f	3.00 e	5.25 he
	12.7	2.50 d	3.50 de	3.50 d	5.50 gh
	17.0	3.50 b	3.75 cd	4.25 c	5.75 fg
	21.2	3.25 c	4.00 bc	4.00 c	6.00 cf
Perennial ryegrass	8.5	1.75 i	3.00 f	3.25 de	6.50 cd
	12.7	2.75 d	3.75 cd	4.25 c	6.75 c
	17.0	3.75 b	4.00 bc	5.00 b	7.75 b
	21.2	4.50 a	6.00 a	7.25 a	8.50 a
Poa trivialis‡	.85	2.20 ef	2.60 g	3.20 de	6.00 ef
	1.27	2.33 e	2.67 g	3.00 e	6.00 ef
	1.70	2.25 e	3.50 de	3.25 de	6.00 ef
	2.12	2.50 d	3.50 de	4.00 c	6.25 de

* Overseeding made Oct. 21, 1969, Mississippi State, Mississippi. A rating of 10 = best.
† Means followed by the same letter are not significantly different at 0.05 level.   ‡ 12.7 kg of annual ryegrass was seeded with each rate of *Poa trivialis*.

Table 6—Turf quality produced by cool-season grasses overseeded on bermudagrass putting green turf.

| Species or mixture | Days to emerge | Turf quality ratings for putting* | | | | | Season of transition |
		Nov	Dec	Jan	Feb	Mar	
Annual ryegrass†	7	8	8	7	7	8	April
Red fescue	8	7	9	8	8	9	May
Rough bluegrass	9	6	8	9	9	7	April
Redtop	10	1	3	3	3	5	April
Seaside bentgrass	11	2	4	5	5	6	May
Redtop & Seaside	11	1	3	3	3	5	May
Redtop & Highland	11	1	3	3	3	5	May

* 10 = best; 1 = poorest.   † For seeding rates see Table 2.

17-kg rate was not consistently superior to the 12.7-kg rate. Increasing *Poa trivialis* from 0.85 to 2.12 kg/100 m² with 8.5 kg of annual ryegrass had little influence on turf quality. However, after 10 weeks the mixture produced superior turf quality to the annual ryegrass alone at all seeding rates used.

During spring transition the annual ryegrass alone died out faster than the mixture, which transitioned before the perennial ryegrass.

On June 18, the percentage of bermudagrass coverage in the plots was 85, 75, and 80% for plots seeded to annual ryegrass, perennial ryegrass, and rough bluegrass, respectively.

Soil topdressing

Spreading a 4- to 6-mm layer of soil over the greens immediately after overseeding has been shown to increase the stand density of overseedings. On October 15, 1961, the species shown in Table 1 were overseeded onto a bermudagrass putting green which had been partitioned into eight sections, four of which were vertical mowed prior to seeding. Each grass was seeded in four replicated plots on vertical mowed and nonmowed turf. Following seeding, one-half of each plot was soil topdressed to a depth of 5 to 6 mm. Vertical mowing had no significant effect on the number of seedlings which emerged, however, soil topdressing significantly increased stand density of rough bluegrass, redtop, Seaside bentgrass, and mixtures of redtop and Seaside. Annual ryegrass stand density was not affected by soil topdressing and the number of red fescue seedlings was slightly reduced by soil topdressing. Ratings of subsequent turf quality produced by these monostands and mixtures are shown in Table 6.

A study was initiated in 1971 and repeated in 1972 to determine if the thin layer of soil topdressing applied at time of seeding should be applied before or after overseeding or both before and after. A mixture and monostand were used; the mixture consisted of 65% red fescue, 25% rough bluegrass, and 10% creeping bentgrass seeded at 8.48 kg/100 m², and perennial ryegrass was seeded alone at 16.96 kg/100 m².

The results for the 2 years were very similar, so only the 1971 data are presented. The presence of a thatch layer greater than 50 mm thick reduced

Table 7—Influence of time of application of soil topdressing on the stand density of over-seeded cool-season turfgrasses. The seeding was made Oct. 13, 1971 on a Tifgreen bermudagrass putting green.

Time of application of soil topdressing	Thatch thickness on bermudagrass base*					
	Thick > 50 mm		Medium ≃ 25 mm		Thin < 15	
	P. rye†	Mix‡	P. rye	Mix	P. rye	Mix
			Density on Oct 21§			
Before seeding	25	15	43	15	43	16
After seeding	30	11	57	18	55	16
Before and after seeding	43	16	65	23	60	20
			Density on Nov 16			
Before seeding	20	30	40	60	50	70
After seeding	20	20	30	70	50	70
Before and after seeding	50	60	60	80	60	70
			Density on Mar 30			
Before seeding	30	60	60	60	70	60
After seeding	70	70	80	80	70	60
Before and after seeding	60	60	70	80	70	60

* Thick, medium, and thin thatch accumulation created by no, three, and six core aerifications per year, respectively.   † Medalist perennial ryegrass 16.96 kg/100 m².   ‡ Mix = mixture of 25% rough bluegrass, 65% red fescue, 20% creeping bentgrass seeded at 8.48 kg/100 m². § Density is based on percentage of 100.

the initial stand of the mixture and perennial ryegrass (Table 7). There was little difference in stands obtained on plots with medium and thin thatch. Topdressing with a 4- to 6-mm layer of soil enhanced earlier and more uniform establishment of all plots. Topdressing after seeding improved the germination of perennial ryegrass more than applying soil topdressing before seeding. Applying soil topdressing both before and after seeding, "sandwiching", produced improved turf density for both the ryegrass and mixture during the first 4 weeks after seeding. Where the thickest thatch layer existed, soil topdressing applied immediately after overseeding and the treatment involved topdressing before and after overdressing produced superior stands compared to topdressing before overseeding only. More uniform stands emerged where some topdressing was applied after overseeding rather than all before. Initial emergence was much faster for perennial ryegrass than the mixture, however, after 4 weeks the stand density of the mixture was greater than for perennial ryegrass.

DISCUSSION

The results obtained in overseeding of bermudagrass golf greens with cool-season turfgrasses for winter play can be influenced by many factors. The date of overseeding should come late enough in the fall for competition from the bermudagrass sod to the emerging seedlings to be minimal. Seeding after frost, however, will result in slow and erratic germination and seedling development due to frequent freezing and lower temperatures. Overseeding larger seeded grasses such as perennial ryegrass may be done earlier or later in the season than slower growing species such as bentgrass. Overseeding 20 to 30 days prior to the average date of the first killing frost proved to be the best in early studies and it has worked well for superintendents on golf courses throughout the region. Perennial ryegrass, of which several outstanding varieties are available, has proven to be the best species evaluated in monostands. It may be used in pure stands at 15 to 20 kg/100 m^2 or at half this seeding rate with an equal quantity of Jamestown or Dawson red fescue. The dark green color of these grasses blends exceptionally well.

Amount of play anticipated should be a factor in determining the grass chosen for overseeding. Annual and perennial ryegrasses have a very fast growth rate and should be included in mixtures on golf courses which have heavy play. Conversely, they require more frequent mowing than mixtures of slower growing cultivars.

Due to its lack of frost and low temperature tolerance, annual ryegrass should be omitted from overseedings along the upper limits of the southern region. As insurance against cold damage and other detrimental environmental influences, a mixture of several species is a wise choice. Such mixtures should contain a sufficient quantity of perennial ryegrass or red fescue to provide adequate early establishment. Other species may be added to give a desired color, a slower transition, and textural effect.

A seeding rate to give a dense stand should be used. If the stand is thin, individual plants will develop more tillers and become too coarse for good putting. Seeding at a rate to supply 10 to 15 million seed/100 m^2 is best for monostands of *Lolium* cultivars. When cultivars with smaller seeds such as rough bluegrass and creeping bentgrass are used, a rate to supply 20 to 25 million seed/100 m^2 should be used.

Regardless of the species of cool-season grass used in overseeding, the transition period can be abrupt. However, the overseeded grass(es) can be delayed in fading out by syringing with short irrigation periods near midday or by increasing the height of mowing by 1 or 2 mm as transition time approaches.

Establishment of uniform overseedings can be enhanced by reducing thatch buildup of the bermudagrass in the summer season. Adding a uniform thin layer, 4 to 6 mm, of topsoil as a mulch at the time of seeding improves the rate and uniformity of germination of the overseeded grasses. Soil topdressing is more critical on greens with a heavy thatch and where cultivars with very small seeds are used.

REFERENCES

1. Annual Report of Agronomy Department. 1969. Research on Crops, Soils, and Seed Technology. Mississippi Farm Res. 32(6):3-6.
2. GILL, W. J., W. R. THOMPSON, Jr., and C. Y. WARD. 1964. Species methods for overseeding bermudagrass greens. The Golf Superintendent 35, 9, 10.
3. KNEEBONE, William R., and Gary L. MAJOR. 1969. Differential survival of cool-season turfgrass species overseeded on different selections of bermudagrass. Crop Sci. 9:153-5.

4. MC BEE, G. C. 1970. Performance of certain cool season grasses in overseeding studies on a Tifgreen bermudagrass golf green. Prog. Report 2457. Texas A&M Univ. Texas Agr. Exp. Sta.

5. MC WHIRTER, E. L., and C. Y. WARD. 1970. Grasses tested for golf greens. Mississippi Farm Res. 33(9):7.

6. MENN, W. G., and G. C. MC BEE. 1971. An evaluation of various cool-season grasses and grass mixtures in overseeding a Tifgreen bermudagrass golf green. PR 2878 Texas Agr. Exp. Sta. 16 p.

7. MEYERS, H. G., and G. C. HORN. 1968. Selection of grasses for overseeding. Proc. Univ. Florida Turfgrass Management Conf. 15:47.

8. ———, and ———. 1970. The two-Grass system in Florida. p. 110–117. *In* Proc. First Int. Turfgrass Res. Conf. Sports Turf Research Institute, Bingley, England.

9. SCHMIDT, R. E., and R. E. BLASER. 1966. Cool season grasses for winter turf on bermuda putting greens. U. S. Golf Assoc. J. Turf Manage. 14:25.

10. ———, and ———. 1967. Establishing winter bermuda putting turf. U. S. Golf Assoc. J. Turf Manage. 15:30.

11. SCHMIDT, R. E. 1970. Overseeding cool-season turfgrasses on dormant bermudagrass for winter. p. 124–129. *In* Proc. First Int. Turfgrass Res. Conf. Sports Turf Research Institute, Bingley, England.

12. THOMPSON, W. R., Jr., and C. Y. WARD. 1967. Prevent thatch accumulation on Tifgreen bermudagrass greens. The Golf Superintendent 34:

13. WILSON, C. G., O. J. NOER, and J. M. LATHAM, Jr. 1963. Evaluation of cool-season grasses for winter overseeding of southern golf greens. Agron. Abstr. p. 120.

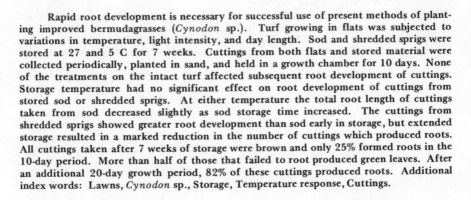

62

Rooting responses of bermudagrass cuttings to preplant treatment[1]

R.E. BURNS

Rapid root development is necessary for successful use of present methods of planting improved bermudagrasses (*Cynodon* sp.). Turf growing in flats was subjected to variations in temperature, light intensity, and day length. Sod and shredded sprigs were stored at 27 and 5 C for 7 weeks. Cuttings from both flats and stored material were collected periodically, planted in sand, and held in a growth chamber for 10 days. None of the treatments on the intact turf affected subsequent root development of cuttings. Storage temperature had no significant effect on root development of cuttings from stored sod or shredded sprigs. At either temperature the total root length of cuttings taken from sod decreased slightly as sod storage time increased. The cuttings from shredded sprigs showed greater root development than sod early in storage, but extended storage resulted in a marked reduction in the number of cuttings which produced roots. All cuttings taken after 7 weeks of storage were brown and only 25% formed roots in the 10-day period. More than half of those that failed to root produced green leaves. After an additional 20-day growth period, 82% of these cuttings produced roots. Additional index words: Lawns, *Cynodon* sp., Storage, Temperature response, Cuttings.

Bermudagrass (*Cynodon* sp.) is the predominant turfgrass in much of the southern United States. The introduction of sterile hybrids has necessitated vegetative planting, which requires transporting and holding of perishable sod or stolons. Up to this time, work on rooting of bermudagrass has been limited to the study of conditions at the time of rooting (1, 3, 5, 6). Little work has been reported on the effect of treatment of the grass prior to planting on subsequent rooting. This study was undertaken to determine 1) the effect of preplant environment and 2) the duration and types of storage on subsequent rooting of bermudagrass.

MATERIALS AND METHODS

Established 'FB-137' bermudagrass sod in greenhouse flats was grown under different environmental conditions for 2 weeks to determine preharvest treatment effects on subsequent rooting of cuttings. These condi-

[1]Contribution of Univ. of Ga. College of Agriculture. Georgia Experiment Station, Experiment, Ga.

Table 1—Effect of environmental variables on rooting of bermudagrass cuttings.

	Percent change due to decrease in:		
	Daylength, 16–10 hours	Light intensity, 16,150 to 8,600 lux	Temperature, 32 to 34–27 to 15 C
Total root length	–34	–32	–35
Average length per root	–17	–24	–16
Number of roots	–19	–11	–19
Roots with branching	0	–42	–67

tions were: day length of 16 and 8 hours, 16,150 and 8,600 lux light intensity, and 32 to 24 C versus 27 to 15 C regimes. Cuttings were then made from these sods and rooted at 16,150 lux, 16 hour days, and 32 to 24 C.

'Tifway' bermudagrass sod (approximately 2-cm thick) was removed from established turf to determine the effect of storage conditions on subsequent rooting of cuttings. A portion of the fresh sod was shredded in a compost grinder and placed in 8-liter perforated plastic bags. The intact sod was stacked. Then sod and sprigs were stored at 5 and 27 C for periods up to 7 weeks; water was applied as necessary. Cuttings were collected twice weekly thereafter. At each harvest, two replicates of 18 cuttings each were rooted in moist sand under the same light and temperature conditions as above. Cuttings were removed from the sand after 10 days for root counts and measurements.

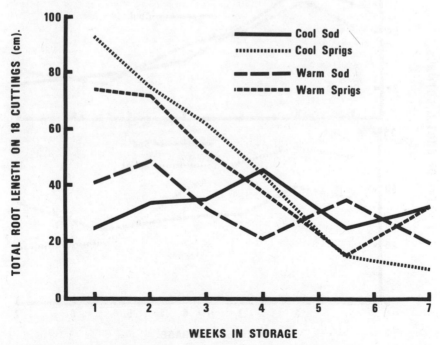

Fig. 1—Total root length on 18 cuttings as affected by temperature and time in storage prior to rooting of the cutting.

RESULTS AND DISCUSSION

A decrease in day length, light intensity, or temperature during the rooting period caused a reduction in root formation in cuttings of FB-137 bermudagrass as reported by Burns in earlier work (1). The total root length of the cuttings was reduced one-third by decreasing any of these factors (Table 1). The average length of individual roots was most affected by light intensity with a corresponding lower effect on number of roots. The amount of root branching, which was not included in root length, was most affected by the temperature variable but was not affected by day length change.

There were no differences in root formation on FB-137 cuttings that had been subjected to temperature, light intensity, and day length variables for 2 weeks prior to taking the cuttings.

The treatment of harvested Tifway bermudagrass sod was limited to temperature, since day length or light intensity would not be involved under storage conditions. The temperature at which the sod or sprigs were stored had no consistent effect on root length (Fig. 1) or on percent of cuttings which formed roots (Fig. 2). In contrast, the form of storage had a definite effect on rooting of cuttings. For the first 5 weeks in storage the cuttings from shredded sprigs performed better than did those from intact sod. This was probably due to an injury-induced increase in enzyme activity. After

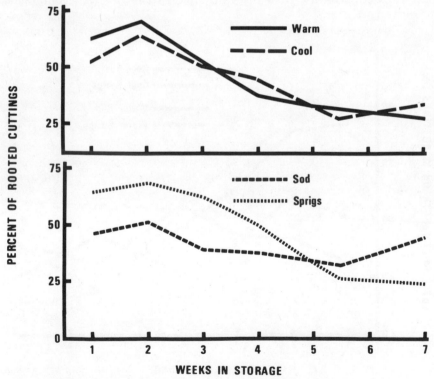

Fig. 2—Percent of cuttings producing roots as affected by storage conditions prior to rooting of cuttings.

Table 2—Average values of root measurements on Tifway bermudagrass cuttings for both temperatures of stored sod and sprigs.

	Weeks in storage*					
	1	2	3	4	5-6	7
Rooted cuttings out of 18	11	12	9	8	6	6
Total root length per 18 cutting, cm	66	58	45	35	22	21
Number of roots per 18 cuttings	19	19	14	11	7	8
Average length per root, cm	3.0	3.0	3.2	3.1	3.1	2.4
Nodes per rooted sprig	1.4	1.4	1.4	1.2	1.1	1.0
Roots per node	1.4	1.2	1.2	1.2	1.1	1.1

* Each value is average of two harvests except for 7 weeks which represents only one harvest.

the second week of storage, the shredded sprigs began to deteriorate more rapidly than the sod and this resulted in lower performance of the cuttings from shredded sprigs after the fourth week in storage (Fig. 1 and 2).

However, the major factor influencing the performance of the cuttings was the time in storage (Table 2). The number of cuttings producing roots decreased approximately 40% from the first to seventh week of storage, while the total root length decreased almost 70%. The reduction in root length was due to both fewer and shorter roots on the cuttings with a reduction in the number of roots being the predominate factor.

The reduction in number of roots was due largely to a reduction in the number of active nodes (Table 2). The number of roots per node decreased only 15% during the storage period. At the final harvest, no cutting produced roots at more than one node compared to as many as four active nodes on some cuttings early in storage.

After 7 weeks in storage all cuttings were brown and dead in appearance. Only 25% of them produced roots in the 10-day period used in this study. When the nonrooted cuttings were left in the rooting media for an additional 20 days only 18% failed to root. Rooting was always preceded by formation of a green leaf. Thus, death of the cutting was not the reason for lack of rooting. One cause may have been the lack of a viable green leaf for the production of the auxin co-factor which is necessary for adventitious root formation (2, 4). In addition to auxin, a rhizocaline compound is necessary for the formation of roots on cuttings (2).

REFERENCES

1. BURNS, R. E. 1972. Environmental factors affecting root development and reserve carbohydrates of bermudagrass cuttings. Agron. J. 64:44–45.
2. MAKOTO, K. 1964. Centrifugation, rhizocaline and rooting of Salix alba L. Physiol. Plant. 17:855–865.
3. SCHMIDT, R. E., and R. E. BLASER. 1969. Effect of temperature, light, and nitrogen on growth and metabolism of Tifgreen bermudagrass (*Cynodon* spp). Crop Sci. 9:5–9.
4. VAN OVERBEEK, J., S. A. GORDON, and E. GREGORY. 1946. An analysis of the function of the leaf in the process of root formation in cuttings. Amer. J. Bot. 33: 100–107.
5. YOUNGNER, V. B. 1959. Growth of U-3 bermudagrass under various day and night temperatures and light intensities. Agron. J. 51:557–559.
6. ———. 1968. The effects of temperature and light on vegetative growth. Proc. 39th Int. Turf Conf. 15:10–12.

63

Influence of mineral nutrition on the cold tolerance and soluble protein fraction of centipedegrass[1]

H. D. PALMERTREE, C. Y. WARD, R. H.PLUENNEKE

A prepared soil, purposely low in the major plant nutrients, was established to a solid sod of centipedegrass, *Eremochloa ophiuroides* (Munro) Hack, under field conditions. During Summer 1971, plots of the centipedegrass turf were fertilized with 0.98, 1.96, and 2.94 kg of N; 0.49, 0.98, and 1.47 kg of P_2O_5; and 0.98, 1.96, and 2.94 kg of K_2O/ 100 m^2 in a factorial arrangement. In midfall, prior to the first frost, a portion of the sod and soil was removed intact from each plot and transferred to a greenhouse and grown as unhardened sod. The sod remaining in the field plots was designated as hardened sod.

Sod portions from each fertility treatment of both hardened and unhardened centipedegrass were subjected to low temperature freezing studies to determine the minimum critical temperature for centipedegrass. Centipedegrass which had been fertilized with N rates greater than 1.96 kg/100 m^2 was significantly less tolerant of low temperatures. Varying rates of P and K had no effect on cold damage in the low temperature chamber, but under field conditions, K at 1.96 and 2.94 kg/100 m^2 increased winter survival of centipedegrass compared to the lower rate of K. Under field conditions, 1.96 kg of N was needed to maintain turf quality and this rate of N actually gave a slight increase in winterhardiness over the lower rate. No difference in the low temperature tolerance was found between field-hardened and unhardened greenhouse sod, suggesting that this grass might obtain maximum hardiness with shortened photoperiod.

Polyacrylamide gel electrophoresis of extracts from centipedegrass leaves revealed that the number of soluble protein bands decreased upon hardening, while the number of soluble protein bands in gels loaded with extract from stolons and crowns increased with hardening. Gels from leaf tissue extract contained more bands than did the gels containing the soluble protein from stolons and crowns. The total soluble protein concentration in stolons and crowns was increased by low temperature hardening. Total soluble proteins also increased with increased N fertilization up to the 1.96 kg rate, but decreased significantly when 2.94 kg of N were applied. Additional index words: Cold hardiness, Soluble proteins, Electrophoresis, Centipedegrass.

One of the most popular home lawn grasses in the lower South is centipedegrass [*Eremochloa ophiuroides* (Munro) Hack.]. It is estimated that about 40% of the lawns within 120 km of the Mississippi Gulf Coast are established with this grass. Even though centipedegrass is used extensively as a lawn grass, it does have a severe weakness—lack of winter survival. This

[1]Journal article of the Mississippi Agricultural and Forestry Experiment Station, Mississippi State, MS 39762.

grass is the least cold tolerant of any of the perennial southern turfgrasses, and each year many homeowners with centipede lawns are plagued with dead spots in the spring. Several factors contribute to this problem, but among the least understood of the known factors affecting cold tolerance in centipedegrass is mineral nutrition.

Literature on effects of soil fertility levels on centipedegrass is limited. Ward (21) found that 2.94 kg of N/100 m² applied annually reduced the winter survival of centipedegrass, while 1.47 kg had no visible effect on winter injury. Heavy N applications in the fall were found to cause loss of cold resistance in 16 turfgrasses common to Ohio (5). Beard (3) found that injury to turfgrasses was increased by late fall applications of N which produced succulent, tender growth. Kentucky bluegrass (*Poa pratensis* L.) was less resistant to low temperature when nitrogen fertilizer was applied (6).

Deal (10) suggested that golf course superintendents may be enhancing low-temperature kill of turf on putting greens by maintaining high levels of P. He noted that grasses absorb N, P, and K in a ratio of 4-1-3, and concluded that balance of nutrients was as important as concentration. Davis (8) and Gilbert and Davis (9) reported a ratio of 4-1-5 as the optimum level of N, P, K, respectively, for increasing cold tolerance in 'Tifdwarf' and 'Tifgreen' bermudagrass. Plants receiving the most N were least resistant to low temperatures; however, a lower killing temperature was observed with increased N, provided the P and K were supplied in a ratio of 1-3. In other work on Tifgreen bermudagrass, it was reported that a high ratio of P to K increased winterkill while a low ratio resulted in little damage. Wagner (20) suggested that when K was not supplied in sufficient quantities to balance high N rates on turfgrasses, lack of winterhardiness could be expected. Hendricks (12) proposed that K protected the plant against protein degradation.

Alexander and Gilbert (2) proposed that an excess of N and/or a low level of K might be the cause of damage to bermudagrass golf greens. Morgan (16) found that K increased vigor and winterhardiness of turfgrasses.

Several workers have reported the relationship of nitrogen fractions to low temperature injury (4, 13, 18, 19). It is generally agreed that a positive correlation exists between soluble protein fraction and cold hardiness (9, 13, 14, 17, 22). Davis and Gilbert (9) used polyacrylamide gel electrophoresis (PAGE) to characterize the soluble protein changes in Tifdwarf and Tifgreen bermudagrass [*Cynodon dactylon* (L.) Pers.]. They found that generally the number of soluble protein bands increased with hardening.

To elucidate the winterkill problem and provide answers for centipedegrass growers, a series of experiments was initiated to study various aspects of centipedegrass low temperature survival as affected by soil nutritional levels. The objectives were as follows:

1) To determine the lowest temperature at which this grass would survive and produce regrowth at several levels of nitrogen, phosphorus, and potassium.
2) To compare naturally cold-hardened centipedegrass turf with sod that had been protected from cold weather. Meeting this objective should provide an insight into the effects of cold hardening on cold tolerance and winter survival.

3) To estimate the optimum level and ratio of N, P, and K for acceptable turf quality with maximum resistance to cold damage.
4) To compare the soluble protein changes of cold-hardened and unhardened sod at selected fertility levels and to compare these treatments with cold tolerance of centipedegrass under field conditions.

METHODS

In Summer 1971, metal drums 209 liters in volume were cut in half, lined with polyethylene bags, and filled with a prepared soil mixture low in available N, P, and K. Centipedegrass sod, washed free of all soil, was placed on the prepared soil and fertilized with 0.98, 1.96, and 2.94 kg of N; 0.49, 0.98, and 1.47 kg of P_2O_5; and 0.98, 1.96, and 2.94 kg of $K_2O/100$ m^2. The statistical design was a randomized complete block with a $3 \times 3 \times 3$ factorial arrangement, replicated three times. The high rates of N and K were split into three equal applications, while all P was applied in a single application.

Portions of sod from each plot in the study were placed in flats and moved to a greenhouse about 2 weeks prior to the first expected frost. This unhardened sod served as a duplicate of the cold-hardened sod left in the field in a minimum critical temperature (killing temperature) study.

The minimum critical temperature of both the hardened and unhardened sod was determined on all fertility treatments in a cold chamber. The cold chamber trials were divided into three phases, as outlined by Davis (8).

Ocular ratings for turf quality in the field were made throughout Fall 1971 and the Spring 1972. The amount of sod surviving the winter under field conditions was determined by a count of live stolons in May 1972.

Sod from five of the fertility treatments was selected to supply tissue for soluble protein analysis. Two grams of leaf and stolon tissue were collected from each of the five treatments and prepared for PAGE according to the methods of Davis (7). Electropherograms resulting from individual gels from each treatment were recorded and band densities were estimated visually. To obtain a quantitative measurement of soluble protein in the stolon and crown tissue, the procedure outlined by Lowry (15) was followed.

RESULTS AND DISCUSSION

The minimum critical temperatures resulting from a programmed temperature reduction scheme in the cold chamber are summarized in Table 1. Nitrogen fertilization influenced low temperature survival more than any other fertility treatment. The addition of 1.96 kg of N significantly increased the minimum critical temperature of the unhardened sod and slightly, although not significantly, increased the survival temperature of the hardened sod. Varying rates of P and K had no significant effect on the killing temperature of either the hardened or unhardened sod. These data also show that while unhardened sod was consistently killed at a slightly higher temperature than hardened sod, the response of the two sods was otherwise similar. It is possible that shortened day length may have provided a near maximum hardening of centipedegrass as was reported in alfalfa (*Medicago*

Table 1—Minimum critical temperature (killing temperature, °C) of hardened and un-hardened centipedegrass sod determined in the cold chamber as influenced by various rates of nitrogen, phosphorus, and potassium fertilization.*

Fertilization level, kg/100 m²	Hardened field sod	Unhardened greenhouse sod
Nitrogen		
0.98	-12.51 a	-11.81 a
1.96	-12.18 a	-11.19 b
2.94	-9.04 b	-8.93 c
Phosphorus (P₂O₅)		
0.49	-11.52 a	-10.62 a
0.98	-11.1Î a	-10.62 a
1.47	-11.48 a	-10.74 a
Potassium (K₂O)		
0.98	-11.07 a	-10.74 a
1.96	-11.23 a	-10.53 a
2.94	-11.48 a	-10.66 a
LSD		
0.05	0.778	0.605
0.01	1.02	0.795

Note: In this and all subsequent tables means not followed by the same letter are significantly different from each other.

sativa L.) by Hodgson (13) and in bermudagrass by Ahring and Irwing (1).

Since the primary use of centipedegrass is for home lawn turf the aesthetic value was considered. Ocular turf quality ratings were recorded in early fall and midfall (Table 2). A minimum rating of 5 was arbitrarily selected as the lowest acceptable turf quality. These data indicate that P and K had no influence on the quality except in midfall. At this rating the

Table 2—Effect of nitrogen, phosphorus, and potassium on visual quality of centipede-grass turf, Fall 1971.

Fertilization level, kg/100 m²	Turf quality*		% green leaves after frost†
	Early fall	Mid-fall	
Nitrogen			
0.98	3.33 a	3.35 a	28.70 a
1.96	6.52 b	6.83 b	28.89 a
2.94	9.52 c	9.92 c	27.22 a
Phosphorus (P₂O₅)			
0.49	6.11 a	6.33 a	30.56 a
0.98	6.66 a	6.98 b	29.56 a
1.47	6.59 a	6.80 b	25.00 a
Potassium (K₂O)			
0.98	6.67 a	6.72 a	24.81 a
1.96	6.44 a	6.76 a	27.60 a
2.94	6.26 a	6.63 a	32.41 b
LSD			
0.05	0.53	0.69	4.98
0.01	0.45	0.59	6.55

* A visual rating from 1 to 10, with 10 as the highest quality; a rating of 5 or more was considered acceptable quality for a home lawn turf. † Visual estimate with 100% representing no frost damage to leaves and 0% representing completely brown turf due to frost.

Table 3—Influence of nitrogen, phosphorus, and potassium on the survival of centipedegrass sprigs, May 1972.

Fertilization level, kg/100 m²	Live sprigs per 28.8 cm
Nitrogen	
0.98	6.07 a
1.96	5.85 a
2.94	2.67 b
Phosphorus (P₂O₅)	
0.49	2.96 a
0.98	5.15 a
1.47	4.48 a
Potassium (K₂O)	
0.98	3.93 a
1.96	5.52 b
2.94	5.15 b
LSD	
0.05	1.24
0.01	1.63

medium and high rates of P increased the turf quality. Each increase in N fertilization resulted in a concomittant increase in quality at both rating dates. Unacceptable quality was obtained with N fertilization at 0.98 kg/100 m².

One week after the first frost, visual ratings for percent green leaves were recorded. Means reported in Table 2 indicate that N and P fertilization did not influence leaf degeneration rate after frost. However, a significant increase in green leaves was noted in centipedegrass fertilized with the high rates of K, indicating that frost affected high K fertilized centipedegrass leaves less rapidly.

To obtain information on the amount of low temperature damage to sod in field plots during the winter, stolon viability counts were made in May 1972. The number of living sprigs in a 28.8-cm cross section of the field plots is summarized in Table 3. The high rate of N significantly reduced the amount of centipedegrass surviving the winter, while the medium rate of N produced only a slight reduction in live sprigs as compared to the low rate of N. The reduction in sprigs surviving the winter when fertilized with 2.94 kg N/100 m² agrees not only with most of the literature but also with the cold chamber study results discussed earlier; the high rate of N fertilization reduced winterhardiness. No effect of P on winter survival could be found, but it was noted that the addition of K significantly increased stolon viability.

Duplicate samples of centipedegrass sod fertilized at selected levels of N, P, and K were grown in the greenhouse (unhardened) and in an environmental chamber programmed to induce hardening of the centipedegrass. Results of anodic PAGE studies of leaf tissue indicated that soluble protein bands decreased in number and density when leaves were cold hardened. The main difference found in tissue of unhardened leaves was the increase in number of bands with increased N fertilization, an increase from 18 bands for the low N treatment to 24 bands for the high N treatment. The area of greatest increase was Rm 0.75 to Rm 1.00. Gels containing protein from hardened leaves also increased in number of bands with increased N fertilization, but

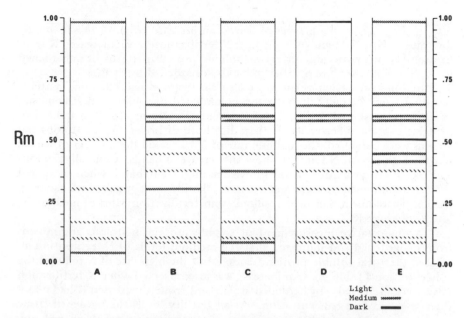

Fig. 1—Soluble protein banding patterns of unhardened centipedegrass stolons and crowns.
A. 0.98-0.49-0.98; B. 1.96-0.49-0.98; C. 1.96-0.49-1.96; D. 1.96-0.49-2.94; E. 2.94-1.47-2.94.

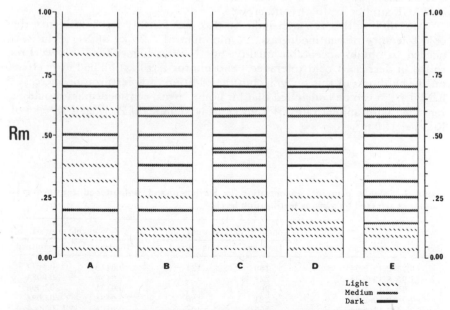

Fig. 2—Soluble protein banding patterns of hardened centipedegrass stolons and crowns.
A. 0.98-0.49-0.98; B. 1.96-0.49-0.98; C. 1.96-0.49-1.96; D. 1.96-0.49-2.94; E. 2.94-1.47-2.94.

not to the extent of unhardened leaves; an increase from 16 bands for the low rate of N to 22 bands for the high N fertilization rate. Increased K fertilization had no noticeable effect on soluble protein patterns of unhardened leaves, but increased the number of bands in hardened leaf tissue.

Stolon and crown tissue were also electrophoresed. Banding patterns resulting from extracts of both the unhardened and hardened stolons and crowns are presented in Fig. 1 and 2. Banding patterns of stolon and crown proteins contained fewer bands than did those of leaves. When stolons and crowns were hardened, the medium rate of N increased the number of bands, but the high rate of N failed to show an increase in bands. Generally, stolons and crowns from hardened sod showed an increase in bands when compared to the unhardened stolons and crowns. The highest number of bands in hardened stolons and crowns resulted from fertilization rates of medium N, low P, and high K.

A quantitative measurement of soluble protein in stolons and crowns from unhardened sod indicated that the medium levels of N fertilization increased the total soluble protein fraction, but the high rate of N reduced the concentration (Table 4). An increase was also observed when K fertilization rates were increased. In hardened stolon and crowns increased K had no influence on protein concentration. At all fertility levels the hardened tissue contained a higher soluble protein concentration than the unhardened sod. This increase in soluble protein with hardening supports the bulk of the literature which suggests that soluble proteins increase as plant hardening processes occur. The quantitative measurements of soluble protein concentration also support the increased number of soluble protein bands observed by PAGE studies in stolons and crowns.

Results of this research indicate that soil fertility levels influence the cold tolerance of centipedegrass. A minimum of 1.96 kg of N/100 m^2 was needed to obtain acceptable quality, but N rates higher than this level resulted in decreased cold tolerance. Phosphorus fertilization had little effect on the hardiness of this turfgrass but the addition of K fertilization increased hardiness. It can be concluded that for home lawns, centipedegrass should be fertilized with annual rates of 1.96 kg of N, 0.98 kg of P$_2$O$_5$, and 1.96 kg of K$_2$O per 100 m^2.

Table 4—Soluble protein concentration in hardened and unhardened centipedegrass stolons as affected by various fertilization levels.*

Fertilization rate, kg/100 m^2	Soluble protein concentration*		% soluble protein†	
	Hardened	Unhardened	Hardened	Unhardened
0.98–0.49–0.98	180	124	0.0113	0.0077
1.96–0.49–0.98	221	134	0.0138	0.0084
1.96–0.49–1.96	209	144	0.0131	0.0090
1.96–0.49–2.94	221	150	0.0138	0.0094
2.94–1.47–2.94	166	107	0.0104	0.0064

* μg/ml extracted from 2 g green tissue, determined by Lowry method.   † Percent soluble protein in tissue, green weight basis.

REFERENCES

1. AHRING, R. M., and R. M. IRWING. 1969. A laboratory method of determining cold hardiness in bermudagrass, *Cynodon dactylon* (L.) Pers. Crop Sci. 9:615–618.
2. ALEXANDER, P. M., and W. B. GILBERT. 1963. Winter damage to bermuda greens. Golf Course Rep. 31:50–53.
3. BEARD, J. B. 1963. Winter injury of turfgrasses associated with ice sheets. U.S. Golf Ass. Green Sec. Rec. 1:1–3.
4. BULA, R. J., Dale SMITH, and R. J. HODGSON. 1956. Cold resistance in alfalfa at two diverse latitudes. Agron. J. 48:153–156.
5. CARROLL, J. C. 1943. Effects of drought, temperature, and nitrogen on turfgrasses. Plant Physiol. 18:19–36.
6. ———, and F. A. WELTON. 1939. Effect of heavy and late applications of nitrogeneous fertilizer on the cold resistance of Kentucky bluegrass. Plant Physiol. 14:297–308.
7. DAVIS, B. J. 1964. Disc electrophoresis. II. Method and application to human serum proteins. Ann. New York Acad. Sci. 121:404–427.
8. DAVIS, D. L. 1967. Changes in soluble protein fraction during cold acclimation plus the effects of certain nutrients and stress conditions on winterkill of *Cynodon* spp. Ph.D. thesis, Dept. of Crop Sci., North Carolina State Univ., Raleigh, N. C.
9. ———, and W. B. GILBERT. 1970. Winterhardiness and changes in soluble protein fractions of bermudagrass. Crop Sci. 10:7–9.
10. DEAL, Elwyn E. 1967. Phosphorus fertilization. Golf Supt. 35:39–41.
11. GILBERT, W. B., and D. L. DAVIS. 1971. Influence of fertility ratios on winterhardiness of bermudagrass. Agron. J. 63:591–593.
12. HENDRICKS, S. B. 1966. Salt entry into plants. Soil Sci. Soc. Amer. Proc. 30:1–7.
13. HODGSON, H. J. 1964. Effect of photoperiod on development of cold resistance in alfalfa. Crop Sci. 4:302–305.
14. ———, and R. J. BULA. 1956. Hardening behavior of sweetclover varieties in a subartic environment. Agron. J. 48:147–160.
15. LOWRY, O. H., N. J. ROSEBROUGH, A. L. FARR, and Rose J. RANDAEL. 1951. Protein measurement with folinphenol reagent. J. Biol. Chem. 193:265–275.
16. MORGAN, Wayne C. 1968. Effects of nutrients on the grass plant. Golf Supt. 36:36–47.
17. PAULI, A. W., and H. L. MITCHELL. 1960. Changes in certain nitrogenous constituents of winter wheat as related to cold hardiness. Plant Physiol. 35:539–542.
18. SIMINOVITCH, D., and D. R. BRIGGS. 1949. The chemistry of the living bark of the black locus tree in relation to frost hardiness. I. Seasonal variation in protein content. Arch. Biochem. 23:8–17.
19. ———, and ———. 1953. Studies on the chemistry of the living bark of the black locust tree in relation to frost hardiness. IV. Effects of ringing on translocation, protein synthesis and the development of hardiness. Plant Physiol. 28:177–200.
20. WAGNER, R. E. 1969. The role of potassium in the metabolism of turfgrasses. Ext. leaflet. Maryland Agr. Ext. Service, College Park, Md.
21. WARD, C. Y. 1968. Effect of nitrogen on winter damage to centipedegrass. Proc. Miss. Turfgrass Ass. Annual Meeting. Mississippi State, Mississippi.
22. ZECH, A. C., and A. W. PAULI. 1960. Cold resistance in three varieties of winter wheat as related to nitrogen fractions and total sugar. Agron. J. 52:334–337.

64

Turfgrass research and results at the Netherlands Sports Federation

J. P. VAN DER HORST

The Netherlands Sports Federation conducted studies evaluating wear tolerance of grasses and turf response to various mowing heights, fertilization, overseeding, and disease. Additional index words: Netherlands, Wear machine, Sports fields, *Poa* spp.

The Netherlands Sports Federation research program is largely designed to improve the Netherland's 6,000 ha of sports field turf. Effort is also devoted to the study of fine turf.

Since the First International Turfgrass Conference, the Netherlands Sports Federation has increased both its facilities and its research programs. New training facilities have been constructed. A main building with medical and guest quarters has been built as well as a new sports hall and Rekortan (manufactured by Voigt Castrup Rauxl, Germany) running track (polyurethane).

Socker, hockey, and rugby demand rugged turf. Research studies are designed to evaluate:

1) Ability of grass to withstand mowing
2) Wear tolerance of grasses
3) Methods for improving root and top density
4) Ability of grasses to germinate rapidly
5) Dates for sowing grass seed
6) The utilization of nitrogen by grasses

Standard procedures include mowing trials at 1 and 3 cm, plus the use of a "wear machine" (discussed later in this paper). The use of different nitrogen rates is also a standard practice.

Data are recorded and reports issued to contractors, seed companies, and advisory officials. Close cooperation exists with agricultural universities and institutes.

Both monoculture and grass mixture trials are conducted. Monocultures of perennial ryegrass (*Lolium perenne* L.) and Kentucky bluegrass (*Poa pratensis* L.) may be utilized for certain purposes. However, for most uses, mixtures of two or three cultivars of these species are established. The use of mixtures reduces risks associated with sports field turf.

Table 1—Composition of turfgrass mixtures established September 1971.

Source of mixture	L. perenne	P. pratensis	P. pratense	P. nodosum	F. rubra commutata	F. rubra	F. ovina	C. cristatus	A. tenuis	F. arundinacea
					%					
Dutch variety list										
New SVA	30	60	10	or 10						
New SV5	20	50			10	20				
New SV6		95	5	or 5						
New R1	20	20			10	20	20		10	
Old SV1	20	20			20	20			20	
Old SV2	20	20	20		10	20			10	
Old SV3	25	25	25			25				
Seed companies										
van der Have A		75	10			15				
B	60	20	20							
C	35	20	15			30				
Cebeco D		75		10		15				
E		90		10						
Mommersteeg F		70	10			20				
G	20	15		10		25		10	20	
Barenbrug H	30	60								
Van Engelen I	10	70								
J	15	75		10				20		
Sports federation										
1	60			5				35		
2		60		5				35		
3	95			5						
4		70			15	15				
5		40								60

MIXTURE TRIALS

Grass mixtures developed by the Federation as well as experimental varieties from seed companies are being tested. Mixtures listed in the Dutch variety list (yearbook) are also established along with older formulas. Table 1 summarizes the composition of mixtures established in September 1971, along with references to mixture sources. Perennial ryegrass and Kentucky bluegrass are the basic species. Also included are hexaploid and diploid timothy (*Phleum pratense* L. and *Phleum nodosum* L.), chewings fescue (*Festuca rubra* var. *commutata* Gaud.), red fescue (*Festuca rubra* var. *rubra* L.), crested dogtail (*Cynosurus cristatus* L.), and to a lesser extent, bentgrass (*Agrostis tenuis* Sibth.), sheep fescue (*Festuca ovina* L.), and tall fescue (*Festuca arundinacea* Schreb.).

MONOCULTURE TRIALS

The present variety tests were established in 1968, 1971, and 1972. From the 1968 trials, differences in the ability of grasses to withstand winter sports season traffic have been identified by the use of a "wear machine."

Kentucky bluegrass varieties differ substantially in their ability to withstand injury. To date, the least damaged cultivars have been 'Sydsport,' 'Merion,' and 'Aron.' Cultivars badly damaged by *Helminthosporium vagans,* such as 'Prato' and 'Arista,' have not stood up under wear.

Table 2—Turfgrasses established in June 1972 trials.

Species	Total number of cultivars	New cultivars	Cultivars previously tested
Poa pratensis	36	28	Apoll, Arista, Baron, Fylking, Merion, Monopoly, Newport Sydsport
Lolium perenne	18	16	Pelo Barenza
Phleum pratense	5	3	Olympia, Tiran
Phleum nodosum	8	6	S50, Sport
Poa trivialis	2	2	
Cynosurus cristatus	2		Encresta, Credo
Festuca arundinacea	5	4	Festal
Festuca ovina duriuscula	3	2	Biljart
Festuca rubra commutata	12	10	Highlight, Waldorf
Festuca rubra rubra	4	2	Dawson, Novorubra
Agrostis tenuis	5	2	Bardot, Tracenta
Dactylis glomerata	2	2	
Total	102	77	

Little difference was noted in the wearability of the perennial ryegrass varieties. At 3-cm mowing height, perennial ryegrasses did not withstand wear and the stands were thin. 'Manhattan' may be a promising cultivar for this purpose.

Species which did not wear as well as Kentucky bluegrass and perennial ryegrass were *Phleum pratense, Phleum nodosum, Festuca rubra,* and *Agrostis* spp.

Poa annua became dominant in the wear-treated areas with as much as 15% of the ground covered by annual bluegrass.

Insufficient time has passed to draw firm conclusions from the 1971 trials. Some observations to date include:

1) Crested dogtail was badly damaged by *Fusarium* spp.
2) Two varieties of Kentucky bluegrass were killed by *Helminthosporium vagans.* Prato and Arista have been badly injured by this disease.
3) Perennial ryegrass varieties are seldom attacked by the red thread organism (*Corticium fuciforme*). However, Manhattan and 'Sprinter' were injured by this disease during fall.

Of the 102 entries established in the June 1972 trial, 75% were new cultivars (Table 2).

FERTILIZER TRIALS

Available nitrogen is often limited during the winter sports season, and contributes to poor quality turf. Studies have been initiated to evaluate the influence of nitrogen rates on turf quality. Nitrogen was applied to 200 kg and 400 kg/ha of mixed stands of Kentucky bluegrass and perennial ryegrass.

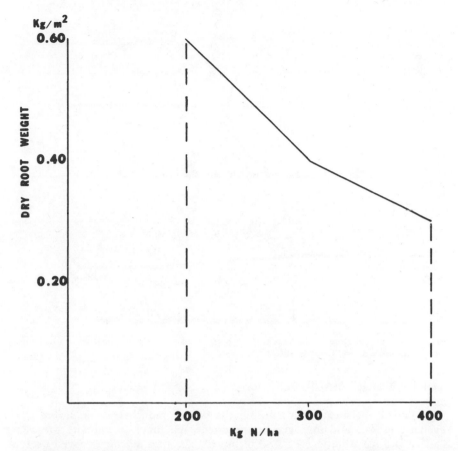

Fig. 1—Influence of nitrogen on the root weight of mixed Kentucky bluegrass-perennial ryegrass turf.

Through the use of a wear machine, we have been able to demonstrate more turf injury at the 400 kg/ha level. With this quantity of nitrogen applied, root growth was adversely influenced (Fig. 1).

In the Netherlands, fertilizer ingredients are supplied individually. Nitrogen is the most important. Phosphorous, potassium, and manganese are applied as their needs are indicated by soil test. Organic matter and pH are also considered important. Sand is used as topdressing to relieve excessive thatch build-up.

RENOVATION

The renovation of weedy turf is of considerable concern. New trials have been established to study this problem. Following vertical mowing at 2-cm depth with grooves 5 cm apart, Manhattan ryegrass was overseeded. The wear machine was used to simulate further traffic damage.

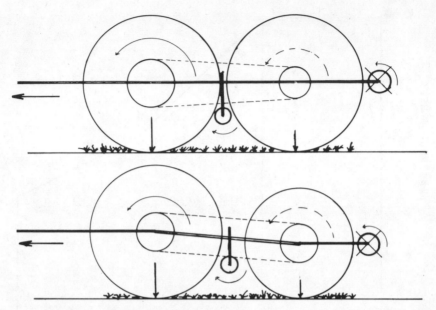

Fig. 2—Top model shows wear machine with equal-sized cylinders; bottom model shows wear machine with cylinders of different sizes.

TURF "WEAR" MACHINES

Traffic on sports fields during the winter months can be severe. To evaluate grasses and management practices, machines to simulate the wear caused during athletic events were built. The first machine proved useful, but too much time was required to obtain results. A second machine was built, and a third unit is being designed at this time.

The new machines incorporate the use of two cleated cylinders of different sizes (Fig. 2). The first roller is of a larger diameter and heavier than the rear roller. The two cylinders rotate at different speeds, which causes some skidding of the rear cylinder and an intensification of the damage. We estimate the new machines will provide results in about one-fourth the time required with the first model.

65

Diagrammatic aid to turfgrass management [1]

F.J. WRAY

Different grass species have individual responses to water and fertilizer requirement, mowing height, shade tolerance, wear, and other factors. It is often difficult to determine the suitability of grasses for given management, climatic, or survival situations. It is also difficult to determine whether two or more grasses are compatible in any given situation, and the effect that management practices will have on their respective survivals.

The triangular diagram enables the turfgrass manager, research worker, or breeder to visualize the degree of compatibility of different species under selected circumstances, and infer consequences arising from changes of management practices or new situations.

The three most useful characteristics of grasses are their individual water requirements, fertilizer requirements, and mowing heights. Numerical values are assigned to each of these characteristics and the results plotted on a triangular diagram. Grasses with similar requirements are automatically placed near each other on the diagram.

Other important characteristics, such as shade tolerance and wear resistance, can be used for situations where those characteristics are important.

The numerical values presented here are chosen to suit cool, wet conditions, but can be changed to suit other regions or specific circumstances. A good turfgrass manager will be able to substitute values based on his own experience. Additional index words: Triangular diagram, Turfgrass requirements, Turfgrass competition, Ecological interactions, Environmental adaptation.

Turfgrass managers, as well as research workers and teachers in turfgrass science, are often faced with comparative data on turf performance which is difficult to interpret. Many articles state that "grass X is superior to grass Y" under certain environmental conditions, or that "Mixture A responded better than Mixture B" to a certain experimental treatment.

These statements are simple comparisons, and are almost impossible to use because the performance of any turfgrass species is subject to more than one external variable, and most comparisons usually consider only one variable. This situation is improved by presenting data in tabular or graphical form, which often shows the interaction between two or three variables simultaneously.

[1] Plant Science Department, Nova Scotia Agricultural College, Truro, Nova Scotia, Canada.

Another difficulty in data presentation is that turfgrasses, like other plants, will tolerate a range of conditions, their performances being satisfactory within two moderately distinct limits.

These difficulties become most pronounced when trying to present information regarding turfgrass performance and characteristics to students.

For the first stage of this work, quantitative data for each major turfgrass species were tabulated in order to give simple numerical comparisons. This was done with great difficulty, the information being first obtained from the ASA Monograph *Turfgrass Science* (2). Primary quantitative information sought was fertility requirements, expressed in kilograms of nitrogen per month per 93 m² assuming there was adequate potassium and phosphorus; mowing height in centimeters; and water requirement in centimeters per week. Secondary quantitative information sought was wear resistance, waterlogging tolerance, shade tolerance, pH requirement, and similar data.

At this preliminary stage single numerical values were grossly misleading, and quantitative data used had to be expressed as a range where these two values are specified. The first ranges obtained were guesses, which were improved by further reading and literature comparisons. The final improved guesses were submitted to fellow lecturers and practical turfgrass managers (J. L. Eggens, J. Fairhurst, personal communications). These final improved guesses are given in Table 1 for turfgrass species used in Canada. Additional information was obtained from several tables in the Proceedings of the First International Turfgrass Research Conference (1).

It is essential to realize that the range of values presented are obtained from practical data and are refined by practical people. Similar information concerning southern grass species was obtained by writing to the appropriate research workers in those areas.

Table 1—Range of values for several characteristics of turfgrass species between which satisfactory performance is normally obtained.

Species	Fertility* requirement, kg of N/month per 93 m²	Mowing height, cm	Water requirement, cm/week	pH range, pH units	Shade tolerance, 10 high, 0 low
Poa pratensis L.					
Common Kentucky	0.4–0.7	3.2–4.8	1–1.5	6.0–7.7	2.0–3.0
Merion Kentucky	0.45–0.9	1.9–3.9	0.8–1.8	6.0–7.7	1.5–2.5
Fylking Kentucky	0.6–0.9	1.3–3.9	0.8–1.7	6.0–7.7	1.5–2.5
Poa annua L.					
Annual bluegrass	0.22–0.7	0.6–3.2	1.3–2.54	5.1–7.7	5.5–7.5
Festuca rubra L.					
Creeping red fescue	0.2–0.4	2.2–3.9	0.5–1.0	5.4–7.6	7.0–8.5
Lolium perenne L.					
Perennial ryegrass	0.3–0.45	4.1–5.0	1.0–1.8	5.5–8.1	2.5–4.0
Agrostis tenuis Sibth.					
Colonial bentgrass	0.4–0.7	1.0–2.0	1.5–2.2	5.4–7.6	3.0–4.2
Agrostris palustris Huds.					
Creeping bentgrass	0.45–0.9	0.6–1.3	1.5–2.2	5.4–7.6	4.0–6.0

* Assumes that adequate P and K are supplied.

The second stage was the utilization of this data for the management of grasses. Although good turfgrass management involves drastic modifications of the grass environment by mowing, fertilizing, irrigation, and other practices, the turf response is primarily ecological. Each grass species or cultivar will tolerate a range of each of these management practices. Outside this range, the grass will die or suffer adversely from weed or other grass competition. Consequently, if this information can be presented concisely and clearly, it may be used as a management tool to determine what will happen to specific grasses in a given location under certain management practices. Stated in reverse, these numerical limits specify the ecological niches within which each turfgrass species performs satisfactorily for a particular site.

Fortunately there are three major management practices which influence quality turfgrass performance. These are nutrient requirement, water requirement, and cutting height. This immediately suggested the triangular diagram format similar to that used as a guide for the textural classification of soils (3) and shown in Fig. 1.

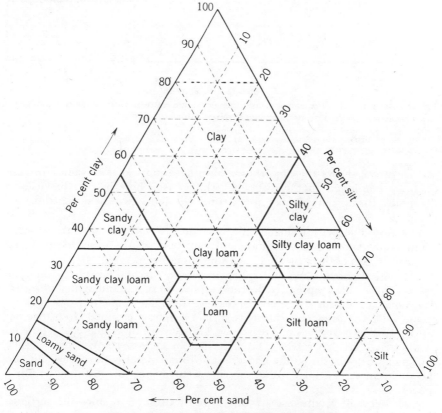

Fig. 1—Guide for textural classification of soils.

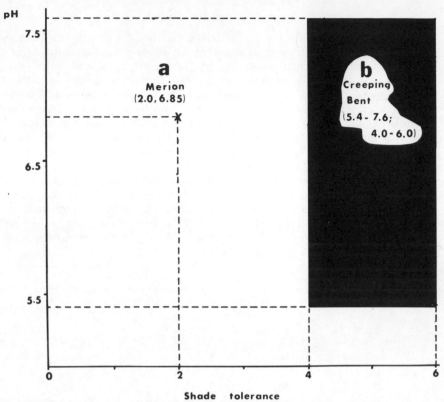

Fig. 2—Difference in format when using single numerical values for each coordinate (a) and a range represented by two numerical values (b).

Figure 2 shows the importance of using a range of two values for each quantity employed in the diagram. This is seen here in two-dimensional "graphic" form. The shaded area defines the limits within which the grass will exist.

Figure 3 shows a triangular diagram where a range of two values for nutrient requirement, water requirement, and cutting height are used. Again the shaded area defines the limits within which the grass exists.

Figure 4 shows a triangular diagram where 'Merion' Kentucky bluegrass *Poa pratensis* L., creeping red fescue *Festuca rubra* L., and annual bluegrass *Poa annua* L. appear together. Grasses with similar characteristics, requirements, and responses to treatments specified appear grouped close together on the diagram. By the same reasoning, grasses with dissimilar characteristics would be widely separated. The difference in their respective areas on such a diagram not only shows the important differences between species, but also shows improvements or variations in performance of cultivars within a species, as seen in Fig. 5.

Consequently, the use of this type of diagram enables the turfgrass specialist to determine whether two or more grasses are compatible in any

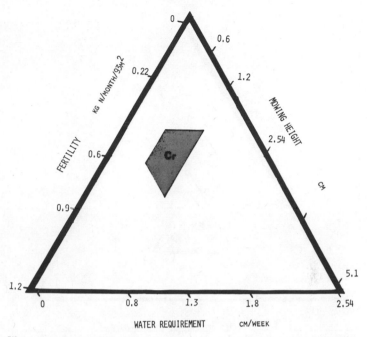

Fig. 3—Water requirement, fertility, and mowing height for creeping bentgrass *Agrostis palustris* Huds. using data from Table 1.

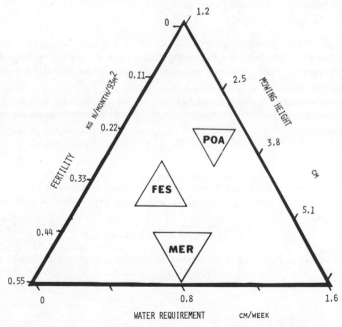

Fig. 4—Water requirement, fertility, and mowing height for 'Merion' bluegrass *Poa pratensis* L., creeping red fescue *Festuca rubra* L. and annual bluegrass *Poa annua* L. using data from Table 1.

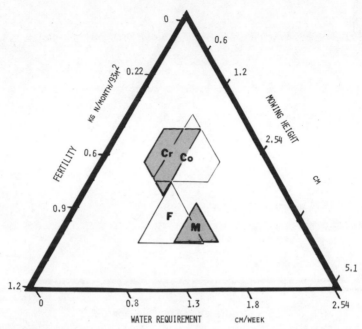

Fig. 5—Water requirement, fertility, and mowing height for *Poa pratensis* L. cultivars 'Merion' and 'Fylking', *Agrostis tenuis* Sibth. colonial bentgrass, and *Agrostis palustris* Huds. creeping bentgrass using data from Table 1.

given environmental or management situation. Further, it is possible to estimate the effect on the botanical composition of a sward of various important management practices, or conversely, how management practices may be used to suppress unwanted weed species.

Research workers and/or grass breeders may be able to use such a diagram to show similarities, differences, or compatibilities of turfgrass species.

REFERENCES

1. BEARD, J. B. 1970. Turfgrass shade adaptation. p. 273-282. *In* Proc. First Int. Turfgrass Res. Conf. Sports Turf Research Institute, Bingley, England.
2. HANSON, A. A., and F. V. JUSKA (eds.). 1969. Turfgrass science. Agronomy 14. Amer. Soc. Agron., Madison, Wis.
3. SOIL SURVEY STAFF. 1960. Soil classification, a comprehensive system, 7th Approximation. Soil Conservation Service, USDA, Washington, D. C.
4. WOOD, G. M. 1970. Shade tolerant turfgrasses of the U. S. and Canada. p. 283-290. *In* Proc. First Int. Turfgrass Res. Conf. Sports Turf Research Institute, Bingley, England.

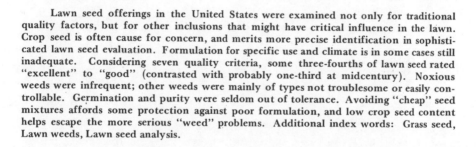

66

Quality of lawn seed on the American market

R.W. SCHERY

Lawn seed offerings in the United States were examined not only for traditional quality factors, but for other inclusions that might have critical influence in the lawn. Crop seed is often cause for concern, and merits more precise identification in sophisticated lawn seed evaluation. Formulation for specific use and climate is in some cases still inadequate. Considering seven quality criteria, some three-fourths of lawn seed rated "excellent" to "good" (contrasted with probably one-third at midcentury). Noxious weeds were infrequent; other weeds were mainly of types not troublesome or easily controllable. Germination and purity were seldom out of tolerance. Avoiding "cheap" seed mixtures affords some protection against poor formulation, and low crop seed content helps escape the more serious "weed" problems. Additional index words: Grass seed, Lawn weeds, Lawn seed analysis.

In the early 1950's, Dr. E. N. Fergus of Kentucky surveyed lawn seed nationally for the American Society of Agronomy. From 1955 through 1958. Drs. L. Everson and L. N. Bass, Iowa State University, sampled lawn seed in Iowa, noting relative abundance of "basic" (permanently satisfactory) and "filler" (impermanent or undesirable) species. In 1958-59, William Heckendorn of the American Seed Trade Association engaged Ernst & Ernst, a prominent accounting firm, to undertake confidential reporting within the trade. These and other evaluations showed that only about one-third of the lawn seed reaching the consumer at midcentury could be considered as having reasonably high quality (even by standards prevailing then); one-third was only "fair," and one-third essentially worthless. Judgment was based primarily upon formulation (the prevalence of perennial species, later identified in labeling as "fine-textured"; improved named cultivars were not yet generally available), with secondary consideration being given purity and other conventional trade standards. It must be remembered that lawn expectations were not as high then as today, and that inclusions not too obviously "weedy" were tolerated and even appreciated. The typical lawn custodian has since become more sophisticated and appreciative of consistently attractive weed-free turf; the many pedigreed lawn cultivars now reaching market give promise of even higher quality in the future.

Table 1—Number of seed offerings examined and metropolitan areas sampled.

Climate*	No. seed offerings	Metropolitan area
Temperate		
Continental conditions	77	Chicago, Denver, New York St. Louis, Washington, D. C.
Benign-humid coastal	13	Seattle
Subtropical		
Humid coastal	10	Houston, Miami
Semiarid inland	25	Oklahoma City, Los Angeles

* Climate is felt least hospitable for achieving performance potential in Los Angeles and Oklahoma City, only fair for Washington, D. C. and St. Louis; thus some leniency was shown in quality ratings for these locations.

Table 2—Rating basis: Characteristics considered in arriving at overall quality score showing which proved most important in pointing up deficiencies.

Characteristic	Maximum penalty points	% not penalized
Formulation	50	50
Germination	20	90
Purity	10	20
Noxious weeds	3	80
Other weeds	4	20
Crop	18	25
Label	4	45

MATERIALS AND METHODS

During 1972, a thorough evaluation of 125 lawn seed samplings purchased at retail stores in 10 metropolitan areas of the United States was made. Each sample was coded, and neither label nor brand identification was revealed until test results had been recorded. Eventually the labels (boxes) were evaluated for factual information.

A rating scheme was constructed in which point scores were given for formulation, germination, purity, noxious weeds, "other" weeds, crop, and label adequacy. Demerit points were subtracted from 100 for inadequacies in any of these categories, always keeping in mind how performance *in the lawn* might be influenced. Penalties proved most severe for poor formulation (inappropriateness for the kind of use suggested, or for climate where offered), moderate for crop content, and fairly light for other categories. A general background on samplings is given in Tables 1–3 and an overall summary of ratings is given in Table 4 (100 is perfect). Analysis by the registered seed technologists was exceptionally thorough, calling for large-sample (usually 25 g) verification, and identification of all foreign seeds (weeds and crop). Value judgments in the several categories gave consideration to the following points.

Table 3—Average penalty assessed seed offerings due to weeds or mechanical inadequacies, and metropolitan areas faring "worst" and "best" for each categorization. Offerings seem more carefully tailored for climates where performance potential is best (See Table 1).

| Weeds | Penalty points | Metropolitan area faring | |
		Worst	Best
Noxious weeds	0.4	Los Angeles	Seattle
Other weeds	1.0	Los Angeles	—
Crop	2.1		Denver
Mechanical inadequacy			
Formulation	4.5	St. Louis	New York
Purity	1.4	Los Angeles	Chicago

Table 4—Overall scores for quality (approximate percentage).

Region	Average Score	Excellent 95–100%	Good 90–94%	Fair 85–89%	Poor 80–84%	Inadequate <80%
New York	91.7	50	25	15	5	5
Washington, D.C.	89.3	44	22	17	6	11
Chicago	87.5	46	36	—	—	18
St. Louis	81.1	19	25	19	6	31
Denver	92.6	39	39	22	—	—
Seattle	86.0	62	15	—	—	23
Los Angeles	90.9	11	56	22	11	—
National	88.4					

Formulation

Formulation was criticized for conditions anticipated in the area where sold. Improved cultivars could doubtless lay claim to special merit, but mixtures containing them were not graded on that account (although typically seed of elite cultivars is better cleaned and handled, and therefore superior in other features). Nevertheless, all species generally accepted as being attractively fine textured and providing good perennial performance for the climate were accorded full rating regardless of the cultivars involved.

Mixtures designed for particular growing conditions (such as shade or temporary cover) were not downgraded for what would be inappropriateness of certain components for other environments, so long as the label clearly indicated the special nature of the formulations; where adaptation was not indicated on the box, it was presumed that the seed was intended for typical lawns on open ground or light shade, given "usual" (not extravagent) care. Likewise, it was presumed that a purchaser bought seed knowingly; that if he purchased clearly identified bentgrass he anticipated providing it appropriate bentgrass care, or with wintergrass for dormant turf he expected only season-long performance.

Greater tolerance was accorded certain formulations in some climates than in others. This related chiefly to coarse species such as tall fescue, more tolerable in some border state climates and southern California (where little else may survive) than in northerly locations where the usual fine-turf species perform well. Thus tall fescue blends were not so severely marked down for Washington, D. C. and St. Louis as they were for New York, Chicago, and Denver.

Obviously, these and similar considerations involve subjective judgment based upon experience with lawns in different areas. Greatest tolerance was shown in Los Angeles, where almost no grass is ideally suited, and where frequent renovations are an accepted "way of life." Some formulations considered acceptable for Los Angeles (say those containing a hodgepodge of species including meadow fescue) would have been severely downrated in climates where the bluegrasses, fine fescues, and bentgrasses do well.

Germination

This conventional standard determinable by laboratory tests was found acceptable in almost all cases; only one sample was markedly out of tolerance with label claims. As can be noted in the Table 2, 90% of the samples met expectations fully, and others were only slightly out of tolerance.

Purity

As with germination, purity claims, enforced by seed laws, were generally well met. A few samples were mildly out of tolerance and thus slightly penalized. Some others were penalized if it seemed that a higher purity (less chaff) should have been chosen to yield a higher PLS (pure live seed) count.

Noxious weeds

Considering the legal prohibitions for interstate sale of seed containing noxious weeds, it is not surprising that very few instances of downgrading were necessary because of noxious weed content. Most occurrences were understandable, involving species not everywhere considered noxious (such as *Poa annua* L.). Most noxious weeds, where they did occur, were very infrequent (one seed in hundreds of thousands), and not felt to be cause for great concern in lawns.

Other weeds

Most seed seems reasonably devoid of weeds today. Although only 20% of the samples were completely free of weed seed, in almost all cases the weeds were quite infrequent by individual count, and typically of kinds not apt to be a problem in lawns (disappearing under mowing, in competition with grass, or easily controlled by phenoxy herbicides). No sample was encountered where it was felt necessary to assess a penalty of more than four points for "other" weeds.

Crop

Only 25% of the samples were completely free from crop (agricultural species not regarded as weeds). Included among crop species are some of the major pests in lawns, particularly coarse perennial grasses for which there is no selective control in a fine-textured lawn. Ryegrass (*Lolium* spp.) and brome (*Bromus* spp.) were frequent contaminants, and to a lesser extent clover (*Trifolium* sp.), orchardgrass (*Dactylis glomerata* L.), coarse fescue (*Festuca arundinacea* Schreb.), timothy (*Phleum pratense* L.), etc.

Bentgrass (*Agrostis* sp.) is a special situation; it is sometimes intentionally included in seed mixtures, and being a fine-textured perennial has much to recommend it for fine turf. Yet it is frowned upon for bluegrass sod, and for lawn plantings in areas where bentgrass has not naturalized. In the ratings some exception was taken to bentgrass as crop (i.e., not as a declared component) in bluegrass blends, but it was not viewed as being so pernicious overall as are coarse species. Certainly traces of bentgrass where bentgrass is already adventive (much of the Northeast and the humid Pacific slopes) would cause little concern.

Label

There were no instances of deliberate misrepresentation noted in labeling, but numerous cases of scanty directions, or instructions somewhat unrelated to the locality were found. About half of the offerings were slightly penalized on this account.

RESULTS AND DISCUSSION

Results are most meaningful for the northern states, where lawn seeding (as opposed to vegetative planting) is widely practiced. As already noted, Los Angeles, with a highly varied local ecology, lacks clear-cut quality indicators that northern locations enjoy. Oklahoma City does not represent a big enough market for the specialized formulations it should have, and suffers because nationally distributed mixtures are a bit "off base" for the climate. Miami and Houston (and to an extent Los Angeles) represent climates where limited seed marketing leaves little to criticize so long as label claims are met (the typical unblended bermuda and dichondra offerings contain no foreign seed considered a serious threat; and bahia, by nature a coarse grass, would hardly be hampered by the crop or weed inclusions noted). Of the other sampling areas, Denver, followed closely by New York, leads in average quality (highest average rating) with St. Louis at the lower end of the scale (Table 4).

Table 5 indicates that noxious weeds (except perhaps *Poa annua* L.) are found infrequently and not abundantly (many of the finds would not even have been discovered in typical 1 or 2 g test samples). The frequency of non-noxious weeds is given in Table 6. The most common, *Festuca myuros* L. and *Apera*, are of little consequence, hardly troublesome in lawns. The most

Table 5—Most prevalent noxious weeds found in seed offerings and their frequency per 100 g sample.

Species	% Approximate	Frequency/100g			
		0–10	10–C	C–M	>M
Poa annua	15	3	6	6	1
Rumex acetosella	7	7	–	–	–
Thlaspi arvense	5	5	–	–	–
Rumex crispus	3	3	–	–	–
Bromus tectorum	2	–	2	–	–
Plantago lanceolata	2	2	–	–	–
All other	3	3	–	–	–

Table 6—Most common "other" weeds found in lawn seed offerings nationally and their comparative frequency.

Weed*	%	Frequency/100 g			
		0–10	10–C	C–M	>M
Festuca myuros	30	6	2	10	12
Apera	25	4	14	3	4
Capsella	21	2	13	3	3
Taraxacum	13	9	2	2	–
Stellaria	12	3	1	4	4
Alopecurus	12	2	3	3	4
Carex	9	3	2	4	–
Lamium	8	4	3	–	1
Airia	6	2	2	1	1
Amaranthus	6	5	–	1	–
Anthoxanthum	6	3	1	–	2
Bromus	6	2	1	1	2
Holcus	6	2	–	3	1
Anthemis	5	1	3	–	1
Camellina	5	2	2	–	1
Hypochoeris	5	3	2	–	–
Crepis	4	2	1	1	–
Myosotis	4	1	1	1	1
Sisymbrium	4	2	–	–	2

* "Other" weeds in <3% of samples: *Hordeum, Achillea, Anthriscus, Cerastium, Chenopodium, Lepidium, Poa palustris, Tanacetum, Spergula, Erodium, Hieracium, Potentilla, Stipa, Matricaria, Polygonum, Glyceria, Ventenata, Geum.*

frequent broadleaf weeds, *Capsella, Taraxacum,* and *Stellaria,* are definitely a detriment to quality; however, they are readily controlled with phenoxy herbicides. Most of the remaining weeds are of little consequence, although a few, such as *Holcus*, can be both persistent and not amenable to easy herbicidal control.

Crop findings, Table 7, are more a cause for concern. The fairly frequent occurrence of bentgrass (*Agrostis*), a fine-textured species capable of making an excellent turf under proper care, is perhaps partly explainable in that paying a premium for seed free of bentgrass would be foolish for regions where

Table 7—Crop most often encountered in lawn seed offerings nationally and frequency of the genera.

	%	Frequency/100 g				
		0–10	10–C	C–M	M–10M	>10M
Agrostis	39	14	14	5	4	2
Lolium	37	9	8	7	7	6
Bromus	24	11	5	6	2	—
Agropyron	20	8	2	8	2	—
Poa pratensis	16	1	3	2	—	10
Poa bulbosa	15	6	3	4	2	—
Trifolium	13	6	3	3	1	—
Dactylis	8	1	—	2	5	—
Festuca, tall	8	3	—	3	2	—
Phleum	8	1	2	1	2	2
Poa compressa	6	—	—	—	4	2
Festuca, red	5	—	2	1	—	2
Linum	3	1	1	1	—	—

bentgrass is already prevalent. Bentgrass-free (or "crop-free") seed is available upon specification for sod and sterilized seedbeds.

Not much good can be said for the next two most frequent crop contaminants, *Lolium* and *Bromus*, either of which can become an unattractive "weed" in most climates. Clover (*Trifolium*) is a weed where it is not wanted. Slender wheatgrass (*Agropyron*) would probably not persist in most lawns. The two *Poas* are hardly a problem; they would pass unnoticed and soon disappear in Merion bluegrass (about the only place they are listed as crop). Orchardgrass, tall fescue, and timothy are all very unpleasant in seed blends, a concern even though they occur in only about 8% of the offerings.

Crop constitutes a quality hazard which cannot be specifically detected under present labeling requirements; the chief measure an average consumer can take to protect himself against perennial coarse grass inclusions, aside from patronizing reliable sources, is to choose products containing little or no crop at all.

Shown below is the average times the five most common noxious weeds, nonnoxious weeds, and crops appear in lawn seed nationally.

Most frequent weed types	%	Greatest frequency
Noxious weeds	6.4	0-10
"Other" weeds	20.2	10-100
Crop species	27.2	wide range

The noxious weeds are only infrequently encountered, but nearly one-fifth of the samplings contained nonnoxious weeds and about one-fourth crop species, both offering potentiality for trouble. The following tabulations show the average occurrence of species judged serious "weeds" in the lawn for nationally marketed lawn seed.

"Weeds"	%	Quantitative frequency
Noxious	5.8	Very light
"Other"	8.7	Light to medium
Crop (coarse)	16.3	Often heavy

Noxious weeds offer little hazard, "other" weeds a slightly more frequent risk, but coarse crop a possibility in about 16% of the samplings. It seems evident that crop, an unfamiliar concept to most seed users, must be regarded as the most serious source of detrimental contamination in lawn seed.

CONCLUSIONS

Scoring for all samples is not detailed here. Quality evaluations, as explained in the text, are partly subjective. One must make value judgments as to what is likely to be the outcome of seeding a particular formulation in a given climate, entirely aside from measurable quality factors such as purity, germination, and weed content. Likewise, a value judgment must be made as to whether higher cost for seed so thoroughly cleaned as to be free from all contamination would be worth the benefits; this well might be the case for a sod grower or professional, but it is of questionable importance for the great majority of lawns where *Poa annua, Taraxacum, Stellaria,* and even *Agrostis* are already prevalent. This raises the question whether the majority of users should be charged for the ultimate in mechanical quality when it is of little benefit to them.

On the whole, quality was commendable in the seed mixtures investigated. Compared to only a few years ago, it appears that seed purveyors for the most part offer well-founded formulations, and, at least with reliable brands, endeavor to include seed of good mechanical quality (high purity, ample germination, limited weed and crop content). There is room for improvement with crop inclusions in many offerings, but compared to conditions only a few decades ago (when such factors were not even considered), change has been marked and for the better. Moreover, the recent availability of named cultivars augurs well for even greater quality advances in the years ahead.

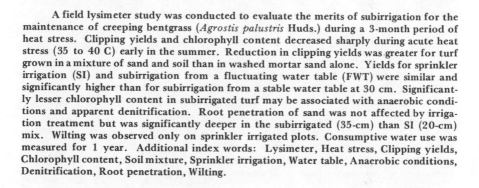

67

Subirrigation and fertilization of bentgrass during prolonged heat stress[1]

J.V. KRANS & G.V. JOHNSON

A field lysimeter study was conducted to evaluate the merits of subirrigation for the maintenance of creeping bentgrass (*Agrostis palustris* Huds.) during a 3-month period of heat stress. Clipping yields and chlorophyll content decreased sharply during acute heat stress (35 to 40 C) early in the summer. Reduction in clipping yields was greater for turf grown in a mixture of sand and soil than in washed mortar sand alone. Yields for sprinkler irrigation (SI) and subirrigation from a fluctuating water table (FWT) were similar and significantly higher than for subirrigation from a stable water table at 30 cm. Significantly lesser chlorophyll content in subirrigated turf may be associated with anaerobic conditions and apparent denitrification. Root penetration of sand was not affected by irrigation treatment but was significantly deeper in the subirrigated (35-cm) than SI (20-cm) mix. Wilting was observed only on sprinkler irrigated plots. Consumptive water use was measured for 1 year. Additional index words: Lysimeter, Heat stress, Clipping yields, Chlorophyll content, Soil mixture, Sprinkler irrigation, Water table, Anaerobic conditions, Denitrification, Root penetration, Wilting.

Irrigation is often the single management practice which has the greatest influence on the development and maintenance of quality turfgrass. The problems associated with improper irrigation are magnified when cool-season grasses which have poor drought resistance are cultured in hot, arid, and semiarid climates typical of the southwestern United States. Nitrogen fertilization is also of primary importance because the soils of this region are inherently low in organic mineralizable N. In spite of the fact that cool-season turfgrass is poorly adapted to the hot summers of this region, creeping bentgrass (*Agrostis palustris* Huds.) is often used on golf greens because it provides an excellent putting surface. Culture of this species is complicated by late summer rain concurrent with temperatures above 32 C. The susceptibility of this species to numerous diseases is most often in evidence during this critical period, especially when available N and soil moisture are excessive.

The following study was conducted to evaluate the suitability of subirrigation for properly providing water and N to the turf during a hot summer period.

[1]Journal paper No. 64 of the Arizona Agr. Exp. Sta., Tucson.

MATERIALS AND METHODS

The study conducted at The University of Arizona Turfgrass Research Center, Tucson, utilized 30 lysimeter units constructed as illustrated in Fig. 1. The upper 30 cm of each m² unit was filled with either washed mortar sand or a volumetric mixture of 52% washed sand, 24% Loamite[2], and 24% soil. 'Penncross' bentgrass was seeded in January 1973, on the lysimeter and surrounding area at a rate of 19.2 g/m².

The seed was germinated by subirrigation in all the lysimeter units. Irrigation treatments were applied to the two soils in a factorial arrangement beginning 3 weeks later. These treatments included sprinkler irrigation (SI), subirrigation with a stable water table (SWT) at about 30 cm, and subirrigation with a fluctuating water table (FWT) maintained between 12 (after subirrigation) and 50 cm (after depletion). The interval between water additions to the FWT treatment varied from 7 to 15 days depending on rainfall and moisture use. SI treatment was watered daily using 4 to 8 liters depending on weather conditions. The water table for SWT treatments was maintained from calibrated 20-liter reservoirs using a Mariotte siphon located in the water control unit (Fig. 1). The calibrated reservoirs were used to obtain water-use data. The SI and SWT treatments were each replicated six times and the FWT treatment three times on each soil.

Ammonium sulfate was applied in the irrigation water on a schedule of 2.4 g of N/m² per 2 weeks. Additional N was applied to the FWT and SWT treatments during midsummer to compensate for apparent large losses of N by denitrification. Nutrition was monitored by N, P, and salt analyses of the upper 10 cm of soil, by visual observations, and by Kjeldahl N analyses of clippings and soil solution obtained from vertical access tubes (Fig. 1).

The turf was mowed daily to a height of 0.6 cm, except when yield and chlorophyll determinations were obtained from 2 days' growth. Chlorophyll

---

[2] A product formerly processed from wood by the Loamite Corporation, Santa Rosa, California.

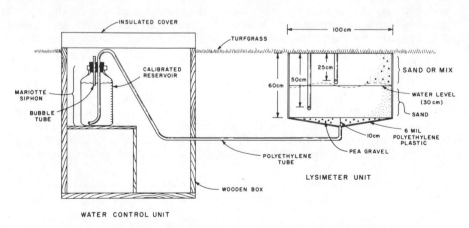

Fig. 1—Lysimeter system used for controlled irrigation.

was measured using a procedure similar to that described by Madison (1) modified to extract chlorophyll from dry clippings. Temperature measurements were obtained from a recording hygrothermograph. Vertical distribution of root mass was determined from 7.5-cm dia cores taken at the end of September.

RESULTS AND DISCUSSION

Color, growth, and root development

The initial effects of high temperatures on growth and color were not observed until the first week in July, following about 1 month of daily maximum temperatures above 35 C. Yield decreased sharply in July and continued to decline until night temperatures became cooler in late September (Fig. 2). Color, as evidenced by chlorophyll content, was affected less by

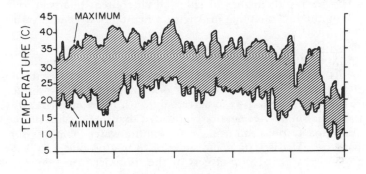

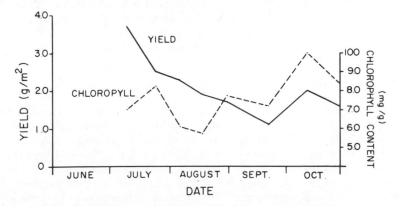

Fig. 2—Yield and chlorophyll content (average of all plots) of creeping bentgrass and maximum and minimum air temperatures during prolonged hot weather.

high temperature. Lightest turf color occurred during and just following the highest temperatures in August.

During the highest summer temperatures in July and early August, yields were significantly greater (difference = 0.5 g) from the mix than the sand plots. With continued high temperatures during the remainder of the summer and during cooler weather in October, yield was significantly greater (difference = 0.5 to 1 g) from sand than mix plots. Although significant differences were found for only four of the eight sampling dates, a similar trend was found for the influence of soils on chlorophyll content.

Following the initial decline in mid-July, yield was not affected significantly by irrigation treatments until mid-August. For the last two evaluations in August and in September, yields were significantly lower from SWT than SI or FWT treatments. Yields were highest from the FWT treatment but the difference between FWT and SI was significant only in September. For the first yield evaluation in July and during the apparent recovery in October, yield differences were all significant. Yield from FWT was greatest and SWT least for early July; SI was greatest and SWT least in October. Comparison of irrigation treatments pooled over soils showed sprinkler-irrigated plots significantly higher in chlorophyll content than subirrigated plots, except for the last sampling in August when there were no significant differences.

Root mass was significantly greater and its extension deeper in the sand (50 cm) than mix (30 cm). Significantly greater root masses were found for FWT treatments than for SWT treatments which in turn were significantly greater than SI treatments. The poor root development under sprinkler irrigation during drought periods is in agreement with other investigators (3).

In general, the summer evaluations indicated that turf quality produced by subirrigation and fertilization using a fluctuating water table was similar to that receiving sprinkler irrigation and superior to that produced by a stable water table. The greatest adverse effects of the sprinkler irrigation and surface fertilization were that 1) this practice tended to encourage shallow root development, especially on the mix soil; and 2) the turf required afternoon syringing on hot, windy days. The major disadvantage associated with the subirrigation and fertilization practice was the production of noticeably lighter green turf, especially from the SWT treatment. Salt content at 10-cm depth increased in subirrigated plots on the average from about 0.5 to 1.6 mmhos/cm over the summer but did not noticeably affect the turf.

Nitrogen nutrition

When lighter green turf on the subirrigated plots first occurred in early July, additional N (SWT = 12.2 g/m^2, FWT = 16.8 g/m^2) was added to the water (mid-July). Chlorophyll content was not improved. Color became lighter on all plots, but subirrigated plots were affected most. Plants on the subirrigated plots exhibited a pronounced chlorosis typical of N deficiency. Chemical analysis of tissue samples revealed a range of 4.0 to 4.4% and 5.0 to 5.2% total N for subirrigated and SI treatments, respectively. Tissue N levels below 4.5% have been suggested as deficient for sprinkler-irrigated bentgrass under similar temperature conditions (G. V. Johnson, unpublished data).

Table 1—Available soil N in relation to irrigation method, kind of soil, and time.

	Irrigation Method					
	SI		SWT		FWT	
Date	Sand	Mix	Sand	Mix	Sand	Mix
			— ppm NO_3^--N†			
Jun 14	3.9	3.2	3.5	4.8	3.3	3.6
Jul 14	9.3	7.1	8.9	7.4	8.1	8.5
Sep 20	5.6	6.1	4.1	3.7	3.8	3.1
Oct 28	4.8	5.0	3.6	3.6	3.8	3.6

* SI—Sprinkler irrigation; SWT—Subirrigation with stable water table; FWT—Subirrigation with fluctuating table.   † Average of all replicates sampled at 10-cm depth.

Continued efforts during August to promote darker green color by high N application in the water of subirrigated plots failed. Only after temperatures became cooler in late September and October was adequate color restored to the subirrigated turf.

Some insight into the problem of lighter green turf associated with subirrigated plots during hot summer weather was possible from data on N use and consideration of differences in physical conditions of the soils in relation to irrigation treatments.

Available soil N at 10-cm depth was similar for all treatments during the summer and, except for the increase in July, remained fairly constant with time (Table 1). Utilization of applied N, however, was extremely poor for the subirrigated treatments (Fig. 3). This inefficient use of N may be related to the anaerobic conditions which exist near and below the water table which could have stimulated gaseous N losses through denitrification. The detection of as much as 2.5 ppm NO_2^- in the soil solution on August 15 and odors characteristic of anaerobic conditions in the subirrigated plots support this

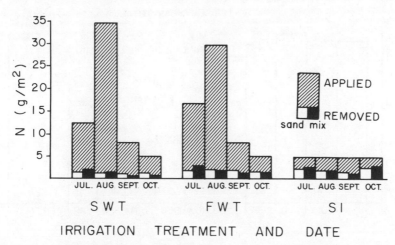

Fig. 3—Removal of applied nitrogen in creeping bentgrass clippings as influenced by irrigation treatment and kind of soil during prolonged hot weather.

supposition. The high rates of N applied during August may have promoted denitrification in spite of the form of N used, as nitrification and denitrification may have occurred within a zone just above and at the water table. For example, applied ammonium may be transported upward with water use to an aerobic zone and be nitrified, followed by diffusion of the more mobile nitrate ion downward to an anaerobic zone where it could be denitrified. Energy for the denitrification process in the form of easily decomposible organic matter could have been provided by root exudates and/or sloughing off of dead root tissue.

Improved color and apparently lower losses of N during cool weather suggest that the apparent denitrification activity may be of concern only during prolonged hot weather. This problem has not been reported with subirrigation of bentgrass turf in cool climates (2). Poor utilization of N applied to SI plots may be explained by the low cation exchange capacity (< 5 meq/ 100 g) and high permeability of both soils which would allow considerable N to be lost by leaching. Nitrogen utilization might be improved by lightly watering in surface applied N to subirrigated turf.

Consumptive use

Consumptive use of water by bentgrass irrigated from a stable water table is summarized for 1 year in Fig. 4. On a daily basis, use ranged from about 5 mm in August to 2 mm in January. Slightly greater use associated with the sand material may be related to greater root development for this treatment.

SUMMARY

Bentgrass turf which was subirrigated with a fluctuating water table was less subject to summer heat stress than sprinkler-irrigated turf. A major

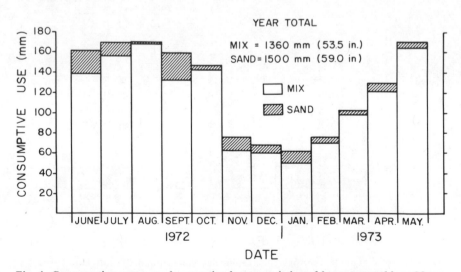

Fig. 4—Consumptive water use by creeping bentgrass irrigated by a water table at 30 cm.

problem experienced with subirrigation and fertilization was that of maintaining dark green turf during the hottest weather. The problem appeared to be related to losses of N due to denitrification.

REFERENCES

1. MADISON. J. J., and A. H. ANDERSON. 1963. A chlorophyll index to measure turfgrass response. Agron. J. 55:461–464.
2. RALSTON, D. S., and W. H. DANIEL. 1973. Effect of porous rootzone materials underlined with plastic on the growth of creeping bentgrass (*Agrostis palustris* Huds.) Agron. J. 65:229–232.
3. SKIRDE, W. 1970. Reactions of turfgrasses to watering. p. 311–325. *In* Proc. First Int. Turfgrass Res. Conf. Sports Turf Research Institute, Bingley, England.

ABSTRACTS

Abstracts of all papers not published herein but presented at the Conference are included below to round off this Section. These abstracts, unlike the printed papers, have not been refereed.

SECTION 7 ABSTRACT—TURFGRASS GROWTH CONTROL WITH CHEMICALS

Mowing, clipping, or trimming turfgrasses remains one of the more time-consuming maintenance procedures common to professional turf managers and homeowners alike. Chemical growth inhibitors would seem to be a logical alternative. The problem with existing chemicals has been that unacceptable discoloration has usually accompanied the growth retardation produced by their use on turfgrass. This research was carried out in an attempt to find suitable chemicals, or combinations of chemicals, or methods of application that would reduce the number of mowings necessary without affecting the quality of the turfgrass.

Established stands of mixed turf (mainly Kentucky bluegrass, *Poa pratensis* L.) and red fescue (*Festuca rubra* L.) were treated at several times in the early spring, in the autumn, and at various times relative to mowing of the grass during 1971 and 1972. Some treatments also were applied to bentgrass (*Agrostis* spp.). The chemicals used were mainly maleic hydrazide or MH (1,2-dihydro-3,6-pyridazinedione) and chlorflurenol (methyl 2-chloro-9-hydroxyfluorene-9-carboxylate) although some new compounds known only by code numbers were also included. Visual effects and fresh weight of clippings were used to assess the effectiveness of the various treatments.

Best results were obtained on mixed turf by the use of mixtures of MH and chlorflurenol, at 3.45 + 1.15 kg/ha, applied when grass growth was beginning in the spring (April 23, 1971 and April 28, 1972). Up to 90% growth inhibition without excessive discoloration was obtained for about 8 weeks. Late fall (October 15 and November 3) application also gave considerable spring growth retardation, but seemed to predispose the grass to winter injury. None of the chemicals tested appeared useful on bentgrass.

These results indicate that MH and chlorflurenol when applied early in the spring can be used to reduce the number of mowings required without causing appreciable discoloration. Where some discoloration is inconsequential, as in certain areas of the golf course or around trees or buildings, higher rates will extend time of retardation, resulting in appreciable savings.— Clayton M. Switzer, University of Guelph, Ontario, Canada.

DISCUSSION

E. W. SCHWEIZER—Very little emphasis has been placed on techniques of application of chemicals, and I feel that this is an important factor. In Switzerland we have found distinct differences on the discoloration of grasses with Knapsack spraying [Ed. Note: Knapsack spraying is a method of application and refers to many sprayers that are portable and hand pumped.] and larger scale application. For slopes we have a special pump with a magnetic counter regulating precisely the amount of liquid applied in relation to the speed of ground coverage and the width of the spray pattern. We have also found on plot trials that with the bentgrasses we observe practically no discoloration from growth retardant applications when a special roller apparatus, marketed in Europe under the name Driftmaster, is used. With use of common pump-type sprayers, discoloration is to be expected. With all chemicals, a spray delivered under too much pressure causes discoloration and burning. Shouldn't greater care be exercised in the application of chemicals?

C. M. SWITZER—Yes, greater care should be exercised in the application of chemicals. Our plots were treated with a Knapsack sprayer under relatively high pressure (2.8 kg/cm^2) and 933 liters/ha of spray. Other methods of application could very well give different results. I agree that with bentgrass at low clipping heights, the higher pressure will force more chemical down into the turf and greater damage may be expected. I don't know what the right pressure should be. I have never thought of 2.8 kg/cm^2 as being particularly high although it may be relatively high in comparison with the application technique used in Switzerland; I'm not familiar with this apparatus.

W. H. DANIEL —It seems to me that we are reporting here work with many growth regulators that are already out of date. Many of these chemicals are being replaced with second and third generation growth regulators and I believe now that we should be placing emphasis on these. I would anticipate that at the next meeting of the International Turfgrass Society (ITS), reports on work of this type will leave a significant imprint on the management of turfgrasses. Finally, it seems obvious that if we are to use these materials effectively on turf, we must have a highly educated clientele that will be using growth regulators as one element of increasingly sophisticated programs.

R. P. FREEBORG—Was CCC applied as a soil drench or as a foliar application? Was zoysia treated so that observations could be made on continuation of foliage color in the fall and early green up in the spring?

V. B. YOUNGNER—Yes, we have used soil drenches, foliar application, and applications in solution culture on a large number of warm-season species and cultivars. In general, we obtained fairly consistent results with different methods of application. With regard to color of zoysiagrass, we have not made these kinds of treatments. We have had some field experiments with CCC on bermudagrass. Our results indicated that CCC did not significantly improve fall color.

K. T. PAYNE—Has injury to turfgrasses been observed in Canada in the spring following a spring application of growth retardants the previous year? Observations were made that injury in the spring following a fall application had been noted.

C. M. SWITZER—Following spring application the preceding year, at the rates we've used, there haven't been any results persisting longer than 6 to 8 weeks. Not only have injuries disappeared but also any signs of growth retardation. One plot could not be distinguished from another.

R. C. WAKEFIELD—In work conducted in Canada has damage to shrubs and trees resulted from applications of chlorflurenol to roadside turf?

C. M. SWITZER—In the same way that we are concerned about the effects of 2,4-D on shrubs and trees, we are concerned about chlorflurenol; i.e., when it is not applied carefully and drifts where it shouldn't. We have used several of these growth regulators on several cultivars of shrubs, and the chemical has a pronounced effect on them. I have not observed injury to shrubs when chlorflurenol was sprayed on the ground near them. Now, it may be that at high rates and with persistent applications movement through the soil could cause injury to shrubs.

W. A. SMALL—Were the thatch decomposition studies in Texas conducted with or without benefit of topdressing?

R. L. DUBLE—No topdressing was applied. Verticle mowing and aerifying were not practiced on any of these plots. We were trying to grow thatch.

P. MC MAUGH—Have you given any attention to Collembola and Nematodes in thatch decomposition? Do you have counts of these?

R. L. DUBLE—All we looked at were the fungi and the bacteria. We didn't look at protozoa or any of the other microorganisms. I'm sure that they'd have a significant effect.

H. D. NIEMCZYK—Are insecticides used on bermudagrass in your area and if the answer is yes, would you comment on their influence on thatch decomposition?

R. L. DUBLE—Yes, insecticides are used regularly on bermudagrass. I have not observed any effect of insecticides on thatch accumulation. We have seen a definite influence of fungicides on thatch accumulation, but no effect of insecticides.

R. E. BLASER—With reference to the proposal for a diagrammatic aid to turfgrass management, there are some very interesting implications presented. However, the issue here is that the turfgrass plant is surprisingly plastic, and the various relationships discussed vary sharply with season. As a matter of fact, I think that for a given species we should never consider any one good cutting practice or even a range. At times a species should be managed one way and at another time in a different way. Close cutting of grasses under favorable conditions may even give them an advantage over bentgrass while under unfavorable conditions or in other seasons this response would be sharply reversed. Grasses have adaptive morphological and physiological mechanisms that interact sharply with other factors that influence growth during different seasons. Thus, although I believe that this is an interesting endeavor, the use of this diagrammatic aid will be restricted to the very, very general because of plant plasticity and natural adaptation.

F. J. WRAY—This is quite true. Seasonal variation in performance must be taken into consideration.

H. C. H. GHIJSEN—What observations have been made in Mississippi with respect to perennial ryegrass taking over a bermudagrass turf following overseeding?

C. Y. WARD —In our locality and, I think, throughout the southern United States where bermudagrass is used (from the 34th to the 25th parallel) perennial ryegrass never takes over in any significant way. Sometimes a few plants persist through the summer season, but generally by late spring 75 to 95% of the perennial ryegrass is gone. This is largely because of close mowing, which pushes it past its capacity to continue growth.

D. T. HAWES—On what type of areas is the use of growth regulators on Kentucky bluegrass economically feasible with presently available commercial materials?

T. L. WATSCHKE —Work that's been done in several states on controlling turfgrass vegetation and on reducing maintenance costs in the mowing operation has yielded several areas where recommendations can now be made. Use of these chemicals on roadsides has proven to be economically feasible. On roadsides regular maintenance operations on turf have proven to be hazardous because of highway traffic. Use of these materials on large areas as a substitute for mowing requires that the material last for a longer time and cause less discoloration of the turf than most materials now on the market. Some of the materials that we're looking at this year are far more encouraging than those reported in the 1972 data. These new materials are both longer lasting and discoloration is not as severe. In other words, they have increased activity with decreased phytotoxicity and this is the combination we're looking for.

W. C. MORGAN—Where did the seed sampling information for the Los Angeles area originate?

R. W. SCHERY—I'm not privileged to say where the sampling came from, but I've been in Los Angeles a number of times and looked at the lawns in this area. I know that you offer quite a few grasses that are not offered in other parts of the country, such as meadow fescue, in some of the mixtures. Of course *Dichondra* is used in the area too. You have the full range of southern grasses as well as the northern grasses. Because of this diversity of plant types used, as well as the great many ecological niches in this area that are not found in other parts of the country, we felt that Los Angeles was treated very leniently in comparison with the rest of the United States. I would put Denver, Colorado at one extreme of the quality scale and Los Angeles, California at the other.

Roadsides

Section VIII

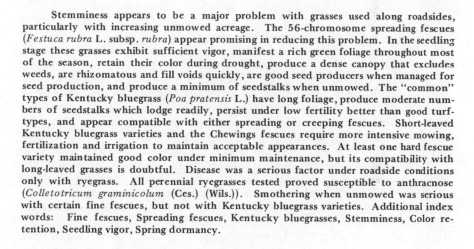

68

Grass varieties for roadsides[1]

R.W. DUELL & R.M. SCHMIT

Stemminess appears to be a major problem with grasses used along roadsides, particularly with increasing unmowed acreage. The 56-chromosome spreading fescues (*Festuca rubra* L. subsp. *rubra*) appear promising in reducing this problem. In the seedling stage these grasses exhibit sufficient vigor, manifest a rich green foliage throughout most of the season, retain their color during drought, produce a dense canopy that excludes weeds, are rhizomatous and fill voids quickly, are good seed producers when managed for seed production, and produce a minimum of seedstalks when unmowed. The "common" types of Kentucky bluegrass (*Poa pratensis* L.) have long foliage, produce moderate numbers of seedstalks which lodge readily, persist under low fertility better than good turf-types, and appear compatible with either spreading or creeping fescues. Short-leaved Kentucky bluegrass varieties and the Chewings fescues require more intensive mowing, fertilization and irrigation to maintain acceptable appearances. At least one hard fescue variety maintained good color under minimum maintenance, but its compatibility with long-leaved grasses is doubtful. Disease was a serious factor under roadside conditions only with ryegrass. All perennial ryegrasses tested proved susceptible to anthracnose (*Colletotricum graminicolum* (Ces.) (Wils.)). Smothering when unmowed was serious with certain fine fescues, but not with Kentucky bluegrass varieties. Additional index words: Fine fescues, Spreading fescues, Kentucky bluegrasses, Stemminess, Color retention, Seedling vigor, Spring dormancy.

The search for superior roadside grasses was prompted by the increasing cost of maintaining more miles of roadsides on restricted budgets and an increasing public awareness of environmental quality. Roadside grass mixtures have evolved out of agricultural experiences where production was an asset utilized in the form of pasture or hay.

Tall fescue (*Festuca arundinacea* Schreb.) is widely used along roadsides today largely because of the impetus given by the Soil Conservation Service to this widely adapted, robust plant. Redtop (*Agrostis alba* L.) is frequently included in roadside mixtures as a fast-starting grass that is adapted to wet acid soils. Ryegrasses, both perennial (*Lolium perenne* L.) and annual (*Lolium multiflorum* L.), are commonly included, particularly for their early emergence and great seedling vigor. These grasses excel in quick initial cover-

[1]Paper of the Journal Series, Soils and Crops Department, New Jersey Agr. Exp. Sta., Rutgers University, New Brunswick, NJ 08903.

age, thereby diminishing opportunities for loss of soil by erosion. With widespread and superior mulching techniques, one may question the need for such vigor, particularly when subsequent mowing needs and appearance are considered.

Kentucky bluegrass (*Poa pratensis* L.) is generally accepted as having a better appearance then the aforementioned species. This grass is commonly included in roadside mixtures as a small percentage, with the hope that it will be manifest on the more productive soils. The fine fescues, particularly creeping (*Festuca rubra* L. subsp. *rubra*), and Chewings (*Festuca rubra* L. subsp. *commutata* Gaud.), are also included in roadside mixtures with the aspiration that they might contribute where infertile, dry, and acid soils occur. Martin and Kaufman (7) reported that from mixtures of perennial ryegrass, Kentucky bluegrass, and red fescue, the dominant grasses after 4 years were Kentucky bluegrass on a loamy-clay site and red fescue on a sandy site. The Kentucky bluegrasses and fine fescues are less vigorous components of most roadside mixtures, and in competition with taller species may be unable to survive on most roadsides. Ryegrasses and redtop commonly disappear in the second year after seeding, and tall fescue frequently becomes the dominant component of the stand.

Apparently it mattered little in the past that tall fescue was more productive and required more frequent mowing to maintain a good appearance because mowing machines were becoming more efficient. As road systems expanded and rights of way widened (a present average of 6 to 7 ha of grass/ km of interstate highway), the cost of mowing grass became a large factor in road maintenance. When roadsides are left unmowed because of budgetary restrictions, the unsightliness of productive grasses and their seedstalks were recognized as a major negative feature of the landscape.

According to a survey made by Hottenstein (4), species were generally specified in mixtures of grasses for roadsides, but *cultivars* were seldom specified. 'Kentucky 31' tall fescue was the cultivar most frequently mentioned in the above-mentioned mixtures. When no cultivar is designated the natural inclination is to use common types, for these are usually cheaper than named cultivars. With increased numbers of named turfgrass cultivars available, the likelihood of "common" seed being a named cultivar that has failed to meet certification requirements is increasing. Thus, differences between lots of seed of "common" of any one species may become increasingly variable.

Establishment of the more productive or hay-type species occurs through viable grass seed in the hay mulch applied over the grass seeding. These frequently include orchardgrass (*Dactylis glomerata* L.), timothy (*Phleum pratense* L.), bromegrass (*Bromus inermis* Leyss.), and reed canarygrass (*Phalaris arundinacea* L.). Unlike legumes and broad-leaf weeds that can be controlled with selective herbicides, these grasses cannot be removed with selective herbicides. The hay-type species resulting from seed in hay mulches may dominate certain areas, often as distinctive patches.

The less productive, finer turfgrasses are more attractive, require less mowing for roadside maintenance, and look better if unmowed. Boeker (1) pointed out the advantages of low-growing grasses along roadsides in

Germany. He also indicated the inappropriateness of complex mixtures including coarse grasses and herbs. He believed that mixtures of three or four species, *Agrostis tenius, Festuca ovina, Festuca rubra,* and *Poa pratensis,* should suffice. Langvad (6) indicated that the aesthetic function of grass must be considered in addition to the erosion control aspect and the vehicular safety feature. Hence, seed of tall, coarse grasses used in Sweden until 1963 were replaced in subsequent mixtures with lower growing grasses needing no mowing.

OBJECTIVES

The practical objective in evaluating grass varieties for roadsides should be to develop mixtures that will provide the best appearance for the most months of the year with the least maintenance, and still provide sufficient certainty of establishment over variable situations. In addition, these grasses should be serviceable with regard to erosion control, weed exclusion, and support for vehicles leaving the pavement. They should be tolerant of roadside environments and not constitute a hazard by way of obstructing vision, causing snow to be deposited on roads, or burning readily.

METHODS

Grasses currently specified for roadsides in New Jersey were compared with commercially available turfgrass cultivars, plant introductions, local selections, and progenies of specific breeding programs. Testing was done in replicated four square meter plots along newly constructed roadsides, or under conditions simulating roadsides, with emphasis on minimum fertilization and mowing.

RESULTS AND DISCUSSION

Evaluation of grass varieties for roadsides since 1968 has resulted in an appreciation for the importance of recognizing stages of growth. Quality ratings may change from the seedling stage → juvenile → mature → possible senescence → possible loss of stand of a variety. In the seedling stage sufficient vigor to allay erosion is desirable, but excessive vigor so as to make a variety overly competitive with associated grasses is undesirable. These characteristics develop more completely and become more obvious when the grass grows unchecked by mowing.

The following data illustrate that seedlings of the finer turfgrasses, sown in the fall and measured prior to heading in the spring, are less vigorous than a coarse grass such as meadow fescue (*F. pratensis* L.).

Cultivar	cm
Meadow fescue	34.0
130-16 spreading fescue	17.2
130-17 spreading fescue	18.3

Atlanta Chewings fescue	11.7
Wintergreen Chewings fescue	13.5
C-26 Hard fescue	8.0
Kenblue Kentucky bluegrass	12.5
South Dakota Kentucky bluegrass	10.0
Merion Kentucky bluegrass	5.5
Sydsport Kentucky bluegrass	5.2

LDS (0.01) = 5.0

The 56-chromosome spreading fescues (1) are more vigorous than the Chewings fescues, and the hard fescues still less vigorous. The common type Kentucky bluegrasses, represented by 'Kenblue' and 'South Dakota Certified' are more vigorous in the seedling stage than the fine turf types such as 'Merion' and 'Sydsport.' Ryegrass cultivars in a separate but similar study indicated that the common type 'Linn' was 41-cm tall while 'Manhattan,' a turf type, was 23-cm tall. Seedling heights of 10 to 20 cm may be sufficient for roadside purposes. More vigorous plants may be excessively aggressive, and smaller plant associates may fail to persist.

Seedling characteristics foretell subsequent plant development in unmowed turf. The more vigorous seedlings may attain sufficient size in a fall seeding to be induced to flower the following spring. This is particularly true of the more vigorous spreading fescues and the common type Kentucky bluegrasses, while the smaller Chewings fescues and fine turf type Kentucky bluegrasses usually do not flower under the same conditions. Other species of roadside grasses typically flower in the spring following fall seeding. These include the ryegrasses, Canada bluegrass (*Poa compressa* L.), redtop, tall fescue, sheeps fescue (*Festuca ovina* L.), hard fescue (*F. longifolia* Thuill), and *F. pseudovina*.

In a mature stand of unmowed grasses the seedstalk characteristics are important quality features. The profusion of seedstalks and their persistance affects appearance. Among the Kentucky bluegrasses, Newport produces a large number of seedstalks annually, even when not mowed for 5 years. These stalks remain upright and conspicuous for months. Common Kentucky bluegrasses such as Kenblue, 'Delta,' and South Dakota produce fewer seedstalks, and these lodge more readily and are covered over by the long leaves of these cultivars. 'Fylking' produced few seedheads and maintained a good foliar cover under fertile soil conditions (Fig. 1 and 2). A rating of Kentucky bluegrass cultivars for seedstalk is listed below.

Kentucky bluegrass cultivars	Rating, 1 = most stalks 9 = no stalks
Newport	1.4
Merion	3.6
South Dakota	4.2
Delta	4.6
Kenblue	4.9
Belturf	7.4
Fylking	8.7

LSD (0.01) = 1.0

Fig. 1—Newport Kentucky bluegrass consistently produces more seedstalks than Kenblue Kentucky bluegrass even when unmowed for several years.

Fig. 2—Merion Kentucky bluegrass annually produces more seedstalks than Fylking, but fewer than Newport.

Fig. 3—Second spring after fall seeding, vigorous Ruby suppressed seedstalks more than did Highlight in background.

While seedstalk production characteristics of Kentucky bluegrass varieties continue perennially after maturity, those of the fine fescues do not. It was noted that in the first spring, after a late fall seeding, no seedstalks were produced by red fescue cultivars but foliar production the next summer on the unmowed plots was particularly good for the vigorous cultivar 'Ruby' and least for 'Highlight.' The information below and Fig. 3 illustrate differential production of seedstalks in unmowed plots the second spring after a late fall seeding.

Fescue cultivars	Rating, 1 = most stalks 9 = no stalks
Highlight	2.4
Pennlawn	4.8
Golfrood	6.2
Atlanta	7.0
Ruby	7.8
LDS (0.05) = 1.5	

The vigorous types, such as Ruby, had sufficient foliar growth to inhibit seedstalk production the second season. By the third spring all varieties had made excessive growth, and few seedstalks were produced on any varieties. Smothering was manifest, and Highlight was notable in its failure to reestablish full cover the fourth year.

Under a no-mow management, smothering of pure stands of fine fescues poses a problem on productive sites. Along roadsides and in mixtures this problem is of little practical importance. The Kentucky bluegrass cultivars have never smothered even under highly productive conditions and no mowing for 5 years. Under poor soil conditions and minimum management, adequacy of cover becomes questionable for fine turf types of Kentucky bluegrass. Common types of Kentucky bluegrass succeed better under such conditions, but not as well as the fine fescues.

Color retention by these fine grasses varies with the season. During summer droughts the Chewings fescues lose color markedly when unmowed on poor sites. In contrast, 'C-26' hard fescue and the spreading fescue selections retained good color, as indicated by the data below. Ruby creeping red fescue retained better color than 'Pennlawn' creeping red fescue.

Fescue cultivars	Rating, 1 = straw color 9 = best green color
Jamestown —Chewings	4.8
Highlight —Chewings	6.0
Pennlawn —creeping	5.5
Ruby —creeping	7.8
C-26 —hard fescue	7.5
Fortress —spreading	7.8
C.P. Shade —spreading	8.0
LDS (0.01) = 0.9	

Ruby and Pennlawn red fescue are called "creeping" in current seed-trade terminology. There is evidence that within these cultivars many plants may be spreading types and possess 2n = 56 chromosomes. The spreading fescue selections were consistent in retaining good color during summer drought under these conditions. In another series sheep fescues (*Festuca ovina* L.) were found to retain good color during summer drought, as did C-26 hard fescue. The following evaluation of color retention during summer drought shows that two Chewings fescues performed poorly in this regard, and that Ruby red fescue again looked better than Pennlawn. Chewings fescues turned brown while selected spreading fescues remained green (Fig. 4 and 5).

Cultivar	Rating, 1 = straw color 9 = best green color
Pennlawn creeping fescue	2.2
Highlight Chewings fescue	3.2
Wintergreen Chewings fescue	4.2
Ruby creeping fescue	6.2
KO-17 sheep fescue	7.5
Golfrood creeping	8.8
C-26 hard fescue	8.8
Alaska Station sheep fescue	9.0
LSD (0.05) = 1.9	

Breaking spring dormancy, or the ability to develop new green leaves,

Fig. 4—During summer drought Ruby creeping red fescue retained better color than Highlight Chewings fescue.

Fig. 5—Ruby creeping red fescue generally appeared greener than Pennlawn.

varies among fine fescue and Kentucky bluegrass varieties. The data below show a few characteristic fine fescue cultivars which differed in early spring greenness. The sheep and hard fescues were notably tardy in spring recovery, and the creeping fescue varieties were somewhat better than the Chewings fescues.

Fig. 6—Taller growing Delta Kentucky bluegrass (right) consistently broke dormancy earlier in the spring ("greened up" quicker) than did shorter growing cultivars like Newport (left).

Cultivar	Rating, 1 = straw color 9 = best green color
C-26 hard fescue	1.3
KO-17 sheep fescue	1.7
Alaska Station sheep tescue	2.0
Golfrood	5.0
Wintergreen—Chewings	6.0
Highlight—Chewings	6.0
Pennlawn—Creeping	6.3
Ruby	6.7
LSD (0.01) = 1.9	

Similarly, the following data show that the taller growing common-type Kentucky bluegrasses were less dormant than the shorter growing turf types (Fig. 6). Increasing rates of fall applied soluble nitrogenous fertilizer increased the production of green foliage of these varieties in the spring.

Cultivar	Rating, 1 = straw color 9 = best green color
Fylking	2.3
Belturf	3.4
Newport	3.4
Merion	3.9
South Dakota	5.9
Kenblue	6.7
Delta	7.9
LSD (0.01) = 1.1	

Differences in disease susceptibility among grass varieties does not appear to be a factor of importance in the roadside environment as it is where turf is intensively managed. The perennial ryegrasses might possibly constitute an exception, however. All of the perennial ryegrasses tested proved short-lived in roadside plots. Even the well-adapted 'Manhattan' cultivar dissipates after 2 or 3 years without mowing. It, and the other varieties, exhibited an abundance of anthracnose (*Colletotricum graminicolum* (Ces.) (Wils.)).

CONCLUSIONS

The best roadside grass mixtures are composed of selected varieties of a few species. Contracts which fail to specify cultivars of superior adaptation will likely result in various qualities of turf—generally poor. The selection of better cultivars for a particular roadside situation will require several years of testing on numerous sites. Cultivars or species that appear promising in early stages may not be the best vegetative cover to perpetually fulfill the basics of "the complete highway"; that is, roadsides designed for utility, safety, economy, and beauty.

ACKNOWLEDGMENT

The authors wish to acknowledge the financial support for research by the New Jersey Department of Transportation and the U. S. Department of Transportation, Federal Highway Administration. Views expressed herein are those of the authors and not necessarily those of the above agencies.

REFERENCES

1. BOEKER, P. 1970. Turfgrasses for roadsides. p. 576–579. *In* Proc. First Int. Turfgrass Res. Conf. Sports Turf Research Institute, Bingley, England
2. COWAN, J. R. 1962. The fescues. p. 300–307. *In* Hughes, Heath, and Metcalf (eds.) Forages, the science of grassland agriculture. The Iowa State College Press, Ames, Iowa.
3. DUELL, R. W. 1969. Highway vegetation. New Jersey Agr. Exp. Sta. Bull. 822, New Brunswick, N. J.
4. HOTTENSTEIN, W. L. 1969. Highway roadsides. *In* A. A. Hanson and F. V. Juska (eds.) Turfgrass science. Agronomy 14:603–637. Amer. Soc. Agron., Madison, Wis.
5. HUBBARD, C. E. 1968. Grasses. Penquin Books, Middlesex, England, Baltimore, Maryland, Victoria, Australia.
6. LANGVAD, B. 1969. Seed techniques for establishing grass on Swedish roadsides. p. 580–582. *In* Proc. First Int. Turfgrass Res. Conf. Sports Turf Research Institute, Bingley, England.
7. MARTIN, D. P., and J. E. KAUFMANN. 1970. Ecological relationships in establishment of roadside grass communities in Michigan. p. 73. Agronomy Abstr. 62nd Ann. Meeting, Tucson, Ariz. Amer. Soc. Agron., Madison, Wis.
8. SCHERY, R. W. 1970. The essentials for roadside vegetation. p. 63–75. *In* W. J. Garmhausen (ed.) Twenty-ninth short course on roadside development (Columbus, Ohio), The Ohio Dept. of Highways and the Dept. of Landscape Architecture, The Ohio State University.
9. SCHMIT, R. M., C. R. FUNK, and R. W. DUELL. 1974. Isolation barriers and self-incompatibility in selected fine fescues. p. 9–17. *In* E. C. Roberts (ed.) Proc. Second Int. Turfgrass Res. Conf. Amer. Soc. Agron., Madison, Wis.

69

Review of grasses for saline and alkali areas

J.D. BUTLER, J.L. FULTS, G.D. SANKS

Highway deicing and utilization of naturally contaminated soils for urban development have increased the demands for grasses adapted to saline and alkali conditions. In the northern areas of the United States only ten to twelve grasses are adapted to these adverse conditions. Furthermore, critical review of these grasses indicated that only three or four have desirable characteristics for turf use. Of these, alkaligrass (*Puccinellia* spp.) and desert saltgrass (*Distichlis stricta* (Torr.) Rydb.) are found spontaneously vegetating saline and alkali areas over a wide geographic range. In 1969, weeping alkaligrass (*P. distans* (L.) Parl.) was observed growing along an Illinois highway where salt from deicing had destroyed the other vegetation. Since 1969, this grass has become widespread along the northern Illinois highways, and soil tests indicate that sodium levels in excess of 10,000 ppm and soluble salt levels over 30,000 ppm exist where the weeping alkaligrass grows. In Colorado, establishment of both weeping and Lemmon alkaligrass (*P. lemmoni* (Vasey) Scribn.) on salty and alkali areas has provided a satisfactory turf for both athletic and residential grounds.

Work directed toward either improved turf quality or increased salt tolerance of grasses adapted to saline and alkali conditions has received little attention. However, plant variants of both alkaligrass and saltgrass are being collected and screened in the United States. A selection of weeping alkaligrass (Colorado Accession 666) that exhibits good turf quality has been increased and distributed for extensive testing. Additional index words: Highway deicing, Alkaligrass, Desert saltgrass, *Puccinellia* spp., *Distichlis stricta*, Salt tolerance.

In the interior regions of the United States salt problems associated with turf production have become critical during the last two decades. Urbanization of areas that were previously avoided because they were naturally high in salts has caused significant problems. Also, the use of salt for deicing highways has injured turf and other vegetation, especially in cooler, humid, and heavily populated areas.

Saline and alkali conditions in the arid west are most common where internal soil drainage is poor, and where drainage basins have no outlets. In such areas salt levels may be so high that all vegetation is excluded.

Direct plant injury from brine flow from highways that receive salt for deicing is pronounced near the paved surface and in stream beds and catchment basins. Brine splash can cause noticeable injury to the vegetative cover.

The salt spray that occurs some distance from the highway is not normally detrimental to turf, but may seriously injure trees and shrubs.

The importance of the deicing problem of highways is described in various reports (4, 5, 10). Hanes (10) determined that several states applied more than 18.1 metric tons of deicing salt per season per lane kilometer to some highways. Thirteen states reported plant injury. Highway salt problems are not diminishing, and solutions must be sought.

The use of grasses known to have a high salt tolerance is frequently only a short-term solution for vegetating a contaminated area. Through continuous applications of deicing salt levels may build until they exceed the limits of the most tolerant species. In areas once naturally salty, copious irrigation can reduce the salt levels and change the grass population from one with a high salt tolerance to one of moderate to low tolerance.

LITERATURE REVIEW

Considering the magnitude of the problems associated with saline and alkali soils there is a paucity of information; however, there is general agreement on a few grasses that have good tolerance to salt.

A review of research on salt tolerance by Beard (1) has resulted in categorization of four turfgrasses as having a relatively good ($EC_e \times 10^{-3}$ of 8 to 16) salinity tolerance. Of the four, only creeping bentgrass (*Agrostis palustris* Huds.) is well adapted to the colder areas of the United States. A listing of forage crops in *Agriculture Handbook No. 60* (17) indicates nine grasses and one forb have high ($EC_e \times 10^{-3}$ of 12 to 18) salt tolerance. The nine grasses listed in order of decreasing salt tolerance are: alkali sacaton (*Sporobolus airoides* (Torr.) Torr.), saltgrass (*Distichlis stricta* (Torr.) Rydb.), Nuttall alkaligrass (*Puccinellia airoides* (Nutt.) Wats & Coult.), bermudagrass (*Cynodon dactylon* (L.) Pers.), Rhodesgrass (*Chloris gayana* Kunth.), rescuegrass (*Bromus catharticus* Vahl.), Canada wildrye (*Elymus canadensis* L.), western wheatgrass (*Agropyron smithii* Rydb.), and barley (hay) (*Hordeum vulgare* L.). Exceptionally good tolerance of tall wheatgrass (*Agropyron elongatum* (Host.) Beauv.) has been noted by Bernstein (2) and Hamilton (9). Among the grasses that Roberts (15) demonstrated to be most salt tolerant were desert saltgrass, Nuttall alkaligrass, alkali sacaton, and western wheatgrass.

Alkaligrass and desert saltgrass are found spontaneously vegetating saline and alkali areas over a wide geographic range. Lunt (13, 14) showed that *Puccinellia distans* (L.) Parl. (weeping alkaligrass) exhibited good tolerance to salt (NaCl). More recent publications (3, 7, 9, 12) have revealed the wide distribution as well as the salt tolerance of several species of *Puccinellia*. *The Manual of Grasses of the United States* (11) lists ten species of alkaligrass. Seven are perennial and three are annual. Fults (7) listed weeping alkaligrass, Nuttall alkaligrass, and Lemmon alkaligrass (*P. lemmoni* (Vasey) Scribn.) as the most valuable species for turf.

Studies with desert saltgrass by Dudeck (6) indicated that 5,000 ppm of salt (NaCl) in gravel culture could significantly increase top growth. Furthermore, he observed no mortality at 20,000 ppm. Jones (12) reported three alkaligrasses to be salt tolerant, but not obligated halophytes, i.e., requiring salt for normal growth.

A review (3) of salt-tolerant grasses for roadsides emphasized the advantages and disadvantages of specific grasses, but the report did not dwell on the use of these grasses for fine turf.

SALT TOLERANT GRASSES

A brief examination of the above grasses emphasizes the scarcity of those adapted to colder areas as well as to turf situations and turf maintenance.

Barley is a tall annual that might serve as a "nurse" grass in salty areas. Rescuegrass is an annual or biennial and grows quite tall. Rhodesgrass, like rescuegrass, grows in warmer areas where highways are not salted.

Alkali sacaton is considered a tall bunchgrass, although Griffiths (8) reported a continuous uniform growth that approached a turf. Canada wildrye is a tall, coarse, cool-season bunchgrass that might be useful, not as a turf, but for cover in low, unmowed areas. Tall wheatgrass is a tall, coarse, bunchgrass that normally forms only a sparse cover.

Western wheatgrass shows promise as a turf, especially if cultivars are developed that will produce a dense, fine-textured cover. Inland saltgrass is a strongly rhizomatous, warm-season perennial that can be found growing in competition with Kentucky bluegrass (*Poa pratensis* L.). The strong rhizomes of saltgrass frequently grow through and destroy hard road surfaces. This western grass has a low growing habit and is moderately fine textured. Saltgrass shows promise as a turf for erosion control and heavily used summer athletic areas. This grass is dioecious and a poor seed producer. Vegetative propagation of saltgrass is practiced. It is a warm-season grass that would be most useful in combination with other warm-season grasses.

The alkaligrasses mentioned by Fults (7) as having turf potential are cool-season, low-growing, perennial bunchgrasses. Of the three, Lemmon alkaligrass is the finest textured and lowest growing while Nuttall alkaligrass is coarser and most upright. Weeping alkaligrass is intermediate. Griffiths (8) noted that Nuttall alkaligrass could stand large amounts of soluble salts in solution for a month or more at a time. This is important in highway salting because of standing water, whether in basins or on frozen grounds, and salt splash.

These three alkaligrasses tiller and spread rapidly, have unusual seedling vigor, and provide quick cover. These grasses are, under some situations, extremely heavy seed producers. This seeding habit can cause a deterioration of other turf, because abundant seed may spread rapidly over an area from a few isolated plants. Mowed turf of these grasses may at times appear to be intermediate between creeping bentgrass and Kentucky bluegrass. At other times, especially if seeding is heavy, it may be stemmy, open, and of poor quality.

RESEARCH AND OBSERVATIONS

Research with alkaligrass was undertaken at about the same time at both the University of Illinois at Urbana and Colorado State University at

Fort Collins. Work at Illinois started when alkaligrass was found growing along an Interstate highway where salt had destroyed all other vegetation. In Colorado, work with this grass was instigated when it was found vegetating salty areas on golf courses.

Positive identification, whether morphological or cytological, of species of *Puccinellia* can be quite difficult (3, 4, 12). It should be noted that the alkaligrass now found so commonly along Illinois highways and on Colorado golf courses, is primarily weeping alkaligrass.

Much of the originally planted Kentucky bluegrass and tall fescue (*Festuca arundinacea* Schreb.) on Chicago, Illinois, area roadsides is succeeded by quackgrass (*Agropyron repens* (L.) Beauv.). Weeping alkaligrass then invades the quackgrass, which disappears. Mexican fireweed (*Kochia scoparia* (L.) Schrad.) and orache (*Atriplex patula* L.) accompany the weeping alkaligrass on sites of high salt content (4).

Recent extensive soil tests from a Colorado golf course indicated that Kentucky bluegrass will grow in soil containing up to 4 mmhos/cm (EC_e), or approximately 2,800 ppm soluble salts. However, above that level, and up to 14 mmhos/cm, only alkaligrass grew well. At higher salt levels along Illinois highways, alkaligrass has been found growing at levels of approximately 4,000 to 10,000 ppm sodium and 20,000 to 30,000 ppm total soluble salts (3, 4).

The problem of salt splash along highways prompted Sanks (16) to make applications of salt solutions (NaCl) to four western grasses—weeping alkaligrass, crested wheatgrass, western wheatgrass, and Nuttall alkaligrass. Three of these were found to have good salt tolerance, while crested wheatgrass (*Agropyron cristatum* (L.) Gaertn.) did not. The solutions were applied weekly for 8 weeks with the last application on March 4, 1971. The grasses were rated 6 weeks later. In Table 1 a rating of 10 indicates no visual damage (compared to the control) and a rating of 1 indicated that the plants all appeared to be dead.

Since sod is frequently used along highways in salty areas, and since sod is more tolerant of salt than seedlings, Sanks (16) determined the sod handling characteristics of several grass mixtures. Preliminary studies indicated that pure stands of western and crested wheatgrass did not form a sod that could be lifted. Smooth bromegrass (*Bromus inermis* Leyss.) was used because of its strong rhizomes. These mixtures were seeded at Urbana, Illinois, on August 1, 1970, and tested May 8, 1971. Table 2 indicates the strength of sod of several mixtures. In Table 2, a "0" indicates that the sod could not be lifted. A sod that could support more than 13.5 kg without tearing was satisfactory for highway use. The sod was cut 0.305 m wide, and

Table 1—Tolerance ratings of various grasses to foliar applications of NaCl.

Treatment, metric tons per lane km of NaCl	Average rating			
	P. distans	*A. cristatum*	*A. smithii*	*P. airoides*
0	10	10	10	10
19.1	9	1	7	9
38.2	8	1	2	8

Table 2—Weight necessary to tear grass mixture sods grown for highway use.

Grass mixture	Sod produced from seed ratios of		
	9:1	3:1	1:1
		kg	
Western wheatgrass to Kentucky bluegrass	>22.7	>22.7	>22.7
Crested wheatgrass to Kentucky bluegrass	19.1	>22.7	>22.7
Western wheatgrass to smooth bromegrass	0	0	0
Crested wheatgrass to smooth bromegrass	0	0	0
Spreading meadowgrass to Kentucky bluegrass	>22.7	---	>22.7

2.5-cm deep. It was concluded that when 10% or more Kentucky bluegrass was used in the mixture, satisfactory sod could be produced in a relatively short time. Since the salt tolerance of Kentucky bluegrass is low it would be replaced by more tolerant species.

At Colorado State University several species of alkaligrass are being tested under turf conditions. One weeping alkaligrass (Accession 666) is a promising turf type that has been increased and distributed over a wide geographic area for testing. Other work is currently under way to improve desert saltgrass for turf use.

There is a great need for research concerned with plant problems associated with salt. Much of the information available on salt grasses has been gathered from diverse and often artificial situations. Thus, more workable models for studying salt problems need to be devised. In the western United States, and in areas where salt is used for deicing, salt problems associated with turf production are common and often severe.

REFERENCES

1. BEARD, J. B. 1973. Turfgrass: science and culture. Prentice-Hall, Inc., Englewood Cliffs, N. J. p. 344–348.
2. BERNSTEIN, L. 1958. Salt tolerance of grasses and forage legumes. U. S. Dep. Agr. Agr. Bull. 194. 7 p.
3. BUTLER, J. D. 1972. Salt tolerant grasses for roadsides. Highway Res. Record 411:1–6.
4. ———, T. D. HUGHES, G. D. SANKS, and P. E. CRAIG. 1971. Salt causes problems along Illinois highways. Illinois Res. 35(4):3–4.
5. DICKINSON, W. E. 1968. Snow and ice control—a critical look at its critics. p. 6–14. In E. D. Carpenter (ed.) Pollutants in the roadside environment, Univ. of Conn. and Conn. Dept. Trans.
6. DUDECK, A. E. 1970. Response of desert saltgrass, *Distichlis stricta* (Torr.) Rydb. to sodium chloride and clipping. Agron. Abst. p. 72.
7. FULTS, J. 1972. Grasses for saline and alkali areas. p. 44–55. Proc. 18th Rocky Mountain Reg. Turf. Conf.
8. GRIFFITHS, D., G. L. BIDWELL, and C. E. GOODRICH. 1915. Native pasture grasses of the United States. U. S. Dep. Agr. Bull. 201. 52 p.
9. HAMILTON, G. J. 1972. Investigations into the reclamation of dryland saline soils. Soil Conserv. J. N.S.W. 28:191–211.
10. HANES, R. E., L. W. ZELOZNY, and R. E. BLASER. 1970. Effects of deicing salts on water quality and biota—literature review and recommended research. Highway Res. Info. Serv Abstr. 3(4):17.

11. HITCHCOCK, A. S., and A. CHASE. 1961. Manual of the grasses of the United States. U. S. Dep. Agr. Misc. Publ. 200. 1051 p.

12. JONES, B. M. G., and L. E. NEWTON. 1970. The status of *Puccinellia pseudodistans* (Crep.) Jansen and Wachter in Great Britain. Watsonia 3:17–26.

13. LUNT, O. R. 1961. Salinity tolerance of five turfgrass varieties. Agron. J. 53: 247–249.

14. ———. 1964. Tolerance of five turfgrass species to soil alkali. Agron. J. 56: 481–483.

15. ROBERTS, E. C. 1968. Salt tolerance and accumulation in soils. Ohio State Univ. Short Course on Roadside Dev. 26:74–83.

16. SANKS, G. D. 1971. Adaptability of alkaligrass for roadside use. Univ. of Ill., Dept. of Hort. M.S. thesis. 40 p.

17. U. S. SALINITY LABORATORY STAFF. 1969. Diagnosis and improvement of saline and alkali soils. U. S. Dep. Agr. Agr. Handbook 60. p. 66–67.

70

Suitability of cool- and warm-season species for dormant winter seedings [1]

J.T. GREEN, JR., H.D. PERRY, J.M. WOODRUFF,
R.E. BLASER

Late fall-winter-spring seedings were made to delineate differences in seedling emergence, winter survival, maintenance of seed viability, and soil protection among several turf species. Cereal rye (*Secale cereale*) was the best species for late fall-spring seedings followed by creeping red fescue (*Festuca ruba*) and roughstalk bluegrass (*Poa trivialis*); results from tall fescue (*Festuca arundinacea*) were fair. The data indicate that higher seeding rates should be used for late fall-winter seedings to obtain better vegetative cover. For winter seedings, a recommended mixture of 'Abruzzi' rye (50 kg), creeping red fescue (40 kg), and 'Kentucky 31' tall fescue (70 kg) with possibly roughstalk bluegrass at 30 kg/ha is proposed. Information on persistence and competitive effects of these grasses as mixed is inadequate. The ryegrasses (*Lolium* spp.) are not recommended for winter seedings. Successful stands of crownvetch (*Coronilla varia*) and sericea lespedeza (*Lespedesa sericea*) were obtained by dormant seeding. The warm-season grasses, bermudagrass (*Cynodon dactylon*) and weeping lovegrass (*Eragrostis curvula*), were not suitable for winter seedings as poor stands were observed the following summer. Additional index words: Mixtures, Germination, Erosion control, Dormant seeding.

Past experience indicates that late fall or winter seeding of perennial species such as tall fescues (*Festuca arundinacea*) and sericea lespedeza (*Lespedeza sericea*) have generally failed to produce a satisfactory vegetative cover; hence, contractors delayed seeding until the following favorable spring season. Severe erosion from such unseeded slopes has been of concern to highway personnel and the public because of the associated siltation and water pollution. Thus, the need of establishing protective vegetative cover during all seasons of the year while highway construction is underway has been recognized. There is now a federal statute that no more than 6.75 hectares per any one contract may be left unseeded beyond 30 days. Seed can be held in place and fair to good erosion control can be obtained during the late fall-winter season by various persistent mulches with chemical binders (11).

Species which germinate and grow at very cool temperatures improve the slope stabilization provided by mulches and provide a vegetative cover

[1]Contribution by the Department of Agronomy, Virginia Polytechnic Institute and State University, Blacksburg, VA 24061.

while persistent species such as tall fescue and sericea lespedeza or crown-vetch are being established. Species vary widely in their ability to germinate at low temperatures (6, 9). These investigations were planned to ascertain the suitability of selected cool- and warm-season species for dormant seedings by obtaining information on seed viability, seedling emergence, and soil cover the following spring.

PROCEDURES

All species were surface seeded in blocks replicated three times in field plots where the soil was relatively level (0 to 2% slope). Seeding rates, dates, and species used for the dormant seedings are listed in the tables. Plot sizes at Blacksburg, Virginia, were 2.44 m² and 3.05 m² at Warsaw and Charlotte Court House, Virginia. Experiments at Blacksburg for several seeding dates were treated with a 10–20–10 fertilizer at the rate of 1,344 kg/ha and wood-fiber cellulose mulch at 1,680 kg/ha. The seedings at Warsaw received 10–20–10 at 672 kg/ha and woodfiber cellulose mulch at 1,522 kg/ha on November 17, 1972. The seeding at Charlotte Court House received no mulch and 672 kg/ha of 10–20–10 fertilizer on December 5, 1972. The following species were used.

Common name	Cultivar	Latin binomial
Redtop	--	*Agrostis alba* L.
Bentgrass	'Colonial'	*Agrostis tenuis* (Sibth.)
Oats	'Clinton'	*Avena sativa* L.
Crownvetch	'Emerald'	
	'Penngift'	*Coronilla varia* L.
Bermudagrass	'Common'	*Cynodon dactylon* L. Pers.
Orchardgrass	'Potomac'	*Dactylis glomerata* L.
Weeping lovegrass	--	*Eragrostis curvula* L. (Schrad) Wees
Russian wild rye	--	*Elymus junceus* Tisch
Tall fescue	'Kentucky 31'	*Festuca arundinacea* Shreb
Creeping red fescue	'Pennlawn'	*Festuca rubra* L.
Barley	'Wong'	*Hordeum vulgare* L.
Lespedesz sericea	--	*Lespedeza cuneata* (Dumont) G. Don
Annual ryegrass	--	*Lolium multiflorum* Lam.
Perennial ryegrass	'Pennfine'	*Lolium perenne* L.
Perennial ryegrass	'Lynn'	*Lolium perenne* L.
Perennial ryegrass	'Manhattan'	*Lolium perenne* L.
Timothy	'Clair'	*Phleum pratense* L.
Kentucky bluegrass	'Common'	*Poa pratensis* L.
Roughstalk bluegrass	--	*Poa trivialis* L.
Rye	'Balboa'	*Secale cereale* L.
Rye	'Abruzzi'	*Secale cereale* L.
Wheat	'Blueboy'	*Triticum aestivum* L.

All initial seedbeds were prepared by plowing, disking, and leveling. The soil at Blacksburg was lightly scarified by hand raking for the December, January, March, and May seedings.

Data obtained included seedling population per 18.6 dm² at three dates after seeding and recorded as a percent of the total number of seeds of each species planted, and vegetative cover for each species at three dates. The later was based on mean estimates by two or three individuals.

RESULTS AND DISCUSSION

Blacksburg experiments

The monthly maximum and minimum temperatures during October through June are given in Table 1. Seedling populations (percent of sown seed) and soil covered with vegetation during early seedling development, on April 18 and on June 1, for different dates of seeding are given in Tables 2, 3, and 4, respectively.

Early seedling development

Data obtained 30 to 69 days after seeding of all species showed the best stands for October and May seedings (Table 2) when temperatures were the most favorable for germination and seedling growth. Seedling stands for the December and March seedings were quite similar. Mild autumn temperatures favored germination and seedling growth. The rather low seedling populations for March seedings are attributed to the cool ambient temperatures; also the lagging soil temperatures, resulting from earlier low ambient temperatures, undoubtedly inhibited germination and growth. Seedling mortality would be expected to be highest for the December and March seedings because of the small seedlings resulting from low temperature growth conditions.

The significant interaction (species X dates of seeding) is evident from data in Table 2. The three warm-season species, weeping lovegrass, bermuda-

Table 1—Monthly average maximum-minimum temperatures (C) at Blacksburg, Charlotte Court House, and Warsaw, Virginia, for the critical months of germination and seedling development.

		Blacksburg 1971–72	Charlotte C. H. 1972–73	Warsaw 1972–73
October	Max	19.0	19.6	19.0
	Min	8.4	6.7	7.3
November	Max	11.2	6.7	13.4
	Min	– 2.2	14.0	3.4
December	Max	11.7	11.2	12.3
	Min	0.0	1.1	2.8
January	Max	7.8	9.5	7.4
	Min	– 5.6	– 2.8	– 2.8
February	Max	5.0	9.5	7.3
	Min	– 7.8	– 3.9	– 2.8
March	Max	11.2	15.7	15.7
	Min	– 2.8	– 5.0	– 5.6
April	Max	16.0	19.6	19.6
	Min	1.7	7.3	7.8
May	Max	20.7	24.1	24.1
	Min	6.7	10.1	11.8
June	Max	23.5	---	---
	Min	---	---	---

Table 2—Plant populations and vegetative cover of soil from different species during early seedling development for seedings on different dates during Fall-Spring of 1971-72 at Blacksburg.

		Seeding dates				
		Oct 15	Dec 1	Mar 1	May 1	
		Observation dates				
Species seeded	kg/ha	Dec 18	Feb 11	Apr 18	Jun 1	Mean
		Number of seedlings, % of sown seed				
Abruzzi rye	67.2	65ab*	52a	49a	49b	54a
Annual ryegrass	11.2	70a	25b	26b	66a	46b
'Pennfine' perennial ryegrass	28.0	58b	28b	15c	62a	41c
Kentucky 31 fescue	56.0	46c	20bc	11cd	43bc	30d
Creeping red fescue	44.8	25d	20bc	9cde	28de	20e
Orchardgrass	28.0	25d	12cd	8cde	36cd	20e
Redtop	5.6	23d	10d	10cde	25ef	16ef
'Penngift' crownvetch	22.4	10ef	10d	10cd	34de	16ef
Kentucky bluegrass	28.0	15e	14cd	5cde	19fg	13f
Roughstalk bluegrass	39.2	13e	6de	10cde	24efg	13f
Timothy	16.8	3f	9de	9cde	29de	12fg
Weeping lovegrass	11.2	3f	0e	1de	30de	8g
Bermudagrass	28.0	1	0e	0e	16gh	4h
Sericea	56.0	2f	0e	0e	8h	2h
Mean		26	15	12	34	
		Soil cover, %				
Abruzzi rye	67.2	34b	12a	2def	56a	26a
Roughstalk bluegrass	39.2	3d	1cd	10a	60a	18b
Perennial ryegrass	28.0	9c	4b	10a	43b	16bc
Annual ryegrass	11.2	11c	1cd	5bcd	45b	16c
Orchardgrass	28.0	4d	1cd	5bcd	39bc	12d
Kentucky 31 fescue	56.0	2d	1cd	6b	31cd	10de
Creeping red fescue	44.8	4d	2d	4d	25d	9e
Kentucky bluegrass	28.0	3d	1cd	4bcde	27d	9e
Redtop	5.6	1d	1cd	2def	31cd	9e
Timothy	16.8	1d	1cd	5bc	8ef	4f
Weeping lovegrass	11.2	0d	0d	0f	14e	4f
Penngift crownvetch	22.4	0d	0d	1f	5ef	2fg
Bermudagrass	28.0	0d	0d	1f	9ef	2fg
Sericea	56.0	0d	0d	0f	3f	1g
Mean		5	2	4	28	

* Means within a column followed by the same letter do not differ significantly at the 5% level.

grass, and lespedeza, showed zero seedlings for December and March seedings and relatively high values for the May seeding. Among the cool-season species, Abruzzi rye had consistently high seedling values for all seeding dates as compared to the other species. The best seedling values for rye were obtained with the October seeding; whereas, the other species generally gave the best seedling stands when sown in May. The seedling values for December and March seedings for orchardgrass, ryegrass, redtop, and tall fescue were less than 50% of those for October and May seedings. Creeping red fescue had similar seedling stands for October, December, and May seedings, but the values for the March seeding were low. Seedling stands for crownvetch were similar for the first three seeding dates; the values for May 1 were threefold higher than the other values.

When considering the mean seedling values for the four seeding dates, the best stands occurred for rye, annual ryegrass, perennial ryegrass, and Kentucky 31 tall fescue, in the order mentioned. Among the cool-season species, the poorest seedling number occurred with *Poa* species.

Soil cover with vegetation, averaged for all species, for early seedling development was very poor after the October, December, and March seedings, but good after the May seeding (Table 2). The rather high soil cover 30 days after the May seeding is attributed to the combined influence of high seedling populations and large seedlings because of the favorable temperature environment.

When making comparisons among species for soil cover with vegetation for all dates averaged (Table 2), the best cover (25%) occurred with Abruzzi rye followed by roughstalk bluegrass, perennial ryegrass, and annual ryegrass with values ranging from 16 to 18%.

Vegetative cover varied among species with dates of seeding (significant date by species interaction). The warm-season species gave essentially no soil protection, except for the fourth and last date of seeding.

Abruzzi rye gave a quick vegetative cover for October and May seedings but low values for the other dates. Roughstalk bluegrass gave a poor vegetative cover following the first two seeding dates, an intermediate value for the March seeding, and the best cover among all species for the May seeding.

The bluegrasses and the creeping red fescue had 7 to 11 seedlings per dm^2, but there was little vegetative cover or soil protection for the October and December seedings because of the small seedlings. The vegetative cover was not closely associated with seedling values because it was confounded with seeding rates and the number of seeds per kilogram. This is discussed later.

April data

Live seedlings, as percent of sown seed, and soil cover data were obtained on April 18 for seedings made in October, December, and March. When averaging all dates, the highest seedling values occurred with rye (41%) and annual ryegrass (22%). Values for the warm-season species were lowest. When averaging all species, the stands were better for October than the other two dates of seeding. Most of the species had fewer seedlings per unit area on April 18 than during earlier seedling development (Tables 2 and 3). This indicates considerable seedling mortality during the winter. Red fescue, Kentucky bluegrass, crownvetch, and timothy were either more cold tolerant than tall fescue or more seeds of those species germinated and survived between the original December 18 and April 18 count.

The values for soil cover were generally very low, except for rye, roughstalk bluegrass, creeping red fescue, and timothy for some dates (Table 3). Rye maintained a good soil cover for the October and December seedings, but the values for roughstalk bluegrass increased sharply for the October and December seeding dates (Tables 2 and 3). There was also a sizeable improvement with creeping red fescue for the October seeding.

Table 3—Plant populations and vegetative cover of soil from different species on April 18, 1972, for seedings on different dates during Fall-Spring of 1971-72 at Blacksburg.

| Species seeded | kg/ha | Seeding dates | | | Mean |
		Oct 15	Dec 1	Mar 1	
		Number of seedlings, % of sown seed			
Abruzzi rye	67.2	49a*	24a	49a	41a
Annual ryegrass	11.2	29b	10bcd	26b	22b
Pennfine perennial ryegrass	28.0	16cde	12bc	15c	14c
Creeping red fescue	44.8	21c	12bc	9de	14cd
Penngift crownvetch	22.4	19cd	13b	10cd	14cd
Kentucky bluegrass	28.0	17cd	11bcd	5def	11de
Kentucky 31 fescue	56.0	14def	10bcde	11cd	11cde
Timothy	16.8	10f	11bc	9de	10ef
Roughstalk bluegrass	39.2	11ef	6defg	10cd	9ef
Redtop	5.6	15de	7cdef	4ef	9ef
Orchardgrass	28.0	9f	4efgh	8de	7f
Weeping lovegrass	11.2	4f	2fgh	2f	3g
Sericea	56.0	2f	1gh	1f	2g
Bermudagrass	28.0	0f	0h	0f	0g
Mean		15	9	11	
		Soil cover, %			
Roughstalk bluegrass	39.2	21b	20a	10a	17ab
Abruzzi rye	67.2	41a	13ab	2a	15ab
Creeping red fescue	44.8	25b	8b	4a	12abc
Timothy	16.8	7c	21a	5a	11bc
Pennfine perennial ryegrass	28.0	9c	6b	10a	8cd
Kentucky bluegrass	28.0	7c	4b	4a	5cd
Kentucky 31 fescue	56.0	5c	1b	6a	4cd
Annual rye	11.2	4c	1b	5a	3cd
Orchardgrass	28.0	2c	2b	5a	3cd
Redtop	5.6	4c	1b	2a	2d
Penngift crownvetch	22.4	0c	0b	1a	0d
Bermudagrass	28.0	0c	0b	0a	0d
Sericea	56.0	0c	0b	0a	0d
Weeping lovegrass	11.2	0c	0b	0a	0d
Mean		9	6	4	

* Means within a column followed by the same letter do not differ significantly at the 5% level.

June data

Final and most important data on live seedlings as percent of sown seed and vegetative cover were obtained on June 1 (Table 4). When averaging all species, the highest seedling populations were obtained for the May 1 and March 1 seedings, respectively. The mean values for the other three seeding dates were of similar magnitude. The highest values for the May seeding date are attributed to a good microenvironment for germination and a low seedling mortality. The number of seedlings for the October seeding generally declined between the April and June sampling dates. Annual ryegrass declined by 59%. Conversely, for the December and March seedings, the seedling numbers for all species increased 67 and 118%, respectively. This suggests that many viable seeds germinated between April and June.

Table 4—Plant populations and vegetative cover of soil from different species on June 1, 1972, for seedings on different dates during Fall-Spring of 1971-72 at Blacksburg.

Species seeded	kg/ha	Seeding dates					
		Oct 15	Dec 1	Jan 15	Mar 1	May 1	Mean
				Number of seedlings, % of sown seed			
Abruzzi rye	67.2	38a*	20b	28a	46a	49b	36a
Annual ryegrass	11.2	19bc	29a	27ab	37b	66a	35a
Pennfine perennial ryegrass	28.0	15cde	11cd	21bc	51a	62a	32b
Kentucky 31 fescue	56.0	14cdef	19b	21bc	30c	42c	25c
Penngift crownvetch	22.4	23b	24ab	21bc	22d	34de	25c
Orchardgrass	28.0	8fg	13c	16cde	22de	36d	19d
Timothy	16.8	19bc	21b	13def	15	29ef	19d
Kentucky bluegrass	28.0	16cd	19b	18cd	20def	19g	18d
Redtop	5.6	12defg	8cd	21bc	20def	25f	17d
Creeping red fescue	44.8	12defg	13c	14def	16efg	28ef	17d
Weeping lovegrass	11.2	9efg	8cd	12efg	23d	30ef	16d
Roughstalk bluegrass	39.2	7g	6d	11efg	12g	24f	12e
Sericea lespedeza	56.0	8g	7d	9fg	11gh	8h	9f
Bermudagrass	28.0	6g	5d	6g	6h	16g	8f
Mean		15	15	17	24	33	
				Soil cover, %			
Roughstalk bluegrass	39.2	36ab	35a	97a	88ab	60a	86a
Kentucky 31 fescue	56.0	15def	70abc	87a	79abc	31cd	71b
Creeping red fescue	44.8	73bcd	80ab	82a	57abc	25d	68bc
Orchardgrass	28.0	1f	57abcd	99a	91a	38bc	67bcd
Pennfine perennial ryegrass	28.0	8ef	13def	81a	93a	43b	61cde
Annual ryegrass	11.2	3f	25cdef	89a	95a	45b	59cdef
Kentucky bluegrass	28.0	79abc	53abcde	73ab	41bcde	27d	58def
Redtop	5.6	67bcd	24cdef	82a	55abcd	31cd	56ef
Abruzzi rye	67.2	93a	18def	58ab	32cdef	56a	52f
Timothy	16.8	57bcde	34bcdef	32bc	53abcde	8ef	42g
Bermudagrass	28.0	6ef	6ef	4c	7def	9ef	12h
Weeping lovegrass	11.2	3f	4ef	2c	7ef	14e	9hi
Penngift crownvetch	22.4	1f	2f	5c	5f	5de	5hi
Sericea	56.0	1f	1f	0c	0e	3f	1i
Mean		35	34	57	50	28	

*Means within a column followed by the same letter do not differ significantly at the 5% level.

When averaging all dates of seeding, the best seedling stands based on actual sown seeds were obtained with rye followed by the ryegrasses. Values for creeping red fescue and tall fescue were similar. The lowest values occurred with roughstalk bluegrass, bermudagrass, and lespedeza.

On June 1, the average soil cover with vegetation for the five seeding dates between October 15 and May 1 was best for roughstalk bluegrass (86%) followed by Kentucky 31 tall fescue, creeping red fescue, and orchardgrass (soil cover ranged between 67 to 71%). These high values are attributed to dense seedling populations due to the high seeding rates. Abruzzi rye had a rather low soil cover because of low seedling population (low seeding rate and large seeds). Vegetative cover from the warm-season species are very poor (1 to 12%).

When averaging soil cover for all species on June 1, the best soil cover occurred with the March 1 and January 15 seeding dates; the values for the

May 1 seeding were generally low because of young, small seedlings. The data generally indicate that there was more seedling mortality or a poor growth recovery of seedlings from the October and December seedings than for the January and March seedings. However, there were significant interactions; species behavior varied with season of seeding. With October and December seedings, soil cover was very poor for the two ryegrasses as compared with the other three dates of seeding. This indicates that there was severe winter injury to germinated seedlings and that there were few dormant viable seeds. Orchardgrass and Kentucky 31 tall fescue had poor vegetative cover for the October seedings as compared with values for the other four dates, while soil cover for roughstalk bluegrass was satisfactory for all dates of seeding. Abruzzi rye produced a much better soil cover for October than for other seeding dates. The values for the warm-season species were low at all seeding dates because cool temperatures before June 1 had inhibited growth.

Warsaw and Charlotte Court House experiments

Seedlings (percent of sown seed in January for seedings made the previous November) near Warsaw showed highest values for the ryegrasses, creeping red fescue, roughstalk bluegrass, and the winter annual cereals (Table 5); however, the erosion protection was almost nil (Table 6). The stands for timothy, redtop, and the two legumes were very poor. By March 15 the

Table 5—Seedling populations from different species seeded in late autumn at Warsaw and Charlotte Court House.

		Seeding dates			
		Warsaw Nov 17, 1972		Charlotte C.H. Dec 5, 1972	
		Observation dates			
Species seeded	kg/ha	Jan 24	Mar 14	Mar 15	Mean
		Number of seedlings, % of sown seed			
Abruzzi rye	67.2	50a*	43a	46a	46
Manhattan perennial ryegrass	61.6	36bc	41a	30b	36
Creeping red fescue	33.6	34bcd	32bc	30b	32
Lynn perennial gyegrass	61.6	37b	32bc	16cde	28
Annual ryegrass	61.6	30bcde	31bc	21bcd	27
Wong barley	67.2	31bcde	28bcd	21bcd	27
Blueboy wheat	67.2	34bcd	20def	23bc	26
Kentucky 31 fescue	67.2	21efg	25cde	24bc	23
Roughstalk bluegrass	39.2	30efg	18ef	19bcde	22
Russian wild rye	67.2	24cde	12fg	23bc	20
Potomac orchardgrass	33.6	22def	17ef	12cdef	17
Kentucky bluegrass	39.2	11fgh	17ef	16cde	15
Clinton oats	67.2	22def	7gh	8def	12
Redtop	5.6	9gh	12fg	14cdef	12
Emerald crownvetch	22.4	4h	4gh	9def	6
Sericea lespedeza	44.8	2h	6gh	6ef	5
Clair timothy	22.4	0	1h	1f	1

* Means within a column followed by the same letter do not differ significantly at the 5% level.

stands showed trends similar to January, except that stands of wheat, rough-stalk bluegrass, oats, and Russian wild rye declined. The vegetative cover was good (37%) for rye, but the other species ranged from 0 to 17%. Later, on May 8, annual ryegrass had the best vegetative cover (88%); the two blue-grasses, two perennial ryegrasses, creeping red fescue, and rye gave a vegeta-tive cover of 55% or more.

In the Charlotte Court House experiment the highest seedling numbers occurred with Abruzzi rye, 'Manhattan' perennial ryegrass, and creeping red fescue, respectively (Table 5). The number of seedlings (percent of sown seed) was 17% or less for orchardgrass, Kentucky bluegrass, redtop, crown-vetch, timothy, lespedeza, and oats. By March 15, the vegetative cover was poor for all species; the highest value of 10% occurred with rye and rough-stalk bluegrass (7%). However, by May 22, all of the ryegrasses, both blue-grasses, tall and creeping red fescue, redtop, and cereal rye had developed a vegetative cover of 55% or better (Table 6). Soil cover was nil for the two legumes and timothy and very poor for Russian wild rye and barley.

Seeding rates

An experiment at two locations was conducted to study vegetative covers obtained from late autumn seedings with species at five seeding rates (Table 7). It was postulated that high seeding rates may provide a dense mat of small seedlings for erosion control during winter. The soil cover in Janu-ary at Warsaw generally increased as the seeding rates of species increased;

Table 6—Percent soil cover with vegetation by different plant species from late autumn seedings at Warsaw and Charlotte Court House.

| | | Seeding dates | | | | | |
| | | Warsaw Nov 17, 1972 | | | Charlotte C.H. Dec 5, 1972 | | |
Species seeded	kg/ha	Jan 24	Mar 15	May 8	Mar 15	May 22	Mean
				Soil cover, %			
Annual ryegrass	61.6	2bc*	13bc	88a	3de	83a	38
Abruzzi rye	67.2	3b	37a	65bcd	10a	58cd	35
Manhattan perennial ryegrass	61.6	2bc	10cd	71bc	2ef	79ab	33
Roughstalk bluegrass	39.2	4a	17b	55def	7b	73abc	31
Lynn perennial ryegrass	61.6	2bc	12c	72b	1fg	57cd	29
Creeping red fescue	33.6	1de	6de	63bcd	3d	61bcd	27
Kentucky bluegrass	39.2	1de	5e	56cde	2ef	54cde	24
Kentucky 31 fescue	67.2	1de	2ef	40fg	1fg	57cd	20
Redtop	5.6	1de	0f	28g	1fg	55cde	17
Potomac orchardgrass	33.6	1de	0f	28fg	1fg	42def	14
Blueboy wheat	67.2	2cd	5e	27g	2def	35efg	14
Wong barley	67.2	1de	2ef	25g	1fg	16gh	9
Clinton oats	67.2	1de	0f	6h	1fg	32fg	8
Russian wild rye	67.2	1de	0f	8h	1fg	11h	4
Sericea lespedeza	44.8	0f	0f	0h	1fg	0h	0
Emerald crownvetch	22.4	0f	0f	0h	1fg	0h	0
Clair timothy	22.4	0f	0f	0	0	0	0

* Means within a column followed by the same letter do not differ significantly at the 5% level.

Table 7—Effects of seeding rates of five species on the vegetative cover of soil resulting from late fall seedings at Warsaw and Charlotte Court House.

Species seeded	kg/ha	Seeding dates				
		Warsaw Nov 17, 1972			Charlotte C.H. Dec 5, 1972	
		Jan 24	Mar 14	May 8	Mar 15	May 22
		Soil cover, %				
Kentucky 31 fescue	67.2	1i*	4j	55def	1f	68ab
	201.6	2gh	7hi	59cdef	2f	67ab
	403.2	3f	10g	67cdef	5ef	73a
	604.8	5e	10g	70bcdc	8def	76a
Creeping red fescue	44.8	1hi	5ij	52ef	4f	68ab
	134.4	3f	10g	58cdef	12def	77a
	268.8	7c	40d	64cdef	22cde	79a
	537.6	9a	68b	72bcde	38b	82a
Manhattan perennial ryegrass	56.0	1hi	4j	65cdef	1f	82a
	168.0	3f	9gh	69bcde	2f	72a
	336.0	6de	15f	77bc	6def	82a
	504.0	8b	15f	74bcd	9def	78a
Roughstalk bluegrass	67.2	3fg	9gh	60cdef	17cdef	82a
	201.6	6d	20e	63cdef	30bc	82a
	403.2	9a	65c	68cde	57a	84a
	604.8	9a	67bc	70bcde	58a	86a
Balboa rye	44.8	1i	5ij	50f	2f	41c
	134.4	3fg	10g	78bc	5ef	53bc
	268.8	6cd	42d	88ab	12def	69ab
	537.6	8ab	77a	96a	23bcd	78a

* Means within a column followed by the same letter do not differ significantly at the 5% level.

however, soil cover was poor, reaching maximum values of only 9%. By March 15 there was a sharp improvement in vegetative cover with increases in seeding rates of creeping red fescue, roughstalk bluegrass, and rye. Soil cover ranged from 67 to 77% for the high as compared to only 4 to 9% for the low seeding rates. However, for high seeding rates there was only 10% cover for tall fescue and 15% for perennial ryegrass. The March data for the Charlotte Court House seeding showed similar trends; however, the values for soil cover were lower (Table 7).

Vegetative cover during May, resulting from the late autumn seedings at two locations, generally showed excellent soil cover with values ranging from 50 to 96% at Warsaw and 41 to 84% at Charlotte Court House. Except for roughstalk bluegrass and perennial ryegrass at Charlotte Court House there was a tendency for soil cover to be improved as seeding rates of the five species were increased by one or more increments of respective seeding rates. There were significant increases in vegetative cover from increasing the seeding rate from 44.8 to 537.6 kg/ha.

There were successive increases in number of seedlings as seeding rates increased. It was also apparent that many seedlings died between January 24 and March 14 at Warsaw where temperatures averaged 7.4 C maximum and −2.8 C minimum. The largest percentage of seedling mortality occurred with the highest seeding rates, apparently because competition reduced seedling size as reported by Donald (7). The smallest seeds (roughstalk bluegrass) had the lowest seedling survival (11% of sown seed). The largest seed ('Balboa' rye) averaged 30% survival; Manhattan ryegrass 32%, creeping red fescue 24%, and tall fescue 21%. With the higher seeding rates, the number of seedlings (based on percent of sown seed) decreased. However, the total number of seedlings of each species increased with seeding rate.

CONCLUSIONS AND APPLICATION

There is a critical need for controlling erosion to avoid downstream pollution from soil areas that are disturbed during the fall and winter months when it is difficult to establish vegetation during highway and other construction. Results from the experiments reported here provide information for compounding seed mixtures to develop vegetation to minimize erosion. It has been found that straw mulch, woodchips, or liberal rates of woodfiber with an asphalt binder give prolonged soil protection (11); thus, vegetative cover may be obtained from fall and winter seedings by using the appropriate species. Woodruff and Blaser (11) found from winter seeding experiments with special mulches and seeding mixtures that cereal rye was the best temporary species during the fall-winter low temperature period. These are in agreement with Andrews et al. (1). Among other species, best cover resulted from red fescue and roughstalk bluegrass with results from tall fescue being fair. For within season seedings, Kentucky 31 tall fescue has been found to be the most widely adapted and persistent species along highways (3, 8). In growth chamber experiments, cereal rye germinated and grew at lower temperatures than any other annual or perennial species (R. E. Blaser, unpublished data). Thus, seeding and fertilizing with a stable mulch during the winter can develop a suitable turf and make it unnecessary to disturb an area for a second time. The principle of using a second-step seed application in spring should improve the chances of success (4).

The data suggest that high seeding rates for late fall-winter seedings will improve the chances of obtaining vegetative cover with a mixture of several grasses adapted to low temperature environments. Thus, for winter seedings, species in a mixture with appropriate seeding rates of Abruzzi rye (50 kg), Kentucky 31 tall fescue (70 kg), and creeping red fescue (40 kg/ha) are recommended. Even though Kentucky 31 tall fescue gave only fair results with winter seedings, the survival of seedlings appears adequate for a stand to develop through plant succession. The ryegrasses are not recommended for seeding during low temperature periods because of vulnerability to winter injury. Roughstalk bluegrass at 30 kg/ha might be added to the mixture, but information on its persistence and competitive effects are unknown. Although it is known that the late winter-spring period is the best season for seeding crownvetch and sericea lespedeza (5, 10), it is suggested that one of the legumes be added to the mixture at seeding rates higher than for normal seeding. The results reported have shown some germination and winter mortality of seedlings, but it is known that hard seedcoats prevent germination of a large percentage of the seed of these legumes. Also, results in various states have shown successful stands of these legumes from winter seedings.

Our data were obtained under stress microenvironmental conditions, with little or no mulching, and with sharply fluctuating diurnal temperatures. Warm temperatures during certain periods undoubtedly encouraged germination, and subsequent low temperatures could be lethal. Published results show that straw and other organic mulches applied at liberal rates moderate temperatures and reduce heaving of seedlings (2). Thus, better vegetative cover than obtained here would be expected with good mulching.

The warm-season grasses, bermudagrass and weeping lovegrass, developed few seedlings. Moreover, the poor stands in spring indicate that the seed lost their viability during the winter months; hence, these species are not suitable for winter seedings.

REFERENCES

1. ANDREWS, O. N., Jr., L. E. FOOTE, and J. A. JACKOBS. 1964. Turf establishment on Illinois roadsides as influenced by seeding mixtures and time of seeding. Agron. Abstr. 98. Amer. Soc. Agron., Madison, Wis.

2. BARKLEY, D. G., R. E. BLASER, and R. E. SCHMIDT. 1965. Effect of mulches on microclimate and turf establishment. Agron. J. 57:189–192.

3. BLASER, R. E., and C. Y. WARD. 1958. Seeding highway slopes as influenced by lime and fertilizer and adaptation of species. Highway Res. Board, Roadside Develop. p. 21–39.

4. ————, and J. M. WOODRUFF. 1968. The need for specifying two or three step seeding and fertilization practices for establishing sod on highways. Highway Res. Rec., Roadside Develop. 246:44–49.

5. CARSON, E. W., Jr., and R. E. BLASER. 1962. Establishing sericea on highway slopes. Highway Res. Board, Roadside Develop. p. 3–14.

6. CHIPPINDALE, H. G. 1949. Environment and germination in grass seeds. J. Brit. Grass. Soc. 4:57–61.

7. DONALD, C. M. 1963. Competition among crop and pasture plants. Advan. Agron. 15:1–118.

8. HOTTENSTEIN, W. L. 1969. Highway roadsides. In A. A. Hanson and F. V. Juska (eds.) Turfgrass science. Agronomy 14:603–637. Amer. Soc. Agron., Madison, Wis.

9. SPRAGUE, V. G. 1943. The effects of temperature and day length on seedling emergence and early growth of several pasture species. Soil Sci. Soc. Amer. Proc. 8:287–294.

10. WOODRUFF, J. M., and R. E. BLASER. 1970. Establishing crownvetch on steep acid slopes in Virginia. Highway Res. Record No. 335:19–38.

11. ————, and ————. 1970. Establishing and maintaining turf on steep slopes along Virginia highways. Annual Report, Dep. Agronomy, Virginia Polytechnic Institute and State University, Blacksburg.

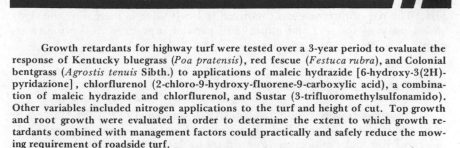

71

Growth control for highway turf [1]

R.C. WAKEFIELD & A.T. DORE

Growth retardants for highway turf were tested over a 3-year period to evaluate the response of Kentucky bluegrass (*Poa pratensis*), red fescue (*Festuca rubra*), and Colonial bentgrass (*Agrostis tenuis* Sibth.) to applications of maleic hydrazide [6-hydroxy-3(2H)-pyridazione], chlorflurenol (2-chloro-9-hydroxy-fluorene-9-carboxylic acid), a combination of maleic hydrazide and chlorflurenol, and Sustar (3-trifluoromethylsulfonamido). Other variables included nitrogen applications to the turf and height of cut. Top growth and root growth were evaluated in order to determine the extent to which growth retardants combined with management factors could practically and safely reduce the mowing requirement of roadside turf.

All retardants significantly reduced vegetative and seedhead top growth. However there was a range of effectiveness depending on material used, rates of application, and the species of grass. Some temporary discoloration of vegetation occurred with some materials but was not considered serious. Root growth was significantly retarded by all materials; the effect closely paralleled that of reducing top growth.

Growth of red fescue was more effectively retarded than Kentucky bluegrass and was less subject to discoloration.

Growth control was much more effective at a mowing height of 10 cm than at 6.3 cm. Supplemental nitrogen was useful in overcoming the discoloration caused by growth retardants by improving color and by increasing the density of growth. Additional index words: Growth retardant, Growth inhibitor, *Poa pratensis, Festuca rubra.*

Use of turfgrass along highways is important to control erosion and improve the appearance of the landscape. Unfortunately, the maintenance of turfgrass along modern highways is expensive and often dangerous to operators of maintenance equipment. The problem is particularly acute during the flush period of growth in the spring.

Growth retardants represent a practical means to reduce the mowing requirements and simplify maintenance.

Maleic hydrazide (MH) [6-hydroxy-3(2H)-pyridazione] has been used for many years but with varying degrees of success (2, 4, 6, 9). Problems cited include critical requirements with respect to time of application (3, 7, 8, 9) and lack of control of broadleaved weeds (1, 3, 9). Results with maleic hydrazide have been enhanced by increasing mowing height (4, 6, 7). Other

[1] Contribution No. 1509 Agricultural Experiment Station, Kingston, RI 02881.

work has shown that nitrogen fertilizer improved the color and density of grass following spraying (7).

Newly available growth retardants include chlorflurenol (CF) (2-chloro-9-hydroxy-fluorene-9-carboxylic acid) and Sustar (3-trifluoromethylsulfonamido)-p-autotoluidide), also designated as MBR-6033 (3M Company, Minneapolis, Minn.). Chlorflurenol used alone and combined with maleic hydrazide has been effective in controlling growth of both grasses and broad-leaved weeds (1). Sustar has been tested for several years at the Rhode Island Agricultural Experiment Station and found to be an effective growth retardant for turfgrass.

The studies reported in this paper were concerned with a comparison of the three previously mentioned growth retardants on turfgrasses. In order to provide additional variables, other treatments included heights of cut and rates of nitrogen fertilization. The object of these experiments was to not only evaluate effects of growth retardants on vertical growth of turfgrasses but to more adequately assess conditions that result in apparent injury to turf. The use of nitrogen was theorized to be of value in increasing the vigor and density of the turf and improve its general appearance following treatment.

MATERIALS AND METHODS

Experiments were conducted from 1970 through 1972 at the University of Rhode Island, Kingston, R. I. Experiment I was conducted on pure stands of 'Park' Kentucky bluegrass (*Poa pratensis* L.) and 'Pennlawn' red fescue (*Festuca rubra* L.). Experiments II and III were conducted on a mixture of Park Kentucky bluegrass, Pennlawn red fescue, and 'Exeter' Colonial bentgrass (*Agrostis tenuis* Sibth). All grasses were established in 1967 on Bridgehampton silt loam. They were maintained at low fertility and at a mowing height of approximately 10 cm to simulate highway conditions. Prior to initiating each experiment, plots were mowed to 10 cm, raked, and fertilized with a 10-6-4 fertilizer at a rate of 488 kg/ha. Certain plots received a second application of urea fertilizer to provide a double rate of nitrogen (97.6 kg/ha). Chemical growth retardants were applied on May 7, 1970, May 7, 1971, and May 10, 1972, with a boom sprayer delivering 80 dm^3/ha.

Plots were mowed at 10 cm in Experiment I, at 6.35 cm and 10 cm in Experiment II, and at 6.35 cm in Experiment III. In the second experiment, plugs of turf 5 cm in diameter and 5-cm soil depth were removed from field plots after spraying and placed in sand in the greenhouse. Top growth above 6.35 cm and root growth extending beyond the original soil plug were cut at intervals 3, 5, 7, and 9 weeks.

Height measurements, color (a visual rating of greenness on a basis of zero to a most desirable 10), and density (also a visual rating on a basis of zero to a most desirable 10, indicating thinness of the turf due to injury or suppression of new tillers) were recorded weekly in field experiments. Grasses cut to the lower height of 6.35 cm were mowed when growth reached 15 cm, and those maintained at 10 cm were mowed when growth reached 20 cm. Plots were harvested with a rotary mower with sample bag attached to the chute. Total harvest area for each plot was 4.88 m^2.

In Experiments I and II, a segment of each plot was not mowed in order to observe the effect of treatments on seedhead suppression. Seedhead counts and dry weights of grass exceeding 10 cm were taken from a 0.186 m² area of each plot approximately 2 months after spraying.

RESULTS AND DISCUSSION

Growth of Kentucky bluegrass was effectively reduced by all inhibitors with Sustar being the most effective followed by maleic hydrazide (Fig. 1). Sustar at 6.72 kg/ha was more effective than at 3.36 kg/ha in reducing growth. Different degrees of discoloration of turf were noted with the various retardants (Fig. 2). Initial discoloration as a leaf tip "burn" was sub-

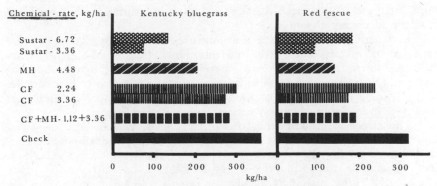

Fig. 1—Effect of growth retardants on dry weight of turf.

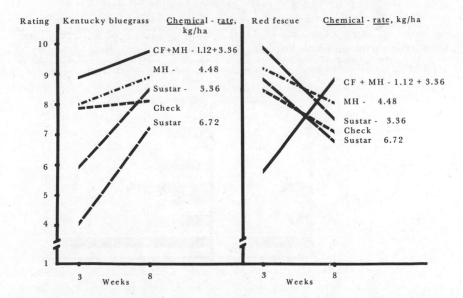

Fig. 2—Effect of growth retardants on appearance of turf. Ratings 1 (poor) to 10 (best).

stantial with Sustar, particularly at the higher rate of application. However a rapid improvement in appearance took place and by the eighth week improvement was noted.

Suppression of red fescue was generally successful with all growth retardants with little or no injury to the grass by most materials (Fig. 1 and 2). Initial discoloration of leaves was noted only with a combination of maleic hydrazide (MH) plus chlorflurenol (CF), but this had largely disappeared by the sixth week. In comparing the two species, it was interesting to note that suppression of red fescue was generally more successful with maleic hydrazide, chlorflurenol, and their combination. Results were again satisfactory with Sustar.

Over the experimental period, a general decline in appearance of red fescue occurred while Kentucky bluegrass improved. This was attributed to the normal growth pattern of these species with the warmer and drier weather of the advancing season.

In general, it would appear that mixtures of these grass species can be expected to react favorably to growth retardants. Because of a slightly varying reaction of the two grasses to the chemicals and the natural seasonal changes in their appearance, a mixture of grasses would appear to be desirable. The spreading growth habit of Kentucky bluegrass would be an additional advantage in its use in a highway turf mixture with red fescue.

The effect of growth retardants on seedhead suppression is shown in Fig. 3. Results indicate that seedheads of Kentucky bluegrass were controlled more readily than those of red fescue. Chlorflurenol was the least effective material with both species. Results indicate that Sustar at the higher rate of 6.72 kg/ha, maleic hydrazide at a rate of 4.48 kg/ha, and a combination of chlorflurenol plus maleic hydrazide at 1.12 + 3.35 kg/ha effectively reduced seedheads of both Kentucky bluegrass and red fescue.

Experiment II was designed to evaluate the effects of growth retardants on both top and root growth of a turf mixture consisting of Kentucky bluegrass, red fescue, and Colonial bentgrass. Plugs were sampled at intervals of 3, 5, 7, and 9 weeks.

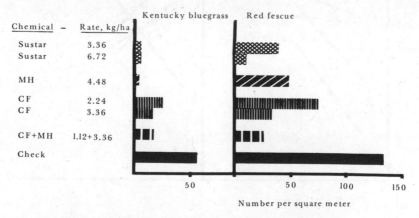

Fig. 3—Effect of growth retardants on seedhead growth.

Table 1—Effect of growth retardants on the top and root growth of treated grass plugs 5 cm in diameter.

| Treatment | | Dry weight, g/plug | | | |
Chemical	Rate, kg/ha a.i.	3 weeks	5 weeks	7 weeks	9 weeks
		Topgrowth			
Maleic hydrazide	5.6	0.39a*	0.41a	0.58abc	0.79bc
Maintain CF 125	3.4+1.1	0.40a	0.43ab	1.15de	1.28e
Sustar	4.5	0.40a	0.44ab	0.92cd	1.40e
Check		0.43ab	0.51ab	2.47f	2.75f
		Root growth			
Maleic hydrazide	5.6	0.17a	0.20a	0.32ab	0.40b
Maintain CF 125	3.4+1.1	0.18a	0.21a	0.42b	0.77c
Sustar	4.5	0.18a	0.19a	0.32ab	0.48b
Check		0.22a	0.34ab	0.71c	1.85d

* Means followed by different letters indicate a significant difference at the 5% level.

Top growth was retarded by all materials for the entire period with maleic hydrazide being particularly effective (Table 1).

Root growth was suppressed to a similar extent for the same period.

The yield data represent extension of growth beyond 6.3 cm for leaves and beyond the original soil plug for roots. No attempt was made to measure new tillers or new root development from the crowns of the plants.

It was apparent from this experiment that for the growth retardants tested, root growth was inhibited severely by materials designed to reduce top growth.

Experiment III was initiated to evaluate the effects of height of cut and supplemental nitrogen on the action of growth retardants on highway turf. In this experiment a mixture of Kentucky bluegrass, red fescue, and Colonial bentgrass was used.

Over a 7-week test period the mowing requirement was increased substantially at 6.3 cm (Fig. 4) as the growth of unsprayed turf was 136% great-

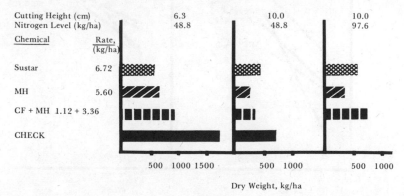

Fig. 4—Effects of growth retardants, cutting height, and nitrogen level on dry weight of turf.

er than at 10.0 cm. Growth retardants were effective at both cutting heights. Growth was reduced, on the average, 48% at 6.3 cm and 52% at 10 cm, compared to the check. Dry weights represent one mowing for treated plots and two mowings for check plots.

Use of supplemental nitrogen at the time of spraying with growth retardants resulted in relatively small increases in growth. All increases due to

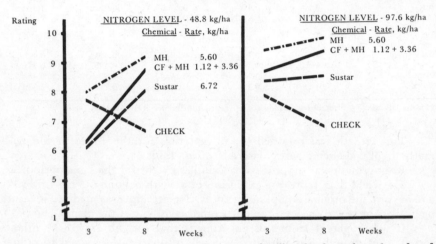

Fig. 5—Effect of growth retardants and nitrogen fertilizer level on the color of turf. Ratings 1 (poor) to 10 (best).

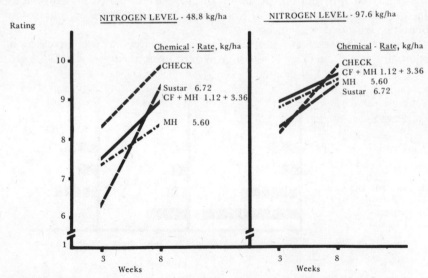

Fig. 6—Effect of growth retardants and nitrogen level on the density of turf. Ratings 1 (poor) to 10 (best).

supplemental nitrogen were less than those recorded for the low cutting level.

Of primary interest was the effect of supplemental nitrogen on injury or discoloration due to growth retardants. Appearance of the turf was evaluated on the basis of color and density (Fig. 5 and 6, respectively.)

Color of turf during the third week following application of growth retardants was adversely affected by Sustar and the combination of chlorflurenol with maleic hydrazide. Use of supplemental nitrogen successfully improved the color of turf treated with growth retardants over that of the check.

Similarly, the density of turf was improved by a supplemental application of N.

Injury to turf from application of growth retardants can take many forms. For example, a leaf tip burn has been previously mentioned as a result of application of Sustar. In these experiments however, the most conspicuous factor affecting appearance was decreased density of the turf. This was particularly noticeable during the second to fourth weeks following use of growth retardants. At this time the turf was not attractive because it lacked density and dead leaves were visible in the undergrowth after the winter. Apparently growth retardants had not only reduced the growth of existing tillers but had also inhibited initiation of new tillers during the early weeks following application. These data indicate that supplemental nitrogen was useful in improving both the color and density of treated turf. Apparently this occurred without affecting the primary value of growth retardants in reducing vertical growth or decreasing the mowing requirements of highway-type turf.

In unmowed subplots the influence of nitrogen on seedhead development was studied following application of growth retardants. Results indicated that all retardants substantially reduced seedheads of Kentucky bluegrass and red fescue and that nitrogen had little influence (Table 2). It was of interest to note that Sustar was not effective in controlling seedhead elongation of Colonial bentgrass and that nitrogen increased the number of seedheads substantially.

Table 2—Effect of growth retardants on seedhead growth of an unmowed turf mixture at two rates of nitrogen fertilization.

Growth retardant			Seedheads/m^2		
Chemical	Rate, kg/ha	Nitrogen, kg/ha	Kentucky bluegrass	Red fescue	Colonial bentgrass
Sustar	6.7	48.8	27b*	92bc	387bc
MH	5.6	48.8	1b	52c	36e
MH + CF	3.4+1.1	48.8	2b	123bc	94de
Check	---	48.8	161a	328a	507ab
Sustar	6.7	97.6	47b	167b	610a
MH	5.6	97.6	0b	27c	5e
MH + CF	3.4+1.1	97.6	2b	46c	54e

* Means followed by different letters indicate a significant difference at the 5% level.

REFERENCES

1. BOCKER, P. 1970. Growth control. p. 464–468. *In* Proc. First Int. Turfgrass Res. Conf. Sports Turf Research Institute, Bingley, England.
2. BROWN, W. G., and C. M. SWITZER. 1970. Growth regulation in turf. Abstracts 1970 Meeting, Weed Science Society of America, Montreal, Canada.
3. CLAPHAM, A. J., R. C. WAKEFIELD, and R. S. BELL. 1969. The effect of Maleic hydrazide on the growth of turfgrasses. Univ. Rhode Island, Agr. Exp. Sta. Bull. 399.
4. FOOTE, L. E., and B. F. HIMMELMAN. 1965. Maleic hydrazide as a growth retardant. Minnesota Dep. Highways, Investig. 616.
5. JUSKA, F. V., and A. A. HANSON. 1964. Effects of growth retardants on Kentucky bluegrass turf. Golfcourse Rep. June. p. 60–64.
6. MORGAN, B. S., and P. W. BOHNE. 1965. A progress report on Maleic hydrazide for growth control of grass and trees. Highway Res. Rec. 93. National Academy of Sciences, Washington, D. C. p. 25–30.
7. WAKEFIELD, R. C., and A. J. CLAPHAM. 1968. Management of turfgrass treated with Maleic hydrazide. Highway Res. Rec. National Academy of Sciences, Washington, D. C. p. 36–43.
8. WHITE, D. B., D. HENG, T. B. BAILEY, and L. FOOTE. 1970. Chemical regulation of growth in turfgrass. p. 481–497. *In* Proc. First Int. Turfgrass Res. Conf. Sports Turf Research Institute, Bingley, England.
9. ZUKEL, J. W. 1957. Report on use of maleic hydrazide as a temporary growth inhibitor of grass. *In* Literature summary on Maleic hydrazide, 1949–1957. U. S. Rubber Co., Naugatuck Chemical Division, Naugatuck, Conn.

DISCUSSION

R. W. SCHERY—What was the form of nitrogen used to control growth on highway turf in Rhode Island and what was the timing of application in relation to that of the growth regulating chemicals?

R. C. WAKEFIELD —An additional 0.45 kg of nitrogen as urea was applied at the time the chemicals were put on.

F. J. WRAY—Is the lack of density or decrease in density of the sward due to a lack of tillering where growth regulators are used?

R. C. WAKEFIELD —Yes, its definitely a lack of tillering. It's a suppression of tiller growth; they're there but they don't develop.

F. J. WRAY—When nitrogen is added does an increase in tillering follow?

R. C. WAKEFIELD —Nitrogen seems to promote some increase in tillering.

W. G. BROWN—In the Rhode Island research on growth regulators, how long after nitrogen and growth regulator treatment were the plots evaluated?

R. C. WAKEFIELD—Data were taken 9 weeks following treatment.

W. G. BROWN—Work in Minnesota has shown Sustar to be ineffective after 6 to 8 weeks and at that time a positive effect of nitrogen on reducing growth suppression would be expected. Actually growth may be stimulated without added nitrogen after 6 to 8 weeks.

R. C. WAKEFIELD —We feel that this stimulating effect occurs not only with Sustar but following growth control with other growth retardants. Once there's been a release from the growth retarding effects, there seems to be a degree of stimulation, but we have found this to be minimal, certainly not very dramatic or very great.

W. G. BROWN—Perhaps the interaction between nitrogen and growth retardant is important. We would expect that nitrogen would have no effect on the turf until the growth retardant had expended itself. Up until the time that effects of the retardant had worn off, the nitrogen would not effect turfgrass growth and development.

B. E. BLASER —With regard to growth retardants, in general, we need one of these chemicals that is more effective than any that have been developed to date and it must be reasonably priced. We see an excellent use for it, mainly in the seeding of legumes. A very sparse, noncompeting stand of grass is excellent for establishing beautiful legumes, such as crownvetch and birdsfoot trefoil, along the roadside. We have found that one of the easiest ways to establish these legumes is to thin out the grasses. We are also interested in this practice to aid in the establishment of woody species by direct seeding. Thus, we'd like to have a growth retardant that would thin out the grasses but not leave toxic effects that would interfere with the growth of nongrassy plants. In order to develop practices of this type I believe that we need additional information on physiological effects and morphological interplay with these chemicals.

APPENDIXES

Section IX

Constitution & Bylaws

ARTICLE I

Name

The name of this Society shall be the International Turfgrass Society, hereinafter referred to as the Society.

ARTICLE II

Objects

The objects of the Society shall be:
(a) To encourage research and education in the field of turfgrass science and to further the dissemination of technical information related to turfgrasses and to accept and administer funds for these purposes.
(b) To provide an opportunity for the presentation of research studies before a critical and competent audience.
(c) To strive toward uniform terminology and standard research evaluation techniques.
(d) To maintain liaison with other scientific or educational organizations whose programs are allied to turfgrass science.

ARTICLE III

Membership

Section 1: Membership shall be on an individual basis. Members shall pay such dues or fees as the executive committee shall decide.

Section 2: Members shall be those who have attended the regular quadrennial business meeting at least once of the previous two meetings, or who have requested membership by writing to the executive committee outlining reasons for being unable to fulfill the above requirement.

Section 3: Membership shall be classified as (a) charter member; (b) regular member; (c) student member; (d) sustaining member:
(a) Charter members are those persons who attended the First International Turfgrass Research Conference held in Harrogate, England, July 15–18, 1969.
(b) Regular members are persons who are qualified research or extension workers or teachers in the field of turfgrass science.
(c) Student members are graduate students in any country. No student members shall remain in this category for a period exceeding 4 years.
(d) A sustaining member is any company or organization interested in the objectives of the Society.

ARTICLE IV

Officers

Section 1: The elected officers of the Society shall be a president, a vice president, a secretary, and five directors. These officers, with the past-president, the appointed treasurer, and the appointed historian, shall constitute the executive committee.

Section 2: A minimum of four countries shall be represented on the executive committee, and a maximum of four members of the executive committee shall come from any one country.

Section 3: All elected officers shall serve for 4 years, but the same incumbents may be re-elected. The positions of treasurer and historian shall be filled by appointment by the executive committee who may also reappoint them. The treasurer and historian shall not be voting members of the executive committee.

ARTICLE V

Election of Officers

Section 1: The executive committee shall appoint a nominating committee which shall nominate eligible candidate(s) for each office. As part of the procedure of nominations, the nominating committee will canvass the membership for suggestions for each office. Nominations can be made from the floor.

Section 2: The nominating committee shall consist of the president and the two most recent past presidents plus one member each from three countries not represented by the foregoing. The most recent past president shall be chairman. This committee shall provide an opportunity for the members of the Society to submit names, providing the consent of the nominee and an indication of his willingness to attend general meetings, has been obtained.

Section 3: The nominating committee shall mail the names of the nominees to each member of the Society not less than 4 weeks in advance of the meeting of the Society. Officers will be elected at the regular quadrennial business meeting by those attending.

Section 4: In the event of the death or resignation of any officer of the Society, the executive committee shall designate a successor to serve for the unexpired term.

Section 5: If the office of president becomes vacant, the vice president shall fill that position until the time of the next meeting. If both of the above positions are vacant at the same time, the executive committee shall appoint a director to act as president for the balance of the 4-year term.

ARTICLE VI

Meetings

Section 1: Meetings of the Society will be held at 4-year intervals unless it is otherwise agreed, and will not normally be held consecutively on the same continent. The time and place will be determined not less than 2 years in advance by the executive committee.

Section 2: Special general meetings may be held at the discretion of the executive committee. Written notice stating the purpose of such a meeting should be given to all members of the Society at least 6 months in advance.

Section 3: At all meetings of the Society every question shall be determined by a majority vote of the members present.

ARTICLE VII

Quorum

Section 1: At any meeting of the executive committee a simple majority of the voting members of that Committee shall constitute a quorum.

Section 2: At any general meeting of the Society thirty (30) regular members in good standing shall constitute a quorum.

Section 3: In transacting business of the Society by letter ballot, the ballots returned shall constitute a quorum.

ARTICLE VIII

Amendments

Section 1: The Constitution of the Society may be repealed or amended by a two-thirds majority vote of those members attending any regular quadrennial business meeting, provided that the proposed amendment has been mailed to the membership at least 60 days prior to the meeting.

Section 2: Bylaws of the Society may be enacted, repealed, or amended at any regular quadrennial business meeting by a majority vote of the voting members present.

BYLAWS

Duties of the Officers:

(a) The executive committee shall have general charge of the affairs of the Society and, subject to the constitutional resolutions and Bylaws, may appoint, at any time, committees or individual members for specific purposes, and exercise governing authority in the administration of the Society, including finances and matters of policy.

(b) The president shall preside at all meetings of this Society and of the executive committee. He shall authorize meetings of the Society and of the executive committee when necessary and perform all the necessary functions of his office.

(c) The past president shall advise the president on matters pertaining to the activities of the Society and shall act as chairman of the nominating committee.

(d) The vice president shall exercise the rights and powers of the president in the absence of the latter.

(e) The secretary shall keep a record of all proceedings of this Society, of the executive committee, and of all committees, and shall deliver such records to his successor in office.

(f) The treasurer shall keep a record of all receipts and disbursements and shall present a financial statement at meetings of the Society.

(g) The historian shall maintain the historical record of the activities of the Society and shall present a written report at each quadrennial meeting.

Dues for the different classes of membership shall be as determined from time to time by resolution of the executive committee and approved by a meeting of the Society.

The auditors to audit the account of the Society for the next meeting will be recommended by the executive committee and approved by the membership at the meeting.

Minutes

FIRST SESSION

Chairman R. R. Davis called the first session of the business meeting of the Second International Turfgrass Society Conference to order at 4:10 p.m., June 19, 1973 at the Donaldson Brown Continuing Education Center, Virginia Polytechnic Institute and State University, Blacksburg, Virginia. Dr. Davis commented on the general organization of the research conference and the procedures used in the planning and developing the conference program.

Dr. Davis then discussed the development of a Constitution and Bylaws for the International Turfgrass Society (ITS). He called on Dr. C. M. Switzer, chairman of the Constitution and Bylaws subcommittee, for a report. Dr. Switzer discussed the proposed Constitution and recommended three amendments to the fourth draft, based on suggestions from the membership and accepted by the subcommittee as follows:

1) Article 4, section 1, Officers: delete . . . "who will also be president elect."

2) Article 5, section 1, line 2: delete . . . "not less than two."

3) Article 5, section 2, following first sentence add: . . . "plus 1 member each from 3 other countries not represented by the foregoing. The most recent past president shall be chairman."

D. L. Klingman raised a point on the advisability of charging the Nominating Committee with the responsibility of proposing a slate of officers. Dr. Switzer moved to adopt the constitution. Motion seconded by Ray A. Keen.

Paul E. Rieke questioned the number of candidates (candidate instead of candidates). J. B. Beard moved that the letter "s" on candidate(s) be placed in parentheses. Seconded by K. T. Payne. Motion passed without dissenting vote.

Clarification of the amendment was requested by Earl H. Odell, Gene C. Nutter, and John E. Gallagher.

R. W. Schery moved to add the following sentence after Article 5, section 1: "Nominations can be made from floor." Seconded by R. J. Hull and passed. The question was called for and the Constitution, as amended, was adopted without dissenting vote.

The matter of officers for the next 4 years was discussed by Dr. Davis. He commented that a nominating committee had been appointed. D. B. White raised a question regarding the slate of officers to be elected in 1973. Dr. Davis replied that the Constitution was not in operation until now and that the procedures under way would be followed this year.

Dr. Davis then requested J. R. Watson, chairman of the nominating committee, to report. Dr. Watson identified committee members as follows: J. L. Eggens, Canada; H. Vos, Netherlands, Rudolph Pietsch, West Germany; R. L. Morris, United Kingdom; and Ralph Engel, United States.

Dr. Watson then named the following nominees, stating all had been contacted and agreed to serve, if elected, in the office to which nominated: President—Peter Boeker, West Germany; Vice President—J. P. van der Horst, Netherlands; Secretary—no candidate; Board of Directors—A. C. Ferguson, Canada; Kaoru Ehara, Japan; R. L. Morris, United Kingdom, Werner Skirde, West Germany; and Ralph Engel, United States.

Dr. Davis commented that the executive committee would consist of the immediate past president and treasurer in addition to the elected officers and directors. The floor was then open for nominations. R. E. Blaser moved that nominations be closed and the slate be elected. Seconded by R. L. Goss. C. Y. Ward nominated Fred B. Ledeboer for secretary. Seconded by Hull.

J. B. Beard stressed that it was premature to finalize election at this business session but rather this should be done at the following business session. Second and motion were withdrawn.

J. F. Shoulders moved that the slate as proposed by the nominating committee be accepted. Motion seconded by G. M. Wood. Motion carried.

Meeting recessed at 4:53 p.m. to meet again at 5:00 p.m., Thursday, June 21.

SECOND SESSION

Chairman R. R. Davis called the second session of the recessed business meeting of the Second International Turfgrass Society Conference to order at 5:00 p.m., Thursday, June 21, 1973. Dr. Davis made several announcements, then called for the report of the nominating committee to be given. J. R. Watson, chairman, reported as follows: past president—R. R. Davis, United States; president—Peter Boeker, West Germany; vice president—J. P. van der Horst, Netherlands; secretary—F. B. Ledeboer, United States; directors—A. G. Ferguson, Canada; Kaoru Ehara, Japan; R. L. Morris, United Kingdom; Werner Skirde, West Germany; and Ralph Engel, United States.

Edgar W. Schweizer nominated Mr. P. Mansat, France, for director. The nomination was seconded by R. W. Schery. Considerable discussion followed. Beard commented that officers should be members of the Society and in attendance unless excused by the executive committee. C. M. Switzer supported acceptance of the nomination on basis of rules of order. R. A. Keen moved the slate as presented by the nominating committee, plus Mr. Mansat, be accepted and that nominations be closed. The motion was duly seconded and passed.

R. C. Wakefield asked if more than five directors could be elected. Dr. Davis replied in the negative based on the Constitution as adopted in the first session. Candidates for offices were asked to stand. Dr. Davis stated that a treasurer and historian will be appointed. Moved by G. M. Wood that nominees for president, vice president, and secretary be accepted by acclamation. Seconded by W. C. Morgan and passed without dissenting vote. The chairman requested that directors be elected by secret ballot and asked the outgoing executive committee to count ballots and report the results at the banquet scheduled for later in the evening. (Directors elected were: A. C. Ferguson, Canada; Kaoru Ehara, Japan; R. L. Morris, United Kingdom; Werner Skirde, West Germany; and Ralph Engel, United States.)

Chairman Davis requested J. P. Shildrick to present the financial report of the first conference, a copy of which follows these minutes. Following an explanation that this report was acceptable to the organizing committee for the first conference and to the British Sports Research Institute, the report was accepted.

Treasurer R. E. Schmidt reported that, as far as could be determined at this point, conference fees plus donations from supporting companies and organizations would cover the expenses and obligations of this conference.

E. C. Roberts, editor for Second Proceedings, reported that he had received most papers and announced the following publications schedule: September 1—deadline for papers; January 1—submit to publisher; June or July—ready for distribution.

The subcommittee for resolutions, C. M. Switzer, chairman, presented resolutions for the second conference. Resolutions were accepted as indicated below:

1) Expressed appreciation to John Escritt, John Shildrick, James B. Beard and to their organizations for publication of the Proceedings of the First Conference.
2) Expressed appreciation to Virginia Polytechnic Institute and State University, its leaders, and to John Shoulders, Chairman, Local Arrangements Committee, for hosting the Second Conference.
3) Expressed appreciation to industries and organizations making contributions toward the expenses of the Second Conference.
4) Expressed appreciation to Richard R. Davis for his leadership of the International Turfgrass Society.
5) Paid tribute to the memory of Bjarne Langvad.

J. B. Beard commented that ITS should have a program to increase membership. A discussion of pros and cons of dues followed with no action taken.

On behalf of the Virginia Polytechnic Institute and State University staff, R. E. Blaser expressed appreciation to all delegates for their participation and interest shown throughout the conference.

Davis announced that the selection of the site for the third conference was left up to the executive committee.

On motion by Dr. Beard, seconded by R. A. Keen and passed, the business session adjourned at 5:05 p.m.

Respectfully submitted,

J. F. Shoulders

June 19, 1973

To: International Turfgrass Society Members

From: First International Turfgrass Research Committee (Majority report)

Subject: Disbursements of Monies and Book Inventories of First ITRC

The following instructions were given:

1) Pay £200 to Sports Turf Research Institute as final payment for indirect costs incurred in hosting First International Turfgrass Conference. This brings the total indirect payment to £600.

2) The £40.64 balance from the First International Turfgrass Conference be transferred to the newly elected ITS treasurer.

3) The First International Turfgrass Conference Proceedings inventory (R. R. Davis has 100 copies and Sports Turf Research Institute 143) be held by ITS for future sales at $10 per copy (President to direct).

4) This statement of disbursements shall terminate the affairs of the First International Turfgrass Conference.

5) This action is not intended to establish a precedent for future International Turfgrass Conference affairs and should not be so construed.

Respectively submitted,

J. B. Beard
J. R. Watson
J. P. Shildrick (representing J. R. Escritt)

Organizational Committees

ITS EXECUTIVE COMMITTEE

R. R. Davis, USA, Chairman
Peter Boeker, West Germany
W. H. Daniel, USA
J. B. Beard, USA
J. R. Escritt, United Kingdom
C. M. Switzer, Canada
J. P. van der Horst, Netherlands

PROGRAM COMMITTEE

R. R. Davis, Chairman
J. B. Beard
W. H. Daniel
R. E. Schmidt, Treasurer and ASA
    Representative
J. F. Shoulders

INDEX

Listings of authors and of United States and overseas turfgrass centers for research; names of grasses, chemicals and materials; and items related to genetics, physiology, culture, and management of turfgrasses made part of these proceedings are included herein.

poae-nemoralis Otth.　71
poarum Niels　45, 71
Pumice　264, 266, 268
Pythium blight　335-338, 361, 487
Pythium spp.　106, 361, 440, 450,
　481, 487, 489, 490
　aphanidermatum (Edson) Fitzpatrick
　335-338, 436, 482
　ultimum Trow　335

Q
Quackgrass　554
Quintozene (PCNB)　320-322

R
Race courses　24, 438-440
Radiation
　breeding　18, 20
　gamma　4-7, 18, 21
Radko, A. M.　287-297
Red thread disease　29, 32, 510
Red top　484, 490, 492, 541, 542,
　544, 558, 560, 562-565
Reed canarygrass　542
Regim-8　392, 398
Registration of turfgrasses　62-73
Reproduction, sexual　9-17, 18-22,
　63
Reproductive isolation barriers　9-17
Rescuegrass　552, 553
Respiration　90, 141, 177, 196-208,
　210, 211, 222-230, 239, 393, 396,
　397, 447
Rhizoctonia spp.　359, 440
　solani　106, 438
Rhizomes　4, 6, 7, 10, 12, 13, 17, 18,
　21, 26, 27, 31-34, 38, 49, 58, 59,
　61, 66, 68, 90, 95, 112, 138, 152,
　187, 222, 232, 372, 384, 426, 458-
　462, 554
Rhode Island research　112-119, 186-
　195, 353-357, 399-409, 569-576
Rhodesgrass　552, 553
Rieger, B. A.　390-398
Rieke, P. E.　120-129
Roadside turf　3, 70, 72, 73, 314, 319,
　458, 463, 474, 537, 538, 541-550,
　551-556, 557-568, 569-576, 577
Robey, M. J.　277-280
Root rot disease　42, 360
Roots　21, 26, 27, 55-61, 79, 80, 90,
　99-103, 105, 112, 120, 132-144,
　146-148, 176-184, 187, 188, 190-
　192, 232-240, 258, 262, 266, 271-
　275, 278, 283, 296, 298-300, 325,
　326, 360, 372-377, 384, 393, 395,
　407, 421, 422, 426-428, 436, 438,
　439, 441, 443, 447, 449, 450, 458-
　462, 470-472, 496-499, 511, 529,
　530, 532, 570, 572, 573
Roughstalk bluegrass　See Bluegrass
　rough
Russian wild rye　558, 564, 565
Rust　37, 39, 42, 43, 45, 46

Rye
　'Abruzzi'　558, 560-565, 567
　'Balboa'　558, 566, 567
　Cereal　345, 346, 567
Ryegrass　94, 361, 454, 456, 457,
　490, 493, 523, 542, 544, 550, 567
　annual　335-338, 362, 453-457,
　481-484, 487, 490-492, 541, 558,
　560-565
　annual 'Magnolia'　491
　perennial　24, 232, 250, 482, 483,
　485, 487, 488, 491-494, 508-511,
　514, 538, 541, 542
　perennial 'Aberystwyth S.23'　29,
　30, 32, 39, 43, 44, 46, 132, 133,
　137-143
　perennial 'Aberystwyth S.24'　30
　perennial 'Barenza'　132
　perennial 'Bocage'　463
　perennial 'Kent Indigenous'　29
　perennial 'Lynn'　558, 564, 565
　perennial 'Manhattan'　29, 30, 37,
　39, 361, 400, 402, 453-457, 487,
　510, 511, 544, 550, 558, 564-567
　perennial 'Medalist'　484, 487, 491
　perennial 'Melle Pature'　38, 39
　perennial 'NK-100'　487, 490, 491
　perennial 'Pacey's'　60
　perennial 'Parcour'　39
　perennial 'Pelo'　39, 487
　perennial 'Pennfine'　453-457, 487,
　558, 560-563
　perennial 'Perma'　39
　perennial 'Romney'　29
　perennial 'Scotia'　39
　perennial 'Sprinter'　29, 30, 510
　perennial 'Wilstermarsch'　60

S
S-21634　402, 403, 409
SADH　467
Saint Augustinegrass　74-78, 222-230,
　258, 350-352, 365, 367-371, 422,
　426, 461
　'Floratam'　352
　Decline (SAD)　350-352
Salinity　See Soil Salinity
Saltgrass　552, 553, 555
Salthay　296
Salt-tolerant grasses　551-556
Sand　36, 49, 73, 80, 95, 100, 120-
　122, 127, 128, 156, 178, 197, 215,
　217, 222, 233, 262, 265-269, 271-
　275, 277, 278, 282-285, 287-296,
　298-300, 302, 303, 336, 337, 366,
　380, 392, 432-437, 440, 449, 452,
　454, 483, 485, 511, 515, 528, 530,
　532, 542
Sanders, P.　344-349
Sanks, G. D.　551-556
Saprophytes　316, 326, 327, 333, 360
Sawdust　432
Scald　432
Scalping　447, 449

NOTES

NOTES

NOTES

NOTES